D1229972

Periodic Table

Transition elements

H 1																	He 2
Li 3	Be 4										B 5	C 6	N 7	O 8	F 9	Ne 10	
Na 11	Mg 12										Al 13	Si 14	P 15	S 16	Cl 17	A 18	
K 19	Ca 20	Sc 21	Ti 22	V 23	Cr 24	Mn 25	Fe 26	Co 27	Ni 28	Cu 29	Zn 30	Ga 31	Ge 32	As 33	Se 34	Br 35	Kr 36
Rb 37	Sr 38	Y 39	Zr 40	Nb 41	Mo 42	Tc 43	Ru 44	Rh 45	Pd 46	Ag 47	Cd 48	In 49	Sn 50	Sb 51	Te 52	I 53	Xe 54
Cs 55	Ba 56	Lu 71	Hf 72	Ta 73	W 74	Re 75	Os 76	Ir 77	Pt 78	Au 79	Hg 80	Tl 81	Pb 82	Bi 83	Po 84	At 85	Rn 86
Fr 87	Ra 88																

Rare earths

La 57	Ce 58	Pr 59	Nd 60	Pm 61	Sm 62	Eu 63	Gd 64	Tb 65	Dy 66	Ho 67	Er 68
Ac 89	Th 90	Pa 91	U 92	Np 93	Pu 94	Am 95	Cm 96	Bk 97	Cf 98	E 99	Fm 100

PRENTICE-HALL CHEMISTRY SERIES

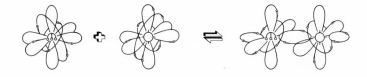

Alan F. Clifford

Associate Professor of Chemistry
Purdue University

Illustrations by
Edward M. Blackwell

Inorganic Chemistry
of Qualitative Analysis

Prentice-Hall, Inc.
Englewood Cliffs, N.J.

© 1961, by Prentice-Hall, Inc., Englewood Cliffs, N.J.
All rights reserved. No part of this book may be reproduced in any form, by mimeograph, or any other means,
without permission in writing from the publishers.

Library of Congress Catalog Card Number 61–8161

First printing .... March , 1961
Second printing .....October , 1961
Third printing........ April , 1963

Printed in the United States of America

74483—C

544
C63

To
Professor Emeritus
Quaesita Cromwell Drake
of the
University of Delaware
who first inspired me
to see the meaning
in qualitative analysis

55388

Preface

It has long been recognized by instructors of undergraduate chemistry that there is little need to teach qualitative analysis for its own sake. Actual analyses are very seldom carried out in this manner any longer. It is nevertheless true that the classical analytical scheme is one of the best vehicles ever devised for teaching the systematics of inorganic chemistry. The purpose of this book, then, is not to teach methods of analysis, but rather to give as thorough a grounding as possible in the chemical relationships in the periodic table on which the classical analytical scheme is founded. This is done in terms of trends in solubility, trends in acidity and basicity, trends in oxidizing and reducing power, and the like. In order to accomplish this intelligibly, such topics as electronegativity, oxidation potentials, and the equilibrium principle are treated, the last extensively.

The book was written for and planned around the chemistry courses 126 and 226 at Purdue University. The former is the second term freshman course for gifted students, whereas the latter is the first term sophomore course for average students which follows two semesters of general chemistry. However, although the book is planned around these courses, it is by no means limited to them and contains far more material than any but the most gifted student could be expected to absorb in one semester. This has been done on the theory that the better students should always have the opportunity to dig by themselves deeper into the subject than they can in the formal course and that the average student should be made aware that what is spooned out to him in lectures is not all that can be said.

The book is divided into sixteen chapters intended to correspond very roughly to the sixteen weeks of the semester. The material is organized insofar as possible to present new background material in the text (and lectures) at the same time as work illustrating it appears in the laboratory. For this reason, the analytical groups are considered in order of increasing complexity, and many additional illustrative experiments have been included. The laboratory procedures have been selected for their pedagogical worth rather than for their analytical utility. For example, the detection of strontium is accomplished with saturated calcium sulfate in order to demonstrate the trend of solubilities of the alkaline earth sulfates, rather than, for example, by complexing calcium with triethanolamine which, from the analytical point of view, is more satisfactory but which teaches very little.   For the same reason, the use of organic spot test reagents has been reduced to a minimum to emphasize inorganic reagents which perhaps are less satisfactory analytically but which nevertheless illustrate fundamental inorganic chemistry better.   Enough organic reagents are discussed, however, to illustrate the nature of lakes (para-nitrobenzeneazoresorcinol and aluminon reagent) and chelation (dimethylglyoxime).

Several new elements have been added to the analytical scheme over the ones usually present, not because they are becoming technically important, but because they demonstrate important principles of chemistry.   Thallium is added to demonstrate the principle of the chemical similarity of neighbors in the periodic table.   Tungsten is added to demonstrate the existence of insoluble acids and the ambivalent nature of reagents (i.e., that addition of HCl brings both H^+ and Cl^- into the solution with the consequent effects of both).   Similarly vanadium demonstrates the existence of insoluble ammonium salts as well as the ambivalence of the NH_4OH—NH_4Cl reagent and certain other points.   Molybdenum is added to demonstrate the existence of amphoteric sulfides for the high oxidation states of the elements on the left-hand side of the periodic table.

In Chemistry 126 and 226 at Purdue the final unknown includes not only a selection of the elements considered in the text but also many other elements, such as Ce, Ge, In, Ta, Th, Ti, Zr, etc., for which no analytical procedures are given.   Each student is told that, in addition to the elements in the regular scheme, he may have some elements from a certain specified list (different in each case).   He must go to the library and devise a scheme which will accommodate these elements and no others.   Thus he must actually study and compare the chemistries of these and the common elements and produce a workable analytical scheme before he goes into the laboratory to analyze the final unknown.   This has proved to be one of the most popular features of the laboratory work.   Besides the textbooks on qualitative analysis listed at the ends of chapters 9, 12, and 14 the following texts on inorganic chemistry may be recommended for this purpose:

GENERAL TEXTBOOKS ON INORGANIC CHEMISTRY

Barnett, E. de Barry, and Wilson, C. L., *Inorganic Chemistry.* New York: Longmans, Green & Co., Inc., 1953.

Hempel, C. A., *Rare Metals Handbook.* New York: Reinhold Publishing Corporation, 1954.

Latimer, W. M., and Hildebrand, J. H., *Reference Book of Inorganic Chemistry,* 3rd ed. New York: Macmillan Company, 1951.

Parkes, G. D., *Mellor's Modern Inorganic Chemistry.* New York: Longmans, Green & Co., Inc.

Remy, H., *Treatise on Inorganic Chemistry.* New York: Elsevier Publishing Company, 1956.

Sidgwick, N. V., *The Chemical Elements and Their Compounds.* Oxford: The Clarendon Press, 1950.

Thorne, P. C. L., and Roberts, E. R., *Fritz Ephraim's Inorganic Chemistry,* 6th ed. New York: Interscience Publishers, Inc., 1955.

Depending on the level of the course, more or less of the textual material may be taken up in class. If it is to be used only as a laboratory manual, the experimental sections only (perhaps with the descriptive material on the individual elements) may be used.

For average students with a moderate background in general chemistry and no previous knowledge of equilibrium, the course might include:

Week	Lecture	Laboratory
1	Chapter 1	Check-in; Section 1-15
2	Chapter 2	Lecture on Section 3-6; Sections 3-12, 3-13 (known)
3	Chapter 3	Sections 3-11, 3-13 (unknown)
4	Sections 4-1, 4-2, 4-4, 4-6, 4-7 (omit if tungsten is to be omitted), 4-8, 4-9 (omit portions on tungsten and molybdenum if desired)	Sections 4-11, 4-12
5	Sections 5-1, 5-2, 5-12, 5-13	Sections 4-11 (unknown), 5-14
6	Sections 5-3, 5-4, 5-5, 5-8	Section 5-15 (unknown)
7	Sections 7-1, 7-2, 7-3	Sections 5-15 (unknown), 7-11
8	Sections 7-5, 7-8, 7-9, 7-10	Sections 7-11, 7-12
9	Sections 9-1, 9-2, 9-4, 9-5	Section 7-12 (unknown)
10	Sections 9-6, 9-8, 9-9	Sections 9-17, 9-18 (unknown)
11	Sections 10-1, 10-2, 10-3, 10-5	Section 9-18 (unknown)
12	Sections 10-6, 10-8, 10-9, 10-12, 10-13	Sections 9-18 (unknown), 11-14, 11-15
13	Sections 11-1 through 11-6	Sections 11-13, 11-15, 12-9 (unknown)
14	Chapter 13	Section 12-9 (unknown)
15	Sections 14-1 through 14-5	Section 12-9 (unknown)
16	Sections 14-6, 14-8	Section 12-9 (unknown); check-out

For average students with a strong background in general chemistry but little knowledge of equilibrium, the foregoing schedule might be used with the laboratory lecture on Section 3-6 substituted for the lecture on Chapter 1. Alternatively the following schedule might be used:

Week	Lecture	Laboratory
1	Section 1-1, Chapter 2	Check-in; Sections 1-15, 3-11
2	Chapter 3	Sections 3-12, 3-13 (known)
3	Sections 1-9, 4-1, 4-2, 4-3	Sections 3-13 (unknown), 4-10
4	Sections 4-4, 4-5, 4-7, etc.	Section 4-11 (unknown)
5	Sections 5-1, 5-2, 5-12, 5-13	Sections 5-14, 5-15
6	Sections 5-3, 5-4, 5-5, 5-8, 5-11	Section 5-15 (unknown)
7	From this week on, the previous schedule would be followed, keeping the laboratory a half-week ahead to give one extra period for the general unknown.	

The calendars above are set up for a four-credit course including one lecture and one recitation (or two lectures) and six hours of laboratory. The following calendar is designed for Chemistry 126 at Purdue which has students with a strong background in general chemistry and some knowledge of equilibrium. Most of the material in Chapters 1 and 2 is considered to be review for these students. The course is a five-credit course having two lectures, one recitation, and six hours of laboratory.

(In the following calendar *a* and *b* represent the first and second lectures or laboratories of the week respectively.)

Week	Lecture	Laboratory
1a	Sections 1-1, 3-6	Check-in; Section 1-15
1b	Chapter 3	Sections 3-7, 3-8, 3-12
2a	Sections 1-9, 1-10, 1-11, 1-12	Sections 3-11, 3-13
2b	Sections 4-1, 4-2, 4-3, 4-7	Section 3-13
3a	Sections 4-4, 4-5, 4-6	Section 3-13 (unknown)
3b	Sections 4-8, 4-9	Section 4-11
4a	Sections 5-1, 5-2	Section 4-12
4b	Sections 5-3 through 5-6	Section 4-12 (unknown)
5a	Sections 5-7 through 5-11	Sections 5-12, 5-13, 5-14
5b	Chapter 6	Section 5-15
6a	Sections 7-1 through 7-5	Section 5-15
6b	Sections 7-6 through 7-10	Section 5-15 (unknown)
7a	Sections 8-1, 8-2, 8-3	Section 7-11
7b	Sections 8-4, 8-5, 8-6	Section 7-12
8a	Sections 8-7, 8-8, 8-9	Section 7-12
8b	Sections 8-10 through 8-13	Section 7-12 (unknown)
9a	Sections 9-1 through 9-7	Section 9-17
9b	Sections 9-8, 9-9, 9-13	Section 9-18
10a	Sections 9-14, 9-15, 9-16	Section 9-18
10b	Sections 10-1 through 10-4	Section 9-18
11a	Sections 10-5 through 10-8	Section 9-18 (unknown)
11b	Sections 10-9 through 10-13	Section 11-13
12b	Sections 11-1 through 11-6	Sections 11-14, 11-15
12a	Chapter 12	Sections 12-9, 14-9, 14-10, 14-11
13a	Sections 13-1 through 13-6	Section 12-9
13b	Sections 13-7 through 13-13	Section 12-9
14a	Sections 14-1 through 14-4	Section 12-9
14b	Sections 14-5 through 14-8	Section 12-9 (unknown) or extra unknown
15a	Sections 14-9, 14-10, 14-11	
15b	Chapter 15 or Chapter 16	
16a	Chapter 15 or Chapter 16	
16b	Examinations	Check-out.

This volume has in large degree been a labor of love. It has had the enthusiastic support of my teaching staff. I am especially grateful to Tom Bydalek for checking the problem sets, to Pat and Ron Olsen for reading the original manuscript, and to Prof. John W. Willard of South Dakota School of Mines for reading proof. The criticisms of the reviewers, including Profs. Kenneth S. Pitzer, Dean W. Robinson of Johns Hopkins University and Samuel B. Knight of the University of North Carolina are gratefully acknowledged.   But most of all I acknowledge the forebearance and constant encouragement of my wife, Shirley.

ALAN F. CLIFFORD

West Lafayette, Indiana

Permission of the publishers to reproduce the following figures is gratefully acknowledged.

Fig. 1-5: Pauling, Linus, *General Chemistry,* 2d ed.   San Francisco: W. H. Freeman and Company, 1950.

Figs. 1-6, 1-9, 1-10, 1-11, 1-12, 1-13, 1-14, 1-16, 1-17, and 10-15: Wyckoff, R. W. G., *Crystal Structures.*   New York: Interscience Publishers, Inc., 1948, 1951, 1957.

Figs. 1-7, and 1-19: Hogness, T. R., and Johnson, Warren C., *Qualitative Analysis and Chemical Equilibrium,* 4th ed.   Copyright 1954.   Reprinted by permission of Henry Holt & Company, Inc., publishers.

Figs. 1-18, and 10-13: Wells, A. F., *Structural Inorganic Chemistry,* 2d ed.   Oxford: The Clarendon Press, 1950.

Fig. 1-24: Reprinted by permission of Clay-Adams, Inc., manufacturer.

Fig. 5-2: Latimer, W. M., and Hildebrand, J. H., *Reference Book of Inorganic Chemistry,* 3rd ed.   New York: The Macmillan Company, 1951.

Fig. 5-3: Reprinted by permission of Fisher Scientific Company.

Figs. 10-2a, 10-2b, and 10-16: Pauling, Linus, *Nature of the Chemical Bond,* 3rd ed.   Ithaca, New York: Cornell University Press, 1960.

Fig. 10-2c: Pearson, R. G., "Crystal Field Explains Inorganic Behavior," *Chemical and Engineering News,* p. 72 (June 19, 1959).

Fig. 14-2: Latimer, W. M., *The Oxidation States of the Elements and their Potentials in Aqueous Solution,* 2d ed.   Englewood Cliffs, N. J.: Prentice-Hall, Inc., 1952.

Contents

Chapter 1

The Philosophy of Qualitative Analysis

The Nature of Matter

1–1. The Philosophy of Qualitative Analysis

The study of inorganic chemistry of necessity entails the memorizing of a great many facts. It is neither necessary nor desirable, however, that these facts be merely a collection of odd items which must be committed to memory by brute force, to be regurgitated unchanged when called for. On the contrary, it is important to realize that the elements of the periodic table are closely related to their neighbors and that their properties fit nicely into trends within the table. Consequently, it is frequently unnecessary to know particular facts if one is familiar with the trends. An appreciation of the trends within the periodic table, then, and an understanding of the reasons for them are much more important aims toward which the beginning student of inorganic chemistry should strive.

One of the most effective devices for teaching inorganic chemistry is the classical scheme of qualitative analysis. Nowadays there is little point in learning qualitative analysis for a grounding in analytic methods, for qualitative analytical schemes are rarely used any more for actual analytical work. Analyses today are much more quickly and surely accomplished by physical methods or by spot tests with a wide variety of selective organic reagents. Neither of these methods, however, can accomplish what the classical analytical scheme can do—to give an integrated general view of the chemistry of the periodic table which the beginning student is capable of understanding.

It must be realized at the outset that the analytical scheme presented here is *only one of many* that could be (or have been) devised. It is selected for what it can teach and because most of the procedures have been well worked out through long usage and are therefore somewhat more dependable than others which might accomplish the same thing. However, as the student

1

becomes more familiar with the chemistry of the elements and with the philosophy of inorganic chemistry, it will be a very useful exercise for him to attempt to devise different schemes, perhaps involving more elements than are covered here. Many modifications can be made. For example, although the sulfide precipitations used in this scheme are a very important part, and from the practical point of view are most satisfactory, they are by no means essential and can be eliminated entirely.

The qualitative scheme is based upon the fact that successive groups of elements can be precipitated away from others left in solution, the precipitating reagents being so selected that the one precipitating the smallest number of elements is used first. The elements precipitated within each group are then separated and identified. The separation procedures depend upon the trends evident in the periodic table with respect to the solubilities of salts, acidic and basic properties, valence and oxidation-reduction properties, and so forth.

Many of the trends which we shall examine and on which the group separations depend are cited in general chemistry as "solubility rules," e.g.

1. All chlorides of the metals are soluble, except $AgCl$, Hg_2Cl_2, and $PbCl_2$ (which is slightly soluble in cold water and moderately soluble in hot water).
2. All sulfides and hydroxides of the metals are insoluble, except those of the alkali and alkaline earth metals. (The hydroxides of the alkaline earth metals are only slightly soluble.)
3. All carbonates (where they exist) and phosphates are insoluble, except those of the alkali metals.
4. All sulfates are soluble, except those of barium, strontium, and lead. (Those of calcium, mercury(II), and silver are only slightly soluble.)
5. All fluorides are insoluble, except those of the alkali metals, silver, and thallium(I).
6. All silver salts are insoluble, except the nitrate, perchlorate, and fluoride. (Silver acetate, sulfate, and chlorate are slightly soluble.)
7. All the salts of the alkali metals and ammonium ion are soluble.
8. All nitrates, perchlorates, and acetates are soluble. (Silver acetate is only slightly soluble.)

These rules are, in fact, not absolute, but are crude representations of trends, and as such will be examined in somewhat more detail as the occasion arises.

1–2. The Structure of Matter

A knowledge of the manner in which atoms combine with one another is necessary for an understanding of the relationships of inorganic chemistry.

Atoms are bound together in compounds in a manner which differs from compound to compound. Thus, when sodium and chlorine react, the sodium atom gives up all interest in its valence electron and passes it over completely to the chlorine, with formation of Na^+ and Cl^- ions which are then attracted to one another by their opposite electrical charges. The complete transfer of the electron is in part the result of the greatly differing abilities of chlorine and sodium to attract electrons (electronegativity).

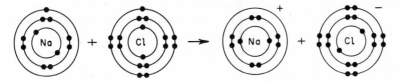

Fig. 1–1. Formation of an Ionic Compound (NaCl).

If, on the other hand, the electronegativities of the two reacting elements are the same (e.g., H and P), then neither atom will be able to attract electrons more than the other and equal sharing, or a covalent bond, will result

$$H : \overset{..}{P} : H$$
$$\overset{..}{H}$$

It is fairly obvious that there will be intermediate cases in which the electronegativities differ somewhat but not enough for complete transfer of electrons. In fact, the majority of bonds fall somewhere between the extremes. In this case a *polar*, but still covalent, bond results. An example is the hydrogen fluoride molecule, HF, in which hydrogen and fluorine differ in electronegativity, but not enough to allow formation of H^+ and F^- ions by complete transfer of the valence electron from hydrogen to fluorine. The result

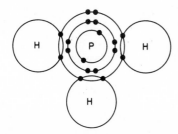

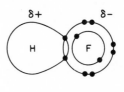

Fig. 1–2. Electronic Structure of a Nonpolar Covalent Compound (PH_3).

Fig. 1–3. Electronic Structure of a Polar Covalent Compound (HF).

is a molecule in which there is an unequally shared electron-pair bond in which the electrons are concentrated toward the more electronegative fluorine atom. This results in a molecule having an *electric dipole*, the atoms carrying permanent charges less than unity

$$\overset{\delta+}{H} \overset{..}{\underset{\rightarrow}{:}} \overset{\delta-}{\underset{..}{F}} :$$

(The symbols $\delta+$ and $\delta-$ mean partial positive and negative charge.) If the charges were unity, there would no longer be any sharing of electrons and the substance would consist of ions, H^+ and F^-. The properties of such a molecule are very strongly affected by this separation of charge which it presents to its neighboring molecules.

Under other circumstances the formation of polar bonds by atoms of different electronegativity may still not result in a polar molecule. An example of this is CCl_4, in which each C—Cl bond is polar in itself ($-\overset{\delta+}{\underset{|}{C}}\overset{\delta-}{\underset{..}{\overset{..}{\rightarrow}Cl:}}$);

yet, because of its complete geometrical symmetry the molecule as a whole is nonpolar, presenting the same aspect to the outside from all angles. Carbon tetrachloride is thus a typical nonpolar substance.

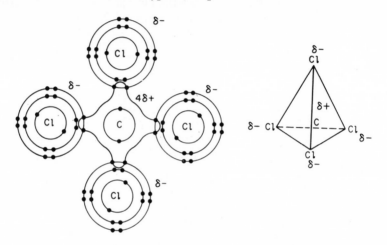

Fig. 1–4. Electron Distribution in CCl_4 Molecule.

1–3. The States of Matter

Matter may exist as solid, liquid, or gas, and most simple substances, under different conditions, may exist as any of the three. The solid and liquid states are "condensed" states (i.e., states in which neighboring molecules are in actual continuous contact with one another) and differ only in their degree of order. The solid state has a perfectly ordered, fixed array of molecules like the bricks in a wall, whereas the liquid state still has order, but less perfect and of a mobile sort, like a tubful of balloons, in which (if the balloons are all of the same size) each balloon will be in contact with a maximum of twelve others; however, there is no well-defined pattern of arrangement in the liquid state, and in any event whatever pattern there is is easily rearranged. This latter is a condition of short-range order but long-range disorder, or randomness. In the gas phase, on the other hand, the molecules are no longer in continuous contact with one another, have a completely random and continuously changing distribution, and may be

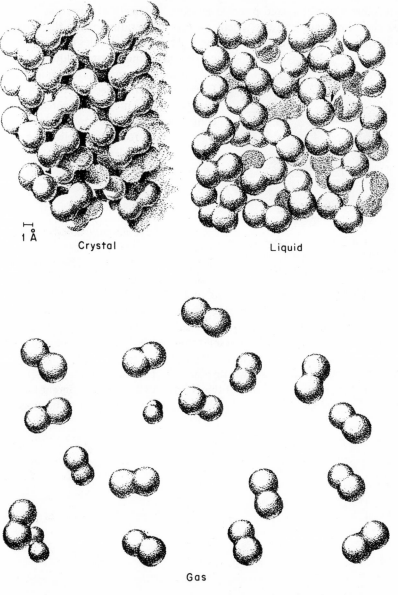

Crystal   Liquid

Gas

Fig. 1–5. Crystal, Liquid, and Gaseous Iodine, Showing Diatomic Molecules, I_2.

likened to bubbles or balloons floating freely in the open. Most of a gas consists merely of the empty space between the molecules.

At all temperatures atoms and molecules are continuously in motion; the higher the temperature, the faster the motion. If, as in the solid state, the average position of the molecule is fixed, then this motion takes the form of vibration about the fixed position and the "intensity of vibration" increases as the temperature rises. When, as the temperature rises, the energy of vibration becomes equal to the energy holding the molecules in the crystal, the

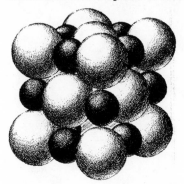

crystal melts and becomes liquid, the molecules now having greater freedom of motion. Eventually, as the energy of motion (kinetic energy) of the molecules increases, it becomes possible for the molecules to break away entirely from their fellows, escaping into the noncondensed gas state, and the liquid (or solid) vaporizes.

Fig. 1–6. A Perspective Drawing of the Unit Cube of NaCl. The large spheres are the chloride ions.

1–4. The Crystalline State

As we have already noted, the crystalline state is characterized by a high degree of fixed order. The regularity of position of the ions or molecules within the crystal is reflected in a definite and characteristic external crystal form. For example, the sodium chloride crystal is built up of a cubic arrangement of alternate sodium ions (Na^+) and chloride ions (Cl^-), and examination of NaCl crystals shows that these are indeed little cubes. (The similar KCl crystal, with identical *internal* arrangement of ions, forms cubes with the corners chopped off, as shown in Fig. 1–7. The difference is a result of the fact that the ratio of the sizes of the Na^+ and Cl^- ions is different from that of the K^+ and Cl^- ions.) In the NaCl crystal, each Na^+ may be considered

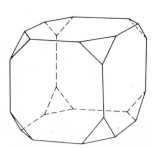

Fig. 1–7. The Crystal Form of Potassium Chloride.

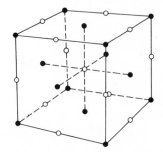

Fig. 1–8. The Crystal Structure of Sodium Chloride.

to be in the center of one of the faces of the cube, and is therefore surrounded by the four Cl^-'s at the corners of the same face, and also by the two Cl^-'s at the centers of the two cubes to which the face is common. Likewise, each Cl^- is surrounded by six Na^+ (Fig. 1–8). This is what the crystallographer calls having a coordination number of six.

The sodium chloride crystal is a typical *ionic* crystal. That is to say, the building units are charged particles or ions (Na^+ and Cl^-) and the crystal is held together by the strong electrostatic attraction of the opposite charges for each other. Crystals of this type are hard and high-melting. The degree of hardness and the elevation of the melting point will depend on the size of the ions and the magnitude of the charges. Both the hardness and the melting point increase as the attraction between the atoms increases. Examples illustrating this point are given in Table 1–1.

TABLE 1–1. RELATIONSHIP OF INTERATOMIC DISTANCE AND CHARGE TO MELTING POINT AND HARDNESS FOR SUBSTANCES HAVING NaCl-Type (OCTAHEDRAL) STRUCTURE

Compound	Interatomic Distance $(r_1 + r_2)$ (Å)	Ionic Charges (e)	$\dfrac{e_1 e_2}{r_1 + r_2}$	Melting Point (°C)	Hardness (Moh)
KCl	3.14	±1	0.319	776	2
NaCl	2.81	±1	0.356	804	2.5
AgCl	2.77	±1	0.361	455	1.3
NaF	2.31	±1	0.433	980	3.5
PbS	2.96	±2	1.350	1114	2.5
MnO	2.22	±2	1.800	1650	5–6
MgO	2.10	±2	1.904	2800	5.5–6.0
NiO	2.08	±2	1.922	2090	5.5

The coordination number in an ionic crystal varies depending on the size and relative number of the ions. Thus in CsCl the Cs^+ and Cl^- have coordination numbers of 8 (Fig. 1–9), whereas in BeO, the Be^{+2} and O^{-2} have coordination numbers of 4 (Fig. 1–10), each ion being surrounded at the corners of a regular tetrahedron by four ions of the opposite charge. In ionic crystals not having a 1:1 ratio of ions, the arrangement is necessarily more complicated. Thus in CaF_2 (Fig. 1–11) and Na_2S, the Ca^{+2} and S^{-2} ions have a coordination number of 8, while the F^- and Na^+ have a co-ordination number of 4. On the other hand, in $MgCl_2$, the Mg^{+2} has coordination number 6 and the Cl^-, 3, whereas in $BeCl_2$, the coordination number of Be^{+2} is 4 and of Cl^-, 2.

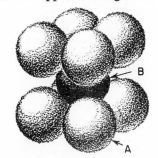

Fig. 1–9. A Perspective Drawing of the Unit Cube of CsCl. Atoms A and B refer to Cs and Cl respectively.

If the ions making up an ionic crystal can be considered as rigid spheres, then the coordination number of an ion M_1 (that is, the number of neighboring ions M_2 in direct contact with M_1) can be predicted on purely geometric grounds as a function of the ratio of the radii of M_1 and M_2, r_{M_1}/r_{M_2}. The coordination numbers so calculated are given in Table 1–2.

When ionic crystals are melted, the ions become free to move. Consequently, molten salts are excellent conductors of electricity, the cations

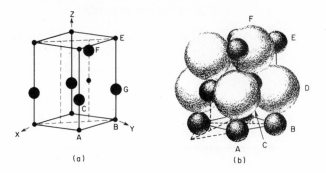

Fig. 1–10. The Crystal Structure of BeO. (a) The Positions of the Atoms in the Hexagonal Unit Cell of BeO. The beryllium atoms are the small black circles. (b) A Perspective Drawing Showing How the Atoms of BeO Would Pack Together if They Were Ions. The small black spheres are beryllium. Letters in this drawing refer to atoms similarly designated in (a).

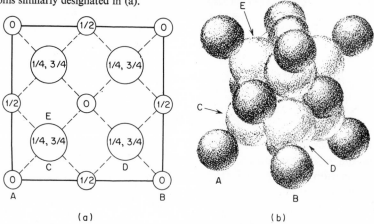

Fig. 1–11. The Crystal Structure of CaF₂. (a) The Positions of Atoms within the Unit Cell of Fluorite, CaF_2. The atoms are projected on a cube face. Lettered circles refer to the corresponding spheres in (b). (b) A Perspective Packing Drawing Showing the Distribution of the Atoms of CaF_2 within the Unit Cube.

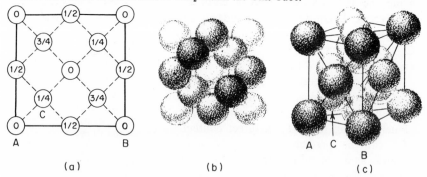

Fig. 1–12. The Crystal Structure of Diamond. (a) The Atomic Positions in the Unit Cube Projected on the Cube Face. (b) A Packing Drawing Corresponding to (a). (c) A Perspective Drawing.

TABLE 1–2. THE RELATIONSHIPS OF RADIUS RATIO AND COORDINATION NUMBER

Radius Ratio (r_{M_1}/r_{M_2})	Coordination Number	Geometrical Configuration
< 0.155	2	Linear
0.155–0.225	3	Triangular
0.225–0.414	4	Tetrahedral
0.414–0.732	6	Octahedral
> 0.732	8	Cubic

(the positive ions) moving toward the cathode and the anions (the negative ions) toward the anode.

Another type is the covalent crystal, in which the atoms are held together not by electrostatic charges on the atoms, but rather by the sharing of electrons between the atoms. Diamond and silicon carbide form crystals of this sort. In diamond, each carbon atom shares a pair of electrons with each of four other carbon atoms which are located at the corners of a regular tetrahedron, with the first carbon atom in the center. In this structure all the atoms are electrically neutral, but are nevertheless tied strongly to one another by sharing electrons (Fig. 1–12). Silicon carbide is the same, except that every other carbon atom of the diamond structure has been replaced by a silicon atom. This type of crystal is also hard and high-melting (Table 1–3).

TABLE 1–3. RELATIONSHIP OF INTERATOMIC DISTANCE AND CHARGE TO MELTING POINT AND HARDNESS FOR SUBSTANCES HAVING SiC-Type (TETRAHEDRAL) STRUCTURES

Compound	Interatomic Distance ($r_1 + r_2$) (Å)	Ionic* Charges (e)	$\dfrac{e_1 e_2}{r_1 + r_2}$	Melting Point (°C)	Hardness (Moh)
AgI	2.80	±1	0.357	552	1
CuI	2.62	±1	0.382	605	2.5–3.0
CuCl	2.35	±1	0.426	422	2.0–2.5
HgS	2.53	±2	1.569	580	2.0–2.5
ZnO	1.975	±2	2.022	1800	4.0–4.5
SiC	1.89	±4	8.473	2700	9.5
C (diamond)	1.54	±4	10.390	3500	10.0

* These charges should be interpreted in the light of the discussion in Sections 1–2 and 1–10.

We have seen that it is possible to combine in one compound both ionic and covalent linkages (e.g., $NaClO_4$, shown in Fig. 1–13, in which the Na^+ and ClO_4^- are ions, but which has covalent Cl—O bonds within the ClO_4^- ions, and KN_3, Fig. 1–14, in which the K^+ and N_3^- are ions, but which has covalent bonds between the nitrogen atoms in the N_3^- or azide ion). Crystals of these substances are held together almost entirely by the attraction of the opposite charges on the ions. It is also possible, however, to have crystals which are bound together both ionically and covalently. Thus crystalline enstatite, $MgSiO_3$, consists of infinite chains of

$$\left[\begin{array}{ccc} O & O & O \\ \| & \| & \| \\ -O-Si-O-Si-O-Si- \\ \| & \| & \| \\ O & O & O \end{array}\right]_{x/3}^{-2x}$$

in which each silicon atom is covalently bound to four oxygens, and one-third of the oxygens are covalently bonded to two different silicons, while the

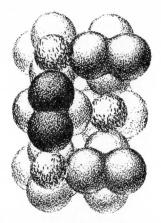

Fig. 1–13. The Crystal Structure of Low-$NaClO_4$. Line-shaded spheres are the sodium ions. Chlorine atoms are completely hidden within their surrounding oxygen tetrahedra.

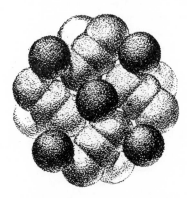

Fig. 1–14. The Crystal Structure of KN_3.

other two-thirds are covalently bound to only single silicon atoms (Fig. 1–15). The whole silicate chain carries an electrical charge of -2 for each silicon atom, or $-2x$ for a chain containing x silicon atoms. On the other hand the magnesiums are present in the crystal as ions, there being x magnesium ions in all, so that the whole crystal is electrically neutral. Such a crystal is held together simultaneously by the covalent bonds within the $(SiO_3^{-2})_x$ anions and by the electrostatic attraction of the negative charge on these anions for the positive charge on the cations.

A third type of crystal is the molecular crystal, which is made up of discrete molecules whose atoms are covalently bonded to each other, the molecules as a whole being attracted to each other by the very weak van der Waals forces, to be described later. An example of such a crystal would be the iodine, I_2, crystal (Fig. 1–16). In this the two iodine atoms are bound to each other by sharing electron pairs in a strong bond within the molecule.

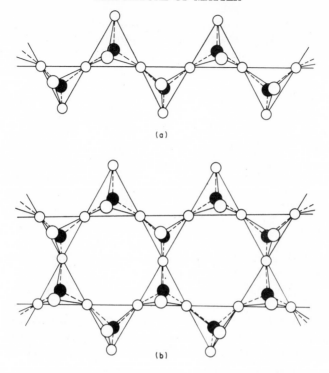

Fig. 1–15. (a) The Structure of the Silicate Chains in Enstatite [MgSiO$_3$].
(b) The Structure of the Silicate Chains in Tremolite
[Ca$_2$Mg$_5$ (OH)$_2$ (Si$_4$O$_{11}$)$_2$].

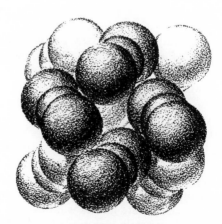

Fig. 1–16. The Crystal
Structure of Solid Iodine.

Fig. 1–17. The Crystal Structure of Solid
CO$_2$. The larger spheres are oxygen atoms.

The individual molecules are attracted to each other to form the crystal, however, only by very weak forces. Consequently, crystals of this type are weak—soft and low-melting (Table 1–4). A similar crystal is that of solid CO_2 (Fig. 1–17).

TABLE 1–4. MELTING POINTS AND HARDNESSES OF SOME MOLECULAR CRYSTALS

Compound	Melting Point (°C)	Hardness (Moh)
Wax (at 0°)	~ 40	0.2
P_4 (white)	44.1	0.5
I_2	113	
S_8 (rhombic)	114.5	1.5–2.5
Se_8 (monoclinic)	200	2.0
As_4S_6 (orpiment)	300	1.5–2.0
As_4S_4 (realgar)	307	1.5–2.0
As_4O_6	315	2.5

Molecular or covalent crystals when melted are poor conductors of electricity, since no ions are liberated.

All possible gradations between these extremes are possible. For example, between the completely nonionic covalent diamond and the ionic BeO crystals lies "Borazon" or cubic boron nitride, BN, whose atoms not only share electron pairs but, because the sharing is unequal, also carry charge. Likewise between the covalent and molecular extremes lie the crystals formed by polar substances. For example, the HF molecule is covalent, the H and F atoms being connected by an electron-pair bond. However, the ability of fluorine to attract electrons (i.e., its electronegativity) is so much greater than that of hydrogen that there is an uneven distribution of charge in the molecule, the hydrogen carrying positive charge and the fluorine, negative charge.

$$\overset{\delta+}{H} \overset{\rightarrow}{:} \overset{\cdot\cdot}{\underset{\cdot\cdot}{F}} \overset{\delta-}{:}$$

Consequently the hydrogen of one molecule will attract electrically the fluorine of another, resulting in attraction stronger than that from van der Waals forces but, because the charges are necessarily less than unity, weaker than would be the case for a crystal made up of H^+ and F^- ions. Depending on the strength of the dipole-dipole attractions, crystals of these substances vary in melting point and hardness.

1–5. Glasses

Glasses are supercooled liquids. They have the short-range order and long-range disorder of liquids but almost the rigidity of solids. In actual fact, under pressure glasses will flow and therefore may be considered to be liquids of extremely high viscosity—so high that under ordinary conditions the rate of flow is infinitesimal. Because of the apparent rigidity, glasses can be used structurally in place of true solids.

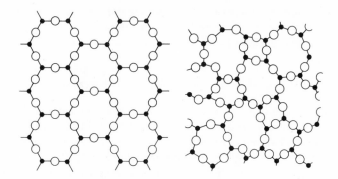

Fig. 1–18. Diagrammatic Representation of the Crystalline and Vitreous Forms of a Compound A_2X_3.

1–6. Dipole Moment

It is useful to be able to express the degree of polarity of a polar molecule. This is done by means of the dipole moment. If a polar substance is placed in an electric field, say between two charged plates, its molecules will tend to line up with the field. That is, the negative ends of the molecules will swing toward the positive plate and the positive ends toward the negative plate. The dipole moment determines the force which the field can exert in orienting the molecule, and depends on the magnitudes of the charges involved and the distance between them within the molecule. The larger the charge and the greater the distance, the greater will be the dipole moment. Molecules which are completely symmetrical and therefore have the same center for positive and negative charge (CCl_4, $HgCl_2$, BF_3), or have only one kind of atom (H_2, Cl_2, P_4, S_8, with certain specific exceptions, such as O_3), or have atoms of identical electronegativity (NCl_3, H_2Te) must necessarily have zero or

TABLE 1–5. DIPOLE MOMENTS IN esu AND DIFFERENCES IN ELECTRONEGATIVITY

	CH$_4$*	NH$_3$	H$_2$O	HF	Ne*
$\mu \times 10^{18}$	0	1.46	1.84	~2	0
Δx†	0.4	0.9	1.4	1.9	—
	SiH$_4$*	PH$_3$	H$_2$S	HCl	A*
$\mu \times 10^{18}$	0	0.55	0.93	1.03	0
Δx	−0.3	0.0	0.4	0.9	—
	GeH$_4$*	AsH$_3$	H$_2$Se	HBr	Kr*
$\mu \times 10^{18}$	0	0.15	~0.4	0.78	0
Δx	−0.3	−0.1	0.3	0.7	—
	SnH$_4$*	SbH$_3$	H$_2$Te	HI	Xe*
$\mu \times 10^{18}$	0	~0.1	~0.2	0.38	0
Δx	−0.4	−0.3	0.1	0.4	—

* Symmetrical molecules.   † Difference in electronegativity.

nearly zero permanent dipole moment. As the difference of electronegativity between two elements increases, however, the greater will be the separation of charge within the molecule and the larger the dipole moment. Examples of this are shown in Table 1–5.

1–7.   Induced Dipole Moment and van der Waals Forces

An imposed electric field may have more effect on a molecule than just to cause it to orient its (permanent) dipole with the field. Let us, for example, consider the monatomic argon molecule, which consists merely of the positive (+18) nucleus and the symmetrical cloud of 18 electrons around it. The permanent dipole of such a completely symmetric molecule is zero.

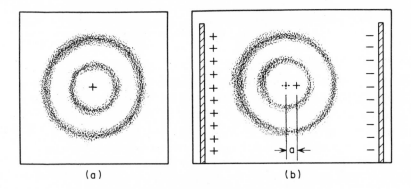

(a)   (b)

Fig. 1–19. (a) The Symmetrical Neon Atom.
(b) The Neon Atom in an Electric Field.

The effect of an external electric field on such a molecule is to cause the centers of positive and negative charge (which originally coincided) to separate. This gives rise to a nonpermanent or induced dipole moment (Fig. 1–19).

It is factors of this sort which give rise to the weak attractive forces known as van der Waals forces. Let us consider two argon atoms close to each other. Although the *centers* of positive and negative charge in each atom are the same, the distributions of positive and negative charge are not. The positive charge is concentrated at the centers, whereas the negative charge is diffused in clouds around the centers. As a consequence, from *very close range* the positive fields of the nuclei will not be completely neutralized or screened by the electrons. The magnitude of the effect by which the inner electrons screen the outer electrons from the nuclear charge depends on the distribution of the electrons and becomes successively less for *s*, *p*, *d*, and *f* electrons (see Section 10–1). This means then that the positive nucleus of one atom will still have some effect on the electron cloud of a nearby atom, resulting in induced polarization and mutual attraction. These necessarily short-range attractive forces are the so-called van der Waals forces.

In addition to these two types of polarity, the dipole moment of a molecule already having a permanent dipole may be increased in an electric field by having the distance between the centers of charge of the permanent dipole increased by an electric field (Fig. 1–20).

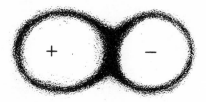

Fig. 1–20. (a) A Polar Molecule.

(b) The Polar Molecule in an Electric Field.

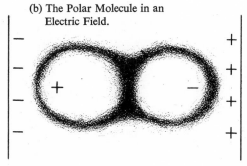

1–8.   Dielectric Constant

The dipole moment is a property of individual molecules. The *dielectric constant* is a measure of how the substance responds *in bulk* to an electric field.

Let us consider what happens to the electrical system of the positive and negative plate described above when a polar substance is placed between the plates. Such a system of plates is called a *condenser*. The amount of positive and negative charge which can be built up on the plates of a condenser (its capacity) is determined by the size of the condenser plates and the distance between them. The larger the plates and the closer the plates are to each other, the higher the capacity. If a polar substance is placed between the plates, this has the effect of moving the plates together, since the positive poles of the molecules will now be closer to the negative plate than the positive plate itself is, and the negative poles are closer to the positive plate than the negative plate is. The result is to increase the capacity of the condenser. The amount by which the capacity is increased is the *dielectric constant* of the substance, i.e.

(capacity with substance)/(capacity in vacuum) = dielectric constant

Another way of looking at it is that the force of attraction between the plates of the condenser has been reduced. The factor by which it has been reduced is the dielectric constant.

It is easy to see that there should be a relationship between the dipole moment and the dielectric constant. However, the relationship is not a simple one. It can also be seen that since an increase of temperature will increase the vibration of the molecules, higher temperatures will tend to prevent the molecular dipoles' orienting themselves in the electric field, thus decreasing the dielectric constant. The value of the dielectric constant is consequently dependent upon the temperature.

If instead of condenser plates we consider the ions of a salt (e.g., $NaCl$), it can be seen that the force of attraction between the ions will be less in a medium of high dielectric constant than it is in air. Consequently, ionic substances have a tendency to go into solution in solvents of high dielectric constant, as, for example, water (dielectric constant 80).

1–9.   Electronegativity

Much has been said about electronegativity. It is merely a measure of the strength with which an atom in a molecule holds or attracts bonding electrons to itself. Electronegativity (x) is roughly a function of the size and effective nuclear charge of the atom

$$x = aZ_{eff}/r^2$$

where a is a constant of proportionality. The "effective nuclear charge" is the real nuclear charge reduced by the "screening" effect of all the inner electrons. For two hypothetical atoms of identical effective nuclear charge but different size, the smaller should be the more electronegative. Conversely, for two atoms of identical size but differing effective nuclear charge, the one of higher effective nuclear charge should be the more electronegative. As we cross the periodic table in any given direction, then, if the atomic size increases faster than the effective nuclear charge, the electronegativity will decrease. On the other hand, if the effective nuclear charge increases faster than the size, the electronegativity will increase. Thus, as we go down

Li   the columns of the alkali metals or the halogens,   F
Na   the size of the atoms increases rapidly, and the   Cl
K   electronegativity decreases. On the other hand, as we   Br
Rb   proceed across the fourth period—K, Ca, Sc, Ti, V,   I
Cs   Cr, Mn, Fe, Co, Ni, Cu—in which the size decreases,   At
Fr   or down a column in which the size remains nearly
                         Cu
              constant, Ag, the electronegativity increases, since the
                         Au
              effective nuclear charge increases in each case.

It may be said that, as one proceeds from the least electronegative of all the elements, francium, in the lower left-hand corner of the table (electronegativity = 0.65), to the most electronegative, fluorine, in the upper right-hand corner (electronegativity = 4.0), the electronegativity *generally* increases. However, reference to the electronegativity map (Fig. 1-21) will

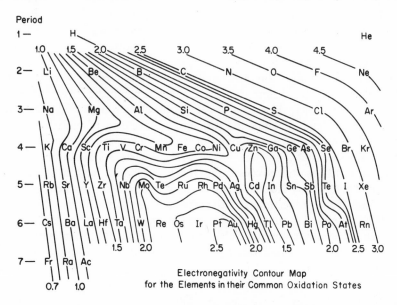

Electronegativity Contour Map
for the Elements in their Common Oxidation States

Fig. 1-21. Electronegativity Contour Map For the Elements in their Common Oxidation States.

show that in actual fact there is a "trough" of low electronegavity centered around zinc and cadmium, and that in reality the electronegativity rises regularly as one goes from left to right, until the Cu-Ag-Au family is reached; falls suddenly with Zn and Cd; and then slowly climbs again to a maximum in the halogens.

The electronegativity values of the second-period elements may be very easily remembered, since they differ from each other by a half unit

Li	Be	B	C	N	O	F
1.0	1.5	2.0	2.5	3.0	3.5	4.0

1-10. The Relationship of Electronegativity and Polarity

It has already been stated that, if two atoms bonded to each other differ in electronegativity, there will be unequal sharing of the electrons in the bond and a dipole will result. The degree of inequality of sharing is expressed as a dipole moment if the distance between the centers of charge is taken into consideration, but may be expressed more generally as a percentage of complete separation or a "degree of ionic character" of the *still-covalent* bond. The quantitative relationship for this, according to Hannay and Smyth, is

$$\text{degree ionic character} = 0.16\,|x_A - x_B| + 0.035\,(x_A - x_B)^2$$

where x_A and x_B are the electronegativities of elements A and B respectively. It follows that a "50 percent ionic" bond will be formed when the difference in electronegativity (Δx) is 2.1. It can be seen that for Δx's less than 0.5, the degree of ionic character is essentially proportional to Δx, since the term $0.035\,(x_A - x_B)^2$ becomes too small to be important.

Since the electronegativity differences between elements close to each other in the periodic table are small, compounds formed between two or more elements situated close to each other will generally be covalent and have little or no polarity, depending on the actual electronegativity differences. On the other hand, a compound formed by two elements moderately separated will be polar, and a compound of two elements widely separated will be ionic. For example, carbon—$(CC)_x$—is completely nonpolar ($\Delta x = 0$); BN ($\Delta x = 1.0$) is still covalent, but the B—N bonds have a considerable polarity; BeO ($\Delta x = 2.0$) has some of the properties of a covalent substance and some of the properties of a salt; whereas LiF ($\Delta x = 3.0$) is a true salt.

If a compound is made up of three elements, two nonmetals lying close to each other in the periodic table, and one metal, the two nonmetals will combine with each other through covalent bonds. The groups so formed will take up the electrons from the metal to form a negative ion, while the resulting positive ion from the metal will be associated with the negative group only by electrostatic attraction. Examples of this are

$Na[OH]$, $K[ClO]$, $K[CN]$, $K_3[AsS_4]$, $Ba[TeI_6]$, $K[SbCl_6]$, $Na_2[S_2O_3]$, $Na[SO_3F]$, $Ca[CN_2]$, $K[H_2PO_4]$, $K[NCO]$, $K[NCSe]$, $K[CH_3COS]$, etc.

If the two elements close together in the periodic table are both metals, then there will be no electrons for them to share with each other (for they will have been given to the nonmetal) and only two discrete positive ions will result. Thus $KMgF_3$ consists of K^+, Mg^{+2}, and 3 F^-; $KCaCl_3$ consists of K^+, Ca^{+2}, and 3 Cl^-; and $NaAl(SO_4)_2 \cdot 12\ H_2O$ consists of Na^+, (hydrated) Al^{+3}, and 2 SO_4^{-2}; $K_2Ce(NO_3)_5 \cdot 4H_2O$ consists of 2 K^+, (hydrated) Ce^{+3}, and 5 NO_3^-; and NH_4MgPO_4 consists of NH_4^+, Mg^{+2}, and PO_4^{-3}. This is not to say that it is impossible to have "double" salts with two or more anions. In fact many of these are known, such as $Mg_2(PO_4)F$, $PbClF$, $KMgClSO_4 \cdot 3H_2O$, and so forth.

1-11. The Structure of Polar Liquids

When we consider a liquid, such as water, which is made up of polar molecules, we can see that its molecules should be much more strongly attracted to one another (head-to-tail) than those of a nonpolar liquid. Consequently, only substances whose attraction for water molecules is about as strong as the attraction of water molecules for one another will be able to force the water molecules apart and mix with them—that is, to dissolve in water. Thus we find that other polar substances, such as alcohols, sugars, and so forth, are very soluble in water. Ionic substances, whose ions have a very powerful attraction for water molecules, are also soluble in water, provided the attraction of the positive and negative ions for each other is not too great, so that they prefer to associate with each other rather than with water molecules. For example, salts like NaCl, KNO_3, and $CaCl_2$ are freely soluble in water, whereas LiF, whose ions are small and attract each other very strongly, is much less soluble. On the other hand, carbon tetrachloride has molecules which have very little attraction for each other, and which by the same token have little attraction for water molecules. Consequently, carbon tetrachloride is almost insoluble in water, and water, likewise, is almost insoluble in carbon tetrachloride.

A salt, such as NaCl, is insoluble in carbon tetrachloride because the Na^+ and Cl^- have far more attraction for each other than they do for nonpolar CCl_4 molecules.

On the other hand, the nonpolar liquid, gasoline, mixes in all proportions with CCl_4. This is not because gasoline molecules have attraction for CCl_4 molecules, but rather because neither kind has much attraction for its fellows, and therefore does not oppose molecules of the other kind intermingling. The justification can now be seen for the statement, "Like dissolves like."

1–12. The Dissolution of a Salt in Water

Since we shall be dealing largely with the solubilities of ionic substances in water, it would be wise to have some conception of what happens when a salt goes into aqueous solution. The surfaces and edges of simple substances like NaCl are made up of alternating positive and negative ions. The ions on the edges, and particularly on the corners, are especially vulnerable to attack by water molecules and are therefore taken into solution more rapidly than those on flat surfaces. The molecules are attracted to the ions (all the same end toward an ion of particular charge) and yet still are pulled away by other water molecules. Consequently, there is a strong pull on the ions on the crystal edges and corners to move out into solution. When a sufficient number of water molecules congregates around a given ion, the pull into solution overcomes the attraction of the other ions in the crystal, and the ion goes into solution. Once the ion is in solution, of course, it becomes completely surrounded (solvated) by water molecules.

1–13. Molecular Weights

From a knowledge of the weight percentages of the various elements in a compound, and from the atomic weights of the elements, it is possible to

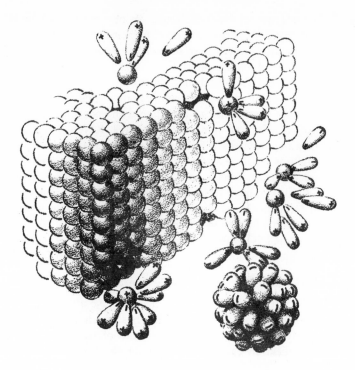

Fig. 1–22. Schematic Representation of the Dissolution of an Ionic Crystal in Water.

calculate the molecular weight of a compound. For example, methane has the analysis 25.13 percent hydrogen and 74.87 percent carbon. Since the atomic weights of hydrogen and carbon are 1.008 and 12.010 respectively, this tell us that methane has four hydrogen atoms for every carbon atom and the formula is CH_4. The sum of the atomic weights of the atoms in the formula is 16.042. Since it is known that methane, whether gaseous, liquid, or solid, consists of discrete CH_4 molecules, the value 16.042 is the molecular weight—or if expressed in grams it is the gram-molecular weight. One gram-molecular weight is frequently called a *mole*.

On the other hand, calcium iodide has the composition 13.64 percent calcium and 86.36 percent iodine. It must therefore have a ratio of one calcium atom to two iodine atoms, with the formula CaI_2, and the sum of the atomic weights is 293.92. In this case, however, there are no discrete CaI_2 molecules, since crystalline CaI_2 is made up of individual Ca^{+2} and I^- ions in the ratio of one to two. It might almost be said that a whole crystal is a single molecule made up of a tremendous number of Ca^{+2} and I^- ions. No matter what the size of the crystal, however, the *ratio* of Ca^{+2} to I^- is always one to two. Consequently, the expression "CaI_2" represents not a molecule but only the ratio of atoms, or the simplest formula. Consequently, the number 293.92, although it is frequently called the molecular weight, is perhaps better called the formula weight. When the formula weight is expressed in grams, we have the gram-formula weight, which is also called a *mole*.

1–14. Concentration Units

Simple solutions are made up of two components, the *solvent* and the *solute*. If the solution consists of a mixture of two liquids, the component present in the larger amount is considered to be the solvent and the other the solute. If one component is normally a solid and the other a liquid, the liquid is considered to be the solvent. If both components in a *homogeneous* mixture are solids (a "solid solution"), again the one present in the larger amount is considered to be the solvent. We shall be concerned primarily with solutions of solids, liquids, and gases in water.

The amount of solute dissolved in a specified amount of solvent is its *concentration*. Concentrations may be expressed in many different ways.

Weight-percent expresses the number of parts by weight of solute dissolved in 100 parts by weight of total solution (solute plus solvent). Thus a 10 weight-percent solution of NaCl in water has 10 grams of NaCl dissolved in 90 grams of water—or 100 grams total of solution.

Mole-percent expresses the number of moles of solute dissolved in 100 moles of total solution. Thus the solution of 10 grams of NaCl dissolved in 90 grams of water, which contains 0.1711 moles of NaCl and 4.9904 moles of H_2O, has a NaCl concentration of

$$\frac{0.1711}{0.1711 + 4.9904} \times 100 = 3.31 \; mole\text{-}percent$$

Molality expresses the number of moles of solute dissolved in 1000 grams of *solvent*. Thus, the solution containing 10 grams of NaCl in 90 grams of water (0.1711 moles of NaCl in 90 grams of water) would contain 1.901 moles of NaCl in 1000 grams of water ($0.1711 \times \frac{1000}{90}$), and is therefore a 1.901 *molal* solution.

Molarity expresses the number of moles of solute dissolved in one liter of final *solution*. Our 10 percent by weight NaCl solution is found to have a density of 1.0707 g/ml. Consequently, one liter of this solution will weigh 1070.7 grams, 10 percent of which, or 107.07 grams, is NaCl. This is thus a 1.831 molar solution. Molarity is frequently given the symbol M.

$$\frac{1000 \; ml \times 1.0706 \; g/ml \times 0.10}{58.46 \; g/(mole \; NaCl)} = 1.831 \; moles/liter = 1.831 \; M$$

Normality is like molarity, except that it expresses the number of gram-equivalent weights dissolved in one liter of solution. If one mole of a substance contains one gram-equivalent weight, then the molarity and normality of solutions of the substance will be the same. Thus our 1.831 *molar* solution of NaCl is also 1.831 *normal*. The gram-equivalent weight is defined (for an acid or base) as the weight of a substance necessary to give one mole of hydrogen ion or hydroxide ion, respectively, in a neutralization reaction; or (for a salt) as the weight of salt resulting from the neutralization of one gram-equivalent weight of acid by one gram-equivalent weight of base; or (for an oxidizing or reducing agent) as a mole of the substance divided by the number of electrons involved in the half-reaction for the reduction or oxidation considered (see Section 11-6).

By far the most important expression of concentration for our purposes is molarity.

It must be emphasized that the *concentration* of a solution bears no relationship to the *amount* of it. Thus a solution of 10.707 grams of NaCl in 100 ml of solution is 1.831 molar, just as truly as the solution of 107.07 grams of NaCl in one liter of solution, since the *ratio* of moles of solute to volume of solution is the same for each

$$\frac{0.1831 \text{ moles}}{100 \text{ ml}} = \frac{1.831 \text{ moles}}{1000 \text{ ml}} = 1.831 \text{ molar}$$

pH. The concentration of hydrogen ion is so important to the chemistry of aqueous solutions that a special unit has been devised to express it. This is *pH*, which is defined as the *negative logarithm of the hydrogen-ion concentration*.

$$\text{pH} = -\log [\text{H}^+]$$

or
$$[\text{H}^+] = 10^{-\text{pH}}$$

The pH scale is based on the self-ionization of water, which is discussed further in Section 7-1. Water undergoes self-ionization

$$\text{H}_2\text{O} \rightleftharpoons \text{H}^+ + \text{OH}^-$$

to a very slight degree. It is found that in water and dilute aqueous solutions

$$[\text{H}^+][\text{OH}^-] = 10^{-14}$$

where the square brackets signify "molar concentration of" the substance indicated inside. This equation means that the product of the concentration of the hydrogen ions in the solution times the concentration of the hydroxide ions in the solution must be a constant, whose value is 10^{-14}. Consequently, if the hydroxide-ion concentration is increased (making the solution more basic), the hydrogen-ion concentration must automatically decrease (i.e., the solution becomes less acidic). In pure water or in a neutral solution, the hydrogen- and hydroxide-ion concentrations must be equal, $[\text{H}^+] = [\text{OH}^-]$, and therefore,

$$[\text{H}^+] = \sqrt{10^{-14}} = 10^{-7} \ M$$

The pH, therefore, is 7. In very basic solution the $[\text{H}^+]$ is much lower and the pH, therefore, higher. Thus in 0.1 M NaOH, the $[\text{H}^+]$ is $1 \times 10^{-13} \ M$, and the pH is 13. In 0.05 M HCl solution, on the other hand, the $[H^+]$ is 5×10^{-2} M or $(10^{0.7} \times 10^{-2})$ M or $10^{-1.3}$ M. The pH is, therefore, 1.3. In very concentrated acid the $[H^+]$ may become very high, the logarithm of the concentration being positive. The pH then becomes negative. Thus, if $[H^+] = 8$ $M = 10^{0.9}$ M, then the pH $= -0.9$. (See Appendix 12 on the use of logarithms.)

1–15. The Laboratory

The laboratory is the workshop in which you will actually examine representative substances and reactions so that you can see at firsthand the qualities and effects about which you are learning. If the laboratory work is approached "cookbook style," and the experiments and procedures are carried out mechanically, they will be of little benefit. On the other hand, if it be realized that *every* observation made in the laboratory, *even if the experiment does not go as expected*, can teach you something about the nature of the substances with which you are working, the laboratory will have done you good. It is, of course, necessary to know pretty much what you are going to do before you go into the laboratory.

In order to be able to interpret your observations correctly, it is necessary that you know exactly what you have done. Therefore, it is essential that housekeeping in the laboratory be of a high degree of excellence. Slovenly housekeeping leads to contaminated solutions and contaminated reagents. The presence of unknown contaminants in your reaction mixtures may lead to reactions quite different from what is reasonable for the substances you think you have present, with consequent misinterpretation of results. Therefore, it is essential to keep all glassware scrupulously clean—with final rinsings with distilled water—and to avoid any physical contact of reagent bottles, or droppers from reagent bottles, with any other equip-

Fig. 1–23. "Let the Drops Fall Free!"

ment or solution. In this respect, drops of reagent solutions from reagent droppers should always be allowed to fall free from the dropper into the vessel to which it is being delivered. Do not allow the dropper to touch the side of the vessel. Do not even allow the *drop* to touch the vessel while it is still in contact with the dropper. There is, of course, some danger of splashing from the free-falling drop, and the drop should be made to fall as short a distance as possible, preferably onto the tilted wall of the vessel. The danger of splashing is much less, however, than the danger of contamination by contact—which is a virtual certainty. Also, to avoid contamination, no reagent, once removed from the bottle, must *ever* be put back Do not take out more reagent than you need in the first place.

Untidy housekeeping is also a source of personal danger. Spilled reagents can lead to damaged clothing and chemical burns which may be very serious. The whole laboratory should be kept scrupulously clean at all times.

The chemicals and apparatus with which you work are potentially dangerous and should be treated with intelligence and respect. The mixing of concentrated acids with water or concentrated bases, for example, should be done only with utmost caution, or not at all. Likewise, the mixing of powerful oxidizing and reducing agents is to be discouraged. When you are working with glass, make sure that all edges are fire-polished and be sure to protect your hands whenever you must apply pressure, as when you are fitting glass tubing into rubber tubing or a rubber stopper, or when pushing a tight stopper into a flask.

However, despite all the precautions you take to handle your equipment properly, there inevitably will be accidents, either your own or your neighbor's (don't forget him!). Consequently you should avail yourself of protective equipment, such as an apron or a lab coat to protect your clothing and, above all, glasses to protect your eyes. Some people also like to wear thin rubber gloves to protect the hands, but these make manipulations more awkward and, in general, unless you are an expert, lead to more accidents than they prevent.

A cardinal rule of conduct in the laboratory—which should be so obvious as to be unworthy of mention—is that there must be absolutely no horseplay.

The various manipulations which you will be performing will include precipitating solids out of solution, separating those solids from the supernatant solution, washing them free of the solution which clings to them, digestion of precipitates, or heating of solutions and evaporation. Such operations as cleaning of glassware and making flame tests will also be carried out.

Precipitation. In order to precipitate a substance from solution, a quantity of the precipitating agent sufficient to cause the solubility-product constant (see Chapter 3) of the substance to be substantially exceeded must be added to the solution. The mixture must then be thoroughly stirred with a clean stirring rod to ensure complete mixing. (Do not shake the tube with your finger over the mouth. This may cause chemical burns and may also contaminate the solution, either with the natural chemicals of the skin, e.g., NaCl, or with deposits from previous shakings.) If the nature of the precipitation is such as to require it, heat the mixture in a water bath, *not* over an open flame. (The intense heat of the flame may cause sudden explosive boiling, or "bumping," which will cause the solution to shoot out of the tube.

The possible danger and loss of time and sample are not sufficiently compensated for by the slight saving of heating time. Be sure that your test tube is never aimed at a neighbor during heating.)

Use of the Centrifuge. When the precipitate has been formed, it must be separated from the supernatant liquid (the "supernate"). This may be

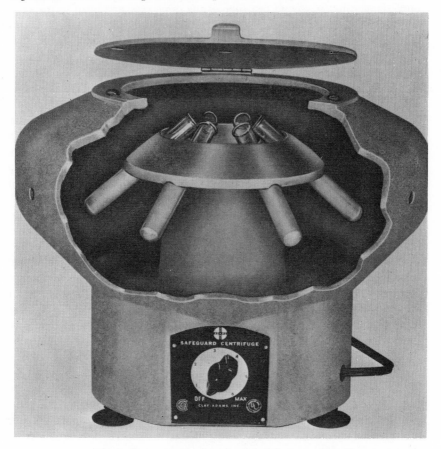

Fig. 1–24. Cut-away View of a Laboratory Centrifuge.

accomplished by filtering the mixture through a paper of the appropriate degree of fineness. In general, however, centrifugation is just as efficient, if not actually more desirable, and results in less loss of solution. A centrifuge is an apparatus which by whirling the samples at high speed in a circle generates centrifugal force considerably greater than the force of gravity, thereby causing the solid (which is usually denser than the liquid) to settle more rapidly than it would settle due to gravity.

$$\text{Centrifugal force (in gravities)} = \frac{\text{diameter (in feet)} \times (\text{rpm})^2}{6000}$$

Thus, if a centrifuge runs at 1500 rpm, and the sample is 6 inches ($\frac{1}{2}$ foot) from the center, the centrifugal force will be 187.5 gravities. Consequently, the precipitate will settle 187.5 times as fast as it would by merely standing and settling under the influence of gravity. It is important that a centrifuge be properly balanced during use. An improperly balanced centrifuge can be quite dangerous. A second test tube of the same size, and filled to the same level as the sample tube, must always be placed opposite the sample in the centrifuge to act as a counterbalance. Occasionally a tube of sample will break in a centrifuge, for example, if it had a little crack in it, some sharp object was left under it, or through some other mishap. Any such spills should be immediately cleaned up lest they corrode the expensive centrifuge mechanism.

Centrifugation should be continued until the supernate is perfectly clear. (Note the distinction between "clear" and "colorless." A colorless solution need not be clear. That is, a solution which has no color—red, green, brown, and so forth—may nevertheless not be clear, i.e., it may be turbid—it may contain suspended colorless—white—material which inhibits the passage of light. If the turbidity is slight, the solution is sometimes described as "milky" or "opalescent." On the other hand, a solution may be perfectly clear but not colorless. For example, a solution of copper nitrate is not colorless—it is blue—but it may be clear, i.e., objects can be seen through it distinctly.) The time required for centrifugation will depend not only on the centrifugal force but also on such factors as the viscosity of the solution, the difference in density between the solid and the solution, and the size of the particles of the solid—the smaller the particles, the slower the sedimentation. In this last respect, it can be seen that colloidal suspensions will take much longer to settle than suspensions of larger particles. After centrifugation is complete, no further benefit can be derived from running the centrifuge longer, so the machine should be made available for others to use.

Testing for Completeness of Precipitation. The supernate must now be tested to make sure that enough precipitating agent was added to give complete precipitation of the desired substance. To this end *one* more drop of precipitating agent solution should be added to the supernate *without stirring the precipitate.* If this causes more precipitation, add a few more drops of precipitant and stir. Centrifuge and repeat the test for completeness of precipitation.

Separation of Precipitate and Supernate. When addition of more precipitant no longer produces any additional precipitation, the supernate may be removed from the centrifuged precipitate by either of two methods. The first of these amounts to simply turning the test tube upside down and letting the supernate run out—into another vessel if more operations are to be carried out on it, or into a waste vessel (or sink) if the liquid is to be discarded. Especially if small centrifuge cones are being used, however, it will be noticed that some liquid will always remain in the tube, being held by capillary action. To remove the remaining liquid, *while the tube is still inverted*, insert a small stirring rod against the inside of the tube so that the tip reaches *almost* to the precipitate (Fig. 1–25). The liquid will then flow out between the rod and the tube wall. *Do not return the test tube to the upright position before removing the last of the liquid with the rod.* If you do, liquid will flow down the inner wall and roil the precipitate so that when the test tube is inverted again *everything* will flow out.

The second method of removing the supernate may be somewhat safer for the novice. For this it will be necessary to make some capillary dropper pipets, either by drawing out glass tubing of appropriate size in the Bunsen flame, or by welding a bit of glass rod to the tip of an ordinary dropper pipet

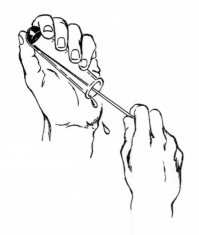

Fig. 1–25. Removal of
Supernate by Decantation.

Fig. 1–26. Dropping
and Capillary Pipets.

and using it as a handle to pull the pipet out to a long capillary form (Fig. 1–26). The capillary tips on these pipets should be thick enough not to break easily and long enough to reach the bottom of a 3 ml test tube. Such a pipet is used to withdraw the supernate from over a centrifuged precipitate. The air is expelled from the pipet *before* it is inserted into the supernate. Since the capacity of the pipet will usually not be as great as the total volume of liquid to be withdrawn, the pipet should *not* be inserted all the way to the bottom, but only far enough to allow the pipet to be filled. When the point has been reached at which one more withdrawal will remove the last of the liquid, the tip of the pipet should be rested against the inner wall of the test tube (to prevent roiling the precipitate through trembling of the hand), just above the surface of the precipitate (Fig. 1–27), and the remaining liquid *slowly* withdrawn so as not to suck up the precipitate along with the liquid. Be sure that no air or liquid is expelled from the pipet while it is in the test tube, since this would roil the precipitate. If the precipitate does becomes roiled, centrifuge again all that remains in the tube.

Washing the Precipitate. Even after all visible liquid has been removed from the precipitate, it will still be mixed with liquid which contains the soluble substances remaining in the supernate. This must also be removed to prevent interference by contaminating ions with the reactions to be carried out. The precipitate therefore must be washed. Distilled water (perhaps 0.5 ml) is added from a wash bottle and used as such or with a few drops of the required reagent added to it. Alternatively, a reagent solution (such as dilute NH_4OH) may be used directly for washing. The precipitate is thoroughly stirred up in the wash liquor. This may be done by holding the tube at the top in one hand and tapping or flicking the bottom of it with a finger of the

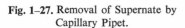

Fig. 1–27. Removal of Supernate by
Capillary Pipet.

Fig. 1–28.
The Washbottle.

other hand. If this does not accomplish complete mixing, a stirring rod should be used; it must be washed off into the tube with a stream of water from the wash bottle after use. The slurried precipitate is now centrifuged down again, the supernatant wash liquor removed and discarded unless otherwise specified, and the washing procedure repeated at least once.

If, on the other hand, it is necessary to transfer a precipitate from one vessel to another, water (or other appropriate reagent) is added, and the precipitate stirred up in it as in the washing procedure. Instead of centrifuging, however, the slurry is poured or removed with a capillary pipet into the new vessel. If a spatula is used to transfer a precipitate, it will be necessary to wash the precipitate which clings to it into the new vessel with a fine stream of water from the wash bottle.

The Wash Bottle. The wash bottle should be made to look like that in Fig. 1–28. It is shown as having been made from an Erlenmeyer flask, but a Florence flask can be used as well. A piece of glass tubing long enough for the left-hand tube should be cut with a file (protect your hands), and the ends fire-polished. Hold the center of the tube above the inner cone of a Bunsen flame equipped with a fishtail. Rotate the tubing in the flame until it is soft enough to bend. *Remove the tubing from the flame* and bend smoothly (taking care not to collapse it) until an angle of about 120 degrees is achieved. Lay aside to cool. A longer piece of tubing is now similarly heated about the same distance from one end and bent to give a 60-degree angle, so that when assembled with the previous piece the two of them will form a straight line. This is done so that you can look straight along the delivery tube when you are blowing into the wash bottle and see where the stream of water is going. After the long piece is cool, the long end of it should be inserted through one hole of the rubber stopper, using water, saliva, or glycerol for lubrication. *Be sure to protect your hand, and do not force the glass.* After the glass is in place, heat it again, well below the stopper, and make a shallow bend in it so that the end will be directed forward into what will be the bottom corner of the wash bottle when it is tilted forward. Adjust the position of the tube in the stopper so that it will not quite touch the bottom when the stopper is firmly fixed in the neck of the flask. Now insert the first tube into the other hole of the stopper and align it with the delivery tube. Draw out a short capillary tip in the same manner as when you made your capillary pipets and attach it to the delivery tube through a piece of rubber tubing. *The lower end of this tip should be higher than the water level in the bottle;* otherwise, the water will syphon out after the first use. Since the upper tube will be in your mouth and will be contaminated with saliva, *water should never be poured through it into a reaction mixture.* It should be cleaned periodically, lest saliva find its way down into the distilled water.

Concentration. After operations have been carried out on a solution, it is frequently necessary to concentrate it in order to carry out further operations effectively. Usually this is done by putting the solution into a small casserole or evaporating dish (which the solution does not more than half fill) and carefully evaporating over a water bath or open flame. If the latter is used, the flame should be low, and the dish should be kept constantly in circular motion to facilitate evaporation and prevent bumping. If evaporation is to be carried to dryness, pains must be taken to avoid spattering toward the end of the heating. The flame should be removed just before the last liquid leaves; otherwise, the solids may be baked into an intractable mass. Placing a watch glass over the casserole toward the end of the evaporation will prevent material from spattering out. The material spattered onto the watch glass should be washed back into the casserole with a fine stream of distilled water after completion of the evaporation. Evaporations liberating corrosive or noxious fumes must always be done in the fume hood.

Another means of concentrating substances in solution is by precipitating them and redissolving them in a smaller volume of solution. This technique is customarily used to concentrate such elements as arsenic, antimony, molybdenum, and tin after they have been leached out of their mixture with the copper-group sulfides by an alkaline reagent such as ammoniacal ammonium sulfide or potassium hydroxide. These elements are precipitated in the concentrated form of their solid sulfides by acidulation of the solution. For example

$$SnS_2 \text{ (s)} + S^{-2} \rightarrow SnS_3{}^{-2}$$
$$SnS_3{}^{-2} + 2 H^+ \rightarrow SnS_2 \text{ (s)} + H_2S \text{ (g)}$$

Determining pH. It will frequently be necessary to test the pH of solutions. This is most easily done with some sort of indicator paper. *Under no circumstances should the paper be dipped into the solution,* for contamination of the solution will result. Always test for pH by removing a drop of the solution to be tested from the test tube with a *clean* stirring rod and touching it to the test paper.

Cleaning the Equipment. It has been mentioned that your apparatus should always be scrupulously clean. If dirty glassware is allowed to stand, especially when dry, it frequently becomes inordinately difficult to clean. Dirty glassware should therefore be cleaned at the earliest possible moment. If it is not possible to clean it immediately, it is good practice to leave it under water. For example, small pieces, such as test tubes, can be kept in a beaker of water while awaiting cleaning.

The most universal cleansing agent and the one which should always be used first is a mixture of soap or detergent and elbow grease. If this fails, then various chemical reagents can be used. For stubborn deposits of metal oxides, concentrated HCl or HCl + HNO_3 (aqua regia) may be used. For sulfides and other oxidizable substances, HNO_3, especially if warmed (*use extreme caution!*), or aqua regia is effective. A very useful cleaning solution can be made by dissolving $K_2Cr_2O_7$ in concentrated sulfuric acid. However, this is much more effective when hot, and may be too dangerous to use. If the deposit can be removed by reducing it (e.g., CeO_2), hydrochloric acid containing a little potassium iodide is useful.

Any of the above reagents is useful for removing basic deposits. On the other hand, acidic deposits dissolve more easily in basic cleansers. A particularly useful one is made by dissolving $KMnO_4$ (or better, $NaMnO_4$) in NaOH. This must be used cold. Glassware should not be left in it too long because of the attack of strong alkalies on glass. This solution may deposit a brownish film of MnO_2 on the glassware, which may be removed by washing with concentrated HCl or with dilute HNO_3 containing some H_2O_2.

After being cleaned with a cleaning agent, the glassware must be thoroughly rinsed with distilled water and set on a paper or clean towel to drain and dry. *Do not put dripping equipment into your locker or desk drawer.*

Reagents. The reagents which you use most frequently are best kept in your desk in individual bottles. The dilute acids and bases may be kept in bottles fitted with droppers having rubber bulbs. Because of their attack on rubber, however, 12 M hydrochloric acid, 15 and 6 M nitric acid and 18 M sulfuric acid should be kept in glass-stoppered bottles. The stoppers or droppers for these bottles must never be laid down on the bench top or other place where they can be contaminated or leave dangerous smears of reagents. The same precautions against contamination must be applied to these re-agents as to the reagents for general use. A list of useful reagents to be kept in the desk is

6 M acetic acid	18 M sulfuric acid (concentrated)
12 M hydrochloric acid (concentrated)	6 M sulfuric acid
6 M hydrochloric acid	6 M ammonium hydroxide
3 M hydrochloric acid	3 M ammonium hydroxide
15 M nitric acid (concentrated)	6 M sodium hydroxide
6 M nitric acid	

Concentrated (15 M) ammonium hydroxide, although frequently used, is best kept in community bottles on the bench top, because by reason of its great volatility it tends to deposit NH_4Cl on the equipment in the desk drawer by reacting with the volatile concentrated HCl.

The Laboratory Notebook. You must have with you in the laboratory at all times a *bound* notebook in which to keep a record of what you do. This is to be a record of what you actually did and what you actually observed. Consequently *it must be written as you perform the experiments.* To write up the procedure ahead of time merely tells what you *expect* to do when you get into the laboratory, whereas what you actually do may be something quite different. Likewise, observations written down afterward from (a fre-quently faulty) memory may be seriously in error and are of no scientific value whatever. Notes taken on slips of paper for subsequent transcription into the bound notebook are subject to loss; they are also poor because of the frequent tendency to take them in abbreviated form with the intention of expanding them when they are transcribed. To those who object that a note-book kept during experimentation is liable to be soiled by chemical stains and smeared by splashes of water, it can only be said that dirty notes which give an accurate account of what was done are invaluable, while unsullied notes which do not give an accurate account are valueless. The notes should be full enough to give a *complete* description of what was done and observed, *and no more.* The following rules should be observed

1. The notes must be made *in ink.*

2. Every *operation and observation* must be written up at the time it is made.

3. Notes must be kept on the analyses of unknowns as well as on the preliminary experiments.

4. *Ionic* equations should be on the same horizontal line as the correspond-ing operations and observations. (These should be added later, so as not to waste laboratory time.)

5. Each page should be signed and dated at the bottom.

6. A *suggested* format for the notebook is given on page 32.

NOTEBOOK

Left-hand page   Right-hand page

Title*.................   Group No.
                                       Date Started
                                       Date Completed

EQUATIONS   *OPERATIONS*   *OBSERVATIONS*

Balanced ionic equations for all   Include brief résumé of   Indicate color of ppts.
reactions here. This applies to   method for carrying out   and solns. Solubility of
all preliminary tests and analyses the test.   ppts., etc.
for unknown solutions.

* Title will be as follows (indicate proper one)
        Preliminary tests for group no....................................
        Analysis of unknown solution for group no. ....
        Other appropriate title ....

1–16. Questions and Problems

1. Why are small crystals more soluble than large ones?

2. What is the difference between a crystal and a glass?

3. What is the dielectric constant of a liquid?

4. Explain what is meant by an induced dipole moment.

5. What is a dipole moment?

6. How many ml of 0.10 M NaOH are required to neutralize the following amounts of acids?
   (a) 35 ml of 0.12 M HCl
   (b) 46 ml of 0.32 M H_2SO_4
   (c) 10 ml of 0.55 M HNO_3
   (d) 5 ml of 0.05 M H_3PO_4
   (e) 25 ml of 0.25 M $HC_2H_3O_2$

7. What is the normality of the following solutions?
   (a) 52 grams NaOH/liter
   (b) 6.2 grams KOH/liter
   (c) 5 grams $NaHCO_3$/250 ml
   (d) 15 grams $HClO_4$/liter
   (e) 9.8 grams H_2SO_4/liter
   (f) 7.3 grams HCl/500 ml

8. What is the molarity of the following solutions?
   (a) 0.2 grams $MnCl_2$/250 ml
   (b) 52 grams NaOH/liter
   (c) 9.3 grams $KMnO_4$/100 ml
   (d) 10.5 grams KCl/500 ml
   (e) 0.036 grams $Al_2(SO_4)_3$/liter
   (f) 15 grams $NaClO_4$/100 ml

9. What is the normality of a 40 percent HCl solution whose density is 1.20 g/ml?

10. How many milliliters of 70 percent HNO_3 (density 1.42) will be required to prepare 100 ml of a 5 N HNO_3 solution?

1–17.   References

GENERAL

Pauling, Linus, *General Chemistry*, 2d ed. San Francisco: W. M. Freeman and Company, 1950.

Wells, A. F., *Structural Inorganic Chemistry*, 2d ed. Oxford: Clarendon Press, 1950.

Van Arkel, A. E., *Molecules and Crystals in Inorganic Chemistry*, 2d ed. New York: Interscience Publishers, Inc., 1956.

McAlpine, R. K., and Soule, B. A., *Prescott and Johnson's Qualitative Chemical Analysis*, 2d ed. New York: D. Van Nostrand Company, Inc., 1933.

Syrkin, Y. K., and Dyatkina, M. E., *Structure of Molecules and the Chemical Bond*. London: Butterworth's Scientific Publications, 1950.

SPECIFIC

Electronegativity:

Allred, A. L., and Rochow, E. G., *Journal of Inorganic and Nuclear Chemistry*, Vol. 5, pp. 264, 269 (1958).

Haïssinsky, M., *Journal de physique*, Vol. 7, p. 7 (1946).

Gordy, W., and Thomas, W. J. O., *Journal of Chemical Physics*, Vol. 24, p. 439 (1956).

Electronegativity and Polarity:

Hannay, N. B., and Smyth, C. P., *Journal of the American Chemical Society*, Vol. 68, p. 171 (1946).

Chapter 2

The Equilibrium Principle

2–1. The Nature of Chemical Equilibrium

The term *equilibrium* has at least two meanings. The first of these is exemplified by a stone poised or balanced at the top of a hill and prevented from rolling down because it is flat on the bottom or because it sits in a small depression. A little push might send it rolling down the hill, but until it *is* pushed it just sits there. This is a case of *static equilibrium*. If the stone were at the bottom of the hill (and there were absolutely no lower place to which it could go), again it would stay put, and again it would be in *static* equilibrium. The latter case is one of true *stability*. The former, which is potentially unstable, is known as *metastability*. Neither type of static equilibrium, however, is of especial interest to us here, although metastability is not an infrequent chemical phenomenon.

Let us consider a mixture of sulfur dioxide and oxygen. If two moles of SO_2 and one mole of O_2 are mixed at 530°C and the total pressure is maintained at 1 atmosphere, the reaction

$$2 SO_2 + O_2 \rightarrow 2 SO_3$$

proceeds until 94 percent of the SO_2 is converted to SO_3; then, further change ceases. If on the other hand, two moles of SO_3 are heated at a total pressure of 1 atmosphere to 530°C, the decomposition reaction

$$2 SO_3 \rightarrow 2 SO_2 + O_2$$

takes place until 94 percent remains unchanged as SO_3, after which no further change is observed.

If the SO_2–O_2 mixture is taken at 900°C, the reaction between SO_2 and O_2 proceeds much more rapidly than before. However, only 18 percent of the SO_2 is converted to SO_3 before no more reaction can be observed. Likewise, if SO_3 is heated under the same conditions, its decomposition proceeds much more rapidly than at 530°C, and apparent reaction stops when 18 percent of it still remains undecomposed.

On the other hand, if the same experiments are carried out at 50°C, no reaction is observed either with $SO_2 + O_2$ or with SO_3 until a vanadium pentoxide or platinum catalyst is introduced into the reaction mixture, whereupon reaction occurs at a relatively slow rate to give essentially 100 percent SO_3, regardless of whether $SO_2 + O_2$ or SO_3 are the starting materials. The introduction of this catalyst into the reaction mixtures at 530°C is found to speed up the reaction considerably, but the composition of the final mixture is the same as before (i.e., 94 percent SO_3).

In all cases where reaction proceeds until a definite limit is reached, it can be said that equilibrium is established. In the case of the uncatalyzed reaction at 50°C, however, true equilibrium is not attained, despite the fact that the SO_2 and O_2 should give 100 percent conversion to SO_3. This, then is a metastable system in which the reaction rate is either zero or negligibly slow.

In those cases in which reaction does take place at an appreciable rate, it will be noticed that the same final composition is reached for each set of conditions regardless of whether the starting point was $SO_2 + O_2$ or SO_3. Therefore, it may be surmised that at equilibrium, both the forward and the reverse reactions are still taking place, but *at equal rates*, so that no further over-all change can be observed. This is a state of *dynamic equilibrium*.

2–2. The Factors Affecting Reaction Rates

In order for two molecules, A and B, to react, it is necessary first of all that they come in contact with each other. Consequently, the rate of a reaction will depend upon the probability that any molecule, A, will collide within a unit time with another molecule, B, with which it can react. Consequently, factors which affect this probability of collision will affect the reaction rate. One such factor is the "population density" of the molecules, i.e., how many molecules of the right kind inhabit the space in which the reaction is to take place. If one molecule, A, moves around in the space, the probability that it will collide with a B molecule depends on how many B molecules there are in the space; i.e., the probability or frequency of collision is proportional to the concentration of B molecules. Likewise, if several A molecules are present, the probability that one of the A's will collide with any B must also be proportional to the number of A molecules in the space, or again, to the concentration of A. Since in gases the concentration (number of molecules per unit volume) is proportional to the pressure, it also follows that for gases the rate of reaction will be proportional to the pressure.

However, every collision of A and B will not necessarily result in reaction, since A and B must collide with enough energy to react. At any given temperature, the molecules have an *average* energy characteristic of that temperature. However, the energies of all the molecules are not the same.

Rather, there is a distribution of energies among the molecules like that shown in Fig. 2–1. If the energy E_a is the energy required for colliding molecules to react, it can be seen that at the low temperature, T_1, very few molecules have the necessary energy to react; at the intermediate temperature, T_2, a small fraction have sufficient energy to react and consequently reaction will proceed slowly; and at the high temperature, T_3, a larger fraction have energies above E_a, resulting in faster reaction.

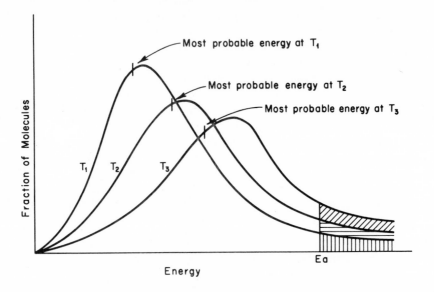

Fig. 2–1. Energy Distribution of Molecules at Various Temperatures.

The energy, E_a, is known as the "activation energy". It can be found experimentally by measuring the reaction rate at two different temperatures. The rate constant is related to T and E_a through the equation

$$k = k'e^{-E_a/RT}$$

where k is the rate constant (see Section 2–3), T is the absolute temperature, R is the gas constant, and e is the mathematical base of natural logarithms. The factor $e^{-E_a/RT}$ comes from the *Boltzmann principle* which states that, for equilibrium at any absolute temperature, T, the ratio of the number of molecules with large energy to the number with small energy is a function of the factor $e^{-\Delta E/RT}$, where ΔE is the difference in the energies. From a mechanistic point of view, it may be considered that two molecules, A and B, which have energies higher than the activation energy, collide and stick together momentarily in an "activated complex," AB, which then rearranges or decomposes to give the product molecules, C and D

$$A + B \rightarrow (AB) \rightarrow C + D$$

The relationships of the energies of the reactants, activated complex, and products are shown in Fig. 2–2. It can be seen that the over-all or net energy of the reaction is the difference between the activation energy and the energy given off when the activated complex decomposes, $E_a - E_{off}$. If this difference is negative, then the reaction may proceed spontaneously; i.e., it is *exothermic*—energy is given out. If the difference is positive, the reaction

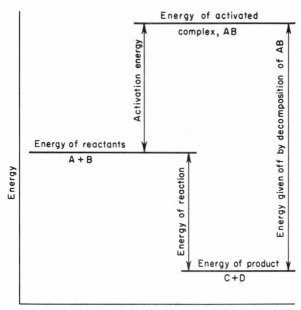

Fig. 2–2. Energy Diagram of the Reaction $A+B \rightleftarrows C+D$.

is *endothermic*; i.e., energy must be supplied to make it proceed. There is no necessary relationship between the activation energy and the energy of reaction.

A second effect of increased temperature is that, because the molecules travel faster at a higher temperature, less time elapses between successive collisions. That is, there are more collisions in a given time. Both of these effects, then, result in increasing the rate of reaction as the temperature rises. *As a general rule-of-thumb, the reaction rate doubles for each 10-degree rise in temperature.*

One further factor which may affect the rate of reaction is the presence of a catalyst. A catalyst speeds up a reaction without affecting it otherwise. It may be considered merely to lower the value of E_a, the lower limit of the energy required for two molecules to react. If the activation energy is lowered for the reaction

$$A+B \rightarrow C+D$$

however, it will be lowered likewise for the reaction

$$C+D \rightarrow A+B$$

and it will be lowered by the same amount (Fig. 2–2). Consequently, *both* the forward and the reverse reactions are speeded up by the same amount. Therefore, as will become apparent later, although a catalyst speeds up a reaction, it does not change the position of the equilibrium. (It should be noted that there are also *negative* catalysts, which correspondingly raise the activation energy and consequently *decrease* the rates of reaction for some systems.)

It is commonly said that a catalyst will not change the course of a chemical reaction. In the strictest sense this is true. For example, when A and B react, if the only reasonable products are C and D, these will be the products whether the reaction is catalyzed or not. However, if C and D are not the only possible products, i.e., if A and B may react in two different ways, the principal or perhaps (for practical purposes) the only products will depend on which way is faster. Under normal conditions, the faster reaction may produce C and D, while the alternative reaction producing E and F is too slow to be observed. If, now, a catalyst is applied which tremendously accelerates the reaction giving E and F without affecting the other reaction, E and F will now become the principal or only products. An example of such a set of competing reactions is that of the oxidation of ammonia by molecular oxygen. In the absence of a catalyst, ammonia burns in air according to the equation

$$4\,NH_3 + 3\,O_2 \rightarrow 2\,N_2 + 6\,H_2O$$

In the presence of a platinum catalyst, however, the reaction is

$$4\,NH_3 + 5\,O_2 \overset{Pt}{\rightarrow} 4\,NO + 6\,H_2O$$

Catalysts may be of two types: (1) contact catalysts, which merely provide a suitable surface on which the reaction can more readily take place, and (2) internal or homogeneous catalysts, which actually enter into the reaction, but are returned to their original state when the reaction has taken place. The distinction between the two types of catalyst is not always clear, however. For example, the platinum catalyst cited above for the oxidation of NH_3 and for SO_2 is fairly clearly a contact catalyst. At first sight so also is the vanadium pentoxide cited for the oxidation of SO_2 to SO_3. However, in all probability some such sequence of reactions as indicated below takes place

$$SO_2\,(g) + V_2O_5\,(s) \rightarrow (VO_2)_2SO_3\,(s)$$
$$(VO_2)_2SO_3\,(s) \rightarrow VOSO_4\,(s) + VO_2\,(s)$$
$$4\,VO_2\,(s) + O_2\,(g) \rightarrow 2\,V_2O_5\,(s)$$
$$4\,VOSO_4\,(s) + O_2\,(g) \rightarrow 2\,(VO_2)_2S_2O_7\,(s)$$
$$(VO_2)_2S_2O_7\,(s) \rightarrow (VO_2)_2SO_4\,(s) + SO_3\,(g)$$
$$(VO_2)_2SO_4\,(s) \rightarrow V_2O_5\,(s) + SO_3\,(g)$$

Ferric oxide can also act as a catalyst for SO_2 oxidation above $480°C$—the decomposition temperature of $Fe_2(SO_4)_3$

$$Fe_2O_3 \text{ (s)} + SO_2 \text{ (g)} \rightarrow (FeO)_2SO_3 \text{ (s)}$$
$$(FeO)_2SO_3 \text{ (s)} \rightarrow FeO \text{ (s)} + FeSO_4 \text{ (s)}$$
$$4 \text{ FeO (s)} + O_2 \text{ (g)} \rightarrow 2 \text{ Fe}_2O_3 \text{ (s)}$$
$$4 \text{ FeSO}_4 \text{ (s)} + O_2 \text{ (g)} \rightarrow 2 \text{ Fe}_2O(SO_4)_2 \text{ (s)}$$
$$Fe_2O(SO_4)_2 \text{ (s)} \rightarrow Fe_2O_3 \text{ (g)} + 2 \text{ SO}_3 \text{ (g)}$$

When all these reactions are added up, the net result is

$$2 \text{ SO}_2 \text{ (g)} + O_2 \text{ (g)} \rightarrow 2 \text{ SO}_3 \text{ (g)}$$

Although both V_2O_5 and Fe_2O_3 are handled in exactly the same way as the platinum catalyst, and outwardly are merely contact catalysts, nevertheless they are intimately involved in the oxidation-reduction scheme of the system and consequently partake of some of the characteristics of each type of catalyst.

On the other hand, in the lead-chamber process for the manufacture of sulfuric acid, the oxides-of-nitrogen catalyst is clearly of the internal type, the reactions being

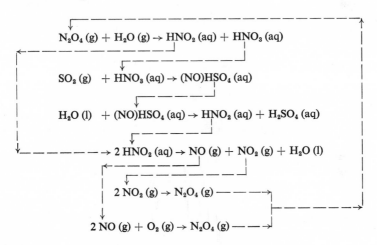

Adding all the equations for this case gives the net reaction

$$2 \text{ SO}_2 + 2 \text{ H}_2O + O_2 \rightarrow 2 \text{ H}_2SO_4$$

2–3.   The Law of Mass Action

We have seen that the rate at which a chemical reaction proceeds is a function of temperature and catalysis and is proportional to the absolute concentrations of the reacting species. If the conditions of temperature and catalysis are held constant, then, for simple reactions, the rate will be proportional to the concentrations of the reactants. If, for example, the reaction

is $A \rightarrow$ products

the mathematical expression is

$$\text{rate} \propto [A]$$

or

$$\text{rate} = k[A]$$

where k is a constant of proportionality known as the *rate constant*. If the reaction is

$$A + B \rightarrow \text{products}$$

then

$$\text{rate} = k'[A][B]$$

If the reaction is

$$2A \rightarrow \text{products} \; (A + A \rightarrow \text{products})$$

then

$$\text{rate} = k''[A][A] = k''[A]^2$$

If, however, we have the somewhat more complicated reaction

$$2A + B \rightarrow C + D$$

the situation becomes more complex. We find that it is extremely unlikely that two A molecules and one B molecule will collide simultaneously to give products, since this would require a three-body collision, the probability of which is very small. The process almost invariably is in fact a succession of two-body collisions, for example

$$A + B \rightarrow AB$$
$$A + AB \rightarrow C + D$$

Even for a more complicated reaction such as this, the rate expression *may* be a simple relationship of the concentrations of the reactants. Instances of this sort may arise as follows. As before, the rate expression for the first step is

$$\text{rate}_1 = k_1[A][B]$$

The rate expression for the second step is

$$\text{rate}_2 = k_2'[A][AB]$$

After the reaction has started, if rate_1 is slow in comparison to rate_2, then AB will be used up just as fast as it is formed, and therefore its concentration will be essentially constant ("steady state"). Since the constant $[AB]$ may be lumped with the constant k_2' to give a new constant k_2, we have

$$\text{rate}_2 = k_2[A]$$

(It should be noted that $[A]$ in the rate_2 expression is smaller than for rate_1, since $[A]$-original will have been diminished by the A that reacted in step 1. However, for all normal chemical reactions, the total number of molecules is so large—0.1 mole $= 6 \times 10^{22}$ molecules—that the difference—$6 \times 10^{22} - 1$ —after one molecule has reacted is negligible. Consequently the two $[A]$'s are for all practical purposes the same.) The over-all rate for the reaction $2A + B \rightarrow C + D$ is then

$$\text{rate}_{12} = k_1 k_2 [A][A][B] = k[A]^2[B]$$

Alternatively, if rate_1 is faster than rate_2, then there is a high probability that AB may decompose into its starting materials $(A + B)$ and equilibrium $A + B \rightleftharpoons AB$ be set up. The mathematical expression for this equilibrium (see below) is

$$\frac{[AB]}{[A][B]} = K$$

If now

$$\text{rate} = k'[A][AB], \quad \frac{\text{rate}}{k'[A]} = [AB]$$

then

$$\frac{\text{rate}}{k'[A]} = K[A][B]$$

and

$$\text{rate} = k'K[A]^2[B] = k[A]^2[B]$$

Provided the above or similar conditions are met, then in exactly the same way, the rate of *any* reaction

$$rA + sB + tC \cdots \rightarrow uD + vE + wF \cdots$$

is

$$\text{rate}_f = [A]^r[B]^s[C]^t \cdots$$

This is the *law of mass action*; i.e., *the rate of a chemical reaction is directly proportional to the product of the active concentrations of the reactants, each raised to the power corresponding to the coefficient of the substance appearing in the balanced chemical equation.* It is absolutely essential to realize, however, that *this statement of the law of mass action is true only if* (1) *the equation used really represents the reaction under consideration, and* (2) *if the equation used is that for the real mechanism of the reaction.* Many instances of reactions which do not meet these qualifications are discussed in Chapter 15.

Exactly the same arguments apply to the reverse reaction

$$uD + vE + wF \cdots \rightarrow rA + sB + tC \cdots$$

$$\text{rate}_r = k_r[D]^u[E]^v[F]^w \cdots$$

Let us now consider the specific reversible reaction

$$rA + sB + tC \rightleftharpoons uD + vE + wF$$

the forward and reverse parts of which both conform to the above requirements. Starting out with a mixture containing only A, B, and C, at the instant of mixing (time $= 0$) the forward reaction will proceed at a rate proportional to the initial concentrations of A, B, and C. However, as the reaction proceeds, these concentrations will decrease, and the rate of reaction

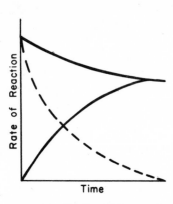

Fig. 2–3. The Establishment of Equilibrium.

must therefore become slower. On the other hand, at zero time the concentrations of D, E, and F are zero; consequently, at the instant of mixing, the rate of the reverse reaction must be zero. However, as the forward reaction ($rA + sB + tC$) proceeds, the concentrations of D, E, and F must increase, resulting in an increase in the rate of the reverse reaction. Eventually the forward reaction will have decreased in rate to the same point to which the rate of the reverse reaction will have increased. In other words, the rates of the forward and reverse reactions will have become equal, $\text{rate}_f = \text{rate}_r$. At this point, then, dynamic equilibrium will have been established (this is shown in Fig. 2–3). Since $\text{rate}_f = \text{rate}_r$, it must follow that

$$k_f[A]^r[B]^s[C]^t = k_r[D]^u[E]^v[F]^w$$

or

$$\frac{k_f}{k_r} = \frac{[D]^u[E]^v[F]^w}{[A]^r[B]^s[C]^t}$$

Since the ratio of two constants is itself a constant, $k_f/k_r = K$,

then

$$\frac{[D]^u[E]^v[F]^w}{[A]^r[B]^s[C]^t} = K$$

This K is known as the *equilibrium constant*, K_{eq}. By convention, the concentrations of the products are written in the numerator of the expression and the concentrations of the reactants in the denominator.

The foregoing derivation of the equilibrium relationship was made on the assumption that the law of mass action was valid for the over-all reactions, both forward and reverse. *Even if the mass action law is not applicable, however, the equilibrium relationship still holds true.* This fact may be demonstrated by considering the following case. Let us assume that the over-all reaction

$$2A + B + C \rightleftharpoons A_2BC$$

proceeds by the steps

$$A + B \rightarrow AB$$
$$A + AB \rightarrow A_2B$$
$$C + A_2B \rightarrow A_2BC$$

all of which are reversible. When over-all equilibrium is attained, each of these steps must also necessarily be in equilibrium

$$A + B \rightleftharpoons AB$$
$$A + AB \rightleftharpoons A_2B$$
$$C + A_2B \rightleftharpoons A_2BC$$

The individual equilibrium expressions for these are

$$\frac{[AB]}{[A][B]} = K_1$$

$$\frac{[A_2B]}{[A][AB]} = K_2$$

$$\frac{[A_2BC]}{[C][A_2B]} = K_3$$

When these are multiplied together, the concentrations of all the intermediates cancel out giving

$$\frac{[A_2BC]}{[A]^2[B][C]} = K_1K_2K_3 = K$$

which is the expression for the over-all equilibrium.

If the reaction had proceeded by quite a different set of steps, say

$$A + C \rightleftharpoons AC$$
$$B + AC \rightleftharpoons ABC$$
$$A + ABC \rightleftharpoons A_2BC$$

exactly the same final result would have been obtained. It follows, then, *that the equilibrium relationship derived above is perfectly general and does not depend upon the mechanism by which the reaction takes place.*

Although equilibrium is established when the rate of the forward reaction and the rate of the reverse reaction have become equal, this does not imply that the concentrations of reactants and products are equal—quite the contrary. A simple example will suffice to illustrate this point.

Let us consider two people assigned the task of shoveling coal. One of these, a football player, starts out in room A with a large pile of coal and shovels it through a window into room B, where the other person, an old man, is to shovel it back into room A. Assuming that both men work at top speed and are not subject to fatigue, it can be seen that the vigorous football player should start off sending the coal into room B at a rapid rate, while the old man will have nothing to shovel back (Fig. 2–4a). As the supply of coal in room B increases, however, the old man will be able to shovel it back at an increasing rate, while the football player, whose supply of coal is decreasing and who will have to run around the room to collect a shovelful, will send coal into room B less rapidly. Eventually a situation will be reached in which the football player, hurrying around room A to collect his shovelfuls of coal, will be shoveling it into room B at exactly the same rate as the plodding old man returns it to room A from the large supply which has collected on his side of the window. In short, the rates of the forward and reverse shoveling of coal have become equal, or have reached equilibrium, but the concentrations of coal in the two rooms are very different (Fig. 2–4b).

Thus, the fact that the rates of the forward and reverse reactions at equilibrium are equal cannot be taken to mean that the concentrations of products and reactants are equal.

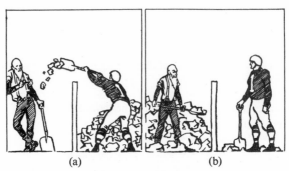

(a)   (b)

Fig. 2–4. A Simple Equilibrium System.

The effect of change in temperature can be seen by assuming that, if the temperature is raised, one of the workers (let us say the old man) is stimulated more than the other to greater activity. Consequently, the old man will shovel the coal much faster, while the football player increases his rate only a little. This will result in the coal going into the football player's side faster than into the old man's. But eventually equilibrium will be re-established, now, however, with a more nearly equal distribution of the coal.

The effect of a catalyst may be illustrated by assuming that the size of the window through which the coal is being shoveled is increased. This will make it easier for both men to shovel and will increase their rates. Their relative rates of shoveling, however, will remain the same.

If now a simple equilibrium system, such as $A + B \rightleftharpoons C + D$, is examined, it will be easy to see what will happen if one of the concentrations is changed. If $[C]$ is increased, it can be seen from the fact that

$$\frac{[C][D]}{[A][B]} = \text{constant}$$

and from the chemical equation, that, since D is used up, $[D]$ must decrease and $[A]$ and $[B]$ must increase until the ratio of $[C] \times [D]$ to $[A] \times [B]$ reaches the same constant value as before. If both $[C]$ and $[A]$ were increased in the same proportion, no change would take place in $[B]$ and $[D]$, since the ratio of the numerator to the denominator would not have been changed.

2–4. The Reversibility of Reactions

In theory, any reaction whatsoever is reversible. That is, if any reaction between $A + B$ produces $C + D$, it is theoretically possible to take C and D under the right conditions and recover A and B. In practice, however, many reactions are not reversible simply because the reverse reaction is so slow or so complicated as to be extremely improbable. Thus, when sugar is heated, it decomposes ultimately to carbon and water

$$C_{12}H_{22}O_{11} \xrightarrow{\Delta} 12\ C + 11\ H_2O$$

However, it is almost inconceivable that sugar could be produced merely by the reaction of carbon and water under any conditions. This would be like asking that a beautiful vase which has been smashed into a thousand pieces reassemble itself without flaw—theoretically possible, but the probability is so close to zero that in fact it could not happen. This reaction is therefore considered to be irreversible.

On the other hand, truly reversible reactions are often considered to be irreversible if the equilibrium lies extremely far in one direction (i.e., if the equilibrium constant is either very large or very small). Thus the reaction

$$Na + H_2O \rightarrow NaOH + \tfrac{1}{2} H_2$$

goes so far to the right that for practical purposes it may be considered to be complete and irreversible. Yet in actual fact it is reversible. The equilibrium constant for this reaction in aqueous solution has the very large value 10^{33}.

Easily reversible reactions, by contrast, have equilibrium constants closer to one. The reaction

$$Tl + H_2O \rightleftharpoons TlOH + \tfrac{1}{2} H_2$$

in water solution has the equilibrium constant 10^{-8}. This reaction can be demonstrated in the laboratory to be easily reversible.

2–5.   The Treatment of Heterogeneous Equilibria

Heterogeneous equilibria differ from homogeneous equilibria in that the reactions of a homogeneous equilibrium take place entirely within a single physical phase, whereas those of the former involve more than one phase.

Examples of homogeneous equilibria are the uncatalyzed equilibrium between SO_3 and $SO_2 + O_2$ at high temperature (where all the reactants are in the gas phase) and the ionization of a weak acid in aqueous solution, such as $HNO_2 \rightleftharpoons H^+ + NO_2^-$ (where all the reactants are in a single liquid phase).

Heterogeneous systems may be much more complex. A few examples follow

(1) $Sn\ (s) + 2\ Cl_2\ (g) \rightleftharpoons SnCl_4\ (l)$

(2) $Sn\ (s) + 2\ I_2$ (in solution in CCl_4) $\rightleftharpoons SnI_4$ (in solution CCl_4)

(3) $Sn\ (s) + 4\ H_2O\ (l) \rightleftharpoons Sn(OH)_4\ (s) + 2\ H_2\ (g)$

(4) Sn (in solution in Hg) $+ 4\ H_2O\ (l) \rightleftharpoons Sn(OH)_4\ (s) + 2\ H_2\ (g)$

(5) $Hg\ (l) + S$ (in solution in CS_2) $\rightleftharpoons HgS\ (s)$

(6) $6\ OH^-$ (in H_2O solution) $+ (2 + 2x)S$ (in CS_2 solution) $\rightleftharpoons 2\ S_x^{-2}$ (in H_2O solution) $+ S_2O_3^{-2}$ (in H_2O solution) $+ 3\ H_2O\ (l)$

(7) $HgS\ (s)[+ H_2O\ (l)] \rightleftharpoons Hg^{+2}$ (in H_2O solution) $+ S^{-2}$ (in H_2O solution)

In the case of homogeneous equilibria we have seen that the equilibrium constant is a function of the concentrations (or activities—Section 5–7) of the reacting substances. In the case of heterogeneous equilibria, the equilibrium constant is a function of the concentrations (or activities) of the reacting substances *in their respective phases*. Thus, in reaction (6) above, the equilibrium constant is

$$K_{eq} = \frac{[S_x^{-2}]_{(aq)}^2 \, [S_2O_3^{-2}]_{(aq)} \, [H_2O]^3}{[OH^-]_{(aq)}^6 \, [S]_{(CS_2)}^{2(1+x)}} \quad *$$

Likewise for reaction (4) of water with tin amalgam (tin in mercury), the equilibrium constant will be a function of the concentration (activity) of the tin in the mercury, as well as a function of the pressure of H_2 gas over the solution. The equilibrium expression for (4) will look different from that for (3), because in (3) the reaction involves *pure tin*. Since the concentration or activity of a reactant in a pure phase does not change in that phase it must be a constant. By convention *the activities of pure solid or liquid phases are taken as equal to one* (which is the same thing as saying that the actual constant concentration of pure phases in themselves are lumped together with the equilibrium constant). Thus the equilibrium expressions for the above reactions become as follows, where the activities of pure phases have been indicated by underlining:

(1)
$$\frac{SnCl_4}{\underline{Sn}\cdot[Cl_2]^2} = \frac{1}{p_{Cl_2}^2} = K_{eq}$$

(2)
$$\frac{[SnI_4]_{(CCl_4)}}{\underline{Sn}\cdot[I_2]_{(CCl_4)}^2} = \frac{[SnI_4]_{(CCl_4)}}{[I_2]_{(CCl_4)}^2} = K_{eq}$$

(3)
$$\frac{Sn(OH)_4\cdot[H_2]^2}{\underline{Sn}\cdot\underline{(H_2O)}^4} = p_{H_2}^2 = K_{eq}$$

(4)
$$\frac{Sn(OH)_4\cdot[H_2]^2}{[Sn]_{(Hg)}\cdot\underline{(H_2O)}^4} = \frac{p_{H_2}^2}{[Sn]_{(Hg)}} = K_{eq}$$

(5)
$$\frac{HgS}{\underline{Hg}\cdot[S]_{(CS_2)}} = \frac{1}{[S]_{(CS_2)}} = K_{eq}$$

(6)
$$\frac{[S_x^{-2}]_{(aq)}^2 \, [S_2O_3^{-2}]_{(aq)} \, \underline{(H_2O)}^3}{[OH^-]_{(aq)}^6 \, [S]_{(CS_2)}^{2(1+x)}} = \frac{[S_x^{-2}]_{(aq)}^2 \, [S_2O_3^{-2}]_{(aq)}}{[OH^-]_{(aq)}^6 \, [S]_{(CS_2)}^{2(1+x)}} = K_{eq}$$

(7)
$$\frac{[Hg^{+2}]_{(aq)} \, [S^{-2}]_{(aq)}}{\underline{HgS}} = [Hg^{+2}]_{(aq)} \, [S^{-2}]_{(aq)} = K_{eq}$$

(In example 6, the water is not a pure phase inasmuch as there are substances dissolved in it; however, *for a dilute aqueous solution*, since there is so much

* The water concentration will be a constant under the conditions discussed in Section 7–1.

more water than anything else, its concentration will remain essentially unchanged, even though the concentrations of the other reactants change many times. Consequently the concentration of water may be taken as constant, as before. See Section 7–1.)

2–6. Le Châtelier's Principle

The effects of changes in equilibrium which have been discussed above are all special cases of Le Châtelier's principle. This is a completely general law whose application is not by any means confined to chemistry, but applies equally well to sociology, economics, physics, and so forth. It states that *if to any system in equilibrium a stress is applied, the system will respond in such a way as to minimize the stress.*

Thus, if pressure is applied to a blown-up balloon, the balloon contracts, which tends to relieve the pressure. If pressure is applied to an equilibrium mixture of water and ice, some of the ice melts because water at 0°C occupies less volume than the same weight of ice, and this tends to relieve the pressure. Again, if an equilibrium mixture of ice and water is heated, some of the ice melts. Since the melting of ice absorbs heat, this tends to prevent the temperature from rising. In the case of a reaction that involves heat, applying heat (i.e., changing the temperature) will shift the equilibrium. For example, the reaction of SO_2 and oxygen is exothermic (evolves heat)

$$SO_2 + \tfrac{1}{2} O_2 \rightleftharpoons SO_3 + 21 \text{ kcal}$$

From Le Châtelier's principle, we should predict that raising the temperature would shift the equilibrium to the left. We have seen (Section 2–1) that this is actually the case. The same effect can be seen in the change of solubility of salts with temperature. In the reaction

$$CdSO_4 \text{ (s)} + \text{water} \rightleftharpoons CdSO_4 \text{ (aq)} + 10.7 \text{ kcal}$$

heat is evolved when solid cadmium sulfate is dissolved in water. It should be predicted that with increasing temperature the equilibrium should shift to the left or, in other words, the solubility should be less at high temperature than at low. We find in actual fact that 100 grams of water at 0°C will dissolve 75.5 grams of $CdSO_4$, but at 100°C, only 60.8 grams. On the other hand, when $Ba(NO_3)_2$ is dissolved in water heat is absorbed.

$$Ba(NO_3)_2 \text{ (s)} + \text{water} \rightleftharpoons Ba(NO_3)_2 \text{ (aq)} - 9.5 \text{ kcal}$$

or $$Ba(NO_3)_2 \text{ (s)} + \text{water} + 9.5 \text{ kcal} \rightleftharpoons Ba(NO_3)_2 \text{ (aq)}$$

In this case, raising the temperature should shift the equilibrium to the right—the solubility should increase with rising temperature. We find in actual fact that the solubility of $Ba(NO_3)_2$ at 20°C is 8.7 grams per hundred grams of water, but at 100°C it is 34.2 grams per hundred grams of water—an increase, as predicted. Increasing solubility of solids with rising temperature is the more general case, since the dissolution of most solids is an endo-thermic reaction (heat is absorbed).

The number of different illustrations of Le Châtelier's principle is legion (an extremely important example from economics is the law of supply and demand). However, the example which most concerns us here is that of the effect of change in concentration on chemical equilibria.

2–7. Questions and Problems

1. Describe the essential difference between homogeneous and heterogeneous equilibria.

2. Explain why the rate of a reaction does not merely double when the absolute temperature is doubled.

3. Derive a general equilibrium constant expression from appropriate rate expressions.

4. Enumerate the cases in which the concentration (or activity) of any reactant in a chemical reaction may be considered to be constant.

5. Describe the effect of change in total pressure on the (SO_3; SO_2, O_2) system.

6. At 450°C and 1 atm pressure, NH_3 decomposes 99.7 percent into N_2 and H_2. At 25°C and 1 atm pressure, the equilibrium mixture contains 97 percent NH_3. Is the reaction
$$N_2 + 3\ H_2 \rightleftharpoons 2\ NH_3$$
endothermic or exothermic?

7. If the reaction velocity in a particular reaction doubles for each 10°C rise in temperature, how much faster will the reaction be at 60°C than at 20°C?

8. If the reaction velocity in a particular reaction increases by 50 percent for each 10°C rise in temperature, how much faster will the reaction be at 75°C than at 20°C?

9. If pressure is applied to liquid $TeCl_4$ at temperatures just above its normal melting point, the substance freezes without lowering of the temperature. Which is more dense—$TeCl_4$ (l) or $TeCl_4$ (s)?

10. Describe the effect on the equilibrium
$$2\ ReO_3\ (s) + Cl_2\ (g) \rightleftharpoons 2\ ReO_3Cl\ (g) + heat$$
of (a) doubling the amount of ReO_3 (volume constant); (b) doubling the amount of Cl_2 (volume constant); (c) doubling the amount of ReO_3Cl (volume constant); (d) doubling the volume; (e) doubling the temperature; (f) doubling the total pressure.

11. A solid alloy of thallium and platinum is reacted with aqueous iodine until equilibrium is reached
$$(aTl + bPt)\ (s) + 3\ I_2\ (aq) \rightleftharpoons Tl_2PtI_6\ (s)$$
Write the equilibrium expression for the reaction and specify what factors will be variable in the equilibrium.

12. The reaction for the decomposition of SO_3 might be written
$$2\ SO_3 \rightleftharpoons 2\ SO_2 + O_2$$
or
$$SO_3 \rightleftharpoons SO_2 + \tfrac{1}{2}\ O_2$$

where $\frac{1}{2} O_2$ means merely half a *mole* of oxygen (i.e., O_2), *not* half a molecule of oxygen (i.e., O). Will this have any effect on the value of the equilibrium constant? (If it does, is there any relationship between the two values?) Does this have any effect on the position of the equilibrium?

13. The equation for the system (SO_3; SO_2, O_2) might be written as

$$2 SO_3 \rightleftharpoons 2 SO_2 + O_2$$

or $$2 SO_2 + O_2 \rightleftharpoons 2 SO_3$$

Will this have any effect on the value of the equilibrium constant? (If it does, is there any relationship between the two values?) Does this have any effect on the position of the equilibrium?

14. At 600°C the reaction

$$2 Al (s) + AlCl_3 (g) \rightleftharpoons 3 AlCl (g)$$

proceeds to the right, whereas at 200°C it goes to the left. Is the reaction exothermic or endothermic as written?

15. Write equilibrium expressions for the following:

(a) HN_3 (aq) $\rightleftharpoons$ H^+ (aq) $+ N_3^-$ (aq)

(b) $2 HI$ (g) $\rightleftharpoons$ H_2 (g) $+ I_2$ (g)

(c) CO (g) $+ 2 F_2$ (g) $\rightleftharpoons CF_3OF$ (g)

(d) N_2O_4 (g) $\rightleftharpoons 2 NO$ (g) $+ O_2$ (g)

(e) N_2O_4 (g) $\rightleftharpoons 2 NO_2$ (g)

(f) $2 H_2S_2$ (g) $\rightleftharpoons H_2S$ (g) $+ H_2S_3$ (g)

(g) $3 O_2$ (g) $\rightleftharpoons 2 O_3$ (g)

16. Write equilibrium expressions for the following, underlining the factors which may be considered constant:

(a) HN_3 (aq) $+ H_2O$ (l) $\rightleftharpoons H_3O^+$ (aq) $+ N_3^-$ (aq)

(b) $2 HI$ (g) $\rightleftharpoons H_2$ (g) $+ I_2$ (s)

(c) CH_3OH (l) $+ 4 F_2$ (g) $\rightleftharpoons CF_3OF$ (g) $+ 4 HF$ (g)

(d) N_2O_3 (l) $\rightleftharpoons NO_2$ (g) $+ NO$ (g)

(e) $2 N_2O_3$ (l) $\rightleftharpoons N_2O_4$ (l) $+ 2 NO$ (g)

(f) $2 H_2S$ (g) $+ SO_2$ (g) $\rightleftharpoons 3 S$ (s) $+ 2 H_2O$ (l)

(g) $2 H_2O_2$ (aq) $\rightleftharpoons 2 H_2O$ (l) $+ O_2$ (g)

17. Show how examination of the solubility equilibrium for Hg_2Cl_2 in water can be used to decide whether mercurous ion is Hg^+ or Hg_2^{+2} in aqueous solution.

2–8.   References

Denbigh, K. G., *The Principles of Chemical Equilibrium with Applications in Chemistry and Chemical Engineering*. Cambridge, England: Cambridge University Press, 1955.

Webb, T. J., *Elementary Principles in Physical Chemistry*. New York: D. Appleton-Century Company, Inc., 1936.

Berkman, S., Morrell, J. C., and Egloff, G., *Catalysis*. New York: Reinhold Publishing Corporation, 1940.

Schwab, G. M., *Catalysis*. New York: D. Van Nostrand Company, Inc., 1937.

Chapter 3

Solubility Products and the Factors Affecting

the Solubilities of Ionic Substances

3–1. Heterogeneous Equilibria

So far we have considered equilibria only from a general point of view. Now we shall examine some specific cases, the first of which will be simple heterogeneous equilibria. Many equilibrium systems involve substances in two or even more phases. These are heterogeneous equilibria. For example, the equilibrium between liquid water and gaseous water in a closed bottle involves the passage of water molecules between the liquid phase and the gas phase, while that between ice and liquid water at 0°C involves the solid and liquid phases. If, on the other hand, we place a piece of ice in a closed bottle below 0°C, we find this soon evaporates (sublimes), until an equilibrium is established between the solid and gaseous phases. These are simple one-component heterogeneous equilibria.

An extremely important example of heterogeneous equilibrium is that between a slightly soluble salt and its ions in its saturated solution. When LiF is shaken up with water, Li^+ ions and F^- ions leave the crystal and go into solution, until an equilibrium between the solid and its ions in solution is reached.

$$LiF\ (s) \rightleftharpoons Li^+ + F^-$$

Such a solution, in equilibrium with a pure solid, is said to be a *saturated* solution. The amount of solid which is dissolved in a saturated solution of a substance is the *solubility* of the substance.

Common expressions of solubility are in terms of the number of grams of salt which will dissolve in 100 grams of water to give a saturated solution, or in terms of the number of moles (gram-formula weights) which are contained in 1 liter of the saturated solution (the molarity).

When the pure, crystalline LiF comes into contact with water containing no Li^+ or F^- ions, Li^+ and F^- ions go into solution at a rate which depends on how many are in contact with the water, or, in other words, at a rate which depends only on the surface area (S) of the solid

$$rate_1 \propto S \quad or \quad rate_1 = k_1 S$$

As soon as there are any Li^+ and F^- ions in solution, however, they can sit back down on the crystal, which is the reverse process. The rate of deposition of the ions on the crystal will also depend on how much surface area is available for the ions to sit down on; but in addition, it will depend on the concentration of the ions in solution, the rate of deposition increasing as the concentration of ions increases.

$$rate_2 \propto S \times [Li^+][F^-] \quad or \quad rate_2 = k_2 S\,[Li^+][F^-]$$

When the concentrations of Li^+ and F^- have increased enough, $rate_2$ will have increased enough to be equal to $rate_1$, and equilibrium will be established. When $rate_2$ equals $rate_1$, then it follows that

$$k_2 S\,[Li^+][F^-] = k_1 S$$

or
$$[Li^+][F^-] = k_1/k_2$$

the surface-area factor cancelling out. Since the ratio of two constants must itself be constant, then
$$[Li^+][F^-] = K$$

This K is usually designated the *solubility product constant*, K_{sp}.

For substances having more than one cation or anion, e.g., $Ca_3(PO_4)_2$

$$Ca_2(PO_4)_2 \text{ (s)} \rightleftharpoons 3\,Ca^{+2} + 2\,PO_4^{-3}$$

arguments similar to those advanced in Chapter 2 will show that the concentration of each ion must be raised to the power which is the same as the coefficient for the ion in the chemical equation,

$$[Ca^{+2}]^3[PO_4^{-3}]^2 = K_{sp}$$

where $[Ca^{+2}]$ and $[PO_4^{-3}]$ are the *actual*, total concentrations of Ca^{+2} and PO_4^{-3}.

3–2. Solubility and K_{sp}; pK_{sp}

The K_{sp} of a substance is thus a measure of its solubility. However, the K_{sp}'s of substances of different stoichiometry must *not* be compared directly. For example, since the K_{sp}'s for CuCl and AgCl are 1.2×10^{-6} and 1.78×10^{-10} respectively, it can be said that AgCl is less soluble than CuCl, because the two compounds have the same stoichiometry. On the other hand, despite the fact that the K_{sp} for Ba $(IO_3)_2$ (1.50×10^{-8}) is smaller than that for $AgIO_3$ (3.1×10^{-8}), it is actually the more soluble of the two in water, as can be shown by calculation: $Ba(IO_3)_2$, 7.2×10^{-4} moles/liter; $AgIO_3$, 1.8×10^{-4} moles/liter.

The calculations can be carried out as follows: In a saturated solution of CuCl *containing no Cu^+ or Cl^- from any other source*, it can be seen that

$$CuCl \ (s) \rightleftharpoons Cu^+ + Cl^-$$

and the concentrations of the Cu^+ and the Cl^- must be the same. Therefore, if $[Cu^+]$ be designated as x moles per liter, the $[Cl^-]$ must also be x moles per liter, or $[Cu^+] = [Cl^-] = x$. Therefore, for $[Cu^+][Cl^-] = 1.2 \times 10^{-6}$

$$x \cdot x = x^2 = 1.2 \times 10^{-6}$$

$$x = [Cu^+] = [Cl^-] = 1.1 \times 10^{-3} \ M$$

which is the solubility of CuCl. In exactly the same way, $y = [Ag^+] = [Cl^-]$ in saturated AgCl solution, so that

$$y^2 = 1.78 \times 10^{-10}$$

and $[Ag^+] = [Cl^-] = 1.33 \times 10^{-5} \ M$, the solubility of AgCl.

In the case of $AgIO_3$, the treatment is identical.

$$[Ag^+] = [IO_3^-] = v$$
$$v^2 = 3.1 \times 10^{-8}$$
$$v = [Ag^+] = [IO_3] = 1.8 \times 10^{-4} \ M$$

However, for $Ba(IO_3)_2$ we must observe that *in a saturated solution containing no Ba^{+2} or IO_3^- from any other source*

$$Ba(IO_3)_2(s) \rightleftharpoons Ba^{+2} + 2 \ IO_3^-$$

there are twice as many IO_3^- ions as Ba^{+2} ions. Therefore, if $[Ba^{+2}]$ be designated as w, then $[IO_3^-]$ must be $2w$, or

$$[Ba^{+2}] = w$$
$$[IO_3^-] = 2w$$

Thus for

$$[Ba^{+2}][IO_3^-]^2 = 1.50 \times 10^{-9}$$

we have 　　　　$w \cdot (2w)^2 = 1.50 \times 10^{-9}$

or 　　　　　　$4w^3 = 1.50 \times 10^{-9}$

Then 　　　　$w^3 = 0.375 \times 10^{-9} = 375 \times 10^{-12}$

and 　　　　　$w = [Ba^{+2}] = \frac{1}{2} [IO_3^-] = 7.2 \times 10^{-4} \ M$

the solubility of $Ba(IO_3)_2$.

By the reverse process, if the solubility of a substance is known, the K_{sp} can be calculated. For example, the solubility of LiF in 100 ml of pure water is 0.16 grams, or 1.6 g/l. The molecular weight of LiF is 25.94, so the molar concentration of this solution is

$$\frac{1.6 \ g/l}{25.94 \ g/mole} = 0.062 \ moles/l$$

Therefore

$$[Li^+] = 0.062 \ M$$

and $\qquad\qquad [F^-] = 0.062 \ M$

Since for the equilibrium

$$LiF \ (s) \rightleftharpoons Li^+ + F^-$$
$$[Li^+][F^-] = K_{sp}$$

then $\qquad\qquad (0.062)(0.062) = 3.8 \times 10^{-3} = K_{sp}$

In the case of $Ca_3(PO_4)_2$ the solubility is 0.000022 grams per hundred milliliters or 0.00022 grams per liter. The molecular weight is 310.28. Consequently, the molar concentration of a saturated solution is

$$\frac{2.2 \times 10^{-4} \ g/l}{310.28 \ g/mole} = 7.13 \times 10^{-7} \ M$$

Now, in the equilibrium

$$Ca_3(PO_4)_2 \ (s) \rightleftharpoons 3 \ Ca^{+2} + 2 \ PO_4^{-3}$$

in pure water, each mole of $Ca_3(PO_4)_2$ dissolving will produce 3 moles of Ca^{+2} and 2 moles of PO_4^{-3}. Consequently, if the molar solubility of $Ca_3(PO_4)_2$ is $7.13 \times 10^{-7} \ M$, the concentration of Ca^{+2} in the saturated solution is

$$[Ca^{+2}] = 3 \times 7.13 \times 10^{-7} \ M = 2.14 \times 10^{-6} \ M$$

and $\qquad\qquad [PO_4^{-3}] = 2 \times 7.13 \times 10^{-7} \ M = 1.43 \times 10^{-6} \ M$

Therefore, for

$$[Ca^{+2}]^3[PO_4^{-3}]^2 = K_{sp}$$
$$(2.14 \times 10^{-6})^3 (1.43 \times 10^{-6})^2 = 2.0 \times 10^{-29} = K_{sp}$$

If, on the other hand, an ion common to the insoluble substance is already present in solution from another source, this must be taken into account. For example, the solubility of LiF in a 0.1 M solution of KF is found to be only 2.9×10^{-2} moles per liter. Consequently, $[Li^+] = 2.9 \times 10^{-2} \ M$. The $[F^-]$, however, is equal to that derived from the KF (0.1 M) plus that which went into solution with the lithium ion ($2.9 \times 10^{-2} \ M$).

Therefore

$$[F^-] = 0.1 + 0.029 = 0.129 \ M$$

From this

$$[Li^+][F^-] = (0.029) (0.129) = 3.7 \times 10^{-3} = K_{sp}$$

in agreement with our previous calculation.

In the case of $Ca_3(PO_4)_2$ dissolving in 0.1 M K_3PO_4, it is found that the concentration of Ca^{+2} in a saturated solution is $1.26 \times 10^{-9} \ M$. (In other words, 4.2×10^{-10} moles of $Ca_3(PO_4)_2$ per liter dissolve.) The concentration of PO_4^{-3} contributed by the $Ca_3(PO_4)_2$ (8.4×10^{-10} moles per liter) is insignificant in comparison to the 0.1 moles per liter from the K_3PO_4, therefore $[PO_4^{-3}] = 0.1 \ M$ and

$$[Ca^{+2}]^3 [PO_4^{-3}]^2 = K_{sp}$$
$$(1.26 \times 10^{-9})^3 (0.1)^2 = 2.0 \times 10^{-29} = K_{sp}$$

in agreement with our earlier calculation.

Taking the established K_{sp}'s, of course, these latter cases could have been turned around to find out what amounts of these substances would have dissolved in the solutions containing the common ions. Thus for LiF dissolving in 0.1 M KF, if $[Li^+] = x$, then $[F^-] = 0.1 + x$, and

$$[Li^+][F^-] = 3.8 \times 10^{-3}$$
$$x\,(0.1 + x) = 3.8 \times 10^{-3}$$
$$x^2 + 0.1\,x - 3.8 \times 10^{-3} = 0$$
$$x = \frac{-0.1 \pm \sqrt{0.01 + 0.0152}}{2} = 0.029\ M$$

the solubility of LiF in 0.1 M KF.

In the case of $Ca_3(PO_4)_2$ in 0.1 M K_3PO_4, if the molar solubility is equal to y, rigorous treatment would give

$$[Ca^{+2}] = 3y$$
$$[PO_4^{-3}] = 0.1 + 2y$$

and
$$[Ca^{+2}]^3\,[PO_4^{-3}]^2 = 2.0 \times 10^{-29}$$
$$(3y)^3\,(0.1 + 2y)^2 = 2.0 \times 10^{-29}$$
$$108y^5 + 10.8y^4 + 0.27y^3 = 2.0 \times 10^{-29}$$

which is too complicated for easy solution. However, from the solubility of $Ca_3(PO_4)_2$ in pure water $(7.13 \times 10^{-7}\ M)$, it can be seen that the contribution from $Ca_3(PO_4)_2$ to the total (PO_4^{-3}) will be so small that it can be neglected in comparison to the 0.1 M contribution from K_3PO_4. Consequently the K_{sp} expression simplifies to

$$(3y)^3\,(0.1)^2 = 2.0 \times 10^{-29}$$

and
$$y = 4.2 \times 10^{-10}\ M$$

which is the molar solubility of $Ca_3(PO_4)_2$ in 0.1 M K_3PO_4. If we had been interested in how much Ca^{+2} would be in this solution, we could have solved for it directly

$$[Ca^{+2}]^3\,(0.1)^2 = 2.0 \times 10^{-29}$$
$$[Ca^{+2}]^3 = 2.0 \times 10^{-27}$$
$$[Ca^{+2}] = 1.26 \times 10^{-9}\ M$$

Solubility product relationships may involve more than two different ions. For example, let us consider the following case: The solubility of syngenite, $K_2Ca(SO_4)_2 \cdot H_2O$, is 0.30 grams per hundred milliliters of saturated aqueous solution. What is its K_{sp}?

$$K_2Ca(SO_4)_2 \cdot H_2O\ (s) \rightleftharpoons 2\,K^+ + Ca^{+2} + 2\,SO_4^{-2} + H_2O$$

Since in dilute aqueous solution the concentration of water will be essentially constant (at 55.5 M), the concentration of water will not appear explicitly in the equilibrium expression. This will therefore take the form

$$[K^+]^2[Ca^{+2}][SO_4^{-2}]^2 = K_{sp}$$

The molecular weight of $K_2Ca(SO_4)_2 \cdot H_2O$ is 328.3; therefore, the molar solubility is

$$\frac{0.30 \text{ g}}{328.4 \text{ g/mole}} \times \frac{1000 \text{ ml/l}}{100 \text{ ml}} = 9.1 \times 10^{-3} \text{ moles/l} = 9.1 \times 10^{-3} \ M$$

Since two K^+ ions and two SO_4^{-2} ions are produced by each molecule of $K_2Ca(SO_4)_2 \cdot H_2O$ dissolving

$$[K^+] = [SO_4^{-2}] = 2 \times 9.1 \times 10^{-3} \ M = 1.82 \times 10^{-2} \ M$$

whereas $[Ca^{+2}] = 9.1 \times 10^{-3} \ M$, since there is only one Ca^{+2} per molecule. The solubility product constant, therefore,

$$K_{sp} = (1.82 \times 10^{-2})^2 \, (9.1 \times 10^{-3}) \, (1.82 \times 10^{-2})^2 = 1.0 \times 10^{-9}$$

Instead of using the K_{sp}, it is sometimes more convenient to use the pK_{sp}, which is defined as the negative logarithm of the K_{sp} (see "pH," Section 1–14). For example, the K_{sp} of $AgIO_3$ may be expressed as 3.1×10^{-8} or $10^{-7.5}$. The pK_{sp} is therefore 7.5. Because the pK_{sp} is the *negative* logarithm of the K_{sp}, the *smaller* the latter is, the *larger* the former must be, algebraically speaking. A very large (positive) pK_{sp}, therefore, is indicative of low solubility, while a very small (negative) pK_{sp} is indicative of high solubility.

3–3. The Effect of Crystal Size on Solubility

It has already been noted (Section 1–11) that the rate at which ions from the corners and edges of crystals go into solution is faster than the rate at which ions from the flat surfaces will go into solution. Consequently, the rate of dissolution of a crystal will be proportional to the surface area

$$\text{rate}_1 = k_1 S$$

only if the ions at the edges do not constitute a significant fraction of the surface ions. If, however, the crystals are so small that the ions on the edges *do* constitute a significant fraction of the surface ions, then the rate of dissolution should be appreciably faster than for larger crystals, i.e., $k_1' > k_1$. On the other hand, there is no reason to expect the rate of deposition on the edges to be faster than on the flat surfaces, in fact the contrary is probably so. Consequently, $k_2' < k_2$. Thus it can be seen that K_{sp} (small crystals) > K_{sp} (large crystals) since

$$\frac{k_1'}{k_2'} > \frac{k_1}{k_2}$$

Therefore small crystals are more soluble than large crystals of the same substance.

It is even possible to estimate mathematically below what size crystal this effect should become noticeable. If the average ionic diameter be taken as approximately 3×10^{-8} cm (3 Å or Ångstrom units), it can be seen that the percentage of surface consisting of atoms lying on the edges of a *perfect* cube jumps from ≈ 0.12 percent for cubes 1×10^{-4} cm on a side to ≈ 1.3 percent for cubes 1×10^{-5} cm and to ≈ 12 percent for cubes 1×10^{-6} cm on a side. *If crystals were perfect*, then, the solubility should begin to increase appreciably for crystals below something between 10^{-5} and 10^{-6} cm. In actual fact, however, real crystals are never perfect, but have cracks and imperfections that increase the actual ratio of "edge" to "flat-surface" ions. Consequently, the solubility will begin to increase for somewhat larger crystals. Thus it is found, for example, that $BaSO_4$ crystals, 10^{-4} cm on edge, are almost twice as soluble as $BaSO_4$ crystals, 2×10^{-3} cm on edge.

It should be easy to see that if a "saturated" solution is in contact with both large and small crystals it cannot be in true equilibrium, since the small crystals will allow a higher concentration of ions in the solution than the large crystals. Consequently, the excess ions must be deposited on the large crystals until their K_{sp} is not exceeded. This, however, will lower the concentration of ions below that required to satisfy the equilibrium for the small crystals and more of these will dissolve. From this it can be seen that the large crystals will increase in size, while the small ones decrease until they disappear. The over-all effect is to reduce the ratio of active "edge" ions to less active "flat-surface" ions.

This process can be used to advantage to increase the crystal size of precipitates that are too fine to manipulate. In particular, since both dissolution and deposition processes are speeded up by raising the temperature, fine precipitates are frequently "digested" at high temperature in order to increase particle size.

Since, when an insoluble salt is precipitated, the first few ions that come together must necessary make a small crystal, it follows that it will in practice require a somewhat higher concentration of ions to start precipitation than the concentration calculated from the solubility-product constant, since the K_{sp} is determined for large crystals. In fact, in the aggregate of the first *eight* ions (of a cubic crystal) which will form the nucleus of the crystal-to-be, *all* the ions are edge ions, and the formation of such nuclei may be very difficult indeed. Consequently, some salts easily form *supersaturated* solutions, in which the product of the ion concentrations may greatly exceed the solubility-product constant. (This is an example of metastability.) If such solutions are "seeded," however, with already-formed nuclei or crystals precipitation rapidly takes place until the equilibrium (K_{sp}) value is reached.

3-4.   Increase in Solubility through Formation of Weak Electrolytes

If a salt is derived from either a weak base or a weak acid, its solubility may be increased by formation of the un-ionized base or acid. Thus ammonium vanadate, NH_4VO_3, has a solubility in water of 5.2 grams per liter

$$NH_4VO_3 \text{ (s)} \rightleftharpoons NH_4^+ + VO_3^-$$

but is much more soluble in NaOH solution because the OH^- and NH_4^+ react to give the un-ionized weak base NH_4OH (or NH_3)

$$NH_4VO_3 \text{ (s)} + OH^- \rightleftharpoons VO_3^- + NH_4OH$$

(or $\qquad NH_4VO_3 \text{ (s)} + OH^- \rightleftharpoons VO_3^- + NH_3 + H_2O$)

The reduction of the NH_4^+ concentration by formation of NH_4OH, requires a correspondingly larger VO_3^- concentration, which means that more NH_4VO_3 must dissolve to satisfy the solubility-product relationship.

The same effect holds for salts of weak acids. For example, $Ba_3(PO_4)_2$, which is insoluble in pure water, nevertheless dissolves easily in dilute acids, according to the equation

$$Ba_3(PO_4)_2 \text{ (s)} + 2\,H^+ \rightleftharpoons 3\,Ba^{+2} + 2\,HPO_4^{-2}$$

because the PO_4^{-3} concentration is reduced through shifting of the equilibrium

$$HPO_4^{-2} \rightleftharpoons H^+ + PO_4^{-3}$$

to the left.

If, of course, the products of such a reaction form an equally insoluble compound, the nature of the compound may change without there being any obvious effect on the solubility. Such an effect is exhibited by mercurous chromate and dichromate

$$2\,Hg_2CrO_4 \text{ (s)} + 2\,H^+ \rightleftharpoons Hg_2^{+2} + Hg_2Cr_2O_7 \text{ (s)} + H_2O$$

3–5. The Limit of Visibility

Even when the conditions for formation of a precipitate are fulfilled, if the amount of the precipitate is too small, it may be impossible to detect it. For example, the eye cannot detect a silver chloride precipitate in an amount less than 2×10^{-5} mole per liter. Consequently, even though a substance may be extremely insoluble and may actually precipitate, it may nevertheless escape detection by being present in an amount below the limit of visibility. It can be calculated that a Zn^{+2} concentration of 10^{-15} molarity should produce a precipitate of ZnS with $10^{-5}\,M\ S^{-2}$, but such a precipitate would be completely invisible and therefore useless as a means of detecting the presence of zinc.

The limit of visibility will vary somewhat depending upon certain factors, e.g., the opacity and particularly the color of the precipitate. A colored precipitate is easier to see than a white one. For this reason, when looking for a small amount of an ion, it is always preferable to precipitate it in colored form if possible. A small amount of Pb^{+2} would be much more easily detected as PbS (black) than as $PbSO_4$ (white). Likewise Hg^{+2} would be more easily detected as HgI_2 (red) than as $HgNH_2Cl$ (white).

3–6. The Effect of Ionic Charge and Radius on the Solubility of Ionic Solids

There are many factors which affect the solubility of a substance in water. However, for solid substances dissolving to give ions, two factors generally outweigh all others—the crystal energy of the solid and the hydration energies of the ions.

Let us consider what happens when an ionic solid dissolves in water, taking sodium chloride as an example (this is the simplest possible ionic crystal). This substance consists of equal numbers of alternate positive and negative ions symmetrically arranged so that each positive ion is surrounded by six negative ions at the corners of a regular octahedron, and each negative ion likewise by six positive ions. The crystal is held together by the electrical (coulombic) attraction of the positive charge for each of the surrounding negative charges and the attraction of the negative charge for each of the surrounding positive charges. This attraction is the "crystal energy" or "lattice energy." It should be easy to see that the smaller the ions (and therefore the smaller the distance between them), and the larger the charges on the ions, the greater will be the crystal energy (i.e., the more stable will be the crystal).

On the other hand, when a sodium ion is dissolved in water, there will be hydration of the sodium ion through the attraction of the positive charge for the negative poles of the polar water molecules, as described in Section 1–11. The same is true of the chloride ions, except, of course, that the attraction is for the positive poles of the water molecules. These attractions are the "hydration energies" of the ions. The hydration energy will also decrease with increasing separation between the charges (i.e., increasing the ionic radius). The crystal energy will tend to keep the ions in the solid, and a high crystal energy will tend to result in low solubility. The hydration energy will tend to pull the ions into solution, and a high hydration energy will tend to result in high solubility. It must be realized, however, that as the ionic size or charge is changed in a series of salts, the crystal energy and the hydration energy will change in the *same* direction. Since it is on the balance between these two energies that the solubility of the substance will depend, a first approximation as to whether the solubility will increase or decrease will depend on which changes more rapidly.

It must furthermore be realized that although the crystal energy will decrease almost linearly as the size of the ions is increased, the hydration energy will not do so for at least two reasons. The first of these concerns the *number* of water molecules engaged in hydrating an ion. In the case of the small lithium ion, the attraction of each water molecule is very strong because of the short distance between ion and molecule, but the number of water molecules that can gather around a lithium ion is severely limited—probably not more than four in actual contact with the ion. With a large cesium ion, however, although the attraction of each water molecule is weak, many more of them can gather around the ion (at least eight). This compensates in part for the decreased attraction of each individual water molecule and results in the hydration energy falling less rapidly than expected.

A second factor involves the polarizability of the water molecules (Section 1–6) and the polarizing power of the ions. A small ion (of high charge density), particularly a cation like Li^+, not only has a strong attraction for the negative end of the permanent dipole of the water molecule, but actually induces additional polarization in the water molecule, thus increasing the attraction beyond what would be expected if the water molecule were not polarizable. As the size of the cation is increased, the attraction of water molecules decreases, not only because of the increasing distance between ion and molecule, but also, over and above that, because of the decreasing ability of the cation to polarize the water molecule. For this reason, then, the solvation energy decreases more rapidly than would be expected as the ionic size is increased. This tends to compensate for the factor previously discussed.

In addition to this, the crystal energy will be affected by the polarizing power of the cations, which is highest for cations of small radius and high charge, and the polarizability of the anions, which increases with increasing anionic size and charge.

It can be seen, then, that the change of solubility with changing ionic size and charge depends on a complicated interplay of several factors. Consequently, it will not be possible to predict how solubilities will change without detailed mathematical analysis of all the factors involved. On the other hand, given a series of salts having a known trend of solubilities, it should be possible to say whether the crystal energy or the hydration energy is changing more rapidly through the series.

Let us consider the case of the alkali halides, taking LiF, CsF, CsI, and LiI as the extremes between which the solubilities of all the other alkali halides vary. The solubility trends are indicated in the diagram below, the arrows pointing in the direction of increasing solubility. The thermodynamic pK_{sp}'s (see Section 3–2) are shown for the purposes of comparison.

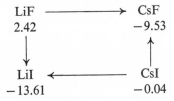

The distances between the ions (to which the crystal energies are inversely proportional) are as follows: LiF 2.01 Å, LiI 3.02 Å, CsF 3.05 Å, and CsI 3.85 Å (where Å is the Ångstrom unit, or 10^{-8} cm). It can be seen that the crystal energy of LiF is high, that of LiI and CsF intermediate and almost identical, and that of CsI low. That the solubility does not increase in this order is due to the fact that the hydration energies decrease in the same order, but at a different rate.

In LiF, the crystal energy is so high that it outweighs the high hydration energies of the small lithium and fluoride ions. In the salts LiI and CsF, the crystal energy is much less, and is outweighed by the very high hydration energy of the small lithium ion in the first case, and the high hydration energy of the small fluoride ion in the second. In CsI, the crystal energy is very low, but the hydration energies of the large cesium and iodide ions are lower yet, so that the crystal energy, even though low, predominates.

It turns out, then, that for series of salts in which the crystal energy starts out high, the solubility increases as the ionic size increases (e.g., LiF, LiCl, LiBr, LiI; LiF, NaF, KF, RbF, CsF; and so forth). For series in which the crystal energy starts out intermediate, the solubility decreases as the ionic size increases.

(1) Thus, if one of the ions is very small or has very high charge, or has very high hydration energy for any other reason, such as having hydrogen atoms in the ion or being derived from a weak acid, then the solubility will increase as the size of the second ion is increased. In this category occur the alkali fluorides, hydroxides, sulfides, nitrites, carbonates, bicarbonates, formates, acetates, phosphates, antimonates, and so forth; the alkaline earth hydroxides, monohydrogen phosphates, and so forth.

(2) If one of the ions is very large or has low charge (i.e., low charge density and low hydration energy) the solubility will decrease as the size of the second ion is increased. In this category occur the alkali iodides, nitrates, perchlorates, permanganates, perrhenates, chloroplatinates, tetraphenyl-borates, the alums, and so forth.

(3) On the other hand, if the reference ion is intermediate in size or charge, then as the size of the second ion is increased, the solubility will first decrease, pass through a minimum, and then increase again. In this category fall the alkali chlorides, bromides, sulfates, and so forth; and the alkaline earth fluorides, oxalates, carbonates, sulfides, and so forth. Examples of these categories are shown in Table 3–1.

TABLE 3–1. EXAMPLES OF THERMODYNAMIC pK_{sp}'s

Category (1) *Increasing Solubility* ──────⟶
        Increasing Ionic Size, or Decreasing Charge ──────⟶

	Li^+	Na^+	K^+	Rb^+	Cs^+
Fluorides	2.4	0.4	−4.3	−6.8	−9.5
Hydroxides	−1.2	−7.1	−11.1	−12.7	−14.6
Bicarbonates	0.3	0.21	−1.5	−2.5	−6.5
Carbonates	2.4	−0.7	−4.2	−8.7	−12.8
Antimonates	?	7.4	2.4	?	?

	Y^{+3}	Ca^{+2}	Na^+ (radii equal)
Hydroxides	22.1	5.1	−7.1

	PO_4^{-3}	SO_4^{-2}	ClO_4^- (radii equal)
Calcium	28.7	4.6	−10.4

Category (2)   *Decreasing Solubility* ———→
                 Increasing Ionic Size, or Decreasing Charge ———→

	Li^+	Na^+	K^+	Rb^+	Cs^+
Iodides	−13.6	−6.0	−2.0	−1.5	0.0
Perchlorates	?	−2.8	1.95	2.3	2.4
		S^{-2}		Cl^- (radii equal)	
Potassium		−12.7		−0.9	
	Th^{+4}	Y^{+3}	Ca^{+2}	Na^+ (radii equal)	
Chlorides	−26.9	−20.5	−11.9	−1.6	

Category (3)   *Solubility Passing through a Minimum*
                 Increasing Ionic Size, or Decreasing Charge ———→

	Mg^{+2}	Ca^{+2}	Sr^{+2}	Ba^{+2}	
Fluorides	8.2	10.4	8.6	6.0	
	Li^+	Na^+	K^+	Rb^+	Cs^+
Sulfates	−0.88	−0.19	+1.69	+0.44	−1.10
	ClO_3^-	BrO_3^-	IO_3^-		
Potassium	0.5	1.5	1.4		
	Ce^{+3}	Ca^{+2}	Na^+		
Sulfates	1.7	4.6	−0.19		

It turns out in practice for the alkali halides that the solubility is at a minimum when the ratio of the radius of the cation to the radius of the anion is about 3:4. The solubility chart of the alkali halides may be modified as follows—where the arrows indicate increasing solubility and the solid line minimum solubility:

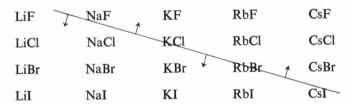

LiF	NaF	KF	RbF	CsF
LiCl	NaCl	KCl	RbCl	CsCl
LiBr	NaBr	KBr	RbBr	CsBr
LiI	NaI	KI	RbI	CsI

An additional example of the effect of ionic radius on solubility is that of the divalent sulfates, MSO_4. The relationship of solubility and cation radius to position in the periodic table is shown in Table 3–2. The relationship between the radius of the cation and the solubility of the sulfate is shown graphically in Fig. 3–1.

3–7.   The Alkali Metals

The alkali metals in the free state are all soft, silvery, easily fused substances. Some of their physical properties are given in Table 3–3.

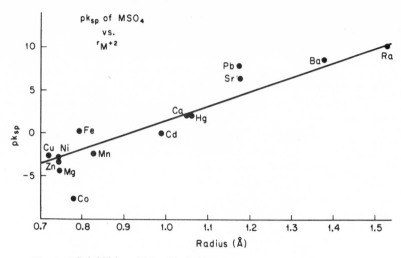

Fig. 3–1. Solubilities of Metallic Sulfates as a Function of Cation Radius.

Since the free metals are so reactive that they vigorously decompose water

$$M \text{ (s)} + H_2O \text{ (l)} \rightarrow M^+ \text{ (aq)} + OH^- \text{ (aq)} + \tfrac{1}{2}H_2 \text{ (g)}$$

and since they have only one oxidation state ($+1$) corresponding to the loss of their only valence electron, the chemistry of these elements in aqueous solution is concerned almost entirely with the $+1$ ions and the salts containing them. Since if the salt of an acid can be prepared at all, its alkali salts can be made, the compounds of the alkali metals are many. We shall confine our discussion, however, to the common salts and to a few of particular interest because of their solubilities.

The solubility relationships of the *alkali halides* have been discussed in the preceding section. They are all at least moderately soluble in water, the least soluble being LiF, which dissolves only to the extent of 0.16 grams per hundred milliliters of water at 18°C. They are all white crystalline solids forming cubic crystals. At room temperature, the internal structure of the crystals is of the face-centered cubic type already described for NaCl (Section 1–4)—except in the cases of CsCl, CsBr, and CsI, which have a body-centered cubic lattice in which each Cs^+ is surrounded symmetrically (at the corners of a cube) by eight X^- ions and each X^- ion is surrounded symmetrically by eight Cs^+ ions.

The alkali metals form *oxides*, M_2O, which react with water, carbon dioxide, and oxygen very readily

$$M_2O + H_2O \rightarrow 2\ MOH$$
$$M_2O + CO_2 \rightarrow M_2CO_3$$
$$M_2O + \tfrac{1}{2}O_2 \rightarrow M_2O_2$$
$$M_2O + \tfrac{3}{2}O_2 \rightarrow 2\ MO_2$$

TABLE 3–2. THERMODYNAMIC pK_{sp}'s AND CATION RADII OF ANHYDROUS DIVALENT SULFATES

	TiSO₄	VSO₄	CrSO₄	MnSO₄	FeSO₄	CoSO₄	NiSO₄	CuSO₄	ZnSO₄		
BeSO₄ —1.68 0.31 Å											—	SnSO₄ (0.38) 1.02 Å
MgSO₄ —4.25 0.75 Å	0.76 Å	0.82Å	0.5 0.80 Å	—2.39 0.83 Å	0.51 0.80 Å	—7.404 0.78 Å	—2.93 0.74 Å	—2.65 0.72 Å	—3.09 0.83 Å	—		
CaSO₄ 4.62 1.06 Å	—	—	—	—	—	—				—	CdSO₄ 0.05 0.99 Å	PbSO₄ 7.80 1.18 Å
SrSO₄ 6.49 1.18 Å							PdSO₄ v. sol. 0.50 Å					
BaSO₄ 10.06 1.38 Å								AuSO₄ dec. —	HgSO₄ 1.43 1.05 Å			
RaSO₄ 14.38 1.52 Å												
EuSO₄ 6 1.1 Å												

TABLE 3–3. PHYSICAL PROPERTIES OF THE ALKALI METALS

Latin Name and Symbol	Lithium Lithium (Li)	Sodium Natrium (Na)	Potassium Kalium (K)	Rubidium Rubidium (Rb)	Cesium Caesium (Cs)	Francium Francium (Fr)
Atomic Weight	6.94	22.997	39.096	85.48	132.91	223*
Atomic Number	3	11	19	37	55	87
Melting Point °C	186	97.5	62.3	38.5	28.5	
Boiling Point °C	1336	880	760	700	670	
Hardness (Moh)	0.6	0.4	0.35	0.3	0.2	
Density 20°C (g/ml)	0.53	0.97	0.86	1.53	1.90	
Standard Oxidation Potential for M (s) $\rightarrow M^+$ (aq) $+ e^-$ (volts)	3.02	2.71	2.92	2.99	3.02	
Heat of Hydration of Gaseous Ions in kcal/mole	123	97	77	70	63	
Electronegativity	1.0	0.9	0.8	0.8	0.75	0.7
Abundance in Earth's Crust (%)	0.007	2.83	2.59	0.031	0.0007	†

* Most stable isotope. Fr^{212} and Fr^{222} are almost as stable.
† The outermost mile of the earth's crust has been estimated to contain only 24.5 grams of Fr^{223}.

the latter two reactions being important only for the heavier alkali metals. The oxides, M_2O, however, are difficult to make and so reactive that they are rarely used.

The *alkali hydroxides* are white crystalline deliquescent solids, dissolving readily in water with considerable evolution of heat (the solution may boil) to give strongly alkaline solutions. They represent the strongest bases obtainable in aqueous solution. The least soluble is LiOH, which dissolves to the extent of 12.7 grams per hundred milliliters of water at 0°C and 17.5 grams at 100°C. By virtue of their free OH^- ion, they neutralize aqueous acids

$$OH^- + H^+ \rightarrow H_2O$$
or
$$OH^- + HA \rightarrow H_2O + A^-$$

The solid hydroxides will react with acidic gases, removing them from the air.

$$MOH + CO_2 \rightarrow NaHCO_3$$
$$MOH + H_2S \rightarrow MSH + H_2O$$

The *carbonates* and *hydrogen carbonates* ("bicarbonates") of the alkali metals are all stable white crystalline solids, the hydrogen carbonates losing CO_2 and H_2O at a relatively low temperature, which is lowest (around room temperature) for $LiHCO_3$.

$$2\,NaHCO_3 \xrightarrow{\;270°C\;} Na_2CO_3 + H_2O + CO_2$$

The *alkali cyanides* are white crystalline soluble substances which are hydrolyzed extensively enough in aqueous solution that the odor of the extremely poisonous HCN can be detected

$$CN^- + H_2O \rightleftharpoons HCN + OH^-$$

The salts themselves are likewise extremely poisonous.

The alkali *arsenates, arsenites, borates, bromates, chlorates, chromates, dichromates, cyanoferrates*(III) (ferricyanides), *cyanoferrates*(II) (ferrocyanides), *nitrates, nitrites, phosphates, phosphites, hypophosphites, selenites, silicates, sulfates, sulfites, sulfides,* and *thiocyanates* are all moderately to highly soluble, except for some of the lithium salts (e.g., the arsenate and phosphate).

The statement has been made (Section 1–1) that *all* the salts of the alkali metals are soluble. Although this is true of almost all the common salts, it does not apply to some of the less common ones. We find, in fact, that true salts composed of large unipositive cations and large uninegative anions have so little ionic hydration energy that their solubility is low. We may expect that the larger the ions the lower the solubility will be. We have already seen that CsI is a compound of low solubility. Since polyatomic ions are larger than monatomic ions, the alkali salts of the uninegative polyatomic anions of strong acids will be only slightly soluble. Reference to Table 3–1 will show that the perchlorates of the heavier alkali metals become difficultly soluble. The even larger tetraphenylborate ion, $B(C_6H_5)_4^-$, forms an extremely insoluble potassium salt, $KB(C_6H_5)_4$ ($K_{sp} = 2 \times 10^{-8}$), whereas the sodium salt is fairly soluble. If the cation is also made polyatomic, the solubility becomes even less. For example, the solubility product constant for tetramethylammonium perchlorate, $[(CH_3)_4N][ClO_4]$, is 4.0×10^{-4} compared with 7.1×10^{-4} for $CsClO_4$, that of nitron perchlorate, $[C_{20}H_{17}N_4]$-$[ClO_4]$, is 2.5×10^{-9}, and that of tetraphenylstibonium tetraphenylborate, $[(C_6H_5)_4Sb][B(C_6H_5)_4]$ is very small indeed.

Even dinegative anions of strong acids may form slightly soluble salts with the larger alkali cations, provided the anions are large enough. Sodium chloroplatinate dissolves in water to the extent of 66 grams per hundred grams of water at 15°C, whereas the potassium salt, K_2PtCl_6, dissolves to the extent of only 0.481 grams at 2°C.

The same applies to trinegative anions, as can be seen by comparing the solubilities of sodium hexanitrocobaltate (cobaltinitrite), $Na_3Co(NO_2)_6$ (>1000 grams per thousand grams of water), and the potassium salt $K_3Co(NO_2)_6$ (0.89 grams per thousand grams of water).

On the other hand, if the anion tends to be highly hydrated or is derived from a weak acid, the solubilities of the salts of the small alkali cations are less, even if the anion itself is large. An example is the case of $NaSb(OH)_6$ and $KSb(OH)_6$, given in Table 3–1.

Again, although certain salts may be quite soluble in dilute aqueous solution, their solubility may be made significantly less by changing the conditions. Thus NaCl, which is soluble in pure water to the extent of about 360 grams per liter can be quantitatively precipitated from concentrated hydrochloric acid.

The molar solubilities of some of the less soluble alkali salts are given in Appendix 11 (Table A11–1a). From these it can be seen that the more common alkali metals, Na and K, can be precipitated quantitatively only by using rather unusual reagents. Furthermore, for each of the less soluble salts of potassium, there is a corresponding insoluble ammonium salt, so that it is always necessary to ensure the absence of ammonium salts before precipitating an insoluble salt of potassium. The converse precaution is not necessary, however, since before testing, ammonium ion is usually distilled as ammonia gas out of the alkaline solution, leaving the nonvolatile potassium salts behind. The tests for ammonium ion (or ammonia) are then performed on the distillate.

3–8.   The Alkaline-Earth Metals

The free alkaline-earth metals are silvery metals whose hardness is greater, whose melting points are higher, and which are less reactive than the alkali metals. In common with the alkai metals, the hardness and melting point decrease, and the reactivity increases, with increasing atomic number. Thus calcium, strontium, and barium will liberate hydrogen from cold water increasingly vigorously in the order named, while magnesium reacts only with steam. Barium may be cut with a knife (with some difficulty). Some of their physical properties are given in Table 3-4.

These metals are all characterized by the fact that they lose both of their valence electrons in aqueous solution, so that the only important oxidation state is the $+2$. Because of the higher positive charge, the kernel electrons are pulled in more than for the corresponding alkali-metal ions, and the radii are smaller, as can be seen from Table 3-5. Therefore the charge densities of the alkaline-earth ions are considerably greater than those of the alkali ions, and the solubility relationships may be expected to be different. The molar solubilities of a number of alkaline-earth salts are given in Table A11-2 (Appendix 11).

TABLE 3-4. PHYSICAL PROPERTIES OF THE ALKALINE-EARTH METALS

	Beryllium	Magnesium	Calcium	Strontium	Barium	Radium
Symbol	Be	Mg	Ca	Sr	Ba	Ra
Atomic Weight	9.02	24.32	40.8	87.63	137.36	226.05
Atomic Number	4	12	20	38	56	88
Melting Point °C	1284	650	850	770	710	700
Boiling Point °C	2970	1103	1440	1380	1500	1140
Hardness (Moh)	>7	2.0	1.5	1.8	1.5	
Density 20°C (g/ml.)	1.73	1.75	1.55	2.6	3.75	6.0
Standard Oxidation Potential (for $M(s) \rightarrow M^{+2}(aq) + 2e^-$) (volts)	1.70	2.34	2.87	2.89	2.90	
Heat of Hydration of Gaseous Ions in kcal/mole		460	395	355	305	
Electronegativity	1.5	1.3	1.1	1.0	0.85	
Abundance in Earth's Crust (%)	10^{-5}	2.09	3.63	10^{-4}	0.05	10^{-12}

TABLE 3-5. COMPARISON OF THE RADII OF METAL IONS (ÅNGSTROM UNITS)

Li^+	Na^+	K^+	Rb^+	Cs^+	Fr^+
0.70	1.00	1.33	1.52	1.70	1.80
Be^{+2}	Mg^{+2}	Ca^{+2}	Sr^{+2}	Ba^{+2}	Ra^{+2}
0.31	0.75	1.06	1.18	1.38	1.42
B^{+3}	Al^{+3}	Sc^{+3}	Y^{+3}	La^{+3}	Ac^{+3}
(0.20)	0.57	0.83	0.88	1.04	1.11

For the purposes of qualitative analysis, the carbonates, oxalates, chromates, sulfates, and the double ammonium phosphates and arsenates (see also Table A11-1b, Appendix 11) are useful. Note the very large change in solubility of the chromates going from Mg to Ba. This is very useful in separating Ba from Sr, and also, especially if the solubility of $SrCrO_4$ is decreased by adding alcohol, in separating Sr from Ca. The lesser solubility of the carbonates of Ca, Sr, and Ba is used in separating these elements from Mg. Likewise, the lesser solubility of $SrSO_4$ may be used, after Ba has been removed, to precipitate Sr away from Ca. Other salts could likewise be used to advantage.

Because of the fact that many of these salts are derived from weak acids, their solubilities increase in acidic solution. This may be used to make their solubility differences more useful. Thus, $SrCrO_4$, which is only slightly soluble in pure water, becomes very soluble in dilute acids because of the reaction

$$2\ SrCrO_4\ (s) + 2\ H^+ \rightleftharpoons 2\ Sr^{+2} + Cr_2O_7^{-2} + H_2O$$

Even the extremely insoluble $Ba_3(PO_4)_2$ is quite soluble in dilute acids, because of the extreme weakness of the third ionization of H_3PO_4.

$$Ba_3(PO_4)_2\ (s) + 2\ H^+ \rightleftharpoons 3\ Ba^{+2} + 2\ HPO_4^{-2}$$

On the other hand, $BaSO_4$, which is not nearly so insoluble in pure water as $Ba_3(PO_4)_2$, requires much stronger acid to be dissolved by the reaction

$$BaSO_4\ (s) + H^+ \rightleftharpoons Ba^{+2} + HSO_4^-$$

because the second ionization of H_2SO_4 is very much stronger than the third ionization of H_3PO_4 ($K_A = 10^{-2}$ for HSO_4^- compared to $K_A = 10^{-12}$ for HPO_4^{-2}).

The solubility of carbonates can likewise be controlled in this way, since carbonic acid, especially in its second ionization, is a weak acid. Thus, even the very weak acid ammonium ion, NH_4^+, can prevent the precipitation of $MgCO_3$, while allowing the less soluble carbonates of Ca, Sr, and Ba to come down.

$$MgCO_3\ (s) + NH_4^+ \rightleftharpoons Mg^{+2} + HCO_3^- + NH_3$$

The precipitation of $CaCO_3$, $SrCO_3$, and $BaCO_3$ is therefore carried out in the presence of NH_4^+ to accomplish a separation from Mg^{+2}.

The *carbonates* of the alkaline earths decompose according to the equation

$$MCO_3\ (s) \rightarrow MO\ (s) + CO_2\ (g)$$

when heated to temperatures which depend upon the charge density of the cation—the lower the charge density, the higher the temperature required. This is illustrated in Table 3–6.

TABLE 3–6. DECOMPOSITION TEMPERATURES OF ALKALINE-EARTH CARBONATES

	Beryllium	Magnesium	Calcium	Strontium	Barium	Radium
°C	100	350	825	1340	1450	

Heating the alkaline-earth carbonates is the usual method for preparation of the *oxides*. Barium oxide, BaO, is a valuable drying agent, and calcium oxide, CaO, is the "quicklime" of commerce. The oxides of calcium and the heavier metals react vigorously with water (but not so vigorously as the alkali oxides), with evolution of much heat, to produce the corresponding hydroxides.

$$MO\ (s) + H_2O\ (l) \rightarrow M(OH)_2\ (aq)$$

Magnesium oxide, if not ignited too strongly, reacts very slowly with water, while beryllium oxide does not react at all. All of the oxides are soft, except for BeO, which is as hard as corundum. All of the oxides have NaCl crystal structure, except BeO, which has diamond (or ZnO) structure. Barium oxide, like the alkali oxides, reacts upon heating with atmospheric oxygen, according to the equation

$$BaO \text{ (s)} + \tfrac{1}{2} O_2 \text{ (g)} \rightarrow BaO_2 \text{ (s)}$$

the product being barium peroxide. At one time this was an important intermediate in the production of hydrogen peroxide.

$$BaO_2 \text{ (s)} + H_2SO_4 \text{ (aq)} \rightarrow BaSO_4 \text{ (s)} + H_2O_2 \text{ (aq)}$$

In addition to certain soluble salts listed in Table A11–2, the *acetates, bromates, bromides, chlorates, perchlorates, chlorides, hypochlorites, cyanides, iodides, permanganates, nitrates, nitrites, sulfides,* and *thiocyanates* of the alkaline-earth elements are soluble. As in the case of the alkali metals, however, under certain conditions some of these normally soluble salts may be insoluble. Thus $BaCl_2$ readily precipitates out of concentrated HCl (compare this to the behavior of NaCl, Section 3–7). This is frequently a source of confusion to the student who knows that $BaSO_4$ dissolves in strong acids and that $BaCl_2$ is "soluble," but who nevertheless finds a white insoluble solid suspended in the concentrated HCl in which he has tried to dissolve $BaSO_4$. A second consideration is the fact that, although two simple salts individually may be soluble, together they may form an insoluble double salt. Thus $Sr(NO_2)_2$ has a solubility of 58.9 grams per hundred grams of water at 0°C, and nickel nitrite likewise does not precipitate from solution when Ni^{+2} and NO_2^{-} ions are brought together; nevertheless, when both Sr^{+2} and Ni^{+2} ions are brought together with NO_2^{-} in solution, a yellow crystalline precipitate of the double salt $SrNi(NO_2)_4$, very similar in appearance to $K_3Co(NO_2)_6$, is obtained. The case of the alums is another case in point. Cesium sulfate, Cs_2SO_4, has a solubility of 167 grams per hundred grams of water at 0°C. Aluminum sulfate, $Al_2(SO_4)_3$, has a solubility of 31.3 grams per hundred grams of water at 0°C. On the other hand, the double salt cesium alum, $CsAl(SO_4)_2 \cdot 12\, H_2O$, has a solubility of only 0.34 grams per hundred grams of water at 0°C. Consequently, on mixing solutions of cesium and aluminum sulfates, the alum will immediately crystallize out. Similarly, the important insoluble triple salt, $NaZn(UO_2)_3(C_2H_3O_2)_9 \cdot 6\, H_2O$, is made up of the soluble sodium, zinc, and uranyl acetates. (Zinc can be replaced in this triple salt by other divalent cations of about the same size without appreciable effect on the solubility. The triple magnesium and nickel salts have been used equally successfully for the determination of sodium.)

3–9. Lakes

Certain organic dyestuffs ("mordant dyes") are capable of dyeing insoluble metal hydroxides. The dye may be described as being adsorbed on the surface of the precipitate. The *dyed* hydroxides produced by precipitation in the presence of the dyes are known as "lakes." The action of a given dye-stuff may be highly specific, and the formation of a lake of characteristic color may be used to identify a particular metallic element among a number of others.

An important example of this is the navy blue lake formed by $Mg(OH)_2$ with the dye *para*-nitrobenzeneazoresorcinol (also known as S. and O. reagent). This can be used to identify magnesium in the presence of certain other ions which may, due to faulty technique, still be present when magnesium is to be identified. Calcium and manganese do not give lakes with this dye, and the lake obtained with $Pb(OH)_2$ is brown rather than blue. The test will detect Mg^{+2} at a concentration of 10 parts per million (ppm).

Another important lake is the bright red one formed by $Al(OH)_3$ and aurintricarboxylic acid (aluminon reagent) which is capable of detecting 0.3 ppm of Al^{+3}. When $Al(OH)_3$ is precipitated from slightly acidic (pH 4.5) ammonia-ammonium salt solutions, the bright red lake is obtained, yellow free dye (free aurintricarboxylic acid) being left in solution. Alumina can be distinguished in this way from hydrous silica, which may precipitate under the same conditions, but which does not form the lake. Likewise, $Cr(OH)_3$ and $Fe(OH)_3$ do not form lakes with aluminon reagent (although care should be taken not to confuse the normally brownish red $Fe(OH)_3$ with the bright red aluminum lake). On the other hand, $Mn(OH)_2$ forms a lake very similar to that of $Al(OH)_3$, as does $Be(OH)_2$.

There are many other lakes which are useful for detecting specific elements under special conditions. A complete discussion of them, however, would occupy a whole volume.

3–10. Flame Tests

The alkali and heavier alkaline-earth elements, whose valence electrons are very loosely bound, are capable of being excited even at the temperature of a Bunsen flame, with emission of visible light. The heat of the flame causes dissociation of the metal salts into ions. The metal ions then pick up electrons, which are abundant in the flame, and the falling of the electrons into the valence orbitals of the metal atoms gives rise to the light emission. The wavelength of light emitted is characteristic of the element involved and, by use of a spectroscope, can be used absolutely to identify the element. Even to the naked eye the flame is usually characteristic enough for identification, although *comparison should always be made with a known sample*. The best flames are obtained with the more volatile halides, rather than with such compounds as the sulfates or nitrates. The flame colors obtained with the alkali and alkaline-earth elements are listed in Table 3–7.

Among the alkaline earths, the color of the strontium flame persists much longer than those of calcium and barium. Since a strontium flame slightly contaminated with sodium may resemble a calcium flame, it is always wise

TABLE 3-7. FLAME COLORS OF ALKALI AND ALKALINE-EARTH ELEMENTS

Element	Color	Element	Color
Lithium	Deep red	Beryllium	None
Sodium	Intense yellow	Magnesium	None
Potassium	Pale lavender	Calcium	Brick red
Rubidium*	Deep red	Strontium	Crimson
Cesium*	Blue	Barium	Pale yellowish green
		Radium	Deep red

* The names of these two elements are derived from their flame colors, *rubidium* from the Latin *rubidus*, red, and *cesium* from the Latin *caesius*, sky blue.

to compare with known samples. The sodium flame is far more intense and persistent than the potassium flame. Since sodium is almost always a contaminant in potassium salts, the potassium flame is always viewed through two thicknesses of cobalt-blue glass, which screens out the yellow sodium light. The potassium flame, so viewed, appears somewhat redder than when seen with the naked eye.

Certain other elements also give colored flames. Some of them are listed in Table 3-8.

TABLE 3-8. FLAME COLORS OF SELECTED ELEMENTS

Element	State or Condition	Color
Boron	Volatile compounds	Apple green
Copper	Halides	Green
Copper	Other compounds	Blue
Indium*	Volatile compounds	Blue
Thallium*	Volatile compounds	Green
Tin	Tin(II): flame impinging on cold surface	Pale blue

* The names *indium* and *thallium* are derived from their spectra—the former from *indigo* and the latter from the Greek *thallos*, a budding twig.

It can be seen that flame tests should not be applied indiscriminately to samples of unknown composition, but should be used only as final identification on material isolated in a systematic way.

3-11.   The Determination of a Solubility Product Constant

Since "seeing is believing," the following experiment is to be performed to show the constancy of a solubility-product *constant* over a range of concentrations. The substance chosen for this experiment is $AgBrO_3$, because its relatively large K_{sp} allows a convenient range of Ag^+ concentrations, and because the actual Ag^+ concentration is easily determined by titration.

Three solutions have been prepared by your instructor and left stirring for 24 hours, and then were allowed to stand for at least one week before your using them, in order to ensure their being at equilibrium. Their compositions are as follows

(1) 1000 ml of 0.010 M $AgNO_3$ + 400 ml of 0.10 M $KBrO_3$ + 1200 ml of 0.102 M KNO_3

(2) 1000 ml of 0.010 M $AgNO_3$ + 1000 ml of 0.10 M $KBrO_3$ + 600 ml of 0.104 M KNO_3

(3) 1000 ml of 0.010 M $AgNO_3$ + 1600 ml of 0.10 M $KBrO_3$

The concentrations in all three solutions are such that the solubility product constant of $AgBrO_3$ is exceeded, and $AgBrO_3$ precipitates. The KNO_3 is added to keep all the solutions at constant ionic strength.

Each solution is to be analyzed as follows: Withdraw 50 ml of the solution through the filter stick provided, and place in a clean 250-ml beaker. Add 1 ml of indicator solution (saturated $Fe_2(SO_4)_3$ in 0.1 M H_2SO_4). Read the level of the KNCS buret. Record it in your notebook.

Stirring constantly, run in slowly 0.005 M KNCS from a buret until the first *permanent* red-orange color develops. (The solution will have become milky from precipitated AgNCS during the titration.) *Do not overtitrate.* Read the final level of the KNCS buret. Record the level, the concentration of the BrO_3^- in the solution, and the temperature. (Remember that Ag^+ and BrO_3^- must have precipitated out in equivalent amounts when the solutions were first made up. Therefore the BrO_3^- concentration is less by what has precipitated.) The red color of the endpoint is due to the formation of the complex $FeNCS^{+2}$.

Repeat for the other two solutions.

Calculate from the amount of KNCS used the concentration of Ag^+ in solution. Knowing the initial concentration of BrO_3^- (after mixing) before precipitation of $AgBrO_3$, calculate the final concentration of BrO_3^-. From these data, determine the K_{sp} for $AgBrO_3$ at this temperature. Plot $[Ag^+]$ versus $1/[BrO_3^-]$ on rectangular graph paper and, from the slope of the curve, again determine the K_{sp} of $AgBrO_3$.

In your report of this experiment (due one week after you perform it), you should include the purpose and procedure of the experiment, as well as the observed data, calculations, and conclusions. Compare your results with literature values. Include any original improvements and variations you may think of.

3–12. Experiments on Solubility Trends

The following experiments are designed to demonstrate the trends in the solubilities of ionic solids described in Section 3–6. Since you are looking for differences in solubility, a precipitate will not form every time. Explain the results of each experiment.

Effect of Ionic Size (Charge Constant). *Category* 1. (Solubility increases as ionic size increases.)

(1) To 5 drops of 5 M KF solution, add 5 drops of 1 M LiCl solution. Explain the result. (i.e., LiF is less soluble than KF, KCl, or LiCl.)

(2) To 10 drops of 1 M LiCl, add 5 drops of 0.1 M Na_2HPO_4 and then 5 drops of 15 M NH_4OH. Look carefully for the crystalline precipitate, which may form rather slowly. What is the function of the NH_4OH? Repeat, using NaCl instead of LiCl.

(3) Dilute a small portion (4–6 drops) of 0.1 M Na^+ solution with an equal quantity of water. To exactly 2 drops of this solution, add exactly 4 drops of glacial (concentrated) acetic acid and exactly 2 drops of zinc uranyl acetate reagent. Mix thoroughly and let stand for at least 10 minutes, with scratching if necessary. The precipitate of a small quantity of pale yellow crystals is $NaZn(UO_2)_3(C_2H_3O_2)_9 \cdot 6\ H_2O$. Repeat, using K^+ instead of Na^+.

Category 2. (Solubility decreases as ionic size increases.)

(1) Dilute 3 drops of 0.1 M K^+ ion solution with 4 drops of water, acidify with a few drops of acetic acid, and add *one* drop of sodium tetraphenylborate solution. The precipitate of $KB(C_6H_5)_4$ should appear immediately on mixing.

(2) Repeat, substituting NH_4^+ for K^+. What does this experiment tell you about the size of the ammonium ion? If $NaB(C_6H_5)_4$ is used to test for K^+, will NH_4^+ interfere? What are the relative solubilities of $NaB(C_6H_5)_4$ and $KB(C_6H_5)_4$?

(3) To a solution of 3 drops of 0.1 M $Sr(NO_3)_2$ solution in 1 ml of water, add 1 ml of saturated $CaSO_4$ solution. What is the precipitate that forms? What are the relative solubilities of $SrSO_4$ and $CaSO_4$?

(4) Into three separate test tubes, put 0.5 ml of water and 5 drops each of 0.1 M Ca^{+2}, Sr^{+2}, and Ba^{+2}. To each tube, add 5 drops of 1 M K_2CrO_4 solution. Stir. What happens? Add alcohol to the tube containing the Sr^{+2}, with stirring, until a reaction takes place. Add the same amount of alcohol to each of the other tubes. Explain.

Category 3. (Solubility passes through a minimum as ionic size increases.)

(1) In three separate tubes, put 5 drops each of 0.1 M magnesium, calcium, and barium ion solutions. To the calcium solution, add with shaking 0.15 M KF solution dropwise until a precipitate forms. Now add the same amount of fluoride to each of the other tubes. What does this illustrate?

Effect of Ionic Charge (Size Constant). *Category* 1. (Solubility increases as ionic charge decreases.)

(1) In three separate tubes, put 5 drops each of 0.1 M cerium, calcium, and sodium salt solutions. To each tube, add 5 drops of 0.15 M KF solution. Centrifuge the tubes in which precipitates have appeared and discard the supernates. To each of the tubes containing a precipitate, add 0.5 ml of water, stir, and then add, dropwise with stirring, 3 M HCl until the precipitates dissolve. Which requires more acid? Explain.

(2) In each of three test tubes, put 5 drops of 0.1 M calcium ion solution. Add the following reagents, dropwise with stirring, each to one tube until a reaction has occurred or until a total of 10 drops has been added: (a) 1 M perchloric acid, (b) 1 M ammonium sulfate, (c) 1 M potassium phosphate. Explain the result.

To 5 drops of saturated calcium sulfate solution, add 5 drops of the phosphate solution. Explain the result.

Category 2. (Solubility decreases as ionic charge decreases.)

(1) Carry out experiment (1) for Category 2 above, using barium ion instead of potassium ion. Explain.

(2) To 5 drops of 1 *M* potassium phosphate solution, add 5 drops of 1 *M* perchloric acid.

Category 3. (Solubility passes through a minimum as ionic charge decreases.)

(1) In three separate tubes, put 5 drops each of 0.1 *M* cerium, calcium, and sodium ion solutions. To the calcium solution, add, dropwise with stirring, a 0.2 *M* ammonium sulfate solution until a reaction occurs. Now add the same amount to each of the other tubes. Explain.

3–13. The Analysis of the Alkali and Alkaline-Earth Groups

The details of the procedure for the analysis of the alkali and alkaline-earth groups are described below. Study them and understand what you are to do before you attempt the analysis of any unknown samples. If you do do not understand any of the procedures, carry out the manipulations on a known solution before you tackle the unknown; or better still, make up a solution containing all the ions to be detected and go through the entire separation and identification procedure. During the analysis of the unknown, whenever you are in doubt about any test, always compare it with the same test performed on a known sample.

When you are properly prepared to analyze the unknown solution, obtain from your laboratory instructor a sample which may contain any number of the ions Ba^{+2}, Sr^{+2}, Ca^{+2}, Mg^{+2}, Na^+, K^+, and NH_4^+.

3–A. Test for NH_4^+ Ion. To 1 ml of the unknown solution in a small casserole or evaporating dish add 6 *M* NaOH dropwise until the solution is alkaline and then 1 ml in excess. (Note: Never dip the litmus or pH indicator paper into the solution to test it! Always remove a drop of the solution on the end of a *clean* stirring rod and touch it to the indicator paper.) Moisten a strip of red litmus paper with *distilled* (or de-ionized) water and place it on the underside of a watch glass just big enough to cover the casserole. Place the watch glass over the casserole and heat *gently*. If NH_3 is present, the litmus paper will turn blue. DO NOT BOIL, for this will spatter the alkaline solution onto the paper, turning it blue even in the absence of NH_4^+. Usually, however, spattering will give blue spots, whereas NH_3 gives a uniform color. If the concentration of NH_3 is high, it may be detected by smell.

3–B. Test for NH_4^+. An alternate, and much more sensitive, test for NH_3 is that with Nessler's reagent (a solution of K_2HgI_4 in excess NaOH). To 1 ml of sample in a test tube add NaOH as in (3–A). In the gas absorption pipet place a few drops of Nessler's reagent and affix the pipet to the top of the test tube by means of a rubber stopper or a gasket made of rubber tubing. Warm the test tube to distill NH_3 through the pipet. The formation of an orange precipitate ($Hg_2I_3NH_2$) shows the presence of NH_3.

$$2\,HgI_4^{-2}\,(aq) + NH_3\,(aq) + OH^-\,(aq) \rightarrow Hg_2I_3NH_2\,(s) + 5\,I^-\,(aq) + H_2O\,(l)$$

The test is extremely delicate, being capable of detecting (as a yellow color) considerably less than 40 ppm of NH_3. At 40 ppm, a distinct orange precipitate is still observable. The test consequently has the disadvantage of being too sensitive for the usual college qualitative analysis laboratory, picking up the ammonia present in the laboratory air.

3–C. *The Separation of* Ba^{+2}, Sr^{+2}, *and* Ca^{+2} *from* Mg^{+2}, Na^+, *and* K^+. The tests for all the other elements in this analytical group are performed in succession on a fresh portion of solution.

If the analysis is to be performed on the supernatant solution from the Al–Zn group, evaporate the supernate to dryness, add 1 ml 6 N HNO_3, and evaporate again, finally dissolving the residue in 1 ml of water. (This procedure destroys the ammonium salts

$$NH_4^+ \text{ (aq)} + NO_3^- \text{ (aq)} \rightarrow N_2O \text{ (g)} + 2 H_2O \text{ (l)}$$

which, if present in too large amount, may prevent the precipitation of the alkaline-earth carbonates.

$$MCO_3 \text{ (s)} + NH_4^+ \rightarrow M^{+2} + HCO_3^- + NH_3$$

It also serves to concentrate the solution.) To this solution (or to 1 ml of a solution of the alkali–alkaline-earth unknown) add 1 ml of 5 M NH_4Cl solution and 15 M NH_4OH until strongly alkaline. Heat in a boiling water bath (to hasten coagulation of the precipitate) and add $(NH_4)_2CO_3$ to precipitate $BaCO_3$, $SrCO_3$, and $CaCO_3$. Centrifuge and test the supernate with 1 drop of $(NH_4)_2CO_3$ solution to check for complete precipitation. If the supernate remains clear, separate the precipitate from it. (Label the supernate 3–G.) Wash the precipitate twice with 3 ml of warm water, discarding the washes, before proceeding.

3–D. *Detection of* Ba^{+2}. To the precipitate from (3–C) add dropwise 6 M HAc, with stirring, until the precipitate is just dissolved. Add 10 drops of 3 M NH₄Ac solution and dilute with 3 ml of water. Stir. Remove a small portion of this solution to another test tube and add to it a few drops of 1 M K_2CrO_4 solution. Stir. If no yellow precipitate is obtained, barium may be presumed to be absent, and the procedure for separating barium may be omitted.

If a precipitate was obtained, combine the two portions of the NH₄Ac–HAc solution and add 10 drops of 1 M K_2CrO_4 solution. Stir and heat. Centrifuge and test for completeness of precipitation. If precipitation is complete, separate the supernate, which may contain Sr^{+2} and Ca^{+2}, and label it (3–E). Wash the $BaCrO_4$ precipitate twice with 3 ml of water. Thorough washing is essential to obviate interference by Ca^{+2}, Sr^{+2}, Na^+, or K^+ with the flame test for Ba^{+2}. Discard the washings.

The presence of Ba^{+2} is confirmed by dissolving the $BaCrO_4$ in 1 ml of 6 M HCl and applying the flame test. This is done by dipping a *clean* platinum wire with a loop at the end of it into the solution and then holding the loop in the side of a Bunsen flame. The presence of Ba^{+2} will be shown by a pale green coloration of the flame. To the HCl solution add 2 drops of 6 M H_2SO_4. The precipitation of white $BaSO_4$ demonstrates the presence of Ba^{+2}. (Centrifuge to make sure the precipitate is white.)

3–E. *Detection of* Sr^{+2}. If K_2CrO_4 was added to the main portion of the solution in (3–D) (i.e., if Ba^{+2} was present), add to the separated supernate

(3–E) NH_4OH, until alkaline, and $(NH_4)_2CO_3$ in excess; heat, centrifuge, and wash exactly as in (3–C). The white precipitate is now free of chromate. (If there is no precipitate, Sr^{+2} and Ca^{+2} are absent.) Dissolve the precipitate in 1 ml of dilute HAc. Divide this solution (or the main portion of solution 3–D if no K_2CrO_4 was added) in half. To one half add at least an equal volume of saturated $CaSO_4$ solution, waiting half an hour, and scratching the inside of the tube below the liquid level with a glass rod if no precipitate appears at once. White turbidity indicates the presence of Sr^{+2}. Centrifuge, wash twice with water, dissolve in 6 M HCl, and carry out a flame test as for Ba^{+2}. A crimson flame confirms the presence of Sr^{+2}.

3–F. *Detection of* Ca^{+2}. While waiting for the $SrSO_4$ precipitate to appear, heat in the water bath the other half of the solution described in (3–E), add dilute H_2SO_4 in excess, allow to stand a half-hour, and centrifuge. The precipitate may contain $SrSO_4$, $CaSO_4$ or both.

To the separated supernate from the H_2SO_4 treatment, add NH_4OH in excess and $(NH_4)_2C_2O_4$. If no precipitate appears at first, rub the inside of the tube with a glass rod at intervals for a half-hour. Heating may hasten precipitation. A white precipitate of CaC_2O_4 shows the presence of calcium. As H_2SO_4 was previously added to remove Sr^{+2}, this precipitate may contain less calcium than was originally present.

Perform the flame test for calcium as described for Ba and Sr. A brick-red flame confirms the presence of Ca^{+2}.

3–G. *The Removal of Ammonium Salts.* The test for K^+ and one of the tests for Mg^{+2} are performed on the solution (3–G) from the carbonate precipitation. The solution should be treated as follows:

To a portion of supernate (3–G) in a casserole add one-third its volume of 15 M HNO_3, evaporate to dryness, and fume to decompose ammonium nitrate. (Hood!) Cool the vessel, add 0.25 ml of water and 0.25 ml of 6 N sodium hydroxide solution (0.25 ml equals 5 drops). Mix well and heat gently to drive off ammonia. Cool nearly to room temperature, dilute to about 4 ml, and transfer half to one small tube and half to another (transferring precipitate as well as solution). Label one half (3–I).

3–H. *Detection of Potassium.* To one of these portions, add one drop of sodium tetraphenylborate solution. If K^+ is present, a white precipitate of potassium tetraphenylborate forms immediately.

To confirm that this precipitate contains potassium, separate and wash the precipitate with water and then perform a potassium flame test using cobalt-blue glass to filter any interfering sodium coloration, as described in Section 3–10. The organic portion of the precipitate burns initially with a luminous flame, and immediately thereafter the potassium flame color can be observed.

3–I. *Detection of Magnesium.* On the other portion (3–I), the test for Mg^{+2} with S. and O. reagent should run as follows: Add 1–3 drops of S. and O. reagent; then add 6 M NaOH dropwise, until alkaline, and then 3 drops in excess. If Mg^{+2} is present, the characteristic blue $Mg(OH)_2$ lake will precipitate. Frequently it is not possible to determine whether the precipitate suspended in the blue solution is itself blue. Consequently, the suspension should be centrifuged so that the color of the precipitate itself can be examined (see Section 3–9).

Divide the remaining portion of the supernate (3–G) from which the NH_4^+ salts were not removed, into two portions. On one of these portions run the precipitation of $MgNH_4PO_4$ as follows: Add, in order, 10 drops of 15 M NH_4OH and 10 drops of 0.5 M Na_2HPO_4 solution. Stir and allow to stand a few minutes. Scratch, if no precipitate appears. The appearance of a white crystalline precipitate of $MgNH_4PO_4$ confirms the presence of Mg^{+2}.

3–H. *Detection of Sodium.* On the remaining portion of the supernate, run the sodium zinc uranyl acetate precipitation as described under "Effect of Ionic Size," (Category 1, Experiment (3), Section 3–12). (Since the reagent has already been saturated with sodium salt in order to increase the sensitivity of the test, *DO NOT* run the flame test on any of precipitate obtained or on the solution itself after zinc uranyl acetate solution has been added. The flame test should be run on the original solution or on the solution (3–H) *before* addition of zinc uranyl acetate. The flame test must be brilliant and long-lasting, since there will almost invariably be traces of sodium present to give a weak flame test.) The appearance of a yellow crystalline precipitate (which may require scratching) confirms the presence of Na^+.

3–14. Questions and Problems

1. Discuss the differences between homogeneous and heterogeneous equilibria with respect to both the descriptions of the systems and the mathematical treatment.

2. Describe the effect on the solubility of solid $MgCO_3$ suspended in water of adding (a) $MgCl_2$, (b) $NaNO_3$, (c) $NaOH$, (d) HCl, and (e) Na_2CO_3.

3. Describe the conditions necessary for the precipitation of a slightly soluble salt.

4. Discuss the effect of crystal size on solubility.

5. Discuss the effect of ionic size and charge on solubility.

6. Is the rule, "All the salts of the alkali metals are soluble," correct? Explain.

7. Discuss the nature of lakes.

8. What is the function of the Fe^{+3} in the $AgBrO_3$ solubility experiment? Why does the red color not develop sooner?

9. Why must NH_4^+ be removed before the lake test for Mg^{+2} is performed?

10. When LaF_3 is precipitated from solution Pu^{+3} is simultaneously precipitated practically quantitatively even though the concentration of Pu^{+3} is many orders of magnitude too low for the solubility product constant $[Pu^{+3}][F^-]^3$ to be exceeded. Explain.

11. Would the explanation for problem 10 explain why $BaSO_4$ precipitated from a solution containing Co^{+2} is always pink?

12. Describe the effect on a saturated solution of $Cu(IO_3)_2$ of adding more solid $Cu(IO_3)_2$.

13. From the solubility of each of the salts given below, calculate the K_{sp}.

Salt	Solubility (g/100 ml)
(a) TlI	0.0064
(b) AgNCS	2.1×10^{-5}
(c) AgN_3	9×10^{-5}
(d) $CsClO_4$	0.8
(e) $FeCO_3$	0.0067
(f) $FePO_4$	0.1
(g) $Cs_2[PtCl_6]$	0.135
(h) $Pb(IO_3)_2$	0.0012
(i) $Th(SO_4)_2 \cdot 9\ H_2O$	1.57
(j) $Ba_2P_2O_7$	0.01
(k) $La(IO_3)_3$	1.7
(l) Tl_3PO_4	0.5
(m) $La_2(C_2O_4)_3 \cdot 9\ H_2O$	0.0008
(n) $Pb_3(PO_4)_2$	1.4×10^{-5}
(o) $Ce(IO_4)_4$	0.015
(p) $Tl_4Fe(CN)_6 \cdot 2\ H_2O$	0.37
(q) $Th_3(PO_4)_4$	10^{-14}
(r) $NH_4MgAsO_4 \cdot 6\ H_2O$	0.038
(s) $NH_4Ce(SO_4)_2 \cdot 4\ H_2O$	5.33
(t) $K_2ThF_6 \cdot 4\ H_2O$	6×10^{-5}
(u) $NaZn(UO_2)_3(C_2H_3O_2)_9 \cdot 6\ H_2O$	3.1

14. From the following K_{sp}'s, calculate the solubilities in grams of solute per hundred milliliters of solution.

Salt	K_{sp}
(a) LiF	5.0×10^{-3}
(b) $Na[Sb(OH)_6]$	4.0×10^{-6}
(c) AuI	1.6×10^{-23}
(d) CuCN	3×10^{-20}
(e) $SrSO_4$	7.6×10^{-7}
(f) $Ra(IO_3)_2$	8.8×10^{-10}
(g) Rb_2PtCl_6	5.5×10^{-5}
(h) BiI_3	1×10^{-28}
(i) $Ag_3[Fe(CN)_6]$	7×10^{-18}
(j) Bi_2Te_3	1×10^{-164}
(k) $Ca_3(PO_4)_2$	1×10^{-25}
(l) $Pu(IO_3)_4$	5×10^{-13}
(m) $Tl_4P_2O_7$	2.6×10^{0}
(n) $Zr_3(PO_4)_4$	1×10^{-132}
(o) $NH_4MnPO_4 \cdot 6\ H_2O$	4.1×10^{-12}
(p) Pb_2OSO_4	6×10^{-20}
(q) $Na_4FPO_4 \cdot 12\ H_2O$	6.2×10^{-2}

15. The solubility of $Ba_3(AsO_4)_2$ in alkaline solution is 0.055 grams per hundred milliliters of solution. What is the K_{sp}?

16. The K_{sp} of dysprosium chromate, $Dy_2(CrO_4)_3$, is 1×10^{-8}. What will be the molar concentration of Dy^{+3} ion if 100 ml of water is saturated with excess $Dy_2(CrO_4)_3$?

17. It is found that if excess solid BaF_2 is shaken up with a 0.1 M $Ba(NO_3)_2$ solution, the fluoride-ion concentration at equilibrium is 4×10^{-3} M. What is the K_{sp} of BaF_2?

18. Calculate how many grams of LiOH will dissolve in one liter of 0.3 M KOH solution ($K_{sp} = 4 \times 10^{-2}$).

19. Calculate how many grams of Ag_2O will dissolve in 750 ml of 0.001 M $AgNO_3$ solution.

20. Calculate how many grams of NaOH must be added to 500 ml of a 0.1 molar solution of $La(NO_3)_3$ just to start precipitation of $La(OH)_3$.

21. Calculate how many grams of $Cd(OH)_2$ will dissolve in 750 ml of a 0.1 M NaOH solution.

22. Calculate the number of grams of $NH_4MgPO_4 \cdot 6\,H_2O$ which will dissolve in 250 ml of an ammoniacal solution containing 10 grams of NH_4Cl.

23. Calculate the number of grams of $RbAl(SO_4)_2 \cdot 12\,H_2O$ which will dissolve in 400 ml of a solution containing 3 grams of $Na_2SO_4 \cdot 10\,H_2O$ at 0°C. The solubility of the rubidium salt in pure water at 0°C is 1.3 grams per hundred milliliters.

24. Calculate the number of grams of $K_2Ca(SO_4)_2 \cdot H_2O$ which will dissolve 300 ml of a solution containing 5 grams of KCl ($K_{sp} = 1.76 \times 10^{-6}$).

25. If solid TlCl is added to a solution containing 0.1 M KBr, what is the ratio of $[Cl^-]$ to $[Br^-]$ when equilibrium is attained?
   What is the $[Tl^+]$ in the saturated solution?

26. Show that when enough $AgNO_3$ is added to a solution containing I^- and NCS^- to precipitate both AgI and AgNCS the ratio of $[NCS^-]$ to $[I^-]$ does not change, regardless of how large an excess of $AgNO_3$ is used.

27. Show that when enough $AgNO_3$ is added to a solution containing I^- and $C_2O_4^{-2}$ to precipitate both AgI and $Ag_2C_2O_4$ the ratio of $[C_2O_4^{-2}]$ to $[I^-]$ is not constant, but depends upon how large an excess of $AgNO_3$ is used.

28. The substances Ag_2SO_4, $CaSO_4$, and $Gd_2(SO_4)_3$ have K_{sp}'s which are all about 2×10^{-5}. (a) If a solution containing each of the ions Ag^+, Ca^{+2}, and Gd^{+3} in 0.01 molar concentration is made 0.1 molar in SO_4^{-2}, what will the final concentration of each of the cations be? (b) If the SO_4^{-2} concentration is raised to 0.5 molarity, what will be the concentrations of the three cations? (c) What is the minimum final concentration of sulfate ion required to start precipitation of all three? (d) What are the concentrations of the cations under these conditions?

29. If the solubility of very small Ag_2CrO_4 crystals is five times that of large crystals, calculate the minimum silver ion concentration required just to begin precipitation of Ag_2CrO_4 from a 0.001 M K_2CrO_4 solution.

3–15. References

Hammett, L. P., *Solutions of Electrolytes*, 2d ed. NewYork: McGraw-Hill Book Company, Inc., 1936.

Mantell, C. L., and Hardy, C., *Calcium Metallurgy and Technology*. New York: Reinhold Publishing Corporation, 1945.

Lithium and Its Compounds. London: Royal Institute of Chemistry, 1957.

Alico, J., *Introduction to Magnesium and Its Alloys*. Chicago: Ziff-Davis Publishing Company, 1945.

Sittig, M., *Sodium, Its Manufacture, Properties and Uses*. New York: Reinhold Publishing Corporation, 1956.

Handling and Uses of the Alkali Metals. ("Advances in Chemistry Series, No. 19.") Washington, D. C.: American Chemical Society, 1957.

Chapter *4*

The Insoluble Halides

Complex Ion Equilibria

4–1. The Insoluble Chloride Groups

It must be realized that elements located near one another in the periodic table will act similarly chemically, *particularly if the oxidation states* are the same.* Thus we find that the first solubility rule cited in Section 1–1 should be expanded and modified to read:

The chlorides of the +1 states of the elements in the *L*-shaped group

Cu

Ag

Au Hg Tl

are insoluble in water, the solubility being lower the closer to the corner of the *L*. In addition, the chlorides of the +2 states of the sixth period elements from Os to Pb (Os, Ir, Pt, Au, Hg, Tl, Pb) are only slightly soluble insofar as they exist. (The compound $AuCl_2$ probably does not exist, although it has been reported. If it does exist, however, it is undoubtedly Au_2Cl_4, i.e., gold(I) chloroaurate(III), $Au^I[Au^{III}Cl_4]$. The known compound Tl_2Cl_4 has been shown to be thallium(I) chlorothallate(III), $Tl^I[Tl^{III}Cl_4]$, and does not contain thallium(II).)

Thus, when dilute hydrochloric acid is added to a solution containing these elements, all the +1 chlorides should precipitate, and partial precipitation

---

* *Oxidation state or oxidation number* has been defined as: "The charge on a simple ion or for a complex ion or molecule: the charge which is assumed on an atom to account for the number of electrons involved in the oxidation (or reduction) of the atom to the free element." *Valence* is very similar in concept and has been defined as: "The number of electron pair bonds which an atom shares with other atoms. In inorganic chemistry the term is often used to mean oxidation state." Latimer, W. M., and Hildebrand, J. H., *Reference Book of Inorganic Chemistry*, 3rd ed. New York: The Macmillan Company, 1951.

should occur of the $+2$ chlorides of the sixth period elements. In practice, the only precipitates observed are AgCl, Hg_2Cl_2, TlCl, and $PbCl_2$. Copper is absent from the precipitate because copper normally is present in solution as Cu^{+2} whose chloride is soluble. Gold is normally present as Au(III), whose chloride is soluble. (Besides, gold is a rare element.) Thallium is not normally present, because of its scarcity, but would precipitate as TlCl if it were present. The elements Os, Ir, and Pt are also rare and, besides, are usually present in some other oxidation state than $+2$. In addition, the sixth period elements easily form complex chlorides which are formed with excess hydrochloric acid and prevent the precipitation of the slightly soluble dichlorides. This tendency is strong with mercury, so that $HgCl_2$, even though only slightly soluble (0.25 molar at 25°C), does not precipitate from HCl solution due to the reaction

$$HgCl_2 + Cl^- \rightleftharpoons HgCl_3^-$$

The tendency is less in the case of lead, so that $PbCl_2$ will *partially* precipitate from dilute HCl, but even in this case, too high a concentration of HCl will prevent the formation of any precipitate because of the reaction

$$PbCl_2 \text{ (s)} + Cl^- \text{ (aq)} \rightleftharpoons PbCl_3^- \text{ (aq)}$$

(All of the insoluble chlorides have a tendency to form complex anions to some extent with excess HCl. Thus AgCl forms $AgCl_2^-$ in the presence of a large excess of HCl. The very low solubility of AgCl, however, prevents loss of significant amounts of the precipitate if the HCl concentration is kept low.)

Under ordinary circumstances, then, the first group precipitate brought down in the qualitative analytical scheme may contain any or all of the compounds AgCl, Hg_2Cl_2, TlCl, and $PbCl_2$.

Separation of the precipitated chlorides into two parts is accomplished by taking advantage of the fact that the solubility of insoluble chlorides is always greater in hot water than in cold, by roughly the same order of magnitude, as can be seen from Table 4–1. The solubilities of $PbCl_2$ and TlCl are

TABLE 4–1. SOLUBILITY IN GRAMS PER HUNDRED MILLILITERS OF WATER

Salt	Cold (°C)	Hot (°C)	Ratio: Hot to Cold
AgCl	0.000195 (25°)	0.0021 (100°)	10.8
Hg_2Cl_2	0.00020 (25°)	0.001 (43°)	—
$PbCl_2$	0.945 (25°)	3.34 (100°)	3.5
TlCl	0.384 (25°)	1.97 (100°)	5.1
$HgCl_2$	6.89 (25°)	61.3 (100°)	8.9

high enough to begin with, so that any $PbCl_2$ and TlCl precipitated in the cold water can be dissolved in a reasonable volume of hot water. Thus, they can be separated from AgCl and Hg_2Cl_2, whose solubilities are more than a thousandfold smaller.

4–2. The Heavy Metal Amides

Both silver and mercury fall within the area of the periodic table where ammonia complexes (ammines) are formed. Thus, in the same way that Ag^+ will combine with Cl^- to form $AgCl$, or with excess Cl^- to form $AgCl_2^-$, so it will combine with neutral NH_3 molecules to form an ammine complex ion.

$$Ag^+ + 2Cl^- \rightleftharpoons AgCl_2^-$$

$$Ag^+ + 2NH_3 \rightleftharpoons Ag(NH_3)_2^+$$

The formation of ammine complexes is not so general a phenomenon in water solution as the formation of chloro complexes, however, and for practical purposes is confined to the center of the periodic table to the group of elements

(Fe)	Co	Ni	Cu	Zn
(Ru)	Rh	Pd	Ag	Cd
(Os)	Ir	Pt	Au	Hg

The more electronegative elements in the group (those with the highest affinity for nitrogen) are capable of actually replacing the hydrogen from the ammonia to form amides (compounds containing the ion NH_2^-), or even nitrides (compounds containing the ion N^{-3}). Of the more common elements in the group, mercury forms amides by far the most rapidly, the reaction being almost instantaneous. Silver, on the other hand, forms amides only on long standing in ammonium hydroxide solution. The difference in rate of amide formation can be used to separate $AgCl$ from Hg_2Cl_2, since $AgCl$ merely dissolves in NH_4OH to give the ammonia complex

$$AgCl\,(s) + 2\,NH_3 \rightleftharpoons Ag(NH_3)_2^+ + Cl^-$$

whereas Hg_2Cl_2 undergoes a more complicated disproportionation reaction, forming a double amide and chloride of mercury(II) (white, insoluble) and finely divided droplets of metallic mercury (black, insoluble).

$$Hg_2Cl_2\,(s) + 2\,NH_3\,(aq) \rightleftharpoons HgNH_2Cl\,(s) + Hg\,(l) + NH_4^+\,(aq) + Cl^-\,(aq)$$

(It should be noted that this amide would also be formed directly from $HgCl_2$.)

$$HgCl_2\,(aq) + 2\,NH_3\,(aq) \rightleftharpoons HgNH_2Cl\,(s) + NH_4^+\,(aq) + Cl^-\,(aq)$$

Since either ammonia or the amide group will be withdrawn from these complexes by hydrogen ions, acid will reverse all of these equilibria.

$$Ag(NH_3)_2^+ + Cl^- + 2\,H^+ \rightleftharpoons AgCl\,(s) + 2\,NH_4^+$$

$$HgNH_2Cl\,(s) + Cl^- + 2\,H^+ \rightleftharpoons HgCl_2 + NH_4^+$$

$$HgNH_2Cl\,(s) + Hg\,(l) + Cl^- + 2\,H^+ \rightleftharpoons Hg_2Cl_2\,(s) + NH_4^+$$

This reaction is frequently used to demonstrate the presence of the colorless $Ag(NH_3)_2{}^+$ ion in solutions in which silver has been separated from mercury(I).

(The very electronegative element osmium in its $+8$ oxidation state goes even farther than mercury in combining with ammonia, replacing all three hydrogens to form the "osmiamate" ion

$$OsO_4 + 2NH_3 \rightleftharpoons NH_4{}^+ + OsO_3N^- + H_2O.)$$

4–3. Insoluble Bromides and Iodides

The solubilities of the bromides and iodides of the heavy metals are similar to those of the chlorides. In particular, the solubilities in water vary in the order $Cl > Br > I$ for many of the nonmetals and for the group

Cu

Ru Rh Pd Ag   Sn Sb

Os Ir Pt Au Hg Tl Pb Bi

Thus the K_{sp}'s of the silver halides are $AgCl = 1.78 \times 10^{-10}$, $AgBr = 4.27 \times 10^{-13}$, $AgI = 8.30 \times 10^{-17}$. This indicates that, in this part of the periodic table (where the difference in electronegativity between the metal and the nonmetal in the compound is small), the smaller the difference in electronegativity, the less will be the ability of the compound to dissociate into ions and, therefore, the lower the solubility. Thus, as we have seen above, AgI (for which the difference in electronegativity, Δx, is 0.7) is less soluble than AgCl ($\Delta x = 1.2$).

It may be generalized, then, that the smaller the difference in electronegativity between B^{+x} and A^{-y}, the greater will be the affinity of one for the other, or the greater will be their tendency to form a covalent association with each other.

4–4. The Halide Complexes

There is no particular reason why this association should be limited to neutral compounds (i.e., equivalent amounts of B^{+x} and A^{-y}). If B^{+x} has a certain tendency to associate with one A^{-y}, it should be expected that it would likewise have a (probably lesser) tendency to associate with two A^{-y}'s. Therefore, we should have not only $Ag^+ + Cl^- \rightleftharpoons AgCl$ (s) but also $Ag^+ + 2\ Cl^- \rightleftharpoons AgCl_2{}^-$, or, in other words, the formation of a complex ion (as we have already seen). The *instability* constant for this particular complex ion (that is to say, the equilibrium constant for the reaction $AgCl_2{}^- \rightleftharpoons Ag^+ + 2\ Cl^-$) is 5.6×10^{-6}.

4–5.　The Stepwise Nature of Complex Ion Dissociation

Although we usually use instability constants for the complete dissociation of a complex ion (e.g., $HgI_4^{-2} \rightleftharpoons Hg^{+2} + 4\,I^-$), the dissociation actually proceeds in steps, each step having its own characteristic instability constant. Thus we have

$$HgCl^+ \rightleftharpoons Hg^{+2} + Cl^- \qquad K = 1.8 \times 10^{-7}$$
$$HgCl_2\,(aq) \rightleftharpoons HgCl^+ + Cl^- \qquad K = 3.3 \times 10^{-7}$$
$$HgCl_3^- \rightleftharpoons HgCl_2\,(aq) + Cl^- \qquad K = 1.4 \times 10^{-1}$$
$$HgCl_4^{-2} \rightleftharpoons HgCl_3^- + Cl^- \qquad K = 1.0 \times 10^{-1}$$

(where $HgCl_2$ (aq) refers to neutral, undissociated $HgCl_2$ in *aqueous* solution, *not* solid $HgCl_2$).

Over-all constants may be computed for each of these species, the over-all constant being the product of the constants for each of the individual steps involved. Thus, for the reaction

$$HgCl_3^- \rightleftharpoons Hg^{+2} + 3Cl^-$$

we have

$$HgCl_3^- \rightleftharpoons HgCl_2\,(aq) + Cl^-, \quad \frac{[HgCl_2][Cl^-]}{[HgCl_3^-]} = 1.4 \times 10^{-1}$$

$$HgCl_2\,(aq) \rightleftharpoons HgCl^+ + Cl^-, \quad \frac{[HgCl^+][Cl^-]}{[HgCl_2]} = 3.3 \times 10^{-7}$$

$$HgCl^+ \rightleftharpoons Hg^{+2} + Cl^-, \qquad \frac{[Hg^{+2}][Cl^-]}{[HgCl^+]} = 1.8 \times 10^{-7}$$

and therefore for $HgCl_3^- \rightleftharpoons Hg^{+2} + 3Cl^-$,

$$\frac{[\cancel{HgCl_2}][Cl^-]}{[HgCl_3^-]} \times \frac{[\cancel{HgCl^+}][Cl^-]}{[\cancel{HgCl_2}]} \times \frac{[Hg^{+2}][Cl^-]}{[\cancel{HgCl^+}]} = \frac{[Hg^{+2}][Cl^-]^3}{[HgCl_3^-]}$$

$$= (1.4 \times 10^{-1}) \times (3.3 \times 10^{-7}) \times (1.8 \times 10^{-7}) = 8.3 \times 10^{-15}$$

For many complex ions, however, only the constant for the over-all dissociation is known.

Again it can be seen that in general, as the difference in electronegativity between the metal and nonmetal decreases, the tendency to dissociate into simple ions decreases (i.e., the complex becomes more stable). Thus we have

$$HgCl_4^{-2} \qquad K_{inst} = 8.5 \times 10^{-16}$$
$$HgBr_4^{-2} \qquad K_{inst} = 1.00 \times 10^{-21}$$
$$HgI_4^{-2} \qquad K_{inst} = 1.48 \times 10^{-30}$$

where the last digit of the subscript on K refers to the number of coordinating groups, or ligands, in the complex. Further examples of this can be seen in Table 4–2.

TABLE 4–2. CUMULATIVE pK_{inst}'s FOR COMPLEX HALIDES

	pK_1	pK_{12}	pK_{123}	pK_{1234}	pK_{12345}	pK_{123456}
Ag^+–Cl	3.23*	5.25	5.5	5.4		
Ag^+–Br	4.30*	7.33	8.56	8.62	8.9	
Ag^+–I	8.13*	15.74	14.1	14.5	14.1	

$(Ag_2Cl^+, 5.20; Ag_3Cl^{+2}, 5.45)$
$(Ag_2Br^+, 9.70; Ag_3Br^{+2}, 8.00; Ag_4Br^{+3}, 8.38; Ag_2Br_6^{-4}, 20.36)$
$(Ag_2I^+, 10.0; Ag_3I^{+2}, 13.6; Ag_4I^{+3}, 13.6; Ag_2I_6^{-4}, 29.9;$
$Ag_2I_7^{-5}, 29.5; Ag_3I_8^{-5}, 45.6)$

	pK_1	pK_{12}	pK_{123}	pK_{1234}	pK_{12345}	pK_{123456}
Am^{+3}–Cl	1.17					
As^{+3}–Cl	1.07[a]	3.47[b]	4.20[c]			

[a] $As(OH)_3 (aq) + H^+ + Cl^- \rightleftharpoons As(OH)_2Cl (aq) + H_2O$
[b] $As(OH)_2Cl (aq) + H^+ + Cl^- \rightleftharpoons As(OH)Cl_2 (aq) + H_2O$
[c] $As(OH)Cl_2 (aq) + H^+ + Cl^- \rightleftharpoons AsCl_3 (aq) + H_2O$

	pK_1	pK_{12}	pK_{123}	pK_{1234}	pK_{12345}	pK_{123456}
Au^+–Cl	?	9.8				
Au^+–Br	?	12.46				
Au^{+3}–Cl	?	?	?	21.30		
Au^{+3}–Br	?	?	?	31.5		
Bi^{+3}–Cl	2.43	4.7	5.0*	5.6	6.1	6.42
Bi^{+3}–Br	2.26	4.45	6.33*	7.84	9.42	9.52
Bi^{+3}–I	3.64	?	?	14.95	16.80	19.1
Cd^{+2}–Cl	2.05	2.60*	2.4	2.9		
Cd^{+2}–Br	2.18	3.05*	2.80	3.21		
Cd^{+2}–I	2.37	3.66*	4.78	6.13		
Ce^{+3}–Cl	0.22					
Ce^{+3}–Br	0.38					
Cm^{+3}–Cl	1.17					
Co^{+2}–Cl	−2.40					
Co^{+2}–Br	−2.30					
Cr^{+3}–Cl	0.60	−0.71				
Cu^+–Cl	?	5.35	5.63			
Cu^+–Br	?	5.92				
Cu^+–I	?	8.85				
Cu^{+2}–Cl	0.07	−0.57*	−2.1			
Cu^{+2}–Br	−0.03					
Fe^{+2}–Cl	0.36	0.40*				
Fe^{+3}–Cl	1.45	2.10	1.10*	−0.85		
Fe^{+3}–Br	0.55	0.82				
Ga^{+3}–Cl	−0.6	−2.3	−4.5*	−6.8		
Hg^{+2}–Cl	6.74	13.22*	14.07	15.07		
Hg^{+2}–Br	9.05	17.33*	19.74	21.00		
Hg^{+2}–I	12.87	23.82*	27.60	29.83		
In^{+3}–Cl	1.0	1.5	1.55*	1.35		
In^{+3}–Br	1.20	1.78	2.48*	3.33		
In^{+3}–I	1.64	2.56	2.48*			
Ir^{+3}–Cl	?	?	?	?	?	14.00
La^{+3}–Cl	−0.15					

	pK_1	pK_{12}	pK_{123}	pK_{1234}	pK_{12345}	pK_{123456}
Mn^{+2}–Cl	ca. 0					
Mn^{+3}–Cl	0.95					
MoO$_2$$^{+2}$–Cl	−0.3	−0.8*	−2.69			
Ni^{+2}–Br	?	−3.24*	?	−8.12		
Pb^{+2}–Cl	1.60	1.78*	1.7	1.4		
Pb^{+2}–Br	1.77	1.92*	3.3	3.00		
Pb^{+2}–I	2.30	3.68*	5.44	6.20		
Pd^{+2}–Cl	6.1	10.5*	12.9	15.5	13.4	11.3
Pd^{+2}–Br	?	?	?	13.10		
Po^{+4}–Cl	?	?	?	?	?	14.00
Pt^{+2}–Cl	?	?	14.00	16.00		
Pt^{+2}–Br	?	?	?	20.5		
Pu^{+3}–Cl	1.17					
Pu^{+4}–Cl	−0.25					
PuO$_2$$^{+2}$–Cl	0.10	−0.35*				
Rh^{+3}–Cl	?	?	?	?	?	12.00
Sn^{+2}–Cl	1.51	2.24*	2.03	1.48		
Sn^{+2}–Br	1.11	1.81*	1.46			
SnOH$^+$–Cl	1.04*					
SnOH$^+$–Br	0.70*					
Sn^{+4}–Cl	?	?	?	?	?	4(?)
Th^{+4}–Cl	1.38	0.38	0.23	−0.51*		
Tl$^+$–Cl	0.52*	0.09	−0.8			
Tl$^+$–Br	0.95*	1.01	0.6	−0.2		
Tl$^+$–I	1.41*	1.82	2.0	1.6		
Tl^{+3}–Cl	8.14	13.60	15.78*	18.00	17.47	
Tl^{+3}–Br	9.7	16.6	21.2*	23.9	25.5	26.2
Tl^{+3}–I	?	?	?	30.29(?)		
U^{+4}–Cl	0.85					
UO$_2$$^{+2}$–Cl	−0.1	−0.92*	−2.62			
VO^{+2}–Cl	0.04					
Zn^{+2}–Cl	−0.5	−1.0*	0.0	−1.0		
Zn^{+2}–Br	−0.8	−2.2*	−2.9	−2.5		
Zn^{+2}–I	−2.9	−1.6*	−1.7	−2.3		
Zr^{+4}–Cl	0.9	1.3	1.5	1.2*		

* Neutral molecule in solution.

4–6. Complex-Ion Equilibria

The only fundamental difference between solubility equilibria and complex-ion equilibria is that the former are heterogeneous (involving more than one phase), whereas the latter are homogeneous (everything being present in a single phase). In solubility equilibria, where the concentration of the solid in the solid itself does not change, its constant concentration (or "activity") is included in the solubility-product constant. One may say that the activity of a pure crystalline solid is equal to 1. Consequently, the concentration of the solid does not appear explicitly in the solubility-product equilibrium expression. On the other hand, in the case of the complex-ion equilibrium, where everything may be in solution, the concentrations of all the species taking part in the equilibrium are variable, and therefore do appear in the equilibrium expression. Thus, in the equilibrium $HgCl_4^{-2} \rightleftharpoons Hg^{+2} + 4Cl^-$, all the species are in solution, their concentrations therefore being variable. The equilibrium expression, then, is

$$\frac{[Hg^{+2}][Cl^-]^4}{[HgCl_4^{-2}]} = K_{inst}$$

Let us calculate from this expression the concentration of free Hg^{+2} present in a solution made by dissolving 10^{-3} moles of $Hg(NO_3)_2$ in one liter of 0.1 M HCl. Since the equilibrium constant, 8.3×10^{-16}, is a very small number, the equilibrium as written above must lie way over on the left and most of the mercury will be present as $HgCl_4^{-2}$. Therefore $[HgCl_4^{-2}] \approx 10^{-3}$ M. The chloride-ion concentration will not be appreciably diminished by formation of the complex ion $(0.1 - 0.004 = 0.096 \ M)$ and consequently we shall assume $[Cl^-] \approx 0.1 \ M$. Therefore

$$\frac{[Hg^{+2}](0.1)^4}{10^{-3}} = 8.3 \times 10^{-16}$$

and $\qquad\qquad [Hg^{+2}] = 8.3 \times 10^{-15} \ M$

In the same way, if 10^{-3} moles of HCl is added to 1 liter of 0.1 M $Hg(NO_3)_2$ solution in nitric acid, the concentration of free chloride ion can be calculated. Since $[Hg^{+2}] \gg [Cl^-]$, it must be assumed that the only important equilibrium will be

$$HgCl^+ \rightleftharpoons Hg^{+2} + Cl^-$$

for which

$$\frac{[Hg^{+2}][Cl^-]}{[HgCl^+]} = 1.8 \times 10^{-7}$$

Assuming that most of the chloride ion will be combined with the mercury, then $[HgCl^+] \approx 10^{-3} \ M$. Consequently

$$\frac{(0.1)[Cl^-]}{10^{-3}} = 1.8 \times 10^{-7}$$

and $\qquad\qquad [Cl^-] = 1.8 \times 10^{-9} \ M$

If 0.01 mole of the "mixed salt" $[HgCl]ClO_4$ is dissolved in 1 liter of an aqueous perchloric acid solution we can again find the concentration of simple ions present. The compound $[HgCl]ClO_4$ may be considered to consist of ClO_4^- anions and complex $[HgCl^+]$ cations. In solution the $HgCl^+$ will be in equilibrium with the simple ions Hg^{+2} and Cl^-, just as in the example above, but since there is no other source of Hg^{+2} or Cl^-, their concentrations now must be equal.

$$HgCl^+ \rightleftharpoons Hg^{+2} + Cl^-$$
$$[Hg^{+2}] = [Cl^-] = x$$

Consequently

$$\frac{x^2}{10^{-2}} = 1.8 \times 10^{-7}$$
$$x = [Hg^{+2}] = [Cl^-] = 4.25 \times 10^{-5} \ M$$

It is also possible to find the concentrations of simple ions present when a substance like K_2HgCl_4 is dissolved in pure water. The treatment of this, however, is much more complicated than that discussed above. Discussion of this subject will therefore be deferred until Chapter 8.

4–7. The Acid-Insoluble Hydroxides

It must now be realized that, when hydrochloric acid is added to a solution in order to precipitate insoluble chlorides, not only is Cl^- being added, but also H^+. Consequently, not only will the elements with insoluble chlorides precipitate, but also those elements whose hydroxides are such weak bases as to be insoluble in acidic solution. Elements whose hydroxides in their normal oxidation states are insoluble in dilute, non-complexing acids are

Si

Ti   V

Nb

Ta   W

In addition, certain hydroxides of less usual intermediate oxidation states or partially dehydrated hydroxides are insoluble in dilute non-complexing acids. The most important of these are $Mn(OH)_4$ or $MnO(OH)_2$ and $SnO(OH)_2$, which we will meet again later; also may be cited Mo_2O_3, MoO_2, ReO_3, OsO_2, IrO_2, PtO_2, and so forth.

Thus, if a solution of sodium niobate is acidified with nitric acid, niobium hydroxide (or niobic acid) precipitates.

$$NbO_3^- + H^+ + 2\,H_2O \rightarrow \text{``}Nb(OH)_5\text{''}$$

The further reaction

$$\text{``}Nb(OH)_5\text{''} + H^+ \rightarrow Nb(OH)_4^+ + H_2O$$

(or similar reactions) is negligible. However, all of these elements except tungsten and silicon form complexes with chloride ion, e.g.

$$NbO_3^- + 5Cl^- + 4H^+ \rightarrow NbOCl_5^{-2} + 2\,H_2O$$

Consequently, if the acid used is HCl, only tungsten and silicon will precipitate from solution as hydroxides.

$$WO_4^{-2} + 2 H^+ \rightarrow H_2WO_4(s) \text{ (tungstic acid)}$$
$$SiO_3^{-2} + 2 H^+ + H_2O \rightarrow Si(OH)_4(s) \text{ (silicic acid)}$$

Samples containing silicates usually require special analytical methods, consequently silicon will not be considered further here. Tungsten, however, which precipitates as insoluble tungstic acid, H_2WO_4, along with the insoluble chlorides may quite conveniently be determined with them. In order to illustrate this point, tungsten will be included in the insoluble chloride (silver) group.

4–8. The Copper-Family Elements

The elements copper, silver, and gold have been known since prehistoric times, because all of them are found in the "native" state, i.e., as the uncombined metals. They are characterized by their inertness (or "nobility") and the ease with which they can be worked (ductility and malleability). Copper is slowly attacked under conditions of weathering, i.e., in the presence of oxygen, water, and carbon dioxide, giving a green basic carbonate. On the other hand, gold is completely unaffected by weathering conditions and even resists the attack of sea water. Whereas the alkali metals have the greatest tendency of all the elements to lose electrons and produce ions, the copper-family elements have the least tendency of all to do so. They are all rare elements, as can be seen from Table 4–3. The abundances given there may be compared with those of the alkali metals, which are Li, 6.5×10^{-3} percent; Na, 2.83 percent; K, 2.59 percent; Rb, 3.1×10^{-2} percent; and Cs, 7×10^{-4} percent of the igneous rocks of the earth's crust. The relatively greater availability of these elements than of Rb and Cs stems from the fact that the insolubility of the salts of Cu, Ag, and Au found in nature, and the inertness of the free elements, results in their occurring in concentrated deposits, whereas the rarer alkali metals, which form only relatively soluble salts, are much more uniformly distributed in the earth's crust. Some of the properties of the copper-family metals (the "coinage" metals) are given in Table 4–3, along with those of the neighboring elements in the same analytical group. Unlike the alkali metals, these are all polyvalent elements. Copper, silver, and gold are the only elements in the periodic table (excluding the lanthanides and actinides) having oxidation states higher than their group (column) number. It has been said that of all the families in the periodic table this one shows the least regularity with respect to oxidation state. It will be shown later (Section 16–3) that this is not so. But for the present, suffice it to say that in aqueous solution the most important oxidation states are Cu(II), Ag(I), and Au(III). In insoluble compounds and complex ions the somewhat less important states Cu(I) and Au(I) are found. Under the

TABLE 4–3. PHYSICAL PROPERTIES OF THE COINAGE METALS, MERCURY, THALLIUM, AND LEAD

	Copper	Silver	Gold	Mercury	Thallium	Lead
Latin Name and Symbol	Cuprum (Cu)	Argentum (Ag)	Aurum (Au)	Hydrargyrum (Hg)	Thallium (Tl)	Plumbum (Pb)
Atomic Number	29	47	79	80	81	82
Atomic Weight	63.54	107.880	197.2	200.61	204.39	207.22
Abundance in earth's crust (%)	1×10^{-4}	10^{-8}	10^{-9}	10^{-7}	10^{-10}	2×10^{-5}
Color of Metal	red	silver	yellow	silver	bluish-white	gray
Melting Point °C	1083	960.5	1063	−38.87	303.5	327.5
Boiling Point °C	2582	2193	2660	356.9	1457	1750
Hardness (Moh)	2.5–3.0	2.5–3.0	2.5–3.0	liquid	ca. 1.5	1.5
Density (g/ml)	8.92	10.5	19.3	14.19 (−40°)	11.85	11.34
Radius of M^+ in crystals (Å)	0.96 (Cu^+) 0.72 (Cu^{+2})	0.97	1.37	1.05 (Hg^{+2})	1.15 (Tl^+) 0.95 (Tl^{+3})	1.18 (Pb^{+2}) 0.70 (Pb^{+4})
Standard Oxidation Potential (for M (s) $\rightarrow M^+$ (aq) $+ e^-$) (volts)	−0.522	−0.799	−1.68	−0.788 (Hg_2^{+2})	+0.3363	+0.126 (Pb^{+2})
Electronegativity	1.65(I) 1.7(II)	1.8(I) 2.15(II)	2.1(I) 2.3(III)	1.8(I) 1.9(II)	1.5(I) 1.95(III)	1.6(II) 1.95(IV)

proper conditions, however, all three elements are found in all three oxidation states, $+1$, $+2$, and $+3$.

The solubility relationships of the $+1$ compounds of the copper family are quite different from those of the alkali metals. Whereas with the latter insolubility is the exception, with the former insolubility is the rule. Furthermore, the trends observed in one case are very likely to be reversed in the other. Thus the solubility increases from NaF to NaI (from 4 grams to 65 grams per hundred milliliters of water), whereas, despite the fact that the radii of Na^+ and Ag^+ are approximately the same, the solubility decreases from AgF to AgI (from 182 grams to 3×10^{-7} grams per hundred milliliters). The reasons for these differences have already been discussed (Sections 3–6 and 4–3).

In the $+2$ and $+3$ states, these elements are typical transition elements. Thus Cu^{+2} is very similar to Ni^{+2} and the other M^{+2} ions of the first transition series. The same can be said of Ag^{+2} and Pd^{+2} and of Au(II) and Pt(II) compounds. Likewise Au(III) is very similar to ions of the preceding third transition series. In general, the solubilities of Cu(II) compounds are greater than those of Cu(I) and Ag(I). The $+3$ states are almost invariably complex, so that we rarely deal with Au^{+3} ion, for example, and comparison of solubilities is less meaningful. The solubilities of certain compounds of these elements are given in Table A11–3. All the common salts of Cu(II) which are not given are soluble to very soluble; some of these are the acetate, bromate, bromide, chlorate, chloride, perchlorate, dichromate, fluoroborate, fluorosilicate, nitrate, selenate, and sulfate. The iodide does not exist, because it rapidly undergoes the reaction

$$CuI_2 \rightarrow CuI \text{ (s)} + \tfrac{1}{2} I_2 \text{ (s)}$$

In exactly the same way

$$Cu(CN)_2 \rightarrow CuCN \text{ (s)} + \tfrac{1}{2} (CN)_2 \text{ (g)}$$

and $$Cu(NCS)_2 \rightarrow CuNCS \text{ (s)} + \tfrac{1}{2} (NCS)_2$$

Such compounds as $Cu_3(AsO_3)_2$, $Cu_3(AsO_4)_2$, $Cu_2Fe(CN)_6$, $Cu_3[Fe(CN)_6]_2$, and $Cu_3(PO_4)_2$, however, are insoluble.

The compound $AuSO_4$, like $CuSO_4$, is soluble in water, but suffers immediate hydrolysis to $3AuO \cdot H_2O$ in the absence of excess H_2SO_4. The sulfides, Au_2S, AuS, and Au_2S_3 are all extremely insoluble in water, as are the other sulfides in this part of the periodic table; but they all decompose fairly easily into free gold and sulfur. Gold, unlike silver and copper, because of its very high electronegativity forms thio complexes such as AuS_2^-. Thus gold follows arsenic in any analytical scheme employing sulfide separations (Electronegativity Chart, Fig. 1–21).

Copper(II) hydroxide and AgOH are very slightly amphoteric (see Chapter 9), sufficiently so that the $Cu(OH)_3^-$ formed imparts a very definite blue color to concentrated NaOH. The acid ionization constants for solid $Cu(OH)_2$ and Ag_2O are

$$Cu(OH)_2 \text{ (s)} + H_2O \rightleftharpoons H^+ + Cu(OH)_3^- \qquad K_A = 1.6 \times 10^{-16}$$
$$\tfrac{1}{2} Ag_2O \text{ (s)} + \tfrac{3}{2} H_2O \rightleftharpoons H^+ + Ag(OH)_2^- \qquad K_A = 2.0 \times 10^{-18}$$

Compared to their basic ionization constants these are unimportant, and the basicity of these compounds far outweighs their acidity. With the more electronegative gold, on the other hand, the hydroxides are distinctly amphoteric. Freshly precipitated AuOH is said to dissolve readily in excess alkali (but eventually disproportionates

$$3 Au(OH)_2^- \rightleftharpoons 2 Au \text{ (s)} + Au(OH)_4^- + 2 OH^-)$$

Gold(III) hydroxide dissolves readily in alkali and forms a series of well-defined salts such as potassium aurate, $KAu(OH)_4$.

4–9. The Other Elements of the Insoluble Chloride Group

The physical properties of the other elements of the insoluble chloride analytical group were given in Table 4–3, except for those of tungsten, which are given in Table 4–4. It can be seen that none of these elements is exceedingly abundant. The relatively high abundance of lead stems in part from its being the end product of the radioactive decay of thorium and uranium.

Mercury is the only metallic element which is liquid at room temperature, although cesium melts at 28.5°C and gallium at 29.78. Liquid gallium can easily be supercooled below room temperature. In addition, certain alloys of Na and K are liquid at room temperature.

Mercury has two oxidation states, $+1$ and $+2$. In the $+1$ state, mercury forms the unique ion Hg_2^{+2}, in which the two mercury atoms are bonded together by an electron pair bond, $^+Hg{:}Hg^+$. No other metallic element forms such an ion, with the exception of cadmium, which forms Cd_2^{+2}. This is very unstable in aqueous solutions, but can be stabilized in such salts as $Cd_2 (AlCl_4)_2$. The ion Hg_2^{+2} is not much more stable than Hg^{+2}, as can be seen from the standard oxidation potentials

Couple	E°
$2 Hg \rightleftharpoons Hg_2^{+2} + 2e^-$	-0.789
$Hg_2^{+2} \rightleftharpoons 2 Hg^{+2} + 2e^-$	-0.920
$Hg \rightleftharpoons Hg^{+2} + 2e^-$	-0.855

Consequently any conditions which favor Hg(II) very much result in disproportionation of Hg(I) into Hg^0 and Hg(II). (Here the symbols Hg(I) and Hg(II) refer to mercury in the $+1$ and $+2$ oxidation states respectively, without specifying the exact nature of the substance. The symbols Hg_2^{+2} and Hg^{+2} refer to the simple ions.)

$$Hg_2O \rightleftharpoons Hg + HgO$$
$$Hg_2S \rightleftharpoons Hg + HgS$$
$$Hg_2Cl_2 + 2\,NH_3 \rightleftharpoons Hg + HgNH_2Cl + NH_4^+ + Cl^-$$
$$Hg_2(CN)_2 + 2\,CN^- \rightleftharpoons Hg + Hg(CN)_4^{-2}$$
$$Hg_2I_2 + 2\,I^- \rightleftharpoons Hg + HgI_4^{-2}$$

The solubilities of mercury salts are generally low, like those of the other elements in this analytical group, the solubilities of the Hg(I) salts being usually lower than the Hg(II). Whereas Hg(II) has an exceptionally high tendency to form complexes, Hg(I) has little or no tendency to do this. Mercury(II) compounds, therefore, have very little tendency to ionize (i.e., the equilibrium HgX_2 (aq) $\rightleftharpoons Hg^{+2}$ (aq) $+2X^-$ (aq) lies way over on the left), only such compounds as the nitrate, perchlorate, fluoroborate, fluoride fluorosilicate, and certain other compounds of the strongest acids being true salts. Thus $Hg(OH)_2$ is one of the weakest bases among the divalent hydroxides because of the very strong tendency of Hg^{+2} to hold on to the OH^-'s.

$$Hg(OH)_2 \text{ (s)} \rightleftharpoons Hg^{+2} \text{ (aq)} + 2\,OH^- \text{ (aq)}$$

The low degree of ionization does not necessarily mean low solubility, however, since a number of mercury(II) compounds are fairly soluble in water (or slightly acidic solution to prevent hydrolysis) without being appreciably ionized. Compounds in this category include $HgCl_2$, $HgBr_2$, $Hg(CN)_2$, $Hg(ClO_3)_2$, $Hg(NO_2)_2$, $Hg(C_2H_3O_2)_2$, $Hg[C(NO_2)_3]_2$, and $Hg(CF_3)_2$. In addition, the solubilities of many other compounds may be raised considerably above their "K_{sp} solubilities" by existing partly as unionized molecules in solution. For example, the measured solubility of $HgBr_2$ in water is 1.4×10^{-2} molar (Table A11–4), whereas the Hg^{+2} concentration is only 3×10^{-7} molar—i.e., the K_{sp} for $HgBr_2$ is 1.12×10^{-19}, and the solution contains 1.4×10^{-2} molar un-ionized $HgBr_2$ molecules. The solubilities of most of these substances are given in Table A11–4, along with the solubilities of other mercury compounds.

Analytically, mercury is usually precipitated as Hg_2Cl_2 or HgS, but many of its other insoluble compounds may also be used to advantage.

Thallium is the only metal outside of the alkali- and copper-family elements which has an important $+1$ state. With respect to the basicity of TlOH, the lack of hydrolysis of its salts, and the solubilities of its ionic compounds, Tl^+ is very similar to K^+. Thus TlOH is a soluble, strong base. It absorbs CO_2 readily from the air, forming the moderately soluble (almost 0.1 molar) Tl_2CO_3. The oxide, Tl_2O, readily absorbs water to give TlOH. However, the hydroxide loses water much more readily than the alkali hydroxides. The decomposition pressure of steam over the hydroxide reaches 1 atm at 139°C. Solutions of thallium salts are only faintly acidic in nature, and the solubilities of salts with large anions of low charge density are relatively low, as are those of K^+. Note, for example, the solubilities given in Table A11–4 for $TlClO_4$, $TlMnO_4$, $TlReO_4$, $TlNO_3$, and Tl_2PtCl_6. Again, as with K^+, $Tl_3Co(NO_2)_6$ is insoluble (10^{-4} M).

On the other hand, in its more covalent compounds, Tl^+ behaves much more like Ag^+ and Pb^{+2}. Thus the solubilities of $TlCl$, $TlBr$, TlI, Tl_2S, Tl_2Se, and Tl_2Te decrease in the order named exactly as for the corresponding compounds of Ag and Pb. Hence, the chemistry of Tl(I) is a curious mixture of the ionic and the covalent.

The standard oxidation potential for the Tl(I)–Tl(III) couple is

$$Tl^+ \text{ (aq)} \rightleftharpoons Tl^{+3} \text{ (aq)} + 2e^- \qquad E° = -1.247 \text{ volts}$$

This means that moderately powerful oxidizing agents are required to oxidize Tl^+ to Tl^{+3}. Reagents which will do this are Cl_2, Br_2, and acidic $KMnO_4$. The weaker I_2 and HNO_3 will not do it. As a matter of fact, Tl^{+3} is reduced by I^-, the slightly soluble TlI_3 which is formed in the reaction being the thallium(I) salt of the triiodide ion, I_3^-.

$$Tl^{+3} + 3I^- \rightleftharpoons Tl^{(I)}(I_3)^{(-I)}$$

Thallium(III) is very similar to Al(III), but more electronegative. Consequently $Tl(OH)_3$ is less basic than $Al(OH)_3$ and its salts are more highly hydrolyzed. Thallium(III), like Hg(II) with which it is isoelectronic, has a strong tendency to form complexes. Thus in aqueous HCl solution, the principal species present is $TlCl_4^-$ which, in common with $AuCl_4^-$, forms sparingly soluble salts with large univalent cations. Consequently, if a thallium(I) salt is added to this solution a compound of the empirical formula $TlCl_2$ is obtained, which appears to be of the +2 state, but which in actual fact has been shown to be thallium(I) tetrachlorothallate(III), $Tl^I[Tl^{III}Cl_4]$.

Lead likewise exists in two well-defined oxidation states, Pb(II) and Pb(IV). The standard oxidation potential for the Pb^{+2}–Pb^{+4} couple is so very negative

$$Pb^{+2} \rightleftharpoons Pb^{+4} + 2e^- \qquad E° = -1.8 \text{ volts}$$

that only the most powerful oxidizing agents are capable of producing simple Pb^{+4}, and very few simple compounds of Pb(IV) are known. Among these are PbF_4, a powerful fluorinating agent; the liquid, unstable $PbCl_4$, which decomposes easily into $PbCl_2 + Cl_2$; $Pb(C_2H_3O_2)_4$, which is a non-ionic oxidizing agent, useful in nonaqueous media, but hydrolyzed in water to $PbO_2 + HC_2H_3O_2$; and PbO_2. This last compound is more stable than the others and is technically of great importance as one of the active principles in the lead storage battery. Because of its greater stability, it is produced from Pb(II) compounds with somewhat milder oxidizing agents than are required for Pb^{+4}.

$$Pb^{+2} + 2 H_2O \rightleftharpoons PbO_2 + 4 H^+ + 2e^- \qquad E° = -1.456 \text{ volts}$$
$$PbSO_4 + 2 H_2O \rightleftharpoons PbO_2 + 4 H^+ + SO_4^{-2} + 2e^- \qquad E° = -1.685 \text{ volts}$$

The tetravalent state can be stabilized by complexing. Thus we find stable $PbF_6{}^{-2}$, $PbCl_6{}^{-2}$, and possibly $PbBr_6{}^{-2}$ and $PbI_6{}^{-2}$, especially in crystalline salts such as Cs_2PbCl_6. In alkaline solution $Pb(OH)_6{}^{-2}$ is easily formed. This ion occurs also in the crystalline plumbates, such as $Na_2Pb(OH)_6$.

By far the most usual, however, are the compounds of Pb(II). These are in many ways similar to those of Tl(I), with which Pb(II) is isoelectronic, but generally somewhat less soluble. Actually, there are very few Pb(II) compounds of more than slight solubility. Among the more soluble ones are $Pb(C_2H_3O_2)_2$, $Pb(ClO_3)_2$, $Pb(ClO_4)_2$, $PbSiF_6$, $Pb(BF_4)_2$, $Pb(NO_3)_2$, and PbS_2O_8.

As in the case of the other elements in this part of the periodic table, the solubilities of lead(II) compounds decrease in solubility in the order $PbCl_2 >$ $PbBr_2 > PbI_2 > PbS > PbSe > PbTe$, which is the result of their covalent character. On the other hand, many of its compounds have the solubilities typical of the ionic compounds of large divalent cations (for example, like Ba^{+2}). In particular PbF_2, $PbSO_4$, $PbPHO_3$, $PbSeO_4$, $PbMoO_4$, $PbWO_4$, $Pb_3(AsO_4)_2$, $Pb_3(PO_4)_2$, and $Pb_2Fe(CN)_6$ are insoluble. Thus lead, like thallium, is a curious blend of the ionic and the covalent. This results in typical ionic trends in solubility overlapping typical covalent trends, as can be seen by examining the molar solubilities given in Table A11–4 for the lead(II) halides, which have the peculiar solubility sequence $PbF_2 < PbCl_2 >$ $PbBr_2 > PbI_2$.

Like gold, lead in both its oxidation states is distinctly amphoteric. Lead(II) hydroxide dissolves in excess alkali to give the plumbite ion

$$Pb(OH)_2\ (s) + H_2O \rightleftharpoons H^+ + Pb(OH)_3{}^- \qquad K_A = 7.4 \times 10^{-16}$$

This can be used to separate lead from the non-amphoteric elements. Thus $BaCrO_4$ and $PbCrO_4$ can be distinguished by the ability of the latter to dissolve in alkali

$$PbCrO_4\ (s) + 3\ OH^- \rightleftharpoons Pb(OH)_3{}^- + CrO_4{}^{-2}$$

The elements tungsten and molybdenum should be considered together since they are very similar in all respects, except for the precipitation of tungsten by hydrochloric acid. Some of the physical properties of tungsten and molybdenum are listed in Table 4–4. The free elements are extremely hard, and tungsten has one of the highest melting points of any known substance. Very high melting points are characteristic of elements in this part of the periodic table (Ta, 2997°C; W, 3380°C; Re, 3147°C; Os, 2700°C).

These elements form compounds in the oxidation states 0, +2, +3, +4, +5, and +6. However, the most important state under ordinary conditions is the +6, to which our discussion will be almost entirely confined. The chemistry of this state is the chemistry of tungstic and molybdic acids,

TABLE 4–4. PHYSICAL PROPERTIES OF MOLYBDENUM AND TUNGSTEN

	Molybdenum	Tungsten
Atomic Number	42	74
Atomic Weight	95.95	183.92
Density (g/ml)	10.2	19.3
Melting Point (°C)	2610	3380
Boiling Point (°C)	4800	5630
Abundance in Earth's Crust (percent)	10^{-6}	5×10^{-5}
Color of Metal	silvery	gray
Standard Oxidation Potential (for		
$M + 4\,H_2O \rightarrow H_2MO_4 + 6\,H^+ + 6\,e^-$)	0 0	0.09
Standard Oxidation Potential (for		
$M + 8\,OH^- \rightarrow MO_4^{-2} + 4\,H_2O + 6\,e^-$)	1.05	1.05
Electronegativity	1.6(IV)	1.6(IV)
	2.1(VI)	2.0(VI)

H_2WO_4 and H_2MoO_4, and their derivatives. Tungstic acid is obtained by digestion of its salts with aqueous HCl. It separates in the cold as $H_2WO_4 \cdot H_2O$ which is slightly soluble in water. From hot solution it separates as H_2WO_4, which dissolves neither in water (solubility $= 1.5 \times 10^{-5}$ molar) nor in any acid except hydrofluoric. Gentle ignition of the acid or of $(NH_4)_2WO_4$ gives WO_3, which has the same solubility characteristics as H_2WO_4.

Molybdic acid is obtained by digestion of molybdates with concentrated HNO_3, $H_2MoO_4 \cdot H_2O$ crystallizing out in the cold. This compound is distinctly more soluble than $H_2WO_4 \cdot H_2O$, a saturated solution at 18°C being 0.0074 molar. Ignition of the acid or of $(NH_4)_2MoO_4$ gives MoO_3. This dissolves in water to give a solution of the acid, which at saturation is, of course, 0.0074 molar. Molybdic acid dissolves in hydrochloric acid to give complexes such as $MoO_2Cl_3^-$ and $MoO_2Cl_4^{-2}$. (Tungstic acid undergoes a comparable reaction to give a complex which may be $WO_2Cl_3^-$ only in concentrated HCl.)

Tungstic and molybdic are relatively weak acids ($K_{A1} = 1.6 \times 10^{-2}$, $K_{A2} = 8 \times 10^{-5}$ for H_2MoO_4; $K_{A2} = 6.5 \times 10^{-5}$ for H_2WO_4). Nevertheless, they form normal salts such as Na_2MoO_4, K_2WO_4, $(NH_4)_2WO_4$, $BaMoO_4$, $PbWO_4$, and so forth. The solubilities of these salts (see Table A11–5) are comparable to those of the corresponding chromates, sulfates, selenates, and so forth. In common with other weak inorganic acids, these readily form polyanions, comparable to $Cr_2O_7^{-2}$. Salts such as $Na_2Mo_2O_7$, $Na_2Mo_3O_{10} \cdot 7\,H_2O$, $Na_2Mo_4O_{13} \cdot 6\,H_2O$, $Na_6Mo_7O_{24} \cdot 22\,H_2O$, $Na_2Mo_8O_{25} \cdot 17\,H_2O$, $Na_2Mo_{10}O_{31} \cdot 2\,H_2O$, and the like, are known. The solubilities of these vary in no apparently systematic way, but presumably depend upon the internal structure of the anion.

Tungsten and molybdenum are almost unique in their formation of *heteropolyacids*. These are formed spontaneously in acidic solutions of molybdic and tungstic acids containing phosphoric, silicic, arsenic, germanic, boric, and certain other weak acids. In each, a central atom of phosphorus, silicon, arsenic, and so forth, is surrounded by up to twelve molybdenum or tungsten oxide groups. Thus we have $(NH_4)_3PO_4 \cdot 12\,MoO_3$ or $(NH_4)_3[P(Mo_3O_{10})_4]$, which is a slightly soluble precipitate very useful in testing for phosphates. These compounds are properly named *molybdophosphates*, *tungstosilicates*, and the like, the central atom being named last. Commonly they are called *phosphomolybdates*, *silicotungstates*, and so forth.

The heteropolyacids (and their anions) of both tungsten and molybdenum are readily (and free tungstic and molybdic acids somewhat less readily) reduced to substances of indefinite composition, known as tungsten or molybdenum blue. They would appear to have formulas such as $(WO_2)_2WO_4 \cdot xH_2O$. These form stable colloidal solutions of intense blue color and are very useful for the analytical determination of these elements.

A second reduction reaction is particularly characteristic of molybdenum. If an acidic solution of Mo(VI) containing NCS^- is treated with Sn(II) or other good reducing agent, a reddish or amber thiocyanate complex of Mo(V), probably $MoO(NCS)_3$, is formed, which can be used to identify the element.

Both tungstic and molybdic acids form with H_2S the extremely insoluble brown trisulfides, WS_3 and MoS_3. The precipitation of MoS_3, however, is frequently not quantitative due to partial reduction to molybdenum blue. The appearance of a blue color in the supernatant liquid after sulfide precipitation may be taken as evidence of the presence of molybdenum. In common with the oxides, the trisulfides have acidic properties. Thus, although MoS_3 does not dissolve even in concentrated HCl, it dissolves readily in alkaline sulfide solutions yielding MoS_4^{-2}. Consequently molybdenum follows arsenic in most analytical schemes. The corresponding reaction of tungsten can be used to separate it from other elements of the insoluble chloride group, whose sulfides are all insoluble in alkaline sulfide solutions.

4–10.   Color in Inorganic Compounds

Color is extremely important for the identification of substances and for control of reactions. The development of an unexpected color or the lack of development of an expected color may give valuable information about whether a process is going incorrectly or in what way it is going astray. Consequently, it is well to know something about when color occurs in inorganic compounds and what colors to expect.

In truly ionic substances, the color is that of the constituent ions. The ions of all the representative elements (i.e., those which are not transition elements) in their usual oxidation states are colorless. In addition, other elements in oxidation states in which they may be conceived of having a kernel of 8 or 18 electrons (i.e., where the oxidation state is the same as the periodic group number) are usually also colorless. The only important exceptions to this last statement are VO_2^+, CrO_4^{-2} (and $Cr_2O_7^{-2}$), UO_2^{+2}, MnO_4^-, and TcO_4^-. Very seldom will two colored ions occur together in a truly ionic substance. When this does happen, the color of the compound is what we should expect from addition of the two individual colors. An example of this is $Nd_2[Pt(CN)_4]_3 \cdot 18\ H_2O$, which contains the rose-violet hydrated Nd^{+3} ion and the yellow $Pt(CN)_4^{-2}$. Since most substances involving two colored ions are compounds of the transition elements, they are likely not to be truly ionic and their colors therefore bear no simple relationship to the colors of the individual ions. Examples of this are $Fe_2(Cr_2O_7)_3$, red-brown; $KFe_2(CN)_6$, deep blue; $Co_2[Fe(CN)_6] \cdot 7\ H_2O$, gray-green; $CuCr_2O_7 \cdot 2\ H_2O$, black; $Cu_2[Fe(CN)_6] \cdot 7\ H_2O$, red-brown; and $Cu[Fe(CN)_5NO] \cdot 2\ H_2O$, greenish ($Fe(CN)_5NO^{-2}$ is red). The colors of the more important ions as they occur uncomplexed in aqueous solution are given in Table 4–5.

TABLE 4–5. COLORS OF INORGANIC IONS

Ion	Color	Ion	Color
$Am(H_2O)_9^{+3}$	Light pink	NpO_2^{+2}	Pale pink (dark yellow-green
$Cr(H_2O)_6^{+2}$	Blue		in 1 M H_2SO_4)
$Cr(H_2O)_6^{+3}$	Blue-violet	$Ni(H_2O)_6^{+2}$	Green
CrO_4^{-2}	Yellow	$Pt(H_2O)_4^{+2}$	Yellow
$Cr_2O_7^{-2}$	Orange	$Pu(H_2O)_9^{+3}$	Violet or blue
CrO_3Cl^-	Red	$Pu(H_2O)_8^{+4}$	Green or brown
$Co(H_2O)_6^{+2}$	Red	PuO_2^+	Nearly colorless
$Cu(H_2O)_6^{+2}$	Blue	PuO_2^{+2}	Orange
$Dy(H_2O)_9^{+3}$	Yellow	$Pr(H_2O)_9^{+3}$	Green
$Er(H_2O)_9^{+3}$	Rose	$Pm(H_2O)_9^{+3}$	Yellow
$Au(H_2O)_4^{+3}$	Yellow	$Rh(H_2O)_6^{+3}$	Pale yellow
$Ho(H_2O)_9^{+3}$	Yellow	$Sm(H_2O)_6^{+2}$	Deep red
$Ir(H_2O)_6^{+3}$	Yellow	$Sm(H_2O)_9^{+3}$	Pale yellow
$Fe(H_2O)_6^{+2}$	Pale bluish-green	TcO_4^-	Pink
$Fe(H_2O)_6^{+3}$	Very pale violet	$Tm(H_2O)_9^{+3}$	Green
FeO_4^{-2}	Deep purple	$Ti(H_2O)_6^{+3}$	Purple
$Mn(H_2O)_6^{+2}$	Pale rose	$U(H_2O)_9^{+3}$	Violet
MnO_4^{-3}	Blue	$U(H_2O)_8^{+4}$	Green
MnO_4^{-2}	Deep green	UO_2^{+2}	Yellow, fluorescent
MnO_4^-	Deep purple	$V(H_2O)_6^{+2}$	Deep violet
$Nd(H_2O)_9^{+3}$	Rose-violet	$V(H_2O)_6^{+3}$	Green
$Np(H_2O)_9^{+3}$	Pale purple	VO^{+2}	Blue
$Np(H_2O)_9^{+4}$	Green	VO_2^+	Yellow
NpO_2^+	Green-blue		

Another source of color in solid substances is covalency. This is capable of producing color even from ions which were originally colorless. Thus yellow CdS is produced from colorless Cd^{+2} and S^{-2}. Likewise, yellow AgI, red CdSe, brown Bi_2S_3 and black PbS all result from the combination of colorless ions. The intensity of the color developed from colorless ions seems to be related to the degree of covalency, although no quantitative comparison can be made. Thus $AsCl_3$ is colorless, $AsBr_3$ is yellowish, and AsI_3 is red. Again ZnI_2 is colorless, GeI_2 is yellow, and AsI_3 is red. The colors of some of the more common precipitates whose colors cannot be predicted from the colors of their ions are listed in Table 4–6.

TABLE 4–6. COLORS OF INORGANIC COMPOUNDS

Compound	Color	Compound	Color
$(NH_4)_3P(Mo_3O_{10})_4 \cdot 3\ H_2O$	Yellow	Hg_2Br_2	Pale yellow
SbI_3	Red or yellow	Hg_2CO_3	Yellow-brown
Sb_2S_3	Orange	Hg_3OCO_3	Brown-red
AsI_3	Red	$HgCrO_4$	Red
As_2S_3	Yellow	Hg_2CrO_4	Red
As_2S_5	Yellow	$Hg_2(IO_3)_2$	Yellowish
BiI_3	Reddish-brown to black	HgI_2	Red* or yellow
Bi_2S_3	Brownish-black	Hg_2I_2	Yellow
CdS	Yellow-orange	$HgIBr$	Yellow
CeO_3 (peroxide)	Orange	$HgICl$	Red
$Co(CN)_2 \cdot 2H_2O$	Buff; blue-violet, anhyd.	HgO	Yellow* or red
$Co_2[Fe(CN)_6]$	Gray-green	Hg_2O	Brownish-black
$Co(OH)_3$	Black	$Hg_4O_3Br_2$	Yellow
CoS	Black	$Hg_4O_3Cl_2$	Yellow
$Cu_4Fe(CN)_6$	Brown-red	$Hg_4O_3I_2$	Yellow-brown
$CuOH$	Yellow	$Hg_3(PO_4)_2$	Pale yellow
Cu_2O	Red	$Hg_3O_2SO_4$	Lemon yellow
Cu_2S	Black	HgS	Black* or red
CuS	Black	Hg_2S	Black
$AuBr$	Yellow	$HgWO_4$	Yellow
$AuCl$	Yellow	Hg_2WO_4	Yellow
$AuCN$	Yellow	MoS_3	Red-brown
$Au(OH)_3$	Yellow-brown	$NiC_4H_8N_2O_2$†	Scarlet
$AuOH$	Dark violet	NiS	Black
AuI	Greenish-yellow	Ag_3AsO_4	Dark red
AuI_3	Dark green	Ag_3AsO_3	Yellow
Au_2O_3	Brown-black	$AgBr$	Pale yellow
Au_2S_3	Brown	Ag_2CO_3	Yellow
Au_2S	Brown-black	Ag_2CrO_4	Red
AuS	Black	$Ag_2Cr_2O_7$	Red
$KFe_2(CN)_6$	Dark blue	$Ag_3Fe(CN)_6$	Orange
$Fe(OH)_3$	Red-brown	$Ag_4Fe(CN)_6$	Yellow
Fe_2S_3	Dark green	AgI	Yellow
FeS	Black	Ag_2O	Brown-black
PbI_2	Yellow	Ag_3PO_4	Yellow
$PbMoO_4$	Yellow	Ag_2S	Black
PbO_2	Brown	Ag_2WO_4	Pale yellow
PbS	Black	TiI_4	Red or yellow*
$Pb_3S_3Cl_2$	Red	TlN_3	Yellow
MnS	Pink (flesh) or green	Tl_2S	Blue-black
MnO_2	Black or brownish-black	UO_2S	Brown-black
$Hg_3(AsO_4)_2$	Yellow	V_2S_5	Blackish-green
$(Hg_2)_3(AsO_4)_2$	Dark red	VS_2	Black
Hg_2HAsO_4	Yellow-red	V_2O_5	Red

* Precipitate from water. Changes to other form on heating.
† Dimethylglyoxime.

The same thing is found for the formation of complex ions, which may result in the development of color from colorless ions or in radical change in the original color sometimes from colored to colorless. Thus Ce^{+4} and Cl^- are both colorless but give the deep red $CeCl_6^{-2}$. Likewise Sn^{+4} and I^- give the black SnI_6^{-2}. The violet Fe^{+3} gives colorless FeF_6^{-3}. Some of the more important cases of this sort are given in Table 4–7.

TABLE 4–7. COLORS OF SOME COMPLEX IONS

Complex Ion	Color	Complex Ion	Color
$CeCl_6^{-2}$	Red	$Fe(PO_4)_2^{-3}$	Colorless
$Ce(NO_3)_6^{-2}$	Deep orange	$PbCl_6^{-2}$	Lemon yellow
$Ce(SO_4)_3^{-2}$	Orange	PbF_6^{-2}	Lemon yellow
$Cr(CN)_6^{-3}$	Yellow	$Mn(CN)_6^{-5}$	Almost colorless
$CrCl^{+2}$	Green	$Mn(CN)_6^{-4}$	Deep blue
$CrCl_2^+$	Green	$Mn(CN)_6^{-3}$	Red
$CrNCS^{+2}$	Wine red	$MnCl_6^{-3}$	Dark brown
$CrSO_4^+$	Green	$Mn(PO_4)_2^{-3}$	Purple
$Co(CN)_6^{-3}$	Very pale yellow	HgI_4^{-2}	Colorless (see Table 4–6)
$Co(NH_3)_6^{+3}$	Yellow-orange	$MoONCS^{+2}$	Red
$Co(NH_3)_5H_2O^{+3}$	Brick red	$Ni(NH_3)_6^{+2}$	Steel- to violet-blue
$Co(NH_3)_5Cl^{+2}$	Dark red-violet	$Ni(NO_2)_4^{-2}$	Yellow
$Co(NH_3)_4(H_2O)Cl^{+2}$	Green	$Os(CN)_6^{-4}$	Colorless
$Co(NCS)_4^{-2}$	Deep blue	$PdCl_6^{-2}$	Red
$Cu(NH_3)_4^{+2}$	Deep blue	$P(Mo_3O_{10})_4^{-3}$	Yellow
$AuBr_4^-$	Red-brown to brown-black	$P(W_3O_{10})_4^{-3}$	Yellow
$Au(CN)_4^-$	Colorless	$PtBr_6^{-2}$	Dark red-brown
$AuCl_4^-$	Yellow	$Pt(CN)_4^{-2}$	Yellow
$IrCl_6^{-3}$	Black	$PtCl_6^{-2}$	Yellow
IrI_6^{-3}	Green	PtI_6^{-2}	Black
$Fe(CN)_6^{-4}$	Lemon yellow	$Pt(NO_2)_4^{-2}$	Colorless
$Fe(CN)_6^{-3}$	Red	$RhCl_6^{-3}$	Red
$FeCl^{+2}$	Yellow	SnI_6^{-2}	Black
FeF_6^{-3}	Colorless	$VO_2Cl_2^-$	Red
$FeNCS^{+2}$	Blood red	VS_3^{-2}	Black
$FeOH^{+2}$	Brown		

In addition, color occasionally arises or is intensified when one element in two different oxidation states occurs in the same solution or compound. For example, a concentrated HCl solution containing both $SbCl_6^{-3}$ and $SbCl_6^-$ is yellow, despite the fact that the two ions individually are colorless. In the same way, the compound K_2SbBr_6, which may be considered to contain equal numbers of $SbBr_6^{-3}$ and $SbBr_6^-$ ions, is black. Likewise CrO_2, which may be considered to consist of green Cr_2O_3 and red CrO_3 (i.e., a chromium(III) chromate(VI)), is black. Colors arising from this last source are very rarely met in qualitative analysis, although one familiar case is $KFe_2(CN)_6$, "Prussian blue."

4–11. Illustrative Experiments

The following experiments are designed to demonstrate the solubility relationships discussed. Since these are studies in solubility, a precipitate may not occur each time. Explain what you observe.

1. (a) To 2 ml of water add 2 drops of 0.1 M AgNO$_3$ solution and 3 drops of 0.1 M KCl. Stir. To this solution add 4 ml of 6 M NH$_4$OH. Stir.

(b) To 2 ml of water add 2 drops of 0.1 M AgNO$_3$ solution and 3 drops of 0.1 M KBr. Stir. To this solution add 4 ml of 6 M NH$_4$OH. Repeat with concentrated NH$_4$OH.

(c) To 2 ml of water add 2 drops of 0.1 M AgNO$_3$ solution and 3 drops of 0.1 M KI. Stir. To this solution add 4 ml of concentrated NH$_4$OH.

2. To 2 ml of water add 2 drops of 0.1 M Pb(NO$_3$)$_2$ solution and then 5 drops of 0.1 M KCl. What is the precipitate? Centrifuge. Transfer the supernate to another tube and to it add 5 drops of 0.1 M KBr. What happens? Centrifuge. Transfer the supernate to a clean tube and to it add 5 drops of 0.1 M KI. What happens? What is the trend of solubilities of the lead halides?

3. (a) To 2 ml of 0.1 M CuSO$_4$ in a 100-mm test tube, add 3 drops of 5 M NH$_4$Cl and a pinch of solid Na$_2$SO$_3$. Stir the solution, centrifuge it, and discard the supernatant liquid. Add 2 ml of 5 M NH$_4$Cl to the precipitate. The reaction of the Cu^{+2} with the SO$_3^{-2}$ is given by the following equation

$$H_2O + 2\,Cu^{+2} + 2\,Cl^- + SO_3^{-2} \rightarrow 2\,CuCl\,(s) + SO_4^{-2} + 2\,H^+$$

(The precipitated CuCl may appear bluish or gray because of occluded CuCl$_2$. DO NOT TRY TO WASH THE CuCl$_2$ OUT.) Write the equation for the reaction between CuCl and NH$_4$Cl.

(b) Prepare another sample of CuCl as above. Wash the precipitate once with 2 ml of water. Add 2 ml of water to the centrifugate. Stir the solution and precipitate for a minute, centrifuge the solution, and pour the centrifugate into another test tube. To the liquid centrifugate add 2 ml of 0.1 M AgNO$_3$.

What did you observe? Which is more soluble, AgCl or CuCl? Explain by the use of Le Châtelier's principle.

4. To 2 ml of water, add 5 drops of 5 M HNO$_3$, 2 drops of Hg(NO$_3$)$_2$, and then one drop of 0.1 M KI. Shake. Continue adding one drop of 0.1 M KI at a time and shaking until two distinct reactions have occurred. What has happened?

5. To 2 ml of Hg$_2$(NO$_3$)$_2$ add as in (4) 0.1 M KI drop by drop until two distinct reactions have occurred. What has happened? Centrifuge. Transfer the supernate to another test tube and add AgNO$_3$ solution to it. The precipitate obtained is Ag$_2$[HgI$_4$]. Explain.

6. Add 1 M NH$_4$OH, dropwise with stirring, to 1 ml of 0.1 M AgNO$_3$ until two distinct reactions have taken place. Explain. Now add a few crystals of NH$_4$NO$_3$ to 1 ml of 0.1 M AgNO$_3$ and again add 1 M NH$_4$OH, dropwise with stirring. Explain the difference.

7. (a) Add 1 ml of 0.1 M Pb(NO$_3$)$_2$ to 2 ml of water, and to this solution add 20 drops of 3 M HCl to precipitate PbCl$_2$. Centrifuge and remove the

supernate. By means of a capillary pipet, wash the crystals with 1 ml of boiling water. Collect the washings and cool. Explain your observations.

(b) Divide the cooled and well-mixed washings obtained in part (a) into two parts, and to one part add 2 drops of 1 M K_2CrO_4. What is the equation for the reaction? Which is more soluble, $PbCl_2$ or $PbCrO_4$? From Table A11–4 predict whether sulfides could convert $PbCrO_4$ to PbS. Add to the mixture a few drops of 1 M thioacetamide and heat to test your conclusion.

(c) Repeat part (b), using solid $Na_3Co(NO_2)_6$ instead of K_2CrO_4.

8. To 1 ml of 0.1 M $Hg_2(NO_3)_2$ in one test tube, and 1 ml of 0.1 M $Hg(NO_3)_2$ in another, add 10 drops each of 6 M HCl. Explain the difference.

9. (a) Add 1 small drop of metallic mercury to 1 ml of 0.1 M $Hg(NO_3)_2$ and heat. Now add a few drops of HCl. Has any reaction taken place between the Hg and the $Hg(NO_3)_2$? Centrifuge the solution and to the supernate add a few drops of $SnCl_2$. (Check the freshness of the $SnCl_2$! See Experiment 15, below.) Was the reaction between Hg and $Hg(NO_3)_2$ complete? Write equations for all the reactions concerned.

10. To 1 ml of 0.1 M $HgCl_2$ in one test tube, and to some freshly prepared Hg_2Cl_2 in another, add a few drops of 1 M NH_4OH. Explain your observations and write equations for the reactions.

11. To 1 ml of 0.1 M $Hg_2(NO_3)_2$ in one test tube, and to 1 ml of 0.1 M $Hg(NO_3)_2$ in a second, add a large excess of 1 M NaOH. What conclusions about the nature of the mercury hydroxides can be drawn from these experiments? Write the equations for the reactions involved.

12. To 1 ml of water made 0.3 normal with HCl in each of five tubes, add (a) 2 drops of 0.1 M $AgNO_3$, (b) 2 drops of 0.1 M $Hg_2(NO_3)_2$, (c) 2 drops of 0.1 M $Pb(NO_3)_2$, (d) 2 drops of 0.1 M $TlNO_3$ (CAUTION! Thallium salts are extremely poisonous!), and (e) 2 drops of 0.1 M Na_2WO_4. Ignore any precipitates which form. Add 10 drops of 1 M thioacetamide solution, stir, and heat for 10 minutes in a boiling-water bath. Explain the results. Let cool and make the solutions strongly alkaline with 15 M NH_4OH. After observing the results, reacidify the tungsten solution with 12 M HCl. Explain your observations. Write equations for the reactions involved.

13. Repeat (7) using $TlNO_3$ instead of $Pb(NO_3)_2$. By any of these reactions can Tl be distinguished from Pb?

14. To 1 ml of 0.1 M $TlNO_3$, add 5 drops of 1 M NH_4SO_4. Do the same with 0.1 M $Pb(NO_3)_2$.

15. To 1 ml of 0.1 M Na_2WO_4 solution, add 5 drops of 3 M HCl. Centrifuge and discard the supernate. Dissolve the precipitate in a minimum quantity of 6 M NH_4OH. Acidify with HCl, add a few drops of $SnCl_2$ solution, and concentrated HCl. Heat to boiling. The presence of tungsten is indicated by the development of a blue color or precipitate. (*Note:* Before using the $SnCl_2$ solution, first test a portion of it with a drop of $HgCl_2$ solution. Stannous chloride is easily oxidized by the air. If the $SnCl_2$ reagent is good, $HgCl_2$ will give a white precipitate, turning black.)

16. Construct a table similar to following showing your observations when AgCl, Hg_2Cl_2, $PbCl_2$, TlCl, and H_2WO_4 are treated with (a) hot water, (b) NH_4OH, (c) NaOH, (d) NaOH in excess, (e) H_2S in 0.3 M H^+, (f) K_2CrO_4.

If some of the information required is not available from the experiments above, devise experiments to give you the information.

Reagent	AgCl	Hg_2Cl_2	$PbCl_2$	TlCl	H_2WO_4
Hot Water					
NH_4OH					
NaOH					
Excess NaOH					
H_2S in 0.3 M H^+					
K_2CrO_4					

17. On the basis of the information acquired in the foregoing experiments, and any other information at your disposal, devise two procedures for the precipitation, separation, and identification of these elements.

4–12. Analysis of the Insoluble Chloride Group

The following is a suggested analytical scheme for the insoluble chloride group. The student is encouraged, however, to make modifications or take different routes according to the results of (17) above.

SCHEMATIC OUTLINE

Add 6 M HCl-Precipitate: AgCl, Hg_2Cl_2, $PbCl_2$, TlCl, H_2WO_4. (Supernate may contain ions of subsequent groups.) Treat with hot water.

Solution: Pb^{+2}, Tl^+ Heat and add 6 M H_2SO_4		Residue: AgCl, Hg_2Cl_2, H_2WO_4 Add 6 M NH_4OH	
Solution: Tl^+ Add KI	Precipitate: $PbSO_4$ Add NH_4Ac	Residue: Hg + $HgNH_2Cl$	Solution: $Ag(NH_3)_2^+$, WO_4^{-2} Add 0.1 M KI
Precipitate: TlI Wash with $Na_2S_2O_3$ solution	Solution: $PbAc_2$ Add K_2CrO_4		Precipitate: AgI	Solution: WO_4^{-2} Evaporate, add 12 M HCl + $SnCl_2$
	Precipitate: $PbCrO_4$			Solution: "Tungsten blue"

The schematic outlines given for each analytical group contain no details. They are designed only to give an over-all picture of the scheme and should not be used as a set of directions in the laboratory.

4–*A*. Test the unknown solution with pH paper to find out whether it is acidic or basic. If it is basic, add sufficient 6 M HNO_3 to a 2-ml portion to neutralize the base; then add 10 drops of 6 M HCl with constant stirring. Heat to ensure precipitation of W, and then cool to ensure precipitation of Pb and Tl. If the unknown solution is neutral or acidic, add the HCl directly, heating and cooling as above. If no precipitation occurs, Ag^+, Hg_2^{+2}, and WO_4^{-2} must be entirely absent, and Pb^{+2} and Tl^+ may be present in no more than minute amounts. If Pb or Tl is present, the solution will deposit glistening platelets or cubes upon cooling. Centrifuge. Add one more drop of HCl to the clear supernate to make sure precipitation is complete. If a precipitate is obtained, centrifuge and test again. Continue until no further precipitation takes place. Remove the supernate and discard it if only the silver group is to be analyzed for, but retain it (marked 5–*A*) for further tests if the sample is part of a general unknown. The precipitate, which may contain any or all of $AgCl$, Hg_2Cl_2, WO_3, $TlCl$, or $PbCl_2$, is washed with cold 2 N HCl and then cold water. Reject the washings.

4–*B*. To the precipitate from (4–*A*) add 1 ml of distilled water, stir, and heat in a boiling water bath. If only $PbCl_2$ and $TlCl$ (not in excessive amount) are present, dissolution of the precipitate will be complete. Centrifuge and separate the supernate by decantation as quickly as possible. Wash by repeating the process with 0.5-ml portions of water until the decanted supernate gives no reaction with K_2CrO_4 solution. Discard the washes. If the hot-water portion contains Pb^{+2} or Tl^+, crystals may be seen to separate as the solution cools.

4–*C*. To the hot solution containing Pb^{+2} and Tl^+ (reheat if necessary), add 8 drops of 5 M H_2SO_4. Stir. If a precipitate of $PbSO_4$ appears, centrifuge and separate the supernate as quickly as possible, not allowing time for the solution to cool. Wash the precipitate with 0.5 ml of water, adding the washings to the supernate. To the precipitate, add 1 ml of 3 M NH_4Ac solution and heat. If a precipitate still appears in the solution on cooling, centrifuge and test the residue for thallium as in (4–*D*). Add 2 drops of K_2CrO_4 to the clear solution. A yellow precipitate of $PbCrO_4$ confirms the presence of Pb^{+2}. Centrifuge the precipitate to make sure that it is actually yellow.

4–*D*. To the supernate from the $PbSO_4$ precipitation, or to the H_2SO_4 solution in (4–*C*) if there was no lead present, add a few drops of 0.1 M KI solution. If a yellow precipitate appears, centrifuge and remove the supernate. Add a few crystals of $Na_2S_2O_3$ and a few drops of water to the precipitate. If the precipitate persists, thallium is present.

4–*E*. If a residue remained in (4–*B*) after the hot-water treatment, add to it 10 drops of 6 M NH_4OH and stir. If the residue becomes black, the presence of Hg_2^{+2} is confirmed, the reaction being

$$Hg_2Cl_2 + 2\ NH_3 \rightarrow Hg\ (black) + HgNH_2Cl\ (white) + NH_4^+ + Cl^-$$

If the residue dissolves completely, no Hg_2^{+2} is present. If a white residue remains, $TlCl$ and/or $PbCl_2$ were not removed completely. Centrifuge. Remove the supernate to another test tube.

4–*F*. Advantage is now taken of the fact that AgI is much less soluble than AgCl (and therefore insoluble in NH_4OH) to separate Ag and W. To the ammoniacal supernate from (4–*E*) add dropwise 0.1 M KI until no further precipitation takes place. Be careful not to add excess. Stir. A pale yellow precipitate of AgI confirms the presence of Ag^+. Centrifuge. Add one more drop of KI solution to the clear supernate to test the completeness of precipitation. If all the silver has been precipitated, centrifuge and remove the supernate to test for tungsten.

4–G. Evaporate the supernate from the AgI precipitation (4–F) to small volume, acidify with HCl, add a few drops of $SnCl_2$ solution and 1 ml of 12 M HCl. Heat to boiling. Development of a blue color ("tungsten blue") confirms the presence of tungsten.

4–13. Questions and Problems

1. Describe what effect the difference in electronegativity between metal and non-metal has on the solubility of such series of compounds as AgCl, AgBr, AgI or CuCl, AgCl, AuCl.

2. Explain why the series PbF_2, $PbCl_2$, $PbBr_2$, PbI_2 has a solubility *maximum* at $PbCl_2$.

3. Find some other solubility trends among the elements in this analytical group and assign an explanation to them.

4. Describe the origins of color in inorganic compounds. Which of these may give predictable colors?

5. Is it reasonable that elements forming insoluble halides should also form halo complexes? Explain.

6. Is it reasonable that many of the elements in this analytical group form ammine complexes? Explain.

7. Explain the separation of Hg_2^{+2} from Ag^+.

8. Because complex ions undergo stepwise dissociation, does it follow that overall instability constants are not valid? Explain.

9. Tungsten(VI) does not form an insoluble chloride. Explain why it is found in the insoluble-chloride group.

10. If HNO_3 were used to precipitate tungsten ahead of the insoluble chloride group (as is sometimes done), would it precipitate alone? Explain.

11. The compounds of Au(I), Hg(II), Pb(IV), and Tl(III), and the compounds of Bi(III), Pb(II), Po(IV), and Tl(III) are in many respects similar. Explain.

12. When $PbCl_2$ is treated with K_2CrO_4, it turns yellow, but when it is treated with $NH_4C_2H_3O_2$, it dissolves. Explain.

13. What experiments could be designed to show that the NH_3 molecule and not NH_4^+ or OH^- is responsible for the dissolution of Ag_2O in NH_4OH?

14. If 0.001 mole of $AgNO_3$ is dissolved in 750 ml of 1 M NH_4OH, what will be the free Ag^+ concentration?

15. If 0.2 gram of HgI_2 is dissolved in 800 ml of 0.1 M KI, what is the free Hg^{+2} concentration?

16. If 0.1 gram of NaCl is added to 500 ml of a 0.1 M $Hg(NO_3)_2$ solution, what will be the concentration of $HgCl^+$? What will be the concentration of free Cl^-?

17. The instability constant of the complex ion $Tl_2Cl_9^{-3}$ is about 10^{-40}. If one gram of $K_3Tl_2Cl_9$ is dissolved in 2 liters of 0.1 M HCl, what is the free Tl^{+3} concentration?

18. In a solution containing both 0.1 M $K_2Zn(CN)_4$ and 0.1 M $K_2Ni(CN)_4$, what is the ratio of $[Zn^{+2}]$ to $[Ni^{+2}]$?

19. In a solution containing 0.1 M K_2HgI_4 and 0.1 M $K_2Hg(SCN)_4$, what is the ratio of $[I^-]$ to $[SCN^-]$?

20. In a 0.1 M KF solution containing 0.01 M K_3FeF_6 and 0.01 M K_2SnF_6, is Sn^{+4} or Fe^{+3} present in larger concentration?

21. If the limit of visibility of $Fe(SCN)_2^+$ is 1×10^{-6} molar, what concentration of KSCN must be added to a solution containing 2×10^{-6} M Fe^{+3} in order to obtain a positive test for iron? Assume K_{inst} for $Fe(SCN)_2^+$ to be 2×10^{-5}.

22. If 0.001 gram $AgNO_3$ be dissolved in 1 liter of 0.5 M NH_4OH, what is the concentration of free Ag^+?

23. If 0.001 gram NH_3 be added to 0.5 liter of 0.1 M $AgNO_3$, how much $AgNH_3^+$ will be formed?

24. If the red color of FeN_3^{+2} can just be detected at a concentration of 10^{-5} molar, what is the minimum concentration of Fe^{+3} which can be detected in a 0.01 M KN_3 solution?

25. If 0.1 gram $HgCl_2$ be dissolved in 900 ml of 0.1 M HCl, what is the concentration of $HgCl_4^{-2}$ present?

26. To a liter of a 10^{-8} molar solution of AgCl in water is added 10^{-6} grams of $AgNO_3$. What is the concentration of Ag_2Cl^+ in the final solution?

27. If, to a liter of a 0.001 molar solution of $As(OH)_3$, 0.001 mole of HCl and 0.001 mole of H_2SO_4 are added, what concentration of $As(OH)_2Cl$ will be present?

4–14. References

Butts, A., *Copper—The Science and Technology of the Metal, Its Alloys and Compounds.* New York: Reinhold Publishing Corporation, 1954.

Whitmore, F. C., *Organic Compounds of Mercury.* New York: Chemical Catalogue Company, Inc., 1921.

Lead. New York: Lead Industries Association, 1952.

Hoffman, W., *Blei und Bleilegierungen, Metalkunde und Technologie.* Berlin: J. Springer, 1941.

Killeffer, D. H., and Linz, A., *Molybdenum Compounds.* New York: Interscience Publishers, Inc., 1952.

Kuo-ch'in Li, and Wang, C. Y., *Tungsten.* New York: Reinhold Publishing Corporation, 1955.

Chapter 5

The Acid-Insoluble Sulfides
Weak Acids and Bases

5–1. The Solubility of Sulfides

The second analytical group consists of those elements whose sulfides are so insoluble that even the concentration of S^{-2} obtainable in 0.3 M acid is capable of precipitating them. By the relationship

$$\frac{[H^+]^2[S^{-2}]}{[H_2S]} = 1.3 \times 10^{-20}$$

we calculate that in 0.3 M acid the sulfide ion concentration of a saturated (0.1 M) solution of H_2S will be almost 10^{-20} M. This is sufficient to precipitate sulfides of the elements

					Cu			Ge	As	Se
Mo	Tc	Ru	Rh	Pd	Ag	Cd	——	Sn	Sb	Te
W	Re	Os	Ir	Pt	Au	Hg	——	Pb	Bi	Po

Variation of the H^+ concentration (and therefore the S^{-2} concentration) will of course, change the boundaries of this group.

Since it would require an excessive attention to detail to consider all of these elements, only certain ones will be selected for examination. Furthermore, Ag(I), Hg(I), and W, having already been disposed of as insoluble chlorides or hydroxides, will not be found in the group. Therefore, we shall reduce the group under discussion to the representative elements

					Cu			As
Mo	——	——	——	——	Cd	——	Sn	Sb
					Hg(II)	——	Pb	Bi

The various elements in this group may assume a wide variety of oxidation states, from $+1$ for Ag and Tl to $+8$ for Os. Under normal conditions, the most likely states are. Mo $(+6)$, W $(+6)$, Tc $(+4)$, Re $(+7)$, Ru $(+3, +4)$, Os $(+4, +6, +8)$, Rh $(+3)$, Ir $(+3, +4)$, Pd $(+2)$, Pt $(+4)$, Cu $(+2)$, Ag $(+1)$, Au $(+3)$, Cd $(+2)$, Hg $(+1, +2)$, Tl $(+1)$, Ge $(+4)$, Sn $(+2, +4)$, Pb $(+2)$, As $(+3, +5)$, Sb $(+3, +5)$, Bi $(+3)$. Many of these are eliminated by treatment of the solution with oxidants and reductants before precipitation. Thus, for the selected group, the following sulfides will be expected: CuS, CdS, HgS, SnS_2, PbS, As_2S_3, Sb_2S_3, Bi_2S_3 and MoS_3.

Solubilities of compounds depend on a number of factors. For ionized salts, the important factors are the size, shape, and charges of the ions involved, as well as the stoichiometry of the substances, as has been discussed in Chapter 3.

For covalent substances which separate into ions on dissolving, however, a further important (and frequently dominating) factor is the difference in electronegativity between the elements involved in the ionization, as was suggested in Chapter 4. The electronegativity of a given element depends upon two factors—the position of the element in the periodic table and its valence or oxidation state (see Sections 1–8 and 1–9). Since electronegativity is a measure of the pull of an element on its electrons, we may expect that as the electronegativity of a metal combined with sulfur comes closer to the electronegativity of sulfur (2.5), the less will be the ability of the sulfur to withdraw electrons from the metal to form S^{-2} and, therefore, the less will be the tendency for the sulfide to go into solution according to the equation

$$M_2S_n(s) \rightleftharpoons 2\,M^{+n} + nS^{-2}$$

Let us consider, therefore, the solubility product constants of the mono-sulfides (for which oxidation state and stoichiometry are constant) insofar as they are known. We see from Table 5–1 that they vary very nearly according to the electronegativity of the positive element.

TABLE 5–1. VARIATION OF SOLUBILITY PRODUCT CONSTANT WITH ELECTRONEGATIVITY

	MnS	FeS	CoS	NiS	CuS	ZnS	——	GeS
$p_{K_{sp}}$	12.6	17.3	21.3	22.0	35.1	22.8		34.5
x^*	1.4	1.45	1.5	1.5	1.7	1.5		1.7
						CdS	——	SnS
$p_{K_{sp}}$						27.3		26.9
x						1.5		1.55
				PtS	——	HgS	——	PbS
$p_{K_{sp}}$				72.1		51.8		27.9
x				2.1		1.9		1.6

* x = electronegativity.

If the $p_{K_{sp}}$ (i.e., the negative of the logarithm of the K_{sp}) is plotted against the difference in electronegativity between the metal and sulfur (see Fig. 5–1), it is seen that there is a very definite trend, for which the relationship can be written

$$p_{K_{sp}} = 102.5 - 80.6\,\Delta x$$

The deviations observed are in part due to inadequate knowledge of the electronegativities and K_{sp}'s in many cases. In addition, other factors which we have ignored, such as ionic size, and so forth, undoubtedly have their effects. (It will be noticed that the insoluble selenides and tellurides follow the same relationship.)

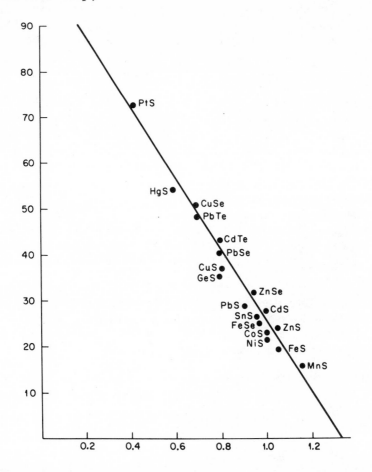

Fig. 5–1. Solubilities of Metallic Chalcogenides as a Function of Difference in Electronegativity.

In exactly the same way, since electronegativity increases with increasing oxidation state, we may expect that, as the oxidation state of any given element is raised, the tendency of its sulfides to dissolve to give M^{+n} and S^{-2} will decrease (K_{sp} relationships can also be given for sulfides of other oxidation states: for M_2S: $p_{K_{sp}} = 124.8 - 100.0\ \Delta x$, for M_2S_3: $p_{K_{sp}} = 235.1 - 171.7\ \Delta x$). In the absence of other complicating factors, then, the solubility of the sulfides of a given element should decrease as the oxidation state of the element is raised. This effect can be seen in the pairs of sulfides listed in Table 5–2.

TABLE 5–2. EFFECT OF OXIDATION STATE ON
SOLUBILITIES OF SULFIDES

Sulfide	Molar Solubility*
FeS	2×10^{-9}
Fe_2S_3	1×10^{-18}
CoS	2×10^{-11}
Co_2S_3	6×10^{-26}
Cu_2S	3×10^{-17}
CuS	3×10^{-18}
Hg_2S	3×10^{-24}
HgS	1×10^{-26}
SnS	4×10^{-14}
SnS_2	3×10^{-24}

* Assuming no hydrolysis.

The sulfide-ion concentration necessary to produce precipitates from 0.01 M solutions of the various metals in their usual oxidation states is listed in Table 5–3.

TABLE 5–3. MINIMUM SULFIDE ION CONCENTRATION REQUIRED TO
PRODUCE PRECIPITATE IN 0.01 M SOLUTION OF CATION

Cation	$[S^{-2}]$	Cation	$[S^{-2}]$
Al^{+3}	2×10^{-1}	Pb^{+2}	1×10^{-26}
Ce^{+3}	3×10^{-3}	Sn^{+2}	1×10^{-25}
La^{+3}	4×10^{-4}	Cd^{+2}	5×10^{-26}
Mn^{+2}	3×10^{-11}	Fe^{+3}	1×10^{-28}
Fe^{+2}	5×10^{-16}	Cu^+	1×10^{-45}
Zn^{+2}	2×10^{-21}	Cu^{+2}	8×10^{-34}
Tl^+	6×10^{-17}	Bi^{+3}	1×10^{-117}
Co^{+2}	5×10^{-20}	Hg_2^{+2}	1×10^{-45}
Ni^{+2}	1×10^{-20}	Ag^+	6×10^{-47}
		Hg^{+2}	2×10^{-50}
		Ir^{+3}	10^{-63}
		Pt^{+2}	8×10^{-71}

Of those listed, Ag_2S and Hg_2S will not be found in the group of elements normally precipitated as acid-insoluble sulfides because of prior precipitation of these cations as chlorides. Likewise, Fe_2S_3 will not be found because, in 0.3 M acid, H_2S reduces Fe^{+3}

$$2 Fe^{+3} (aq) + H_2S (aq) \rightleftharpoons 2 Fe^{+2} (aq) + S (s) + 2 H^+$$

With these exceptions then, it is easy to see that in 0.3 M acid (in which $[S^{-2}] < 10^{-20}$ M) the sulfides in the right-hand column will precipitate, whereas those in the left-hand column will not, since they require a higher sulfide-ion concentration than can exist under these conditions.

It can now be seen that the solubility rule for sulfides quoted in Section 1–1 should be modified to read:

> All the sulfides, selenides, and tellurides of the metals are insoluble in water, except those of the alkali and alkaline-earth elements. The smaller the difference in electronegativity between the metal and the nonmetal in the compound, the lower the solubility will be.

It should be noted, however, that in the case of some sulfides which should precipitate only in alkaline solution, the solubility of the hydroxide may be less than that of the sulfide, and consequently the hydroxide will precipitate instead. Examples of this are Al_2S_3, Ce_2S_3, and Cr_2S_3. These compounds cannot be precipitated from water solution because of the preferential precipitation of $Al(OH)_3$, $Ce(OH)_3$, and $Cr(OH)_3$ (see Section 8–7).

5–2. The Sulfide Complexes

The next separation to be considered is that used to divide the acid-insoluble sulfides into two subgroups. Again advantage is taken of the change in affinity for sulfur with change in electronegativity. The more electronegative elements in the presence of a sufficiently high sulfide-ion concentration will combine with extra sulfide ions to form thio anions.

$$MS_n \text{ (s)} + S^{-2} \text{ (aq)} \rightleftharpoons MS_{n+1}^{-2} \text{ (aq)}$$

(Compare the complex halides, Section 4–4.) The *instability* constants (i.e., for the reactions MS_{n+1}^{-2} (aq) $\rightleftharpoons MS_n$ (s) $+ S^{-2}$ (aq)) for some of these ions are listed in Table 5–4 along with the electronegativities of the metals.

The same is done in Table 5–5 for the sulfides not forming thio anions. It can be seen, that although correspondence is by no means perfect, there is a general trend in affinity for sulfide ion with change in electronegativity.

TABLE 5–4. SULFIDES FORMING THIO ANIONS

Complex Ion	$pK_{inst.}$	*Electronegativity*
AuS_2^-		2.3
PtS_3^{-2}		2.1
MoS_4^{-2}		2.1
AsS_2^- (aq) $\rightleftharpoons \frac{1}{2} As_2S_3$ (s) $+ \frac{1}{2} S^{-2}$	3.6	2.0
$HgS_2^{-2} \rightleftharpoons HgS$ (s) $+ S^{-2}$	−0.6	1.9
GeS_3^{-2}		1.8
SnS_3^{-2} (aq) $\rightleftharpoons SnS_2$ (s) $+ S^{-2}$ (aq)	5.04	1.8
SbS_2^- (aq) $\rightleftharpoons \frac{1}{2} Sb_2S_3$ (s) $+ \frac{1}{2} S^{-2}$ (aq)	0.45	1.8

TABLE 5–5. SULFIDES NOT FORMING THIO ANIONS

Sulfide	*Electronegativity*
Bi_2S_3	1.8
CuS	1.7
PbS	1.6
SnS	1.55

Sulfide	Electronegativity
CdS	1.5
ZnS	1.5
NiS	1.5
CoS	1.5
FeS	1.45
MnS	1.4

It will be noticed that the instability constant for HgS_2^{-2} is quite high. This results in partial dissolution of HgS in alkali sulfide solutions unless the $[S^{-2}]$ is carefully regulated. If the separation is carried out in the NH_4OH solutions of S^{-2} in which $[S^{-2}]$ cannot be very high because of the equilibrium, $NH_4^+ + S^{-2} \rightleftharpoons NH_3 + HS^-$, very little HgS dissolves, whereas if the much stronger base KOH is used, the HgS can be completely dissolved. (Sodium hydroxide is not quite strong enough a base, Appendix 5, to give complete dissolution in a reasonable volume of the amounts of HgS found in the usual qualitative analysis sample.)

The group of elements having amphoteric sulfides is reprecipitated from the ammonium sulfide solution by careful addition of HCl, e.g.,

$$SnS_3^{-2} \text{ (aq)} + 2\ H^+ \text{ (aq)} \rightleftharpoons SnS_2 \text{ (s)} + H_2S \text{ (g)}$$

$$2\ AsS_2^- \text{ (aq)} + 2\ H^+ \text{ (aq)} \rightleftharpoons As_2S_3 \text{ (s)} + H_2S \text{ (g)}$$

The group is now further broken down by taking advantage of the differing solubilities of the sulfides in concentrated hydrochloric acid. The solubility in HCl depends not only on the solubility-product constant of the sulfide, but also on the stability of the chloro complex formed. In general, the smaller the difference in electronegativity between the metal and chlorine, the more stable the complex. Since, however, the electronegativity of chlorine is higher than that of sulfur, the stability of the chloro complexes does not vary as rapidly as the solubility of the sulfides, thus giving rise to differences in the solubility of the sulfides in HCl.

Except for the case of bismuth (which is added for comparison), the values of the equilibrium constants for the following reactions are highly approximate. Nevertheless, they will serve as a comparison to show why As_2S_3 is insoluble in even very concentrated HCl, whereas Sb_2S_3 and Bi_2S_3 are soluble if the concentration is much over one molar. It also shows why SnS_2 fails to precipitate at all unless great care is taken to acidify with the minimum amount of HCl.

$$As_2S_3 \text{ (s)} + 6\ H^+ \text{ (aq)} + 8\ Cl^- \text{ (aq)} \rightleftharpoons 2\ AsCl_4^- \text{ (aq)} + 3\ H_2S \text{ (g)} \quad K = 10^{-64}$$

$$Bi_2S_3 \text{ (s)} + 6\ H^+ \text{ (aq)} + 8\ Cl^- \text{ (aq)} \rightleftharpoons 2\ BiCl_4^- \text{ (aq)} + 3\ H_2S \text{ (g)} \quad K = 10^{-49.8}$$

$$Sb_2S_3 \text{ (s)} + 6\ H^+ \text{ (aq)} + 8\ Cl^- \text{ (aq)} \rightleftharpoons 2\ SbCl_4^- \text{ (aq)} + 3\ H_2S \text{ (g)} \quad K = 10^{-47}$$

$$SnS_2 \text{ (s)} + 4\ H^+ \text{ (aq)} + 6\ Cl^- \text{ (aq)} \rightleftharpoons SnCl_6^{-2} \text{ (aq)} + 2\ H_2S \text{ (g)} \quad K = 10^{-20}$$

On the other hand, As_2S_3 *is* soluble in aqua regia, the reaction

$$As_2S_3 \text{ (s)} + 8 \text{ H}^+ \text{ (aq)} + 2 \text{ NO}_3^- \text{ (aq)} + 8 \text{ Cl}^- \text{ (aq)} \rightleftharpoons 2 \text{ AsCl}_4^- \text{ (aq)}$$
$$+ 2 \text{ NO (g)} + 3 \text{ S (s)} + 4 \text{ H}_2\text{O (l)}$$

having an equilibrium constant $K = 10^{+58}$.

The trend in solubility of the sulfides also makes it possible to separate mercury from the other elements forming non-amphoteric sulfides, since mercury (II) sulfide is the most insoluble of the sulfides in this group. Thus, HgS does not dissolve in the HNO_3 used to dissolve the other members of the group, the equilibrium constant being $10^{-13.8}$ for the reaction

$$3 \text{ HgS (s)} + 2 \text{ NO}_3^- \text{ (aq)} + 8 \text{ H}^+ \rightleftharpoons 2 \text{ NO (g)} + 3 \text{ S (s)} + 3 \text{ Hg}^{+2} \text{ (aq)}$$
$$+ 4 \text{ H}_2\text{O (l)}$$

It will dissolve in aqua regia, however, the equilibrium constant being $10^{+33.8}$ for the reaction

$$3 \text{ HgS (s)} + 2 \text{ NO}_3^- \text{ (aq)} + 12 \text{ Cl}^- \text{ (aq)} + 8 \text{ H}^+ \text{ (aq)} \rightleftharpoons 2 \text{ NO (g)} + 3 \text{ S (s)}$$
$$+ 3 \text{ HgCl}_4^{-2} \text{ (aq)} + 4 \text{ H}_2\text{O (l)}$$

On the other hand, the next most insoluble sulfide in this group, Bi_2S_3, is easily dissolved by HNO_3, $K = 10^{+41}$ for the reaction

$$Bi_2S_3 \text{ (s)} + 2 \text{ NO}_3^- \text{ (aq)} + 8 \text{ H}^+ \rightleftharpoons 2 \text{ NO (g)} + 3 \text{ S (s)} + 2 \text{ Bi}^{+3} \text{ (aq)}$$
$$+ 4 \text{ H}_2\text{O (l)}$$

5–3. Weak Acids and Bases

We have made use of weak acid and base equilibria in the laboratory to adjust the $[\text{H}^+]$ in order to bring about or prevent the precipitation of various substances. For example, adjustment of the $HCO_3^- \text{ (aq)} \rightleftharpoons \text{H}^+ \text{ (aq)} + CO_3^{-2}$ (aq) equilibrium through the $NH_4OH \text{ (aq)} \rightleftharpoons NH_4^+ \text{ (aq)} + OH^- \text{ (aq)}$ equilibrium allowed precipitation of $BaCO_3$, $SrCO_3$, and $CaCO_3$, without precipitating the more soluble $MgCO_3$. Adjustment of the

$$Cr_2O_7^{-2} \text{ (aq)} + H_2O \rightleftharpoons 2 \text{ HCrO}_4^- \text{ (aq)} \rightleftharpoons 2 \text{ CrO}_4^{-2} \text{ (aq)} + 2 \text{ H}^+ \text{ (aq)}$$

equilibrium allowed precipitation of $BaCrO_4$ (and its subsequent dissolution) without precipitating $SrCrO_4$. Ammonium ion was observed to interfere with the blue lake test for magnesium by not allowing a high enough $[\text{OH}^-]$ to precipitate the $Mg(OH)_2$ necessary for lake formation, and adjustment of the $H_2S \rightleftharpoons 2 \text{ H}^+ + \text{S}^{-2}$ equilibrium allowed separation of one group of insoluble sulfides from those of greater solubility.

Although all of these examples are of weak acids and bases in solution (homogeneous equilibria), it is by no means necessary that they be so, and many examples of insoluble weak acids and bases are known whose equilibria with their ions in solution are heterogenous. Examples which you have already met include niobic and tungstic acids,

$$\text{``HNbO}_3\text{''} (s) \rightleftharpoons H^+ (aq) + NbO_3^- (aq)$$
$$H_2WO_4 (s) \rightleftharpoons 2\,H^+ (aq) + WO_4^{-2} (aq)$$

or $\qquad WO_3 (s) + H_2O \rightleftharpoons 2\,H^+ (aq) + WO_4^{-2} (aq)$

and also $\qquad V_2O_5 (s) + 3\,H_2O \rightleftharpoons 6\,H^+ (aq) + 2\,VO_4^{-3} (aq)$

and all the insoluble metal hydroxides, which are weak bases, e.g.,

$$Ag_2O (s) + H_2O \rightleftharpoons 2\,Ag^+ (aq) + 2\,OH^- (aq)$$
$$Mg(OH)_2 (s) \rightleftharpoons Mg^{+2} (aq) + 2\,OH^- (aq)$$
$$Bi(OH)_3 (s) \rightleftharpoons Bi^{+3} (aq) + 3\,OH^- (aq)$$

5-4. Homogeneous Weak Acid Equilibria (Monoprotic Acids)

A weak acid like hydrazoic acid, HN_3, is found to be only slightly ionized in aqueous solution, according to the equation

$$HN_3 (aq) \rightleftharpoons H^+ (aq) + N_3^- (aq)$$

(Henceforth the designation (*aq*) will be omitted except as required for clarity, and it will be assumed that all ions are in water solution unless specifically stated otherwise.) The mathematical expression for this equilibrium is

$$\frac{[H^+][N_3^-]}{[HN_3]} = K_A = 1.9 \times 10^{-5}$$

where 1.9×10^{-5} is the experimentally determined acid-ionization constant at 25°C. It can be seen that, to a first approximation, the $[H^+]$ and $[N_3^-]$ will be the same. If we now set $[H^+] = [N_3^-] = X$, then $[HN_3] = C - X$ where C is the total concentration of hydrazoic acid present in all forms and $(C - X)$ is the concentration of un-ionized acid left after ionization has taken place. Thus, if we have a 0.1 M solution of HN_3 in pure water, we shall have

$$\frac{[H^+][N_3^-]}{[HN_3]} = \frac{X \cdot X}{0.1 - X} = 1.9 \times 10^{-5}$$

Then $X^2 = 1.9 \times 10^{-6} - (1.9 \times 10^{-5})X$ and, using the quadratic formula, $X = [H^+] = [N_3^-] = 1.4 \times 10^{-3}$ M. It can now be seen that the value of $(0.1 - X) = 0.0986$ does not differ significantly from 0.1, and therefore we could have written

$$\frac{X \cdot X}{0.1} = 1.9 \times 10^{-5}$$

For our purposes, the difference between C and $C - X$ can be ignored when X is less than 10 percent of C. This will be the case *unless* C is exceptionally small or K_A is exceptionally large.

If the HN_3 were to have a concentration of 1×10^{-4} M, then, if $C = 1 \times 10^{-4}$ M,

$$\frac{X \cdot X}{1 \times 10^{-4}} = 1.9 \times 10^{-5}$$

and $X = 4.4 \times 10^{-5} M$. This is $\dfrac{4.4 \times 10^{-5}}{1 \times 10^{-4}}$ or 44 percent of the total, so that the calculation is not within the required limits of accuracy. Use of the more accurate expression $\dfrac{X^2}{1 \times 10^{-4} - X} = 1.9 \times 10^{-5}$, and the quadratic formula, gives $X = [H^+] = [N_3^-] = 4.0 \times 10^{-5} M$, which differs from the previous answer by 10 percent.

Carrying this theme to extremes, if the simplified calculation is used for a $1 \times 10^{-5} M$ solution of HN_3

$$\frac{X \cdot X}{1 \times 10^{-5}} = 1.9 \times 10^{-5}, \quad X = 1.4 \times 10^{-5} M$$

which, being greater than the total concentration of acid in the solution, is obviously absurd. Here the more accurate calculation is required to obtain an answer having any meaning at all, the true answer being $X = 7.0 \times 10^{-6}$ or 70 percent dissociation. It can be seen from these calculations that the degree of dissociation of a weak acid increases with decreasing concentration.

The same situation can be demonstrated for acids having large ionization constants. Thus hypophosphorous acid, HPH_2O_2, has a constant $K_A = 1.6 \times 10^{-2}$. In 0.01 M solution, $HPH_2O_2 \rightleftharpoons H^+ + PH_2O_2^-$, and

$$\frac{[H^+][PH_2O_2^-]}{[HPH_2O_2]} = 1.6 \times 10^{-2}$$

Ignoring the difference between C and $C - X$

$\dfrac{X^2}{0.01} = 1.6 \times 10^{-2}$, $X = 1.3 \times 10^{-2}$, which again is obviously absurd. More accurate calculation gives $X = 7 \times 10^{-3} M$, or 70 percent dissociation.

5-5.   The Common Ion Effect

In accordance with Le Châtelier's principle, the ionization equilibrium of a weak acid should shift upon addition of another substance contributing one of the ions derived from the acid, just as we have seen to be the case with insoluble salts and complex ions. Thus, if either H^+ (say, as HCl) or N_3^- (as KN_3) were added to a hydrazoic acid solution, the equilibrium

$$HN_3 \rightleftharpoons H^+ + N_3^-$$

should be shifted to the left, resulting in repression of the ionization of the acid. Thus, if 0.01 mole of KN_3 be added to 1 liter of a 0.1 molar solution of HN_3, since the KN_3 is a salt and 100 percent ionic, the $[N_3^-]$ may be taken as 0.01 M, while the $[HN_3] = 0.1 M$.

Therefore

$$\frac{[H^+][N_3^-]}{[HN_3]} = 1.9 \times 10^{-5} = \frac{[H^+](10^{-2})}{10^{-1}}$$

and $[H^+] = 1.9 \times 10^{-4}\ M$.

That we were justified in taking $[N_3^-] = 0.01\ M$ and ignoring the contribution to $[N_3^-]$ from the ionization of the HN_3 can be shown by setting the problem up rigorously and solving the quadratic obtained. Since the ionization of HN_3 must produce H^+ and N_3^- in equal amounts, the total $[N_3^-] = 0.01 + X$, where $X = [H^+]$. Likewise $[HN_3] = 0.1 - X$. Thus

$$\frac{[H^+][N_3^-]}{[HN_3]} = \frac{X(0.01 + X)}{0.1 - X} = 1.9 \times 10^{-5}$$

and $X^2 + (0.01 + 1.9 \times 10^{-5})X - 1.9 \times 10^{-6} = 0$. Since 1.9×10^{-5} is negligible in comparison to 0.01, this becomes

$$X^2 + 0.01X - 1.9 \times 10^{-6} = 0$$

Applying the quadratic formula

$$X = [H^+] = 2 \times 10^{-4}\ M$$

and the total $N_3^- = 1.02 \times 10^{-2}\ M$, which is not significantly different from what was taken before.

In exactly the same manner, if 0.01 mole of HCl (which is 100 percent ionized in solution) be added to 1 liter of 0.1 M HN_3, then $[H^+] = 10^{-2}\ M$, while $[HN_3]$ is still $10^{-1}\ M$. Therefore

$$\frac{[H^+][N_3^-]}{[HN_3]} = \frac{10^{-2}[N_3^-]}{10^{-1}} = 1.9 \times 10^{-5}$$

and $[N_3^-] = 1.9 \times 10^{-4}\ M$.

5–6.   Strong Acids

Substances like hydrochloric acid have been described as strong acids, 100 percent ionized in solution. However, it must be realized that the laws of chemical equilibrium apply to strong acids just as to weak ones. In the case of the strongest acids, however, the ionization constants are so large that for all intents and purposes ionization is complete, except in the most concentrated solutions. The ionization constant for HCl in water is of the order of 10^7. Thus, if we assume for a 0.1 M solution that essentially 100 percent is ionized into H^+ and Cl^-, and that the concentration of un-ionized HCl is X, then

$$\frac{(0.1)(0.1)}{X} = 10^7$$

and $X = [HCl] = 10^{-9}\ M$, or only 0.000001 percent remains un-ionized. Similarly we calculate for 1 M HCl that 0.00001 percent is un-ionized. This is a negligible amount in either case. In other words, the percentage of ionization is for all practical purposes 100 percent. Likewise, it can be calculated from the estimated ionization constant of 10^{10} that hydriodic acid, HI, is 0.00000001 percent un-ionized in 1 molar solution and only 0.000000001 percent un-ionized in 0.1 molar solution. Thus the concentration of H^+ in a dilute solution of a strong acid is essentially the same as the total acid concentration.

On the other hand, nitric acid, HNO_3, is a weak "strong acid," with an ionization constant of only 22. Thus for a 0.1 molar solution, we calculate the concentration of un-ionized HNO_3 to be 0.45 percent, and in 1 molar solution it is up to 4.5 percent. Consequently, in solutions more concentrated than 1 molar, nitric acid acts appreciably less strong than hydrochloric and the other very strong acids. Estimated ionization constants for the common strong acids and for acids of intermediate and low strength are given in Appendix 4. The difference between weak and strong acids is only one of degree and not one of kind.

5–7. Activity and Activity Coefficients

A factor much more important to the apparent strength of solutions of strong acids than their ionization constants is that of *activity*. The activity, *a*, of a substance is related to its concentration through the expression

$$a = \gamma m$$

where *m* is the molal concentration (equivalent to the molar concentration for dilute aqueous solutions) and γ is the *activity coefficient*.

Activity is a manifestation of the electrical forces which the ions exert on each other as they move through the solution. In very dilute solutions in which the ions are far apart, the attraction of one ion for others of opposite charge is essentially zero. Consequently, at low concentrations (less than 0.01 molar in aqueous solutions), concentration and activity are essentially the same (i.e., $\gamma = 1$). As the concentration is increased, however, the ions are retarded in their passage through solution by the attraction of ions of opposite charge, and the activity becomes less than the concentration (i.e., $\gamma < 1$). On the other hand, at very high concentrations, repulsive forces between ions of like charge and other factors become effective, so that the activity increases again and may considerably exceed the concentration ($\gamma > 1$). Some typical *activity coefficient* functions are shown in Fig. 5–2.

It can be seen from this figure that in 1 molal solutions of HCl and HBr the *effective* hydrogen-ion concentration (activity) is somewhat less than unity. However, above 2 molal, the activity is greater than 2, and increases fast at higher concentrations. Consequently, for strong acids, the changes in activity may far exceed the changes in degree of ionization in concentrated solutions, where the changes in ionization might otherwise be expected to be observed. Thus we have seen (Sections 5–6) that in going from 10^{-3} *M* HCl to 1 M HCl the change in un-ionized HCl is from 10^{-11} percent to 10^{-7} percent, whereas the activity coefficient, 2, changes from 1 to 0.8. This means that the activity changes as though the HCl were essentially 100 percent ionized at 10^{-3}, but only 80 percent ionized at 1 M. The activity effect can

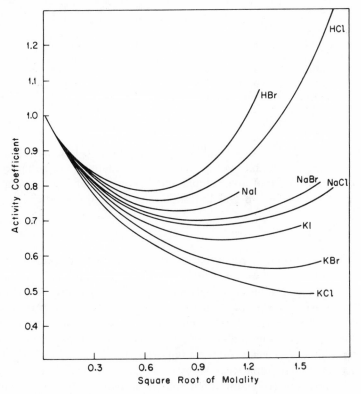

Fig. 5–2. Activity Coefficient of Hydrogen and Alkali Halides.

therefore be seen to swamp utterly any effect due to the ionization constant. This effect can be seen in the data obtained when we try to determine an "ionization constant" for a strong acid like HCl, assuming incomplete ionization. From the data given in Table 5–6 it is obvious that the effects of activity completely outweigh the effect of the ionization constant in the case of the strong acid. Data are also given for acetic acid for comparison.

The activity effect can also be seen in the facts (1) that a half-mole of NaCl does not lower the freezing point of water quite so much as one mole of ethyl alcohol (1.66°C compared to 1.83°C), despite the fact that a half-mole of NaCl contains the same number of particles as one mole of alcohol; (2) that the electrical conductivity is less than twice as great for a 1 M NaCl solution as for a 0.5 M solution; and (3) that although the equilibrium

TABLE 5–6. COMPARISON OF K_A FOR ACETIC ACID WITH THE APPARENT K_A OF HCl

| *Acetic Acid* | | *Hydrochloric Acid* | |
Molar Concentration	K_A	Molar Concentration	Apparent K_A
		0.200	1.56
		0.100	1.05
0.0500	1.81×10^{-5}	0.050	0.73
0.0128	1.80×10^{-5}	0.010	0.32
0.00591	1.80×10^{-5}	0.005	0.23
0.00241	1.80×10^{-5}	0.002	0.15
0.00103	1.78×10^{-5}	0.001	0.12
0.00015	1.78×10^{-5}		

av. 1.80×10^{-5}

principle predicts no effect of a soluble salt having no ions in common with a precipitated salt, the solubility of the precipitate is found in fact to increase when the concentration of the soluble salt becomes high. For example, $BaSO_4$ is more soluble in 1 M NaCl solution than it is in 0.1 M NaCl.

5–8. Weak Bases

Weak bases are quite comparable to weak acids with respect to their ionization equilibria. For example, it is found that ammonium hydroxide, NH_4OH, in 0.1 molar solution is only 1.3 percent ionized into NH_4^+ and OH^-, CH_3HgOH is 0.0005 percent ionized into CH_3Hg^+ and OH^-, and TlOH is 12 percent ionized into Tl^+ and OH^- at the same concentration.

The number of common soluble weak bases is far smaller than the number of common soluble weak acids, the most important one by far being NH_4OH. For the most part, the soluble weak bases are organic compounds of nitrogen (amines, derivatives of NH_3), but a few soluble inorganic and metal-organic weak bases exist, such as TlOH, N_2H_4, $HONH_2$*, CH_3HgOH, C_6H_5HgOH, $(C_2H_5)_2TlOH$, $(CH_3)_3SnOH$, and $(CH_3)_3P$†. Appendix 5 contains some ionization constants for *soluble* weak bases.

5–9. Acids and Bases from the Brønsted Point of View

To date we have generally considered acids to be substances capable of giving up H^+ and bases to be substances capable of giving up OH^-. This is the classical point of view and is adequate for most purposes, but does not give the whole picture. For example, in discussing the ionization of ammonia in water we have used two alternative (but equivalent) points of view: (1) that ammonia in water exists actually as un-ionized NH_4OH and undergoes ionization in the classical sense, $NH_4OH \rightleftharpoons NH_4^+ + OH^-$, or (2) in

---

* This ionizes according to the equation $HONH_2 + H_2O \rightleftharpoons HONH_3^+ + OH^-$.

† This ionizes according to the equation $(CH_3)_3P + H_2O \rightleftharpoons (CH_3)_3PH^+ + OH^-$; compare $NH_3 + H_2O \rightleftharpoons NH_4^+ + OH^-$.

the sense developed by Brønsted and Lowry, $NH_3 + H_2O \rightleftharpoons NH_4^+ + OH^-$, in which the NH_3 is not a hydroxide-ion donor but rather a hydrogen-ion acceptor. The mathematical expressions for the equilibria are equivalent

(1)
$$\frac{[NH_4^+][OH^-]}{[NH_4OH]} = 1.8 \times 10^{-5}$$

or (2)
$$\frac{[NH_4^+][OH^-]}{[NH_3]} = 1.8 \times 10^{-5}$$

The neutralization of HCl may be looked at in the same way

(1) $\qquad NH_4OH + HCl \rightarrow NH_4^+ + Cl^- + H_2O$

or (2) $\qquad NH_3 + HCl \rightarrow NH_4^+ + Cl^-$

where (1) differs from (2) only by having the elements of water added to both sides. The Brønsted definition of a base, then, is *that it is a proton (hydrogen-ion) acceptor*. This applies even in the case of NH_4OH, where the reaction may be conceived as $NH_4OH + HCl \rightleftharpoons NH_4OH_2^+ + Cl^-$, with subsequent decomposition of the $NH_4OH_2^+$

$$NH_4OH_2^+ \rightleftharpoons NH_4^+ + H_2O$$

and in the case of NaOH, where only the OH^- is considered to be the base, and the OH^- is the proton acceptor

$$HCl + OH^- \rightleftharpoons HOH + Cl^-$$

In actual fact, of course, HCl in aqueous solution exists as OH_3^+ (oxonium ion) $+ Cl^-$; and just as only the OH^- in NaOH is the base, so only the OH_3^+ in aqueous HCl is to be considered the acid

$$H_2O + HCl \rightleftharpoons OH_3^+ + Cl^-$$

This reaction can be seen to be the equivalent of the reaction given above between NH_3 and HCl. In this case it can be seen that the acid HCl is reacting with the base H_2O, the H_2O and OH_3^+ playing the same roles as the NH_3 and NH_4^+ respectively. The acidic reactions of an aqueous acid solution are due to the presence of oxonium ion, e.g.

$$OH_3^+ + NH_3 \rightleftharpoons H_2O + NH_4^+$$
$$2\,OH_3^+ + Mg \rightarrow Mg^{+2} + H_2 + 2\,H_2O$$

and so forth. Indeed, the similar ammonium ion can also act as an acid, although a weaker one than OH_3^+. Thus magnesium metal dissolves in aqueous ammonium salt solutions according to the equation

$$2\,NH_4^+ + Mg \rightarrow Mg^{+2} + H_2 + 2\,NH_3$$

It can also be seen that no stipulation has been made that an acid or base must be a neutral molecule. On the contrary, both neutral and charged species have been used as examples, the *only* stipulation being that an acid be a proton donor and a base a proton acceptor. (Even this definition is too narrow for some purposes.) The following are some examples of acids and bases of varying charge

$$\text{acids}\begin{cases} NH_4{}^+ \rightleftharpoons H^+ + NH_3 \\ H_3PO_4 \rightleftharpoons H^+ + H_2PO_4{}^- \\ AuCl_3 + H_2O \rightleftharpoons H^+ + AuCl_3OH^- \\ H_2PO_4{}^- \rightleftharpoons H^+ + HPO_4{}^{-2} \\ Zn(H_2O)(OH)_3{}^- \rightleftharpoons H^+ + Zn(OH)_4{}^{-2} \end{cases}$$

$$\text{bases}\begin{cases} H_2NNH_3{}^+ + H^+ \rightleftharpoons H_3NNH_3{}^{+2} \\ PbOH^+ + H^+ \rightleftharpoons Pb^{+2} + H_2O \\ NH_3 + H^+ \rightleftharpoons NH_4{}^+ \\ H_2PO_4{}^- + H^+ \rightleftharpoons H_3PO_4 \\ PO_4{}^{-3} + H^+ \rightleftharpoons HPO_4{}^{-2} \end{cases}$$

It can now be seen from these examples that, if an acid ($H_2PO_4{}^-$, for example) loses a proton to form $HPO_4{}^{-2}$, the product is capable of taking a proton back again to form the original substance. The product of ionization of an acid (the $HPO_4{}^{-2}$, in this case) is therefore a base. Thus for each acid there is a "conjugate" base, and each base has its conjugate acid. The relationship $pK_A + pK_B = 14$ must hold for any pair of conjugate acids and bases *in water solution.*

It follows that in any neutralization, or acid-base, reaction *two* acids and *two* bases are involved: the original acid, the original base, the product acid, and the product base. That is

$$\text{acid}_1 + \text{base}_1 \rightleftharpoons \text{base}_2 + \text{acid}_2$$

or, to cite specific examples:

$$\underset{\text{acid}_1}{HCl} + \underset{\text{base}_1}{NH_3} \rightleftharpoons \underset{\text{base}_2}{Cl^-} + \underset{\text{acid}_2}{NH_4{}^+}$$

$$\underset{\text{acid}_1}{N_2H_6{}^{+2}} + \underset{\text{base}_1}{H_2O} \rightleftharpoons \underset{\text{base}_2}{N_2H_5{}^+} + \underset{\text{acid}_2}{OH_3{}^+}$$

$$\underset{\text{acid}_1}{NH_4{}^+} + \underset{\text{base}_1}{CO_3{}^{-2}} \rightleftharpoons \underset{\text{base}_2}{NH_3} + \underset{\text{acid}_2}{HCO_3{}^-}$$

$$\underset{\text{acid}_1}{H_2PO_4{}^-} + \underset{\text{base}_1}{OH^-} \rightleftharpoons \underset{\text{base}_2}{HPO_4{}^{-2}} + \underset{\text{acid}_2}{H_2O}$$

$$\underset{\text{acid}_1}{OH_3{}^+} + \underset{\text{base}_1}{OH^-} \rightleftharpoons \underset{\text{base}_2}{H_2O} + \underset{\text{acid}_2}{H_2O}$$

$$\underset{\text{acid}_1}{H_2PO_4{}^-} + \underset{\text{base}_1}{PO_4{}^{-3}} \rightleftharpoons \underset{\text{base}_2}{HPO_4{}^{-2}} + \underset{\text{acid}_2}{HPO_4{}^{-2}}$$

$$\underset{\text{acid}_1}{H_2S} + \underset{\text{base}_1}{S^{-2}} \rightleftharpoons \underset{\text{base}_2}{HS^-} + \underset{\text{acid}_2}{HS^-}$$

Whether an acid in water is weak or strong depends solely on how far to the right lies the equilibrium $HA + H_2O \rightleftharpoons H_3O^+ + A^-$. The same applies to bases: $B + H_2O \rightleftharpoons BH^+ + OH^-$.

5-10.   Ampholytes

It can be seen that many substances (not the least important of which is water itself) are capable of being both acid and base. Thus a solution of NaH_2PO_4 contains, in addition to $H_2PO_4^-$, some H_3PO_4 and HPO_4^{-2} (not to mention minute concentrations of such species as $H_4PO_4^+$ and PO_4^{-3}). Substances of this sort are called *amphoteric*; i.e., they are ampholytes. The K_A and K_B of any ampholyte are characteristics of the particular ampholyte and bear no specific relationship to each other (unlike the case of the conjugate acid-base pair). Although, if ampholyte A is a stronger acid than ampholyte B, it may *generally* be said that ampholyte A will be a weaker base than ampholyte B, this is *not necessarily* or invariably so. For example, Table 5-7 shows that the dihydrogen phosphate ion is at the same time a weaker acid *and* a weaker base than the hydrogen sebacate ion.

TABLE 5-7.

Substance	pK_A	pK_B
$H_2PO_4^-$	7.2	11.9
$HC_{10}H_{16}O_4^-$	5.5	9.5

Whether this *rather unusual* situation may exist will depend upon the particular details of the structures of the substances.

Almost all substances are capable, under extreme conditions, of acting as ampholytes. Very frequently, however, only the basic or the acidic function is important in aqueous solution. For example, ammonia is normally considered to be a base in aqueous solution, the equilibrium constant for the basic ionization, $NH_3 + H_2O \rightleftharpoons NH_4^+ + OH^-$, being 1.8×10^{-5}. Nevertheless, ammonia does undergo ionization as an acid in aqueous solution, $NH_3 + H_2O \rightleftharpoons OH_3^+ + NH_2^-$, with an ionization constant about 10^{-30}. This constant is so small that the degree of ionization as an acid is ordinarily completely negligible. It can be calculated that the concentration of amide ion, $[NH_2^-]$, in a 0.1 M NH_4OH solution is about 10^{-20} M. This is nevertheless sufficient to precipitate certain extremely insoluble amides from aqueous solutions of ammonia, e.g., $HgNH_2Cl$.

(In a 0.1 M NH_4OH solution, the $[NH_4^+] = [OH^-] = 1.3 \times 10^{-3}$ M.

$$\frac{X^2}{0.1} = 1.8 \times 10^{-5}; \quad X = [OH^-] = 1.3 \times 10^{-3} \ M$$

Therefore

$$[H^+] = \frac{10^{-14}}{[OH^-]} = 7.7 \times 10^{-12} \ M$$

and

$$\frac{[H^+][NH_2^-]}{[NH_3]} = \frac{(7.7 \times 10^{-12})[NH_2^-]}{0.1} = 10^{-30}$$

so that

$$[NH_2^-] = 1.3 \times 10^{-20} \ M)$$

Likewise, substances normally considered to be acids may act as bases. Thus nitrous acid, HNO_2 or $NOOH$, whose acid ionization constant is 5×10^{-4} for the reaction $HNO_2 \rightleftharpoons H^+ + NO_2^-$, nevertheless, in very concentrated aqueous solutions of strong acids, produces sufficient nitrosonium ions by the reaction $HNO_2 \rightleftharpoons NO^+ + OH^-$, $K_B = 7 \times 10^{-19}$, to precipitate fairly insoluble nitrosonium salts, such as $NOHSO_4$, $NOClO_4$, $NOBF_4$, and so forth.

5–11. Indicators

A special class of weak acids and bases is that in which the ionized form has a different color from the un-ionized form. Since small concentrations of these substances will therefore change color over a short pH range, by going from one color form to the other as the pH changes, they are of great utility for determination of the pH of solutions, or as indicators to show neutralization of an acid by a base, or vice versa. Indicators may be either inorganic or organic, but by far the most useful and abundant are the organic ones. (An inorganic indicator with which you are familiar is the yellow chromate ion, which changes to orange dichromate in acidic solution:

$$\tfrac{1}{2} Cr_2O_7^{-2} + \tfrac{1}{2} H_2O \rightleftharpoons H^+ + CrO_4^{-2}$$

Unfortunately, the color change in this case is not distinctive enough to be useful.) The color changes of organic indicators, on the other hand, are distinctive and observable at low concentrations. Some of them are bases (e.g., methyl violet, which is violet as the free base and yellow as the salt), while some are acids (e.g., trinitrobenzene, which is colorless as the free acid but red-orange as the salt). The basic indicators may be considered to be weak bases, subject to the equilibrium $Ind + H^+ \rightleftharpoons IndH^+$, while the acids undergo $IndH \rightleftharpoons H^+ + Ind^-$.

It can be seen that when the hydrogen-ion concentration is exactly equal to K_A (pH $= pK_A$) for an acidic indicator, or when the hydroxide-ion concentration is exactly equal to K_B (pOH $= pK_B$) if the indicator is a base, then there must be equal concentrations of the ionized and un-ionized forms, or in other words, the indicator is exactly half neutralized. This will be halfway in the color change for the indicator and will usually constitute the "endpoint" for a titration using it. Thus the pK_A for trinitrobenzene is about 12.5.

$$\frac{[H^+][C_6H_2N_3O_6^-]}{[HC_6H_2N_3O_6]} = 3 \times 10^{-13}$$

pH $= 12.5$ is $[H^+] = 3 \times 10^{-13}$ M.
Therefore,

$$\frac{(3 \times 10^{-13})\,[C_6H_2N_3O_6^-]}{[HC_6H_2N_3O_6]} = 3 \times 10^{-13}$$

or
$$[C_6H_2N_3O_6^-] = [HC_6H_2N_3O_6]$$

Litmus, one of the earliest known indicators, changes from red to blue when the pH changes from 5 to 8. Litmus is thus very useful in changing color so close to neutrality (pH = 7), but the change is too gradual (i.e., over too wide a range) for litmus to be a very accurate indicator. A list of useful indicators is given in Fig. 5–3.

5–12. The Elements of the Acid-Insoluble Sulfide Group—(A) Those having Non-Amphoteric Sulfides

The location in the periodic table of the elements occurring in the acid-insoluble sulfide group has been discussed in Section 5–1. Of the individual ones to be considered, the elements copper, mercury, and lead have already been discussed in Chapter 4. The ones forming non-amphoteric sulfides which remain to be discussed are cadmium and bismuth. Some physical constants for these elements are given in Table 5–8. Since these two elements are not closely related, they will be discussed individually.

Cadmium is an analogue of mercury and is like it in many respects. Unlike mercury, it does not have a stable +1 state. Its basicity is greater and its complex-forming power is less than those of mercury, both properties being a reflection of its considerably lower electronegativity. Its abundance is approximately the same as that of mercury, but because of its much greater

TABLE 5–8. SOME PHYSICAL PROPERTIES OF CADMIUM AND BISMUTH

	Cadmium	*Bismuth*
Symbol	Cd	Bi
Origin of Name	Gr. *Kadmia*, earth	Ger. *Weisse Masse*, white mass (Wismuth)
Atomic Number	48	83
Atomic Weight	112.41	209.00
Melting Point, °C	320.9	271
Boiling Point, °C	767	1420
Hardness (Moh)	2.0	2.5
Density (g/ml)	8.6	9.8
Radius of Cd^{+2}, Bi^{+3} (Å)	0.99	1.20
Electronegativity	1.5	1.8 (Bi^{+3}), 2.2 (Bi^{+5})
Color	Silver-white (bluish tinge)	Gray-white (reddish tinge)
Abundance in earth's crust (%)	2×10^{-7}	10^{-8}
Standard electrode potential (volts)	$+0.403$ ($Cd \rightleftharpoons Cd^{+2} + 2\,e^-$)	-0.43 ($Bi \rightleftharpoons Bi^{+3} + 3\,e^-$) -0.32 ($Bi + H_2O \rightarrow BiO^+ + 2\,H^+ + 3\,e^-$) ≈ -1.6 ($BiO^+ + 2\,H_2O \rightarrow HBiO_3 + 3\,H^+ + 2\,e^-$)

chemical similarity to zinc (which is about two hundred times more abundant), it usually occurs as an impurity in zinc ores, whereas mercury has its

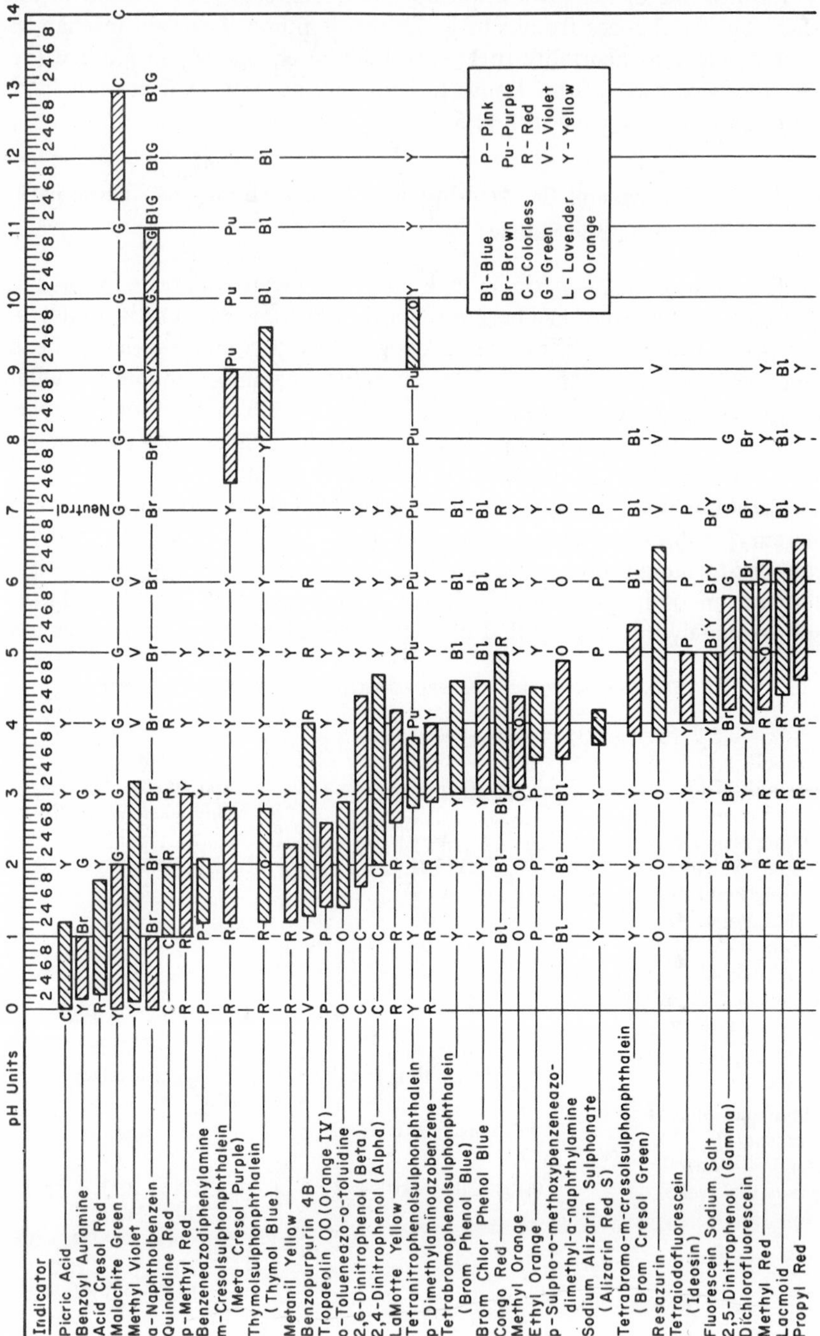

pH Units

Neutral

Legend:

Bl – Blue	P – Pink
Br – Brown	Pu – Purple
C – Colorless	R – Red
G – Green	V – Violet
L – Lavender	Y – Yellow
O – Orange	

Indicator

Picric Acid
Benzoyl Auramine
Acid Cresol Red
Malachite Green
Methyl Violet
α-Naphtholbenzein
Quinaldine Red
p-Methyl Red
Benzeneazodiphenylamine
m-Cresolsulphonphthalein
(Meta Cresol Purple)
Thymolsulphonphthalein
(Thymol Blue)
Metanil Yellow
Benzopurpurin 4B
Tropaeolin OO (Orange IV)
o-Toluenazo-o-toluidine
2,6-Dinitrophenol (Beta)
2,4-Dinitrophenol (Alpha)
LaMotte Yellow
Tetranitrophenolsulphonphthalein
p-Dimethylaminoazobenzene
Tetrabromophenolsulphonphthalein
(Brom Phenol Blue)
Brom Chlor Phenol Blue
Congo Red
Methyl Orange
Ethyl Orange
p-Sulpho-o-methoxybenzeneazo-
dimethyl-α-naphthylamine
Sodium Alizarin Sulphonate
(Alizarin Red S)
Tetrabromo-m-cresolsulphonphthalein
(Brom Cresol Green)
Resazurin
Tetraiodofluorescein
(Ideosin)
Fluorescein Sodium Salt
2,5-Dinitrophenol (Gamma)
Dichlorofluorescein
Methyl Red
Lacmoid
Propyl Red

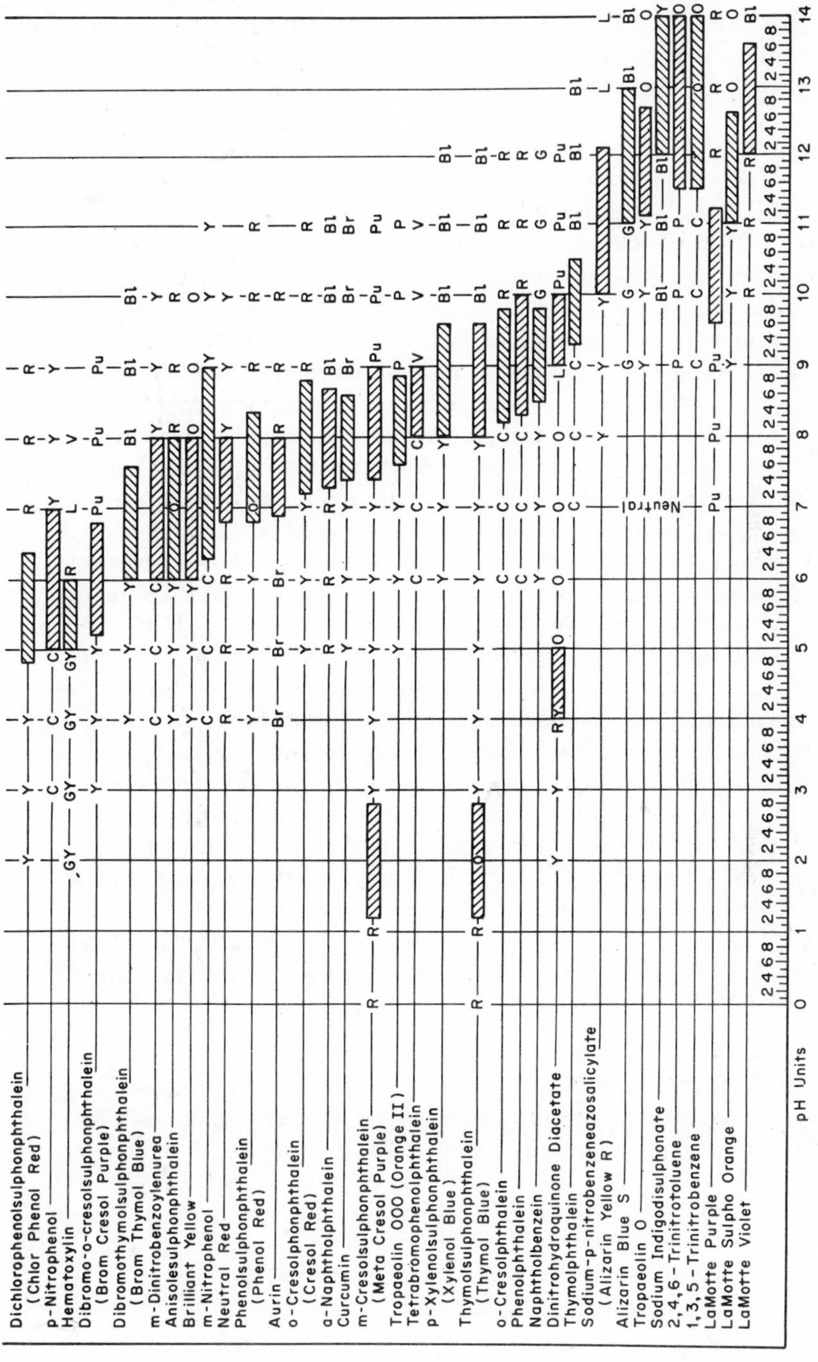

Fig. 5-3. Hydrogen Ion Indicator Chart. Reproduced by Permission of Fisher Scientific Company.

own characteristic ores. As can be seen from Table 5–8, cadmium lies slightly above, and bismuth slightly below, hydrogen in the electromotive series. Like the other elements in this part of the periodic table, then, the free forms are not very reactive and the compounds are easily reduced to the elemental form.

Despite the almost identical electronegativities of cadmium and zinc, $Cd(OH)_2$ is more soluble (and a stronger base) than $Zn(OH)_2$, and CdS is less soluble than ZnS. Whereas both $Hg(OH)_2$ and $Zn(OH)_2$ are amphoteric, $Cd(OH)_2$ seems to be almost exclusively basic.

In common with the copper-family elements and zinc (and mercury), cadmium lies within the region of the periodic table where ammine complexes are formed. The complexes of Zn^{+2}, Cd^{+2}, and Hg^{+2} have the form $M(NH_3)_4^{+2}$. As will be noted below, bismuth lies outside this region, and this fact is frequently used to separate cadmium (and copper) from bismuth.

Since cadmium is less electronegative than the elements discussed in Chapter 4, its compounds tend to be somewhat more ionized and soluble. It nevertheless shows weak complex-forming ability, as can be seen by reference to Table 4–2. The solubilities of some cadmium compounds are given in Table A11–6. It can be seen that the solubilities of the salts of strong acids (bromate, bromide, chlorate, chloride, iodide, nitrate, and sulfate) are high, while, with the exception of the acetate (compare with $Hg(C_2H_3O_2)_2$), the solubilities of the salts of weak acids (carbonate, cyanide, fluoride, hydroxide, iodate, oxalate, sulfide, and tungstate) are low. Because of the low electronegativity of cadmium, neither its hydroxide nor its sulfide is amphoteric. It therefore follows copper and bismuth in the analytical scheme.

Bismuth is the heaviest and most metallic member of the nitrogen family. Its basicity is the greatest of any member of the family, but it is still much less basic than cadmium, and more nearly comparable in basicity and complexing power to mercury. (This is in conformity with the electronegativities of these elements.)

The hydroxide, $Bi(OH)_3$, is such a weak base that the principal characteristic of the normal salts of bismuth, BiX_3, is their hydrolysis in water solution to give basic or "bismuthyl" salts, which are mostly insoluble.

$$BiX_3 + H_2O \rightleftharpoons BiOX \text{ (s)} + 2 H^+ + 2 X^-$$

Besides the bismuthyl salts listed in Table A11–6, also known are bismuthyl bromide, BiOBr; carbonate $(BiO)_2CO_3$; chlorate and perchlorate, $BiOClO_4 \cdot H_2O$ (hygroscopic, loses its water at 80–100°); dichromate, $(BiO)_2Cr_2O_7$; fluoride, BiOF; iodide, BiOI; nitrate, $BiONO_3 \cdot H_2O$; nitrite, $BiONO_2 \cdot \frac{1}{2} H_2O$; and a sulfate, $(BiO)_2SO_4$. All of these salts are insoluble in water but dissolve in an excess of the acid from which they are derived. In most cases, except probably in concentrated $HClO_4$, the solutions do not contain Bi^{+3}, but rather the complex anion related to the acid.

$$BiOCl \text{ (s)} + 2 H^+ + 3 Cl^- \rightleftharpoons BiCl_4^- + H_2O$$
$$BiOC_2H_3O_2 \text{ (s)} + 3 HC_2H_3O_2 \rightleftharpoons Bi(C_2H_3O_2)_4^- + H_3O^+$$

The complexing power of F^- for bismuth is very low, and the fluoride consequently dissolves only in very concentrated HF.

$$BiF_3 \text{ (s)} + HF + H_2O \rightleftharpoons BiF_4^- + OH_3^+$$

Despite the relatively high electronegativity of bismuth, it is still not high enough for bismuth hydroxide and sulfide to be amphoteric. Also, bismuth lies outside the region of the periodic table in which the elements form ammine complexes in aqueous solution. Consequently, bismuth follows copper and cadmium in the analytical scheme, but is separated from them by the fact that, while copper and cadmium form $Cu(NH_3)_4^{+2}$ and $Cd(NH_3)_4^{+2}$ with NH_4OH, bismuth precipitates as $Bi(OH)_3$.

Bismuth, like the other members of the nitrogen family (compare arsenic and antimony, Section 5–13), exhibits a pentavalent state in which it is more electronegative and more acidic than in the trivalent state. It is much less easily attained and much less well-defined, however. It is known in the pentafluoride, BiF_5, and the corresponding hexafluorobismuthates, BiF_6^-, both of which are hydrolyzed by water. In concentrated aqueous HF, pentavalent bismuth is probably present as the pentafluorohydroxybismuthate ion, BiF_5OH^-. Other compounds of pentavalent bismuth include Bi_2O_5, Bi_2O_4 (probably $(Bi^{III}O)(Bi^VO_3)$) and the slightly soluble sodium bismuthate, $NaBiO_3$. This is an important and powerful oxidizing agent, in acidic solution even being able to oxidize manganese(II) ion to permanganate

$$2\,Mn^{+2} + 5\,NaBiO_3 \text{ (s)} + 14\,H^+ \rightarrow 2\,MnO_4^- + 5\,Bi^{+3} + 5\,Na^+ + 7\,H_2O$$

5–13. The Elements of the Acid-Insoluble Sulfide Group—(B) Those having Amphoteric Sulfides

The elements in this group are all somewhat more electronegative than the preceding ones and are therefore amphoteric in nature. The electronegativity of molybdenum is high by reason of its high oxidation state ($+6$), while the others have high electronegativity because of their position in the periodic table. (Molybdenum has already been discussed in Section 4–8.)

The elements arsenic, antimony, and tin lie together in the periodic table among the metalloids—those elements which are neither good metals nor good nonmetals. Arsenic is the least and tin the most metallic of the three.

All of these elements occur in easily reducible ores and arsenic and antimony occasionally occur native. They were all known to the ancients. Although none of them is especially abundant, they all occur in well-defined and easily worked ores.

Because of their relatively high electronegativities their hydroxides and sulfides (except that SnS does not dissolve in excess alkali sulfide) are amphoteric, their salts suffer extensive hydrolysis, and they tend to exist in aqueous solution as complex ions. They are, however, all outside the area of the periodic table where ammine complexes are formed.

TABLE 5–9. PHYSICAL PROPERTIES OF ARSENIC, ANTIMONY, AND TIN

	Arsenic	*Antimony*	*Tin*
Symbol	As	Sb	Sn
Origin of Name	Gr. *arsenikon*, yellow orpiment	L. *antimonium*; L. *stibium*, mark	A.S. *tin*; L. *stannum*
Atomic Number	33	51	50
Atomic Weight	74.91	121.76	118.70
Melting Point (°C)	814 (36 atm)	630.5	231.9
Boiling Point (°C)	610 (subl.)	1440	2337
Hardness (Moh)	3.5	3.0–3.3	1.5–1.8
Density (g/ml)	5.7 (gray) 3.9 (yellow)	6.58 (gray) 5.3 (yellow)	9.8
Radii of Ions (Å)	0.69 (As^{+3}) 0.47 (As^{+5})	0.90 (Sb^{+3}) 0.62 (Sb^{+5})	1.02 (Sn^{+2}) 0.65 (Sn^{+4})
Electronegativity	2.0 (As^{+3})	1.8 (Sb^{+3}) 2.1 (Sb^{+5})	1.55 (Sn^{+2}) 1.8 (Sn^{+4})
Color of Metal	Steel-gray	Blue-white	Silvery-white (or gray < 18°C)
Abundance in earth's crust (%)	10^{-6}	10^{-7}	10^{-6}
Standard electrode potential (metal → M^{+n} + ne^-) (volts)	−0.2475 (→ $HAsO_2$ (aq))	−0.212 (→ SbO^+)	+0.136 (→ Sn^{+2})
(M^{+n} → M^{+n+2} + 2 e^-)	−0.559 (→ H_3AsO_4 (aq))	−0.64 (→ Sb_2O_5 (s))	−0.15 (→ Sn^{+4})

In their trivalent states, arsenic and antimony are like bismuth, but are of course less basic. Thus the trihalides (except SbF_3) hydrolyze in water giving the basic compounds MOX and more complicated hydrolysis products, which, especially in the case of antimony, are extremely insoluble, even dissolving in acids sometimes with extreme difficulty. Occasionally, hydrolyzed antimony precipitates are so resistant to the action of acids that it is necessary first to metathesize them to the sulfide, and then dissolve the sulfide in some strongly oxidizing medium such as aqua regia. A typical set of reactions might be

$$Sb_4O_5Cl_2 (s) + 6 H_2S (aq) \rightarrow 2 Sb_2S_3 (s) + 5 H_2O + 2 H^+ + 2 Cl^-$$
$$3 Sb_2S_3 (s) + 10 NO_3^- + 36 Cl^- + 40 H^+ \rightarrow 6 SbCl_6^- + 9 S (s) + 10 NO (g) + 20 H_2O$$

Again, as with bismuth, these elements are usually present in solution as complexes—$AsCl_4^-$, $SbBr_4^-$, and so forth—rather than simple cations. Compounds of arsenic or antimony in acidic solution are reduced by active metals such as zinc to arsine, AsH_3, or stibine, SbH_3. These are poisonous, reactive gases which are very useful in the detection of these elements. If they are allowed to come in contact with $AgNO_3$ solution (as on a filter paper), a dark spot is formed, according to the reactions

$$AsH_3 (g) + 6 Ag^+ + 3 H_2O \rightarrow 6 Ag (s) + H_3AsO_3 + 6 H^+$$
$$SbH_3 (g) + 3 Ag^+ \rightarrow Ag_3Sb (s) + 3 H^+$$

If this reaction is carried out in solution on a mixture of AsH_3 and SbH_3, it can be used to separate the two elements, the antimony being precipitated as Ag_3Sb, while the arsenic stays in solution as H_3AsO_3.

If the reduction is carried out in an alkaline solution with metallic aluminum, the greater sensitivity of stibine to alkali results in its decomposition

$$SbH_3 \text{ (g)} + OH^- + 3\,H_2O \rightarrow Sb(OH)_4^- + 3\,H_2 \text{ (g)}$$

Consequently, from a mixture of arsenic and antimony compounds only AsH_3 will be released. Because of the increased stability of AsO_4^{-3} in alkaline solution, however, only *trivalent* arsenic can be detected in this way. Consequently, if arsenic is present as arsenate it must first be reduced with Na_2SO_3.

The lower (divalent) state of tin is somewhat more basic than the trivalent states of arsenic and antimony, and the sulfide SnS is not amphoteric, in the sense that it will not dissolve in alkali sulfide solutions (although it will dissolve in alkali hydroxide solutions). Nevertheless, its salts are subject to considerable hydrolysis, it tends to form complexes in solution, and the hydroxide is amphoteric. Because $Sn(II)$ is a fairly strong reducing agent, its solutions tend to be unstable in air with respect to oxidation. Consequently, there are always some tin(IV) compounds present in any tin(II) that has stood in contact with the air, and it is preferable to precipitate tin as amphoteric SnS_2, which follows As_2S_3 and Sb_2S_3, rather than as non-amphoteric SnS, which would follow CuS. To this end ammonium poly-sulfide, $(NH_4)_2S_x$, may be used for the separation of arsenic, antimony, and tin from the nonamphoteric sulfides

$$SnS \text{ (s)} + S_2^{-2} \rightarrow SnS_3^{-2}$$

or the tin may be oxidized with H_2O_2 prior to the group precipitation

$$Sn^{+2} + H_2O_2 + 2\,H^+ \rightarrow Sn^{+4} + 2\,H_2O$$

The highest oxidation states of these three elements are characterized by their (weak) acidity. Arsenic acid, H_3AsO_4, is very similar to phosphoric acid, H_3PO_4, in most of its characteristics, except its much greater ease of reduction. The crystalline phosphates and arsenates are generally isomorphous and similar in solubility. Because of the stability of arsenic acid, arsenic in the pentavalent state forms few complexes in aqueous solution. For example, no evidence can be found for the existence of chloro complexes of $As(V)$, even in $10\,M$ HCl. (In concentrated aqueous HF, however, AsF_5OH^- and AsF_6^- exist.) Even the thio complexes form slowly and incompletely. For this reason, even though As_2S_5 readily forms thio anions, it is preferred to reduce arsenic to the trivalent state before the group precipitation, since formation of As_2S_3 from $As(III)$ is rapid and complete. Consequently, before precipitation of the acid-insoluble sulfides, NH_4I is usually added to reduce $As(V)$ to $As(III)$.

$$H_3AsO_4 + 3\,I^- + 2\,H^+ \rightarrow H_3AsO_3 + I_3^- + H_2O$$

Even if insufficient iodide is added to reduce all the As(V), complete reduction is accomplished during the sulfide precipitation because the iodine (or triiodide ion, I_3^-) produced is reduced back to iodide ion by the H_2S and can then reduce more arsenic acid.

$$I_3^- + H_2S \rightarrow 3\,I^- + S\,(s) + 2H^+$$

The iodide ion thus acts as a catalyst for the reduction of As(V) by H_2S.

The only stable simple halide of As(V) is AsF_5. (The compound $AsCl_5$ is very unstable.)

Pentavalent antimony in alkaline solution exists as hexahydroxyantimonate ion, $Sb(OH)_6^-$. This is quite different from PO_4^{-3} and AsO_4^{-3} and consequently crystalline antimonates produced from aqueous solution are never isomorphous with the corresponding phosphates and arsenates, and their solubilities are quite different. In acidic solution, unlike As(V), but like As(III) and Sb(III), Sb(V) is present in the form of complex ions. In HCl solution, there are present ions of the form $[Sb(OH)_{6-x}Cl_x]^-$ which reach $SbCl_6^-$ in concentrated HCl. Thus, unlike As_2S_5, the precipitation of Sb_2S_5 is rapid and quantitative.

The only simple halides of pentavalent antimony known are SbF_5 and $SbCl_5$, both liquids.

Tetravalent tin is very similar to Sb(V). In alkaline solution, it exists as $Sn(OH)_6^{-2}$, whose salts are isomorphous with, and similar in solubility to, the corresponding plumbates, $Pb(OH)_6^{-2}$, platinates, $Pt(OH)_6^{-2}$, and the like. Like Sb_2S_5, SnS_2 is rapidly and completely precipitated by H_2S. Again like antimony, Sn(IV) rarely exists as a simple cation in acidic solution, but usually as complexes, as for example $[Sn(OH)_{6-x}Cl_x]^{-2}$, which reach $SnCl_6^{-2}$ in more concentrated acid. Nevertheless Sn(IV) is more basic than Sb(V) and in very concentrated solutions of noncomplexing acids (e.g., $HClO_4$), the uncomplexed and unhydrolyzed cation, Sn^{+4}—or rather $Sn(H_2O)_6^{+4}$—may exist.

Because of the ease of preparation of Sn(II) and its good reducing properties, tin is usually determined by reducing it to Sn(II) and observing its action on oxidizing agents (I_2 or $KMnO_4$ quantitatively, or $HgCl_2$ qualitatively).

The solubilities of a number of compounds of arsenic, antimony, and tin are listed in Table A11–7. In Table A11–8, the solubilities of some phosphates and arsenates are also given for comparison. The solubilities of antimonates and stannates are known in only a few instances. The solubilities of a number of compounds containing these elements in the anion are given in Table A11–9, along with certain other similar compounds for comparison.

5–14. Illustrative Experiments

The following experiments are designed to illustrate the relationship just discussed. Recall experiment 2 in Section 4–10.

1. Put into the same test tube 1 ml each of 0.1 M $Hg(NO_3)_2$, $Cu(NO_3)_2$, and $Cd(NO_3)_2$. Add 15 drops of 1 M thioacetamide solution and heat in a water bath for 10 minutes. Centrifuge, discard the supernate, and wash the precipitate thoroughly with water to remove NO_3^-. Pour 2 ml of 6 M HCl over the precipitate, mix thoroughly, and centrifuge. Decant the HCl solution into a clean test tube, neutralize with NH_4OH, and add just enough HCl to make 0.2 molar in H^+. Add 5 drops of thioacetamide and heat. Explain the result.

Wash the residue remaining after the HCl treatment several times with water to remove all Cl^-. To the washed residue, add 1 ml of 3 M HNO_3 and heat for several minutes. Centrifuge, remove the supernate to a clean test tube, and to it add excess NH_4OH. Explain.

2. Make up 5 ml each of the following HCl solutions: 6 M, 2 M, 0.2 M, 0.02 M, and 0.002 M. Add 1 ml of each to 1 ml of each of the following solutions: 0.1 M Cd^{+2}, 0.1 M Cu^{+2}, 0.1 M Zn^{+2}. What are the concentrations of H^+ and metal ion in each of these fifteen solutions? Add 10 drops of thioacetamide to each of these and mix. Heat for 10 minutes in a boiling water bath. Record your observations in a chart similar to that used for experiment 16, Section 4–10.

3. Prepare $Pb(NO_3)_2$ solutions of the following concentrations: (a) 0.01 M, by adding 9 ml of water to 1 ml of 0.1 M $Pb(NO_3)_2$, (b) 0.001 M, by adding 9 ml of water to 1 ml of solution (a), and in like manner (c) 0.0001 M, (d) 10^{-5} M, and (e) 10^{-6} M. To 2 ml of each of these solutions add 10 drops of thioacetamide and heat for ten minutes in the boiling water bath. Cool. Note the limiting concentration which gives a distinct coloration. From the ionization constants of H_2S, and assuming the concentration of H_2S to be 0.1 molar, calculate the K_{sp} of PbS. Is there any evidence of supersaturation of PbS?

4. Make up a chart with a column for each of the ions Hg^{+2}, Pb^{+2}, Bi^{+3}, Cu^{+2}, Cd^{+2}, $AsCl_4^-$, AsO_4^{-3}, MoO_4^{-2}, $SbCl_4^-$, $SbCl_6^-$, Sn^{+2}, and $SnCl_6^{-2}$, and a row for each of the reagents 1 M NH_4I, 3 percent H_2O_2, 6 M NaOH, 6 M NaOH in excess, 3 M NH_4OH, 3 M NH_4OH in excess, 0.1 M NaCl, and thioacetamide in hot 0.3 M HCl. From your knowledge of the chemistry of these elements, fill in the information. If you are not familiar with any particular reaction, devise an experiment which will give you the data you need.

5. Prepare some fresh HgS in each of three test tubes. To each precipitate add 10 drops of 1 M thioacetamide. To one tube add 2 ml of 15 M NH_4OH, to the next 2 ml of 6 M NaOH, and to the third 2 ml of 6 M KOH. Heat. Explain your observations.

6. From your knowledge of the chemistry of these elements construct a chart showing the action of 0.3 M HCl, dilute HNO_3, aqua regia, $(NH_4)_2S$, $(NH_4)_2S_x$, K_2S, and K_2S_x on HgS, PbS, Bi_2S_3, CuS, CdS, As_2S_3, MoS_3, Sb_2S_3, SnS, and SnS_2. Perform any experiments necessary to obtain information not already known to you.

7. Devise some experiments to show the hydrolysis of salts of As(III), Sb(III), Sn(IV), and Bi(III), and whether the hydrolysis is reversible.

8. Devise and carry out experiments to establish the relative concentrations of Cu^{+2} in solutions or suspensions of $CuCl_2$, CuC_2O_4, $Cu(OH)_2$, $Cu(NH_3)_4^{+2}$, and CuS.

9. Make up a solution containing 1 ml of 0.1 M Hg^{+2}, 4 ml of 0.1 M

NCS⁻, and 1 ml 2 M $NaC_2H_3O_2$. If the solution is not clear, add just enough more NCS⁻ to clarify it. Add 10 drops of this solution to 10 drops of each of the following solutions in individual test tubes: 0.1 M Co^{+2}, 0.1 M Cu^{+2}, 0.1 M Cd^{+2}, 0.1 M Ni^{+2}, 0.1 M Pb^{+2}, 0.1 M Bi^{+3}, and 0.1 M Zn^{+2}. Explain. What useful tests could be devised from these reactions?

10. To each of two test tubes, add 2 drops of 0.1 M Na_2SO_4 solution. To one add 2 drops of 0.1 M Ba^{+2} and to the other add 2 drops of 0.1 M Pb^{+2}. To each tube add 3 M $NH_4C_2H_3O_2$ dropwise, until a distinct reaction has occurred in one of the tubes. Explain.

11. To a test tube containing 10 drops of 0.1 M Cd^{+2} and 10 drops of 0.1 M Cu^{+2}, add 1 drop of 6 M HCl and then a pinch of solid sodium dithionite, $Na_2S_2O_4$. Heat. Centrifuge. If any blue color remains in solution, add more dithionite and heat again. Centrifuge. What is the precipitate? Assuming the other product of the reaction to be SO_2, write an equation for the reaction. Remove the colorless supernate, add 10 drops of 1 M thioacetamide and heat. What is the precipitate? Explain.

12. Prepare six strips of filter paper wet with 0.1 M $AgNO_3$ solution. Obtain six small wads of cotton or glass wool. To a series of six test tubes, add individually 10 drops of (a) and (b) 0.1 M Na_3AsO_4, (c) and (d) 0.1 M $AsCl_4^-$, (e) and (f) 0.1 M $SbCl_4^-$. To (a), (c), and (e) add 10 drops of 6 M HCl and 1 ml of water. To (b), (d), and (f) add sufficient 6 M NaOH to redissolve any precipitate which forms, and then add 1 ml more. To (a), (c), and (e) add a few pieces of arsenic-free zinc metal and immediately plug the tubes loosely with the cotton to prevent spattering; place a strip of moist $AgNO_3$ paper over the mouth of each tube. To (b), (d), and (f) add a few pieces of metallic aluminum, immediately inserting the cotton plugs, and covering with $AgNO_3$ paper. Explain the results. Why is haste necessary? What other gas is produced?

13. To four test tubes, containing (a) 10 drops of 0.1 M Na_3PO_4, (b) 10 drops of 0.1 M Na_3AsO_4, (c) 10 drops of 0.1 M $KSb(OH)_6$, and (d) 10 drops of 0.1 M $(NH_4)_2MoO_4$, add 1 ml of "magnesia mixture" (Mg^{+2} in buffered NH_4OH). Allow the solution to stand at least 10 minutes, with shaking. Explain your observations.

14. To each of five test tubes, add two drops of fresh 0.1 M Sn^{+2}. To test tube (a) add 2 ml of H_2O, to (b) 2 ml of 6 M HCl, to (c) 2 ml of 12 M HCl, to (d) 2 ml of 5 M NH_4Cl and to (e) 2 ml of H_2O and excess solid NH_4Cl. Stir tube (e) until no more NH_4Cl dissolves. Now add 2 drops of 0.1 M $HgCl_2$ to each tube and observe the results for a minute or two. Explain the results.

15. Precipitate some $Bi(OH)_3$ in a tube and discard the supernate. In another tube, make 1 ml of 0.1 M Sn^{+2} strongly alkaline with excess 6 M NaOH. Pour half of the NaOH solution into the $Bi(OH)_3$; immediately stopper the tube containing the remaining half, label it, and set it aside in your desk. Observe the $Bi(OH)_3$. Write the equations for what has happened. Wait until the next laboratory period and examine the NaOH solution in the stoppered tube. What is the precipitate? Centrifuge. Treat some freshly precipitated $Bi(OH)_3$ with the supernate. Explain your observations.

16. Put 2 drops of 0.1 M $SbCl_4^-$ into a test tube, and add 10 drops of H_2O. Make the solution ammoniacal and then add just enough 6 M acetic acid to

make the solution acidic. Add one drop more. Ignoring any precipitate which forms, heat the solution almost to boiling, and add a few crystals of sodium thiosulfate, $Na_2S_2O_3 \cdot 5 H_2O$. Allow the test tube to stand *without shaking* for at least five minutes. The orange-red oxysulfide, Sb_2OS_2, formed at the interface is very characteristic of antimony.

17. To 1 ml of 0.1 M $(NH_4)_2MoO_4$ solution, add 10 drops of 15 M HNO_3 and 5 drops of 0.1 M Na_2HPO_4. Warm, but *do not boil*. What is the precipitate? Repeat, using Na_3AsO_4 instead of Na_2HPO_4.

18. To 5 drops of 0.1M $(NH_4)_2MoO_4$ add 10 drops of 1 M NCS^-, 10 drops of 12 M HCl, and then 5 drops of 0.1 M Sn^{+2}. Explain your observations.

5-15.   Analysis of the Acid-Insoluble Sulfide Group

The species usually to be found in this group (as restricted in Section 5-1) are Hg^{+2} or $HgCl_4^{-2}$, Pb^{+2}, $BiCl_4^-$ or BiO^+, Cu^{+2}, Cd^{+2}, H_3AsO_4, $AsCl_4^-$, $SbCl_4^-$, Sn^{+2}, $SnCl_6^{-2}$, and H_2MoO_4. If the solution is the supernate from the precipitation of the insoluble-chloride group, then many of the elements will be present as chloro complexes. For simplicity's sake, these will be referred to henceforth as simple ions.

5-A. Group Precipitation. If the solution to be analyzed for this group of elements is not the supernate from the precipitation of the insoluble chloride group, determine its pH. If it is alkaline, smell to determine whether ammonia is present. If the solution is ammoniacal and clear, Hg^{+2}, Pb^{+2}, and Bi^{+3} must be absent. If it is ammoniacal and colorless Cu^{+2} must be absent. If it is alkaline and clear, but not ammoniacal, Hg^{+2}, Bi^{+3}, Cu^{+2}, and Cd^{+2} must be absent. Any elements which can be eliminated on these or similar grounds need not, of course, be tested for, thus allowing simplification of the analytical scheme.

Make the solution acidic to litmus with 6 M HCl, if it is not already acidic. (The pH should be <1.) To 3 ml of the acidified solution, add 5 drops of 3 percent H_2O_2, and heat in the boiling water bath. After the bubbles of oxygen from the decomposition of the H_2O_2

$$2 H_2O_2 \rightarrow 2 H_2O + O_2$$

no longer are evolved, add one drop of 1 M NH_4I solution. (From the nature of any reaction observed at this point, inferences may be made about what is in the solution.) Adjust the acidity to 0.3 M H^+ with methyl violet paper by adding dilute NH_4OH or HCl. Add 15 drops of 1 M thioacetamide solution and continue to heat for 10 minutes. Cool. Test the acidity. If it is not now at 0.3 M H^+, adjust to 0.3 M and heat again. In any event, add a few more drops of thioacetamide and heat to test for completeness of precipitation. When precipitation is complete, cool, centrifuge, and discard the supernate, or save it for analysis of the alkali-insoluble sulfide and hydroxide groups (7-A). Wash the precipitated sulfides well with water at least twice. Test the washes with a little $AgNO_3$ solution and continue washing until no more Cl^- remains. (The presence of Cl^- would interfere with the subsequent separation of HgS from the other nonamphoteric sulfides by formation of aqua regia.)

5-B. Separation of the Amphoteric and Non-Amphoteric Sulfides. Suspend the sulfides in 3 ml of 9 M NH_4OH (1 ml 15 M NH_4OH + 2 ml. 6 M NH_4OH)

TABLE 5–10. SCHEMATIC OUTLINE FOR THE ANALYSIS OF THE ACID-INSOLUBLE SULFIDE GROUP

Solution: Hg^{+2}, Pb^{+2}, Bi^{+3}, Cu^{+2}, Cd^{+2}, As^{+3}, H_3AsO_4, H_2MoO_4, Sb^{+3}, Sn^{+2}, Sn^{+4}.
Make 0.3 M in H^+. Add 3 percent H_2O_2. Heat. Add 1 M NH_4I. Heat with CH_3CSNH_2. Cool.
Precipitate: HgS, PbS, Bi_2S_3, CuS, CdS, As_2S_3, MoS_3, SnS_2, Sb_2S_3.
Treat with hot ammoniacal CH_3CSNH_2.

Residue: HgS, PbS, Bi_2S_3, CuS, CdS; Treat with 6 M HNO_3				Solution: AsS_3^{-3}, SbS_3^{-3}, SnS_3^{-2}, MoS_4^{-2}; Acidulate with HCl			

Left branch (Residue: HgS, PbS, Bi_2S_3, CuS, CdS; Treat with 6 M HNO_3):

Residue: HgS; Dissolve in aqua regia, Add 0.1 M Sn^{+2}	Solution: Pb^{+2}, Bi^{+3}, Cu^{+2}, Cd^{+2}; Add conc. H_2SO_4 and evaporate	
Precipitate: Hg_2Cl_2 + Hg	Precipitate: $PbSO_4$; Add 3 M NH_4Ac	Solution: Bi^{+3}, Cu^{+2}, Cd^{+2}; Add 15 M NH_4OH
Alternatively, dissolve HgS in aqua regia; Add Co^{+2} and NCS^-	Solution: $PbAc_2$; Add 1 M K_2CrO_4	Precipitate: $Bi(OH)_3$; Add Na_2SnO_2 solution
Precipitate: $CoHg(NCS)_4$	Precipitate: $PbCrO_4$	Precipitate: Bi

Under "Add 15 M NH_4OH" solution branch:

Solution: $Cd(NH_3)_4^{+2}$ $Cu(NH_3)_4^{+2}$ (deep blue indicates Cu^{+2}); Acidulate with HCl; Add $Na_2S_2O_4$

Ppt: Cu

Solution: Cd^{+2}; Make 0.3 M in H^+; Add CH_3CSNH_2; Heat

Ppt: CdS

Right branch (Solution: AsS_3^{-3}, SbS_3^{-3}, SnS_3^{-2}, MoS_4^{-2}; Acidulate with HCl):

Precipitate: As_2S_3, Sb_2S_3, SnS_2, MoS_3; Treat with 6 M HCl

Residue: As_2S_3, MoS_3; Dissolve in aqua regia; Dilute with water; Add magnesia mixture		Solution: Sb^{+3}, Sn^{+4}	
Precipitate: $MgNH_4AsO_4$ Treat with HCl + $NaHSO_3$; Add excess NaOH and Al metal	Solution: H_2MoO_4; Add HCl, KNCS, and $SnCl_2$	Evaporate: Add iron wire (black precipitate: Sb); Remove excess wire; Add $HgCl_2$	Add 6 M NH_4OH; Add 6 M HAc; Add solid $Na_2S_2O_3$
Gas: AsH_3; React with $AgNO_3$	Red solution: Mo complex	Precipitate: Hg_2Cl_2 + Hg (test for Sn)	Red color: Sb_2OS_2
Precipitate: As (test for As)		Alternatively, reduce with Mg instead of Fe; Dip cold crucible in solution; Hold in Bunsen	
		Blue flame: Sn	

Add 15 drops of 1 M thioacetamide and heat for 10 minutes. Centrifuge and remove the supernate to another tube for analysis for Mo, As, Sb, and Sn. Repeat the treatment of the precipitate, adding the supernate to that from the first treatment. The combined supernates are to be treated according to the procedures beginning in (5–I).

5–C. *Isolation of Mercury.* Wash the residue from the above treatment (if there is none, Hg^{+2}, Pb^{+2}, Bi^{+3}, Cu^{+2}, and Cd^{+2} are obviously absent) twice with 3 ml of water containing 5 drops of 4 M NH_4NO_3. (Since sulfides frequently become very intractable on aging, they should be treated immediately.) To the washed residue, add 2 ml of 3 M HNO$_3$, stir, and heat in the water bath, until no more of the residue appears to dissolve. The color of the residue at this point should be black or white, but not brown. (Certain insoluble compounds, such as Hg$_2$S(NO$_3$)$_2$, are white.) Cool, centrifuge, and remove the supernate to another tube (5–E) for tests for Pb^{+2}, Bi^{+3}, Cu^{+2}, and Cd^{+2}. Because this treatment may have formed free sulfur in such a state as to prevent complete dissolution of all the sulfides other than HgS, it is necessary to remove the sulfur and repeat the HNO$_3$ treatment. With the end of a glass rod, remove any particles of sulfur floating in the supernate (5–E), and add them to the residue from the HNO$_3$ treatment. Add to the residue 1 ml of 15 M NH$_4$OH and 10 drops of 1 M thioacetamide and heat. Agitate with a glass rod to aid dissolution of the sulfur. When dissolution appears to be complete, centrifuge, remove and discard the supernate, wash the residue twice with 15 M NH$_4$OH and repeat the HNO$_3$ treatment on any residue which is left. Combine the supernate with (5–E).

5–D. *Confirmation of Mercury(II)*. If a residue remains from the treatment in (5–C), add to it 2 drops of 15 M HNO$_3$ and 10 drops of 12 M HCl. Heat and agitate until most of the residue is dissolved. Add 1 ml of water, centrifuge if necessary, and transfer the liquid to a small casserole. Evaporate the solution over an open flame *in the hood*, stopping when only 2 to 3 drops of liquid remain. If evaporation is carried to dryness, volatile and poisonous HgCl$_2$ will be lost. Add 1 ml of water and transfer to one or two small tubes to perform one or both of the following tests, centrifuging if necessary beforehand.

(a) Add 2 or 3 drops of fresh (check !) 0.1 M SnCl$_2$ solution. The presence of Hg^{+2} is revealed by formation of a white precipitate turning gray. (If copper were present, it would be reduced to white CuCl, but would not turn gray.)

(b) Add 15 drops of 3 M NaC$_2$H$_3$O$_2$ and 5 drops of 0.1 M Co(NO$_3$)$_2$. Stir. Now add with stirring 0.1 M NH$_4$NCS dropwise. A deep-blue precipitate of CoHg(NCS)$_4$ confirms the presence of Hg^{+2}.

5–E. *Isolation and Confirmation of Lead*. The solution (5–E) is transferred to a small casserole. Add 8 drops of 6 M H$_2$SO$_4$ and evaporate *in the hood* until the dense white fumes of SO$_3$ appear. Appearance of SO$_3$ ensures removal of all of the HNO$_3$. This is necessary because HNO$_3$ would interfere with the subsequent precipitation of PbSO$_4$, both through formation of a weak nitrate complex (PbNO$_3^+$, $K_{inst} = 7 \times 10^{-2}$) and through action of the hydrogen ion in the reaction

$$PbSO_4 \text{ (s)} + H^+ \rightleftharpoons Pb^{+2} + HSO_4^-$$

Cool thoroughly and then *very carefully*, with adequate stirring, add 1 ml of water. If white PbSO$_4$ appears, centrifuge. (Too little water added would result in no precipitation because of the high H$_2$SO$_4$ concentration, PbSO$_4$ (s) + H$_2$SO$_4$ $\rightleftharpoons$ Pb^{+2} + 2 HSO$_4^-$. Too much water added may cause precipitation of white (BiO)$_2$SO$_4$, 2 Bi^{+3} + SO$_4^{-2}$ + 2 H$_2$O $\rightleftharpoons$ (BiO)$_2$SO$_4$ (s) + 4 H$^+$.) Transfer the supernate to another test tube (5–F), taking care not to roil the finely divided PbSO$_4$. Wash the precipitate with 1 ml of water to which 2 drops of 6 M H$_2$SO$_4$ have been added. Centrifuge and add the washings to (5–F), again taking care not to roil the precipitate. To the precipitate, add 1 ml of 3 M $NH_4C_2H_3O_2$ and heat. Centrifuge if necessary and discard the precipitate. To the solution, add 2 drops of 1 M K_2CrO_4. The precipitation of yellow $PbCrO_4$ confirms the presence of Pb(II). (Centrifuge the precipitate down to make sure it is really yellow.)

5–F. *Confirmation of Cu(II) and Isolation of Bi(III).* To the supernate from the $PbSO_4$ precipitation add 15 M NH_4OH, dropwise with shaking, until distinctly alkaline and any blue $Cu(OH)_2$ which may have precipitated is redissolved. The deep blue color of $Cu(NH_3)_4^{+2}$ confirms the presence of Cu(II). If a precipitate appears, proceed with (5–G).

5–G. *Confirmation of Bismuth.* Heat the ammoniacal solution if necessary to coagulate any precipitate and centrifuge. Remove the supernate (5–H), and wash the precipitate well with dilute NH_4OH until no blue color can be seen in the washes. Then wash thoroughly with water. Discard the washes. Prepare a sodium stannite solution by adding NaOH to fresh (check!) $SnCl_2$ solution, until the originally formed precipitate dissolves. Pour this onto the suspected $Bi(OH)_3$. Allow to stand at least five minutes if no reaction is immediately apparent. The appearance of black metallic bismuth confirms the presence of Bi(III). The test should be performed even though the precipitate from the ammoniacal solution may be thought to be negligible, since the white $Bi(OH)_3$ may easily escape notice.

5–H. *Removal of Copper and Confirmation of Cadmium. If Cu^{+2} is found to be present* in the solution, proceed as follows: Add dilute HCl until the deep blue of the copper-ammonia complex disappears and any cupric hydroxide has just dissolved. Then, to this solution, add little by little solid sodium dithionite with stirring, until all blue color has disappeared *and* until no further precipitation of red metallic copper takes place. Centrifuge and discard the copper precipitate. To the solution add 15 to 20 drops of 1 M thioacetamide solution and heat for 10 minutes. A yellow precipitate of CdS indicates the presence of Cd^{+2}.

If Cu^{+2} is not present, merely add the thioacetamide directly to the ammoniacal solution (5–H).

5–I. *Concentration of Mo, As, Sb, and Sn.* Acidulate the supernate from the $(NH_4)_2S$ extraction (5–B) with dilute HCl, (i.e., add HCl dropwise until the solution is *barely* acidic. Too much HCl will cause loss of tin through the reaction

$$SnS_2 \text{ (s)} + 6\,Cl^- + 4\,H^+ \rightarrow SnCl_6^{-2} + 2\,H_2S \text{ (g)}$$

It is best to carry out the HCl addition in a large flask and *in the hood* because of the possibly violent evolution of H_2S.) Centrifuge down any precipitate which appears and discard the supernate. Wash the precipitate with water and discard the washings. Add 2 ml of 12 M HCl and heat gently without boiling for 5 minutes. Centrifuge. Pour the supernate into a clean test tube (5–L). Repeat the HCl treatment and add the supernate to (5–L). The procedures in (5–J) and (5–K) are to be performed on the residue.

5–J. *Separation and Confirmation of Arsenic.* To the residue from (5–I) add 2 drops of 15 M HNO_3 and 10 drops of 12 M HCl. Heat until the solid is dissolved, adding more acid if necessary. Evaporate to small volume and make almost neutral but not basic with 6 M NaOH. Add an equal volume of magnesia mixture, making sure the solution is now alkaline. Allow the solution to stand 10 minutes or longer, with occasional shaking if no white crystalline $NH_4MgAsO_4 \cdot 6\,H_2O$ appears. Centrifuge down any precipitate and remove the supernate for the molybdenum test (5–K). Wash the precipitate once with a little magnesia mixture, discarding the wash liquor. Dissolve the precipitate in a minimum amount of 6 M HCl (or if no precipitate appeared, take a portion of the solution) and add a pinch of solid $NaHSO_3$. Make the solution strongly alkaline with 6 M NaOH. (Ignore the precipitated $Mg(OH)_2$.) Warm until no more NH_3 is detectable with red litmus. Prepare a piece of filter paper wet with 0.1 M $AgNO_3$. Add a few pellets of metallic aluminum to the solution and immediately plug the mouth of the tube loosely with a wad of cotton and cover the mouth of the tube with the $AgNO_3$ paper. Warm the tube gently if necessary to start the reaction. Development of a black stain of metallic silver on the paper confirms the presence of arsenic.

5–K. *Confirmation of Molybdenum.* To the supernate from the $MgNH_4AsO_4 \cdot 6\,H_2O$ precipitation (or a portion of the solution if there was no precipitate) add an equal volume of 12 M HCl, 10 drops of fresh 0.1 M $SnCl_2$ (test!) and 1 ml of 1 M KNCS. Development of an amber to orange-red color confirms the presence of molybdenum.

5–L. *Confirmation of Tin.* Divide the supernate from the 12 M HCl extraction (5–I) into three portions and transfer each of these to a casserole. (a) To the first add a few small pieces of fine iron wire and heat in the hood until the solution has evaporated *almost, but not completely,* to dryness. Add water, centrifuge, and pour into a test tube. A few small black pieces of carbon from the wire may wash over, but will cause no difficulty. (If antimony is present, it will be reduced to black antimony metal.) On the other hand, no metallic iron should be allowed to get into the test tube. Add 2 drops of 0.1 M $HgCl_2$. A white or gray precipitate (Hg_2Cl_2 + Hg) confirms presence of tin. In the event that insufficient tin was present to reduce all the $HgCl_2$ added, only the white Hg_2Cl_2 will appear. Since this is not very distinctive, it is advisable to prove its identity. Therefore, if the precipitate is only white, centrifuge, wash with water, and then add NH_4OH. If the white precipitate now turns black, it was Hg_2Cl_2 and tin is confirmed.

$$Hg_2Cl_2 \text{ (s)} + 2\,NH_3 \rightleftharpoons Hg \text{ (l)} + HgNH_2Cl \text{ (s)} + NH_4^+ + Cl^-$$

(b) To the second portion of the solution in a casserole, add some magnesium powder, or a few granules of zinc. Fill a crucible which is clean on the *outside* with cold water. Dip the bottom of it into the liquid in the casserole and then hold it in a Bunsen flame. A bluish luminescent flame clinging to the unglazed portion of the bottom of the crucible confirms the presence of tin.

5–M. *Confirmation of Antimony.* Evaporate the third portion of the liquid (5–I) to half its original volume *in the hood.* Transfer to a small tube and add 6 M NH_4OH until just alkaline. Acidulate with 6 M acetic acid and add one drop in excess. Heat to boiling. Drop into the hot solution a small pinch of $Na_2S_2O_3 \cdot 5\,H_2O$ crystals. Do not agitate. The appearance of an orange-red color on the surface of the crystals confirms the presence of antimony. Gentle heating may be necessary. (Do not confuse a yellowish-white precipitate of free sulfur with Sb_2OS_2.)

5–16. Questions and Problems

1. How does the fact that a half-mole of NaCl does not lower the freezing point of water so much as 1 mole of alcohol demonstrate that activity and concentration are not equal?

2. How does the fact that the electrical conductivity of a 1 M NaCl solution is not twice as great as that of a 0.5 M NaCl solution demonstrate that activity and concentration are not the same?

3. How does the fact that BaSO$_4$ is more soluble in 1 M NaCl solution demonstrate that activity and concentration are not the same?

4. Explain why, although the solubilities of NaCl, NaBr, and NaI in water increase in the order named, the solubilities of AgCl, AgBr, and AgI decrease in the order named, despite the fact that Na$^+$ and Ag$^+$ are of about the same size.

5. Taking the equations for the pK_{sp}'s of the sulfides, selenides, and tellurides (Section 5–1) and noting that $K_{sp} = [M^+]^2[S^{-2}]$; $K'_{sp} = [M^{+2}][S^{-2}]$, and so forth, can be written $pK_{sp} = -2 \log [M^+] - \log [S^{-2}]$; $pK'_{sp} = - \log [M^{+2}] - \log [S^{-2}]$, and so forth, deduce an approximate relationship among the three equations.

6. Does the same principle hold for the relationships for the halides?

$$MX: \ pK_{sp} = 29.0 - 18.1 \, \Delta x$$
$$MX_2: \ pK_{sp} = 46.4 - 24.4 \, \Delta x$$
$$MX_3: \ pK_{sp} = 52.9 - 35.5 \, \Delta x$$
$$MX_4: \ pK_{sp} = 75.0 - 43.8 \, \Delta x$$

7. Explain why HgS does not dissolve appreciably in ammoniacal sulfide solutions but does in solutions containing KOH.

8. Explain why SnS$_2$, whose K_{sp} is on the order of 10^{-70}, dissolves so readily in dilute HCl, whereas CuS, whose K_{sp} is about 10^{-50}, does not.

9. Show why the degree of ionization of a weak acid increases as its total concentration decreases.

10. Explain why a quadratic solution is necessary for calculating the concentrations of ions in solutions of weak acids when the ionization constant is high or when the concentration is low.

11. Show whether weak acids and bases obey Le Châtelier's principle. In this particular case, what is this called?

12. Explain why aqueous solutions of strong acids cannot be treated from the equilibrium point of view.

13. Discuss the Brønsted concept of acids and bases.

14. What are conjugate acids and bases? Is there any relationship between their ionization constants in aqueous solution?

15. What are ampholytes?

16. What is an indicator?

17. What is the pH of solutions having each of the following hydrogen-ion con-

centrations? (a) 1×10^{-2}, (b) 6×10^{-7}, (c) 9.5×10^{-5}, (d) 11.2×10^{-9}, (e) 1.1×10^{-10}.

18. What is the hydrogen-ion concentration in solutions having each of the following pH's? (a) 15.0, (b) 7.0, (c) 8.05, (d) 9.73, (e) -0.35.

19. Calculate the concentration of hydrogen ion in each of the following solutions
    (a) $0.1\ M\ HN_3$
    (b) $0.01\ M\ HN_3$
    (c) $1.0\ M\ HN_3$
    (d) $10^{-6}\ M\ HN_3$
    (e) $0.01\ M\ CCl_3CO_2H$
    (f) $0.07\ M\ HClO$
    (g) $2 \times 10^{-4}\ M\ HCN$
    (h) $0.03\ M\ H_2O_2$
    (i) $3 \times 10^{-3}\ M\ HCl$
    (j) $0.2\ M\ KHSO_4$

20. Calculate the concentration of hydroxide ion in
    (a) $0.1\ M\ NH_4OH$
    (b) $0.01\ M\ NH_4OH$
    (c) $1.0\ M\ NH_4OH$
    (d) $2 \times 10^{-4}\ M\ CH_3HgOH$
    (e) $2 \times 10^{-4}\ M\ (C_2H_5)_2TlOH$
    (f) $3 \times 10^{-3}\ M\ C_2H_5NH_2$
    (g) $0.05\ M\ HNC(NH_2)_2$
    (h) $5 \times 10^{-6}\ M\ AgOH$
    (i) $0.04\ M\ CH_3NH_2$
    (j) $4 \times 10^{-5}\ M\ CH_3NH_2$

21. (a) What is the degree of ionization of each acid in problem 19 above? (b) What is the percentage of ionization of each base in problem 20?

22. Calculate the ionization constant for each of the following substances from the data given.

Solution	Degree of Ionization
(a) $0.1\ M\ NH_4OH$	0.0133
(b) $0.01\ M\ NH_4OH$	0.0415
(c) $0.1\ M\ HNO_2$	0.067
(d) $0.0001\ M\ HCN$	0.002
(e) $0.005\ M\ CH_3HgOH$	0.000245
(f) $0.04\ M\ HIO_3$	0.33
(g) $9 \times 10^{-6}\ M\ AgOH$	0.9991

23. Calculate the hydrogen-ion concentration of each of the following solutions
    (a) $0.2\ M\ HC_2H_3O_2 + 0.1\ M\ NaC_2H_3O_2$
    (b) $0.01\ M\ HClO_2 + 0.2\ M\ NaClO_2$
    (c) $0.05\ M\ HF + 0.07\ M\ KF$
    (d) $0.02\ M\ HN_3 + 0.05\ M\ KN_3$
    (e) $0.1\ M\ H_2S + 0.003\ M\ KSH$

24. Calculate the concentration of the anion of the weak acid or the cation of the weak base in each of the following solutions
    (a) $0.02\ M\ HONH_2 + 0.003\ M\ NaOH$
    (b) $0.01\ M\ HBrO + 0.002\ M\ HClO_4$
    (c) $0.05\ M\ (CH_3)_3SnOH + 0.06\ M\ KOH$
    (d) $0.2\ M\ HN_3 + 0.08\ M\ HCl$
    (e) $0.03\ M\ HF + 0.05\ M\ HCl$

25. How many grams of the appropriate potassium salt of each acid listed below must be added to 1 liter of each of the following solutions to give the indicated pH?

Solution	pH
(a) $0.1\ M\ HC_2H_3O_2$	4.7
(b) $0.0002\ M\ HClO$	5.1
(c) $0.90\ M\ CCl_3CO_2H$	0.0
(d) $0.08\ M\ HF$	3.9
(e) $0.1\ M\ HBr$	1.5

26. A solution containing 0.09 M NH$_4$OH also has some NH$_4$Cl. It is found to have a hydroxide-ion concentration of 0.10×10^{-5} M. How many grams of NH$_4$Cl are in a liter of this solution?

27. If 0.05 moles of HCl are added to the solution in problem 26, what is the hydroxide-ion concentration of the resulting solution?

28. Calculate the molar concentration of an N$_2$H$_4$ solution which is known to be 1 percent ionized.

29. Ten grams of (NH$_4$)$_2$SO$_4$ are added to 500 ml of a 0.1 M NH$_4$OH solution. Calculate the hydroxide concentration in the resulting solution.

30. Calculate the pH of 500 ml of a solution containing 1.7 grams of HCl and 4.5 grams of NaC$_2$H$_3$O$_2$.

31. Show that the chromate-dichromate system would be poor as an indicator because the point of half-neutralization ($[CrO_4^{-2}] = \frac{1}{2}[Cr_2O_7^{-2}]$) is dependent upon the chromate concentration.

32. Using different amounts of NH$_4$Cl and NH$_3$ in each case, calculate three different sets of concentrations which will give an OH$^-$ concentration of 10^{-4} molar.

33. What is the hydrogen-ion concentration in a liter of a solution of 5 grams of NaCN to which 5 grams of gaseous HCl have been added?

34. Using data from Fig. 5–3, calculate approximate ionization constants for five different indicators.

5–17. References

Bell, R. P., *Acids and Bases*. New York: John Wiley and Sons, Inc., 1952.

Clifford, A. F., "The Prediction of Solubility Product Constants," *Journal of the American Chemical Society*, Vol. 79 (1957), p. 5404.

Clifford, A. F., "The Electronegativity of Groups," *Journal of Physical Chemistry*, Vol. 63 (1959), p. 1227

Mantell, C. L., *Tin*. New York: Reinhold Publishing Corporation, 1949.

Audrieth, L. F., *Acids, Bases and Non-Aqueous Systems* ("23rd Annual Priestley Lectures, Pennsylvania State College.") Ypsilanti, Mich.: University Litho-printers, 1949.

Chapter 6

Polybasic Acids

6–1. Polybasic Acids

Although we have so far concentrated largely on monobasic acids (acids having only one ionizable hydrogen), it should be apparent from the discussion in Section 5–10 that it is possible to have acids having more than one ionizable hydrogen. Thus phosphoric acid undergoes the stepwise ionizations

(1) $$H_3PO_4 \rightleftharpoons H_2PO_4^- + H^+$$

(2) $$H_2PO_4^- \rightleftharpoons HPO_4^{-2} + H^+$$

(3) $$HPO_4^{-2} \rightleftharpoons PO_4^{-3} + H^+$$

each step having its own characteristic ionization constant. In general, for simple oxy acids of this sort, the successive ionization constants differ from each other by a factor of about 10^5 (see Section 9–10). For example, K_1, K_2, and K_3 for H_3PO_4 are 7.6×10^{-3}, 6.2×10^{-8} and 1×10^{-12}, respectively. (It should be noted that for acids of other types, and for oxy acids of more complicated structure, e.g., with more than one central atom, this rule is not followed. Thus K_1 and K_2 for H_2S are 1.0×10^{-7} and 1.3×10^{-13}, while K_1 and K_2 for $H_2C_2O_4$ are 3.8×10^{-2} and 5.0×10^{-5}, Section 9–10.)

The extent of the first ionization of H_3PO_4 in 0.1 M solution is about 25 percent, while the concentration of PO_4^{-3} in such a solution is only 10^{-18} M. Sulfuric acid, on the other hand, whose K_1 is about 10^{+3}, is essentially completely ionized to HSO_4^- in 0.1 M solution. The resulting HSO_4^- is further ionized to the extent of about 10 percent. However, the extent of ionization of HSO_4^- in 0.1 M $KHSO_4$ is 30 percent. The reason for this is that in the H_2SO_4 solution, the H^+ from the first ionization represses the second ionization equilibrium. In other words, the successive ionizations of a polybasic acid must represent a series of simultaneous equilibria because of the $[H^+]$ which is common to all of them.

Just as the equilibrium expressions for other simultaneous equilibria can be combined to obtain an over-all expression, so they can be combined for polybasic acids to give an expression for the over-all ionization. With phosphoric acid, whose over-all ionization is given by adding equations given above

(4) $H_3PO_4 \rightleftharpoons 3H^+ + PO_4^{-3}$

we have

(1′) $\dfrac{[H^+][H_2PO_4^-]}{[H_3PO_4]} = 7.6 \times 10^{-3} = K_1$

(2′) $\dfrac{[H^+][HPO_4^{-2}]}{[H_2PO_4^-]} = 6.2 \times 10^{-8} = K_2$

(3′) $\dfrac{[H^+][PO_4^{-3}]}{[HPO_4^{-2}]} = 1 \times 10^{-12} = K_3$

and therefore

(4′) $\dfrac{[H^+]^3[PO_4^{-3}]}{[H_3PO_4]} = 4.7 \times 10^{-22} = K_{123}$

From these equations, we can calculate the $[PO_4^{-3}]$ in 0.1 M H_3PO_4. First of all, since each successive step in the ionization takes place to a lesser extent than the preceding one, *equation (4) cannot be interpreted to mean that there are three hydrogen ions for every* PO_4^{-3}. On the contrary, it must be realized, that if K_2 is reasonably small and considerably smaller than K_1, the principal source of H^+ will be the first ionization. To a first approximation, then, $[H^+] = [H_2PO_4^-]$. Therefore, from equation (1′)

$$\frac{X^2}{0.1 - X} = 7.6 \times 10^{-3}$$

and $X = [H^+] = 2.4 \times 10^{-2}\ M$

Then from equation (4′)

$$\frac{(2.4 \times 10^{-2})^3[PO_4^{-3}]}{0.076} = 4.7 \times 10^{-22}$$

and $[PO_4^{-3}] = 2.6 \times 10^{-18}\ M$

The concentrations of all the species involved can be obtained by similar approximations. Thus, using equation (2′)

$$\frac{(2.4 \times 10^{-2})[HPO_4^{-2}]}{2.4 \times 10^{-2}} = 6.2 \times 10^{-8}$$

and $[HPO_4^{-2}] = 6.2 \times 10^{-8}\ M = K_2$

and it can be seen that where the second ionization contributes a negligible amount to the hydrogen-ion concentration, the concentration of the anion resulting from the second ionization is numerically equal to the second ionization constant. Now, from equation (3')

$$\frac{(2.4 \times 10^{-2})[PO_4^{-3}]}{6.2 \times 10^{-8}} = 1 \times 10^{-12}$$

and $$[PO_4^{-3}] = 2.6 \times 10^{-18} \ M$$

in substantial agreement with the calculation above.

Since $[PO_4^{-3}]$ is an inverse function of the *cube* of $[H^+]$, the phosphate-ion concentration will decrease very rapidly as the pH is lowered. Therefore, even though metal phosphates are generally fairly insoluble in water, all but the most insoluble phosphates of elements of high oxidation state—e.g., $Th_3(PO_4)_4$, $Zr_3(PO_4)_4$—are soluble in acidic solution because of the reaction $M_3(PO_4)_n + nH^+ \rightleftharpoons 3M^{+n} + nHPO_4^{-2}$.

6–2. Hydrosulfuric Acid, H_2S

Another polybasic acid of importance is H_2S (discussed briefly in Section 5–1), upon which are based most of the schemes of qualitative analysis. Since a saturated aqueous solution of H_2S at room temperature and 1 atm pressure is approximately 0.1 molar, and since H_2S is customarily used in solutions in which $[H^+]$ has been fixed, calculations involving H_2S are generally simple. The concentrations of sulfide ion at various pH's in saturated aqueous H_2S, calculated from the relationship

$$\frac{[H^+]^2[S^{-2}]}{[H_2S]} = K_1 \times K_2 = (1 \times 10^{-7}) \times (1.3 \times 10^{-13}) = 1.3 \times 10^{-20} = K_{12}$$

are shown in Table 6–1.

TABLE 6–1. MOLAR CONCENTRATION OF SULFIDE ION IN
SATURATED SOLUTIONS OF VARIOUS pH'S

Conditions	$[S^{-2}]$
pH = 0	1.3×10^{-21}
pH = 1	1.3×10^{-19}
pH = 3	1.3×10^{-15}
pH = 4 (no added acid)	1.3×10^{-13}
pH = 7	1.3×10^{-7}
0.1 M $(NH_4)_2S$	2×10^{-5}
0.1 M Na_2S	5×10^{-2}

How the dependence of the sulfide-ion concentration on pH is used in the separation of analytical groups has already been discussed in Section 5–1.

6–3. The Mechanism of Sulfide Precipitation

The concentration of S^{-2} in a saturated H_2S solution of pH = 0 at room temperature is only 1.3×10^{-21} moles per liter. Since there are 6×10^{23} molecules in a mole, a liter of such a solution contains only about 800 free sulfide ions, or about one ion per milliliter. Despite this vanishingly low concentration, when a heavy metal salt such as $AgNO_3$ is added to this solution, precipitation of the insoluble sulfide is extremely rapid—much more rapid, in fact, than could be expected from such a low concentration of sulfide ion. On the other hand, the concentration of SH^- is much higher (1×10^{-8} M) in this solution, and it might be expected that SH^- could combine rapidly with the heavy metal ion to precipitate a hydrosulfide.

$$Ag^+ + SH^- \rightleftharpoons AgSH$$

According to the principles discussed in Section 5–1, the hydrosulfides of the heavy elements should be expected to be insoluble and their K_{sp}'s should be smaller than those of the corresponding hydroxides. After precipitation, or even during the precipitation process, the hydrosulfide loses H_2S, giving the normal sulfide.

$$2\,AgSH \rightleftharpoons Ag_2S + H_2S$$

The existence of the substance AgSH in solution has been demonstrated by Treadwell and Hepenstrick. The equilibrium constant for the reaction

$$\tfrac{1}{2}\,Ag_2S\,(s) + \tfrac{1}{2}\,H_2S\,(aq) \rightleftharpoons AgSH\,(aq)$$

is $K = 1.4 \times 10^{-6}$. The substance AgSH is a weak acid, but about fifty times stronger than H_2S; the ionization constant for the reaction

$$AgSH \rightleftharpoons H^+ + AgS^-$$

is $K_A = 5.2 \times 10^{-6}$. Treadwell and Schaufelberger have also demonstrated the existence of $Hg(SH)_2$ in solution. The equilibrium constant for the reaction

$$HgS\,(s) + H_2S\,(aq) \rightleftharpoons Hg(SH)_2\,(aq)$$

is $K = 6.3 \times 10^{-7}$ and the over-all acid-ionization constant for

$$Hg(SH)_2 \rightleftharpoons 2\,H^+ + HgS_2^{-2}$$

is $K_{12} = 1.0 \times 10^{-7}$.

The formation of $HAsS_2$ has been investigated by Holje. For $\tfrac{1}{2}\,As_2S_3\,(s) + \tfrac{1}{2}\,H_2S\,(aq) \rightleftharpoons HAsS_2$, $K = 5.0 \times 10^{-6}$, and for $HAsS_2 \rightleftharpoons H^+ + AsS_2^-$, $K_A = 2.0 \times 10^{-4}$.

This type of process is known to occur in the precipitation of many heavy metal oxides. For example, when NaOH is added to $AgNO_3$ solution, yellow AgOH immediately precipitates, and then rapidly dehydrates to brown Ag_2O.

$$Ag^+ + OH^- \rightleftharpoons AgOH\,(s)$$
$$2\,AgOH\,(s) \rightleftharpoons Ag_2O\,(s) + H_2O$$

If this picture of sulfide precipitation is correct, it should be expected that sulfide precipitates would contain excess H_2S. This is in fact found to be the case.

Such a mechanism will have no effect on the K_{sp} relationships of the sulfides, however, since *these depend solely on the initial and final states of the systems*, e.g.

$$2 \, Ag^+ \, (aq) + S^{-2} \, (aq) \rightleftharpoons Ag_2S \, (s)$$

and are not effected by the mechanism by which the equilibrium is attained.

It is also very probable that the thio complexes in solution exist largely as "hydrothio" complexes, e.g., as $Sn(SH)_6^{-2}$ rather than SnS_3^{-2}. This has been demonstrated to be the case with many hydroxy complexes. For example, in alkaline solution Sn(IV) is $Sn(OH)_6^{-2}$, not SnO_3^{-2}. Thus the compounds given in most handbooks as $K_2SnO_3 \cdot 3 \, H_2O$, $K_2PbO_3 \cdot 3 \, H_2O$, $K_2PtO_3 \cdot 3 \, H_2O$, $2 \, NaSbO_3 \cdot 7 \, H_2O$, $KAuO_2 \cdot 2 \, H_2O$, and so on, are in reality $K_2Sn(OH)_6$, $K_2Pb(OH)_6$, $K_2Pt(OH)_6$, $NaSb(OH)_6 \cdot \frac{1}{2} \, H_2O$, $KAu(OH)_4$, and so on. In the same way, the compound listed as $K_2SnS_3 \cdot 3 \, H_2O$ is in all probability $K_2Sn(OH)_3(SH)_3$.

6–4. The Coprecipitation of Sulfides

The coprecipitation of $CoSO_4$ and other salts with $BaSO_4$ has already been mentioned (problem 11, Section 3–14). This takes place under conditions where $CoSO_4$ alone would not normally precipitate. In like manner, when $Mn_3(PO_4)_2$ is precipitated from ammoniacal phosphate solutions containing salts of such metals as copper and zinc, the phosphates of these elements coprecipitate with the isomorphous manganese phosphate, even though they themselves are normally soluble in ammoniacal solution. The Cu^{+2} or Zn^{+2} ions presumably are substituted for Mn^{+2} in the $Mn_3(PO_4)_2$ crystal lattice.

This same phenomenon may be very important in the precipitation of sulfides. Thus if CuS is precipitated with H_2S from a solution too acidic for CdS to precipitate by itself, CdS nevertheless in part precipitates with it. This is also true of ZnS and FeS. In the same way, HgS will carry down CuS and CdS from solutions too acidic for them to precipitate alone. When ZnS is precipitated from acetic acid solution, partial coprecipitation of MnS, FeS, CoS, and NiS occurs, even though normally these compounds cannot be precipitated under these conditions. Likewise, CdS carries ZnS from acidic solution and SnS carries considerable amounts of NiS. That this is not merely mechanical carrying is apparent from the fact that when MnS is coprecipitated with ZnS, CdS, or HgS, much of it remains undissolved even after the precipitate has been digested with acetic acid, although MnS alone is freely soluble under the same conditions. This is true even though the MnS is entirely on the outside of the HgS particles. If an Mn^{+2} solution is added to HgS suspended in aqueous $(NH_4)_2S$, so that the MnS is precipitated entirely on the surface of the HgS, it still is not possible to dissolve the MnS in 20 percent acetic acid, which would easily dissolve MnS alone. Kolthoff has shown that the more soluble sulfide is not precipitated at the same time as the less soluble, but rather subsequently "by H_2S condensed on" the gelatinous, less soluble sulfide. Some such process as the following may be envisioned

$$Hg(SH)_2 + Mn^{+2} \rightleftharpoons MnHgS_2 \text{ (s)} + 2 H^+$$

so that the product is in reality an insoluble thiomercuriate, thiocuprate, or the like, rather than a mixture of simple sulfides. If the sulfides are precipitated under conditions where they are crystalline rather than gelatinous, this coprecipitation phenomenon is less likely to occur, both because crystalline materials naturally precipitate more cleanly than gelatinous ones and because the crystalline precipitates will have a minimum of "H_2S condensed on" them. This is one important reason for preferring thioacetamide precipitation to H_2S (Section 6–6). Thus, when ZnS is precipitated *by H_2S* in the presence of Fe^{+2}, it is invariably gray with coprecipitated FeS. With hot thioacetamide solution, on the other hand, pure white ZnS is obtained. The difference is probably a function of the mechanism of the thioacetamide precipitation, which is discussed in Sections 6–6 and 15–9.

6–5. The Polymorphism of Sulfides

When nickel sulfide is precipitated from 0.1 molar nickel salts with saturated H_2S solution, precipitation does not take place at pH's below 1. Considering supersaturation and the fact (Section 3–3) that small first-formed crystals have a higher K_{sp} than the final large crystals, this agrees with the experimental K_{sp} of 1×10^{-22}. Once the NiS is precipitated, however, especially if it is allowed to stand, it is insoluble in acid much more concentrated than that which will prevent its precipitation initially. It is found that NiS can exist in at least three different crystal structures. Substances which can exist in more than one crystal structure are called *polymorphic*. The various forms of NiS are designated as α, β, and γ. The respective K_{sp}'s of these three forms are 1×10^{-22}, 3×10^{-28}, and 7×10^{-30}. Perhaps because of the mechanism of sulfide precipitation, with the possibility of first precipitating a hydrosulfide, e.g., $Ni(SH)_2$, the α form, mixed with a little β and γ, is what first precipitates. On standing, the α form goes over to the less soluble β and γ forms. The conversion furthermore is favored by acid, so that even fairly fresh precipitates of NiS resist dissolution by acids.

Cobalt sulfide is quite similar to NiS, having α and β forms of $K_{sp} = 5 \times 10^{-22}$ and 6×10^{-29}.

It is possible to prevent the transition of NiS to the less soluble forms by coprecipitating it with another sulfide which itself does not undergo the transition. For example, if NiS be coprecipitated with excess PbS from $(NH_4)_2S$ solution, it can be almost completely redissolved by dilute strong acids in which pure NiS would be quite insoluble.

6–6. Thioacetamide

Although hydrogen sulfide is an extremely useful reagent, it is also an obnoxious and toxic one. Few people realize that H_2S is just about as poisonous as HCN! In addition, metal sulfides precipitated with H_2S have an unfortunate tendency to be gelatinous or even colloidal rather than crystalline. This may be due to the intermediate formation and slow decomposition of hydrosulfides, or it may be the result of the extreme supersaturation resulting from the relatively high concentrations of H_2S and SH^- ions.

There are many compounds of sulfur which hydrolyze to give H_2S and which may be used instead of H_2S itself for the precipitation of sulfides. Among the best substitutes for H_2S is the organic compound thioacetamide, CH_3CSNH_2, which is recommended in this text. This substance is soluble in water and forms aqueous solutions which are stable for months at room temperature. At temperatures approaching that of boiling water, on the other hand, hydrolysis takes place with slow liberation of H_2S, especially in the presence of acids or bases. The reaction in acidic solution is represented by the equation

$$CH_3CSNH_2 + H_2O \rightarrow CH_3CONH_2 + H_2S$$

In basic solution, the reaction is

$$CH_3CSNH_2 + 2\,OH^- \rightarrow CH_3CO_2^- + NH_3 + SH^-$$

The use of hot thioacetamide solution in place of H_2S results in sulfide precipitates that are very seldom colloidal, but much more crystalline and easy to handle than those obtained from H_2S (Section 6–4). Because the H_2S concentration builds up slowly the K_{sp}'s are only slowly exceeded and the sulfides precipitate in order of their increasing K_{sp}'s, or at least in order of their decreasing rates of precipitation. Thus, when H_2S is added to a solution containing both zinc and nickel salts, a black, mixed ZnS–NiS precipitate is immediately formed. With hot CH_3CSNH_2, however, pure white ZnS precipitates in large part before the black NiS is seen.

The greater crystallinity of the precipitates may be a result of the slow increase in H_2S concentration, so that a high degree of supersaturation never takes place and the crystals have time to grow. An alternative explanation is based on the fact that thioacetamide is known to form complex ions with the heavy metals at room temperature. (When CH_3CSNH_2 is added to a cold solution containing heavy metal ions, a precipitate may be formed immediately; this, however, is a metal-thioacetamide complex, which is always lighter in color than the corresponding metal sulfide.) When the temperature is raised, the complex may decompose, giving the metal sulfide directly and not going through the hydrosulfide stage.

6–7. Carbonic Acid

Another important dibasic acid is H_2CO_3. The ionization constants usually quoted for H_2CO_3 are $K_1 = 4.2 \times 10^{-7}$ and $K_2 = 4.8 \times 10^{-11}$. Although K_2 does represent the expected process

$$HCO_3^- \rightleftharpoons H^+ + CO_3^{-2}$$

K_1 is for the more complicated over-all process

$$H_2O + CO_2 \text{ (aq)} \rightleftharpoons H_2CO_3 \text{ (aq)} \rightleftharpoons H^+ + HCO_3^-$$

$$\frac{[H^+][HCO_3^-]}{[CO_2]} = 4.2 \times 10^{-7}$$

Since, however, less than 1 percent of the CO_2 in an aqueous solution of CO_2 is really present as H_2CO_3, the true first ionization constant of H_2CO_3 is 1.5×10^{-4}.

$$\frac{[H^+][HCO_3^-]}{[H_2CO_3]} = 1.5 \times 10^{-4}$$

For most systems involving dissolved CO_2, the apparent $K_1 = 4.2 \times 10^{-7}$ is the appropriate one to use. For systems involving hydrolysis of HCO_3^-, however, (Section 7–6) since CO_2 is rather slowly liberated from dilute H_2CO_3, the true $K_1 = 1.5 \times 10^{-4}$ is more appropriate. We shall confine our attention here to the apparent K_1.

The treatment of carbonic acid is essentially the same as that of H_2S and H_3PO_4. The K_1 expression and the K_2 expression

$$\frac{[H^+][CO_3^{-2}]}{[HCO_3^-]} = 4.8 \times 10^{-11}$$

combine to give

$$\frac{[H^+]^2[CO_3^{-2}]}{[CO_2]} = 2 \times 10^{-17}$$

for the over-all ionization.

Since a saturated solution of carbon dioxide in water at 25°C and 1 atm pressure is about 0.034 molar, and since the second ionization is negligible in comparison to the first

$$[H^+] = [HCO_3^-] = X$$

and

$$\frac{X^2}{0.034} = 4.2 \times 10^{-7}$$

and

$$X = 1.2 \times 10^{-4} \, M$$

The carbonate-ion concentration, therefore, is

$$\frac{(1.2 \times 10^{-4})^2[CO_3^{-2}]}{0.034} = 2 \times 10^{-17}$$

$$[CO_3^{-2}] = 4.8 \times 10^{-11} \, M$$

or essentially the same as K_2.

Because of the much greater difference in electronegativity between metals and oxygen than between metals and sulfur, the carbonates generally follow the solubility trends of ionic substances, rather than the electronegativity relationship of covalent substances. As a class, they are more soluble than the sulfides. As a result of their greater solubility and the volatility of CO_2, carbonates are universally soluble in acids, as opposed to the sulfides. Very few carbonates are precipitated by aqueous CO_2 (Ag_2CO_3 is one of the few which is), whereas most sulfides *are* precipitated by aqueous H_2S.

6–8. Chromic Acid

Chromic acid, H_2CrO_4, represents yet another variation on the polybasic acid theme. When acid is added to a solution of an alkali chromate, the first product is hydrogen chromate ion

$$CrO_4^{-2} + H^+ \rightleftharpoons HCrO_4^-$$

The reverse of this process, which is the second ionization of chromic acid, has the constant

$$\frac{[H^+][CrO_4^{-2}]}{[HCrO_4^-]} = 3.2 \times 10^{-7}$$

The hydrogen chromate ion, however, almost immediately loses water and condenses to give dichromate ion

$$2\, HCrO_4^- \rightleftharpoons H_2O + Cr_2O_7^{-2}$$

For the reverse of this process, we have

$$\frac{[HCrO_4^-]^2}{[Cr_2O_7^{-2}]} = 2.3 \times 10^{-2} \quad \text{or} \quad \frac{[HCrO_4^-]}{[Cr_2O_7^{-2}]^{1/2}} = 1.5 \times 10^{-1}$$

The over-all process, $\frac{1}{2} Cr_2O_7^{-2} + \frac{1}{2} H_2O \rightleftharpoons H^+ + CrO_4^{-2}$, therefore has the constant

$$\frac{[H^+][CrO_4^{-2}]}{[Cr_2O_7^{-2}]^{1/2}} = 4.8 \times 10^{-8}$$

The free acid, H_2CrO_4, is very difficult to obtain, if, indeed, it exists at all as such. Judging from the rule of thumb given in Section 6–1, however, the first ionization constant for the hypothetical H_2CrO_4 should be around 10^{-1}. This agrees with an experimental value of 1.8×10^{-1} reported by Neuss and Rieman.

Because of the relatively small constant for the chromate-dichromate equilibrium, most insoluble chromates, like the carbonates, are soluble in acids, unless the corresponding dichromate happens also to be insoluble. Thus $BaCrO_4$ and $PbCrO_4$ are fairly easily soluble in acids:

$$2\, BaCrO_4\, (s) + 2\, H^+ \rightleftharpoons 2\, Ba^{+2} + Cr_2O_7^{-2} + H_2O$$

whereas Hg_2CrO_4 and Ag_2CrO_4 are much less easily soluble:

$$2\,Hg_2CrO_4\,(s) + 2\,H^+ \rightleftharpoons Hg_2^{+2} + Hg_2Cr_2O_7\,(s) + H_2O$$

6–9. Polyacid Bases

Soluble polyacid bases are less frequently encountered than polybasic acids. Their treatment, however, is exactly the same as for polybasic acids. For example, $Pb(OH)_2$ is soluble in water to the extent of 0.16 gram per liter or 6.6×10^{-4} molar. It is found that a significant fraction of the lead hydroxide in solution is present as un-ionized $Pb(OH)_2$ molecules. Therefore, for all $Pb(OH)_2$ solutions of concentrations lower than 6.6×10^{-4} molar (for which the simple K_{sp} relationship applies), lead hydroxide must be treated as a diacid base in solution, for which the equilibria

$$Pb(OH)_2\,(aq) \rightleftharpoons PbOH^+ + OH^-$$

and

$$PbOH^+ \rightleftharpoons Pb^{+2} + OH^-$$

apply. Thus

$$\frac{[PbOH^+][OH^-]}{[Pb(OH)_2]} = 1.0 \times 10^{-3}$$

$$\frac{[Pb^{+2}][OH^-]}{[PbOH^+]} = 1.5 \times 10^{-8}$$

and

$$\frac{[Pb^{+2}][OH^-]^2}{[Pb(OH)_2]} = 1.5 \times 10^{-11}$$

In a 5×10^{-4} molar solution of lead hydroxide, then, where the first ionization predominates over the second, $[PbOH^+] = [OH^-] = X$, and

$$\frac{X^2}{5 \times 10^{-4} - X} = 1.0 \times 10^{-3}$$

so

$$X = [PbOH^+] = [OH^-] = 3.7 \times 10^{-4}\ M$$

Then, as in the case of the dibasic acids, it can be seen that the concentration of the cation resulting from the second ionization (in this case, Pb^{+2}) is numerically equal to the second ionization constant.

$$\frac{[Pb^{+2}](3.7 \times 10^{-4})}{(3.7 \times 10^{-4})} = 1.5 \times 10^{-8}$$

$$[Pb^{+2}] = 1.5 \times 10^{-8}\ M$$

In the case of $Hg(OH)_2$, which is formally similar, a different situation arises. Mercuric oxide is soluble in water to the extent of 0.0515 gram per liter or 2.4×10^{-4} molar. It is found that the solution contains largely un-ionized $Hg(OH)_2$, for which the first and second basic ionization constants are respectively 1.0×10^{-14} and 1.2×10^{-8}. Let us examine the equilibria for a 1×10^{-4} molar solution, which is below that of a saturated solution. The first ionization expression is

$$\frac{[\text{HgOH}^+][\text{OH}^-]}{[\text{Hg(OH)}_2]} = 1.0 \times 10^{-14}$$

If it be assumed that $[\text{HgOH}^+] = [\text{OH}^-]$, then

$$\frac{X^2}{1 \times 10^{-4}} = 1.0 \times 10^{-14}$$

and
$$X = [\text{OH}^-] = 1.0 \times 10^{-9} \, M$$

However, this is much less than the hydroxide-ion concentration (1×10^{-7} molar) provided by water itself. In other words, of the two simultaneous equilibria $\text{Hg(OH)}_2 \rightleftharpoons \text{HgOH}^+ + \text{OH}^-$ and $\text{H}_2\text{O} \rightleftharpoons \text{H}^+ + \text{OH}^-$, the water equilibrium clearly predominates, and the hydroxide-ion concentration is therefore essentially 1×10^{-7} molar. Consequently

$$\frac{[\text{HgOH}^+](1 \times 10^{-7})}{1 \times 10^{-4}} = 1 \times 10^{-14}$$

and
$$[\text{HgOH}^+] = 1 \times 10^{-11} \, M$$

Now, from the second ionization expression

$$\frac{[\text{Hg}^{+2}][\text{OH}^-]}{[\text{HgOH}^+]} = \frac{[\text{Hg}^{+2}](1 \times 10^{-7})}{1 \times 10^{-11}} = 1.2 \times 10^{-8}$$

$$[\text{Hg}^{+2}] = 1.2 \times 10^{-12} \, M$$

which is a significant fraction of the HgOH^+ concentration. Since, however, neither $[\text{Hg}^{+2}]$ nor $[\text{HgOH}^+]$ is a significant fraction of $[\text{Hg(OH)}_2]$, no correction is necessary, as can be seen by comparing the $[\text{Hg}^{+2}]$ obtained above with that obtained from the over-all ionization expression

$$\frac{[\text{HgOH}^+][\text{OH}^-]}{[\text{Hg(OH)}_2]} \times \frac{[\text{Hg}^{+2}][\text{OH}^-]}{[\text{HgOH}^+]} = \frac{[\text{Hg}^{+2}][\text{OH}^-]^2}{[\text{Hg(OH)}_2]}$$

$$= 1 \times 10^{-14} \times 1.2 \times 10^{-8} = 1.2 \times 10^{-22}$$

$$\frac{[\text{Hg}^{+2}](10^{-7})^2}{1 \times 10^{-4}} = 1.2 \times 10^{-22}$$

$$[\text{Hg}^{+2}] = 1.2 \times 10^{-12} \, M$$

Polyacid bases of the ammonia type should also be considered. Their treatment, however, does not differ from that of the others. Hydrazine, N_2H_4, is such a base.

$$\text{N}_2\text{H}_4 + \text{H}_2\text{O} \rightleftharpoons \text{N}_2\text{H}_5^+ + \text{OH}^-$$

$$\text{N}_2\text{H}_5^+ + \text{H}_2\text{O} \rightleftharpoons \text{N}_2\text{H}_6^{+2} + \text{OH}^-$$

$$\frac{[N_2H_5{}^+][OH^-]}{[N_2H_4]} = 8.5 \times 10^{-7}$$

$$\frac{[N_2H_6{}^{+2}][OH^-]}{[N_2H_5{}^+]} = 8.9 \times 10^{-16}$$

There are many organic compounds, such as ethylenediamine, $H_2NCH_2CH_2NH_2$, which are diacid bases.

6–10. Ampholytes and Zwitter Ions

Many substances which are ampholytes can be treated as dibasic acids (or as diacid bases). For example, the substance glycine, which is amphoteric, exists in acid solution as the cation $\overset{+}{H_3}NCH_2CO_2H$. This undergoes two successive acid ionizations,

$$\overset{+}{H_3}NCH_2CO_2H \rightleftharpoons \overset{+}{H_3}NCH_2CO_2{}^- + H^+$$

$$\overset{+}{H_3}NCH_2CO_2{}^- \rightleftharpoons H_2NCH_2CO_2{}^- + H^+$$

with constants of 4.0×10^{-3} and 1.6×10^{-10} to give the anion $H_2NCH_2CO_2{}^-$. This succession of ionizations may be treated exactly as for any other dibasic acid, and the ion $\overset{+}{H_3}NCH_2CO_2H$ may be considered to be a dibasic acid.

The ampholyte glycine itself is somewhat different from substances that we have considered heretofore, in that it is not an uncharged molecule, such as $H_2NCH_2CO_2H$, but is rather a polar substance, $\overset{+}{H_3}NCH_2CO_2{}^-$. Substances of this sort, which are fairly common in organic chemistry, are known as *zwitter* (double) ions. Inorganic substances of the zwitter-ion type are very rare. Perhaps the most important inorganic zwitter ion is sulfamic acid, $\overset{+}{H_3}NSO_3{}^-$, whose ionization constant is 0.105 for the reaction

$$\overset{+}{H_3}NSO_3{}^- \rightleftharpoons H^+ + H_2NSO_3{}^-$$

(The formula of this substance is frequently erroneously given as HSO_3NH_2.)

6–11. Strong Polybasic Acids

The case of the polybasic acid whose first ionization constant is very large (e.g., H_2SO_4) is very simple, for the completeness of the first ionization dominates the situation and represses the relatively much weaker second ionization. Thus, in $0.1\ M\ H_2SO_4$, the $[H^+] = 0.1\ M$, plus a small contribution from the second ionization, $HSO_4{}^- \rightleftharpoons H^+ + SO_4{}^{-2}$.

$$\frac{[H^+][SO_4{}^{-2}]}{[HSO_4{}^-]} = \frac{(0.1)[SO_4{}^{-2}]}{0.1} = 1.26 \times 10^{-2}$$

Therefore, $[SO_4^{-2}] = 1.26 \times 10^{-2}$ M, or the HSO_4^- is 12.6 percent ionized. In this case, obviously this solution is not quite rigorous because of the large value of K_2, and if 10 percent is not an acceptable error, it should be recalculated. To do this set $[SO_4^{-2}] = y$, $[H^+] = 0.1 + y$, and $[HSO_4^-] = 0.1 - y$

$$\frac{(0.1+y)y}{0.1-y} = 1.26 \times 10^{-2}$$

$$y = [SO_4^{-2}] = 0.010 \ M$$

or 10.0 percent ionization of HSO_4^-.

In the case of polybasic acids with K_1 and K_2 both large and very close together, the situation is more complicated. Such an acid is $H_4P_2O_7$, pyrophosphoric acid, whose constants are $K_1 = 1.4 \times 10^{-1}$, $K_2 = 1.1 \times 10^{-2}$, $K_3 = 2.9 \times 10^{-7}$, and $K_4 = 3.6 \times 10^{-9}$. It can be seen from the arguments already given that the third and fourth ionizations are small enough to be neglected. The second ionization, however, will be appreciable even in the presence of the first.

Let us calculate the degree of ionization for the first and second steps of a 0.1 molar solution of $H_4P_2O_7$. If the assumption is made that the second ionization can be ignored, then $X = [H^+] = [H_3P_2O_7^-]$ and $[H_4P_2O_7] = 0.1 - X$, then

$$\frac{[H^+][H_3P_2O_7^-]}{[H_4P_2O_7]} = \frac{X^2}{0.1-X} = 1.4 \times 10^{-1}$$

$$X = [H^+] = [H_3P_2O_7^-] = 6.8 \times 10^{-2} \ M$$

Then

$$\frac{[H^+][H_2P_3O_7^{-2}]}{[H_3P_2O_7^-]} = \frac{(6.8 \times 10^{-2})[H_2P_3O_7^{-2}]}{6.8 \times 10^{-2}} = 1.1 \times 10^{-2}$$

Therefore

$$[H_2P_2O_7^{-2}] = 1.1 \times 10^{-2} \ M$$

This indicates that the first ionization takes place to the extent of 79 percent and the second to 16 percent. However, 16 percent is not insignificant. Consequently, a more rigorous treatment is required.

Again assuming that the third and fourth ionizations can be ignored, we have

(1)
$$\frac{[H^+][H_3P_2O_7^-]}{[H_4P_2O_7]} = 1.4 \times 10^{-1}$$

and (2)
$$\frac{[H^+][H_2P_2O_7^{-2}]}{[H_3P_2O_7^-]} = 1.1 \times 10^{-2}$$

Since all the species derived from $H_4P_2O_7$ must add up to 0.1 M, we have the conservation equation

(3)
$$[H_4P_2O_7] + [H_3P_2O_7^-] + [H_2P_2O_7^{-2}] = 0.1$$

Since all the H^+ comes from ionization of $H_4P_2O_7$

$$H_4P_2O_7 \rightleftharpoons H^+ + H_3P_2O_7^-$$

and $$H_4P_2O_7 \rightleftharpoons 2\,H^+ + H_2P_2O_7^{-2}$$

(4) $$[H^+] = [H_3P_2O_7^-] + 2[H_2P_2O_7^{-2}]$$

Eliminating $[H_3P_2O_7^-]$ between (1) and (2)

(5) $$\frac{[H^+]^2[H_2P_2O_7^{-2}]}{[H_4P_2O_7]} = 1.5 \times 10^{-3}$$

Eliminating $[H_3P_2O_7^-]$ between (3) and (4)

(6) $$[H^+] - 2[H_2P_2O_7^{-2}] = 0.1 - [H_2P_2O_7^{-2}] - [H_4P_2O_7]$$

Eliminating $[H_3P_2O_7^-]$ between (1) and (4)

(7) $$\frac{[H^+]([H^+] - 2[H_2P_2O_7^{-2}])}{[H_4P_2O_7]} = 1.4 \times 10^{-1}$$

$$[H^+]^2 - 2[H_2P_2O_7^{-2}][H^+] = 1.4 \times 10^{-1}[H_4P_2O_7]$$

Eliminating $[H_4P_2O_7]$ between (5) and (6)

(8) $$\frac{[H^+]^2[H_2P_2O_7^{-2}]}{1.54 \times 10^{-3}} = 0.1 + [H_2P_2O_7^{-2}] - [H^+]$$

Eliminating $[H_4P_2O_7]$ between (5) and (7)

(9) $$\frac{[H^+]^2 - 2[H_2P_2O_7^{-2}][H^+]}{1.4 \times 10^{-1}} = \frac{[H^+]^2[H_2P_2O_7^{-2}]}{1.54 \times 10^{-3}}$$

$$\frac{1.1 \times 10^{-2}[H^+]}{2.2 \times 10^{-2} + [H^+]} = [H_2P_2O_7^{-2}]$$

Eliminating $[H_2P_2O_7^{-2}]$ between (8) and (9)

(10) $$[H^+]^3 + 1.4 \times 10^{-1}[H^+]^2 - 1.245 \times 10^{-2}[H^+] - 3.08 \times 10^{-4} = 0$$

Solving the cubic equation for $[H^+]$ gives

$$[H^+] = 7.7 \times 10^{-2}\ M$$

From (4) $$[H_3P_2O_7^-] + 2[H_2P_2O_7^{-2}] = 7.7 \times 10^{-2}\ M$$

and from (2) $$\frac{(7.7 \times 10^{-2})[H_2P_2O_7^{-2}]}{7.7 \times 10^{-2} - 2[H_2P_2O_7^{-2}]} = 1.1 \times 10^{-2}$$

Therefore

$$[H_2P_2O_7^{-2}] = 8.6 \times 10^{-3}\ M$$
$$[H_3P_2O_7^-] = 6.0 \times 10^{-2}\ M$$
and $$[H_4P_2O_7] = 3.1 \times 10^{-2}\ M$$

Thus the first ionization has occurred to the extent of 69 percent and the second to 14.3 percent, a result which is significantly different from that of the simplified calculation.

From the relationship

$$\frac{[H^+][HP_2O_7^{-3}]}{[H_2P_2O_7^{-2}]} = \frac{(7.7 \times 10^{-2})(HP_2O_7^{-3})}{8.6 \times 10^{-3}} = 2.9 \times 10^{-7}$$

$$[HP_2O_7^{-3}] = 3.2 \times 10^{-8}\ M$$

which is insignificant in comparison to the other concentrations. It was thus justified to ignore the third (and fourth) ionizations.

6–12. Questions and Problems

1. Is there any evidence to suggest that any of the indicators shown in Fig. 5–3 are dibasic acids or diacid bases?

2. Explain in what way the second ionization of H_3PO_4 is affected by the first.

3. Explain why the molar concentration of SO_4^{-2} in a H_2SO_4 solution is not numerically equal to the second ionization constant of the acid.

4. Explain how CuS can be precipitated from a 1 molar strong acid solution while FeS cannot.

5. Explain why ZnS precipitated with H_2S in the presence of Fe^{+2} always contains a little FeS, even though the $[H^+]$ is too high for the precipitation of FeS alone.

6. Explain why in a 10^{-5} molar solution of oxalic acid, you cannot take

$$[H^+] = [HC_2O_4^-]$$

7. Explain why, although most heavy metal phosphates are much less soluble in water than the corresponding heavy metal sulfates, they are much more soluble in dilute acids than the corresponding sulfates.

8. Carbonic acid belongs to the class of substances known as carboxylic acids, for which the general formula is XCO_2H (in H_2CO_3, $X = OH$). For all of these acids $K_A = 10^{-5}$ or larger. Explain why the measured K_A for carbonic acid solutions is only 4.2×10^{-7}.

9. Explain why insoluble carbonates cannot be precipitated from CO_2 solutions as insoluble sulfides can from H_2S solutions.

10. Discuss the mechanism of precipitation of insoluble sulfides.

11. The K_{sp} of $FePO_4$ is $10^{-21.89}$, while that of $CoS(a)$ is $10^{-21.3}$; Yet CoS can be precipitated by adding H_2S to a Co^{+2}, while $FePO_4$ cannot be precipitated by adding H_3PO_4 to a Fe^{+3} solution. Explain.

12. In a saturated solution of $Hg(OH)_2$ $[HgOH^+]$ is not equal to $[OH^-]$. Explain.

13. Calculate the H^+ concentration in each of the following solutions:

(a) 0.05 M H_3BO_3 (d) 0.1 M KHC_2O_4
(b) 0.1 M H_3PO_4 (e) 0.01 M KH_2PO_4
(c) 0.001 M H_2S (f) 0.1 M $K_2Cr_2O_7$

14. Calculate the H^+ concentration of a 0.04 M H_2SO_4 solution.

15. Calculate the sulfide-ion concentration of saturated H_2S solutions having the following pH's
  (a) 0.0   (d) 4.8
  (b) 2.0   (e) 5.9
  (c) 3.5

16. Calculate the concentration of the anion Y^{-n} in each of the following solutions of H_nY
  (a) 0.1 M H_2SeO_4 (e) 10^{-3} M $H_2C_2O_4$
  (b) 10^{-5} M H_2PHO_3 (f) 10^{-2} M H_3AsO_4
  (c) 0.01 M H_2S (g) 10^{-6} M H_3PO_4
  (d) 10^{-3} M $Hg(SH)_2$ (h) 10^{-4} M $H_2Fe(CO)_4$

17. (a) If 0.1 M $CuCl_2$ is precipitated with H_2S, what is the $[H^+]$ after precipitation?
  (b) If 0.1 M $Cu(C_2H_3O_2)_2$ is precipitated with H_2S what is the $[H^+]$ after precipitation?

18. Calculate the concentrations of H_3PO_4, H^+, $H_2PO_4^-$, HPO_4^{-2}, and PO_4^{-3} in a 0.4 M solution of H_3PO_4.

19. What is the minimum concentration of HCl required to dissolve 1 gram of freshly precipitated CuS in 5 liters of solution?

20. What is the $[H^+]$ of a solution containing 0.1 molar $NaHSO_4$ and 0.1 molar Na_2SO_4?

21. What is the pH of a solution containing 0.05 M $NaHC_2O_4$ and 0.01 M $Na_2C_2O_4$?

22. Calculate the total $[H_2SO_4]$ of a solution of H_2SO_4 known to have a pH of 2.3.

6–13. References

COPRECIPITATION OF SULFIDES

Loczka, J., *Journal of the Chemical Society* (London), Vol. 76, II (1899), p. 100.

Hawley, L., *Journal of the American Chemical Society*, Vol. 29 (1907), p. 1011.

Kolthoff, I. M., and Pearson, E., *Journal of Physical Chemistry*, Vol. 36 (1932), p. 549.

Kolthoff, I. M., and Griffith, F. S., *Journal of the American Chemical Society*, Vol. 60 (1938), p. 2036.

SPECIFIC

Chromic Acid: Neuss, J. D., and Rieman, III, W., *Journal of the American Chemical Society*, Vol. 36 (1934), p. 2238.

Ringbom, A., "Solubilities of Sulfides," *Report to Analytical Section*, I.U.P.A.C., July, 1953.

AgSH: Treadwell, W. D., and Hepenstrick, H., *Helvetica Chemica Acta*, Vol. 32 (1949), p. 1872.

Hg(SH)$_2$: Treadwell, W. D., and Schaufelberger, F., *ibid.*, Vol. 29 (1946), p. 1936.

HAsS$_2$: Höltje, R., *Zeitschrift für anorganische Chemie*, Vol. 181 (1929), p. 395.

Chapter 7

Hydrolysis. The Alkali-Insoluble
Hydroxides and Sulfides

7–1. The Ionization of Water

We have already seen that water undergoes self-ionization to a slight degree and is thus a typical ampholyte, acting simultaneously as acid and as base

$$H_2O \rightleftharpoons H^+ + OH^-$$

$$\frac{[H^+][OH^-]}{[H_2O]} = 1.8 \times 10^{-16}$$

Since 1 liter of pure water at 25°C contains 55.35 moles of water, it is easy to see that the concentration of un-ionized water will not be significantly changed (less than 2 percent), even for hydrogen-ion or hydroxide-ion concentrations as high as one molar. Consequently, the concentration of un-ionized water, $[H_2O]$, may be considered as constant, and is customarily lumped with the ionization constant to give what is known as the *ion-product constant*, or the *water constant*, K_w

$$\frac{[H^+][OH^-]}{55.35} = 1.81 \times 10^{-16}$$

$$[H^+][OH^-] = 1.0 \times 10^{-14} = K_w$$

It can now be seen that in pure water, where $[H^+] = [OH^-]$, $X^2 = 1.0 \times 10^{-14}$, and $X = [H^+] = [OH^-] = 10^{-7}$ *M*. Consequently, pure water or *neutral* aqueous solutions have pH = 7 (Section 1–14). If anything is done to change the hydrogen-ion or hydroxide-ion concentration, the equilibrium $H_2O \rightleftharpoons H^+ + OH^-$ must shift, but the product $[H^+] \times [OH^-]$ must always be 1×10^{-14} in dilute solutions. It makes no difference whether NaOH is added to water, increasing the hydroxide-ion concentration, or whether NH_3 is added, lowering the hydrogen-ion concentration $(NH_3 + H^+ \rightleftharpoons NH_4^+)$;

the concentration of the H^+ must decrease or the concentration of the OH^- must increase, so that $[H^+][OH^-] = 1 \times 10^{-14}$. Likewise, it makes no difference whether HCl is added, increasing the H^+ concentration, or whether $AuCl_3$ is added, decreasing the OH^- concentration ($AuCl_3 + OH^- \rightleftharpoons AuCl_3OH^-$); the OH^- concentration must decrease or the H^+ concentration must increase, so that $[H^+][OH^-] = 1 \times 10^{-14}$.

Since water is by far the most common solvent for chemical reactions—almost the only one in qualitative inorganic analysis—the self-ionization of water and its possible effects on the reactions taking place must always be kept in mind.

One consequence of the self-ionization of water is the limiting effect on acidity and basicity, to which we have just referred, since the relationship $[H^+][OH^-] = 10^{-14}$ must always be obeyed in dilute aqueous solution. Thus an increase in $[H^+]$ must always be accompanied by a proportional decrease in $[OH^-]$.

We have also seen the effect of the water ionization on the ionization of very weak electrolytes, such as $Hg(OH)_2$ (Section 6–9), where the extent of the ionization $Hg(OH)_2 \rightleftharpoons HgOH^+ + OH^-$ was limited by the hydroxide-ion concentration, resulting from the fact that water ionizes to a greater degree than $Hg(OH)_2$. The same thing, of course, is true for very weak acids. Thus in solutions of phosphine ($K_A \approx 10^{-21}$) the contribution of H^+ from the ionization of water completely overwhelms that from the ionization of the phosphine.

7–2. The Hydrolysis of Anions

An extremely important effect of water on chemical reactions is through *hydrolysis*. Hydrolysis means merely cleavage or separation of a compound into two different products by reaction with water, according to the general molecular equation

$$BA + HOH \rightleftharpoons BOH + HA$$

as for example

$$NaNH_2 \text{ (s)} + H_2O \rightleftharpoons NaOH + NH_3$$

or actually

$$NaNH_2 \text{ (s)} + H_2O \rightleftharpoons Na^+ + OH^- + NH_3$$

The hydrolysis reaction may be considered to proceed through the prior ionization of water and the subsequent reaction of the ions so produced with the substance to be hydrolyzed. For example, in the hydrolysis of sodium acetate (or better, of the acetate ion), the following scheme may be visualized

$$C_2H_3O_2^- + H^+ \rightleftharpoons HC_2H_3O_2$$
$$+$$
$$OH^-$$
$$\Updownarrow$$
$$H_2O$$

It follows that even in the absence of free acetic acid intentionally added as such, an equilibrium will be established in water solution between the acetate ion and free acetic acid.

It should be fairly easy to see that the strength of the acid from which a given anion is derived will affect the degree of hydrolysis, since the weaker the acid is, the more strongly it holds its proton, and therefore the more strongly will the anion capture the proton from water. From considerations of the fact that the equilibria for both the ionization of the weak acid and for the ionization of water must be simultaneously obeyed, it should be possible to derive an equilibrium expression for the hydrolysis reaction. It should be observed that this is a situation exactly comparable to those to be discussed in Section 8–9, except for the fact that the concentration of one of the acids (H_2O) is constant.

When sodium acetate is dissolved in water, since the substance is a salt, it may be considered to give initially only Na^+ and Ac^-. The Na^+, being derived from a strong base, remains as such. The Ac^-, however, being derived from a weak acid, undergoes the hydrolysis reaction

$$Ac^- + H_2O \rightleftharpoons HAc + OH^-$$

This equation can be obtained by subtracting the equation for the ionization of the acid from that for the ionization of water.

$$H_2O \rightleftharpoons H^+ + OH^-$$
$$-(HAc \rightleftharpoons H^+ + Ac^-)$$
$$\overline{H_2O - HAc \rightleftharpoons OH^- - Ac^-}$$

or $$H_2O + Ac^- \rightleftharpoons OH^- + HAc$$

The corresponding mathematical expression is similarly obtained by dividing the expression for water equilibrium by that for the acid

$$[H^+][OH^-] = K_w$$

$$\frac{[H^+][Ac^-]}{[HAc]} = K_A$$

$$\frac{[H^+][OH^-]}{\dfrac{[H^+][Ac^-]}{[HAc]}} = \frac{[HAc][OH^-]}{[Ac^-]} = \frac{K_w}{K_A}$$

The quantity K_w/K_A is known as the *hydrolysis constant*; i.e., $K_w/K_A = K_H$. In the case of acetate ion, $K_w/K_A = \dfrac{1 \times 10^{-14}}{1.85 \times 10^{-5}} = 5.4 \times 10^{-10}$. It can be seen, then, that in fairly concentrated solution, the degree of hydrolysis of acetate ion is small. For example in a 0.1 M NaAc solution

$$[Ac^-] = 0.1\ M,\ [HAc] = [OH^-] = X$$

$$\frac{X^2}{0.1} = 5.4 \times 10^{-10}$$

and $$X = [HAc] = [OH^-] = 7.3 \times 10^{-6}\ M$$

The degree of hydrolysis, therefore, is

$$\frac{[\text{HAc}]}{[\text{Ac}^-]+[\text{HAc}]} = \frac{7.3 \times 10^{-6}}{0.1} = 7.3 \times 10^{-5} \text{ or } 0.0073 \text{ percent}$$

and the pH of the solution is

$$14.0 - \text{pOH} = 14.0 + \log(7.3 \times 10^{-6}) = 14.0 + (-6 + 0.86) = 8.86$$

The degree of hydrolysis of the salts of weaker acids is much greater. Thus sodium phenoxide, C_6H_5ONa, which is the salt of the weak acid phenol, has the hydrolysis constant

$$K_H = \frac{K_w}{K_A} = \frac{1.0 \times 10^{-14}}{1.0 \times 10^{-10}} = 1.0 \times 10^{-4} = \frac{[C_6H_5OH][OH^-]}{[C_6H_5O^-]}$$

In a 0.1 molar solution of C_6H_5ONa, then

$$[C_6H_5OH] = [OH^-] = X$$

$$[C_6H_5O^-] = 0.1$$

$$\frac{X^2}{0.1} = 1.0 \times 10^{-4}$$

$$X^2 = 1.0 \times 10^{-5}$$

and $$X = [OH^-] = [C_6H_5OH] = 3.2 \times 10^{-3} \ M$$

The degree of hydrolysis is therefore

$$\frac{[C_6H_5OH]}{\text{total}} \text{ or } 0.032 \text{ percent}$$

7–3. The Hydrolysis of Cations

The hydrolysis of the ammonium ion may be considered in the same light as the hydrolysis of anions

(1) $$\qquad NH_4^+ + H_2O \rightleftharpoons NH_4OH + H^+$$

or it may be considered merely as the ionization of NH_4^+ as an acid,

(2) $$\qquad NH_4^+ \rightleftharpoons NH_3 + H^+$$

Just as the mathematic treatments of the ionization of ammonia as a base (Section 5–9) did not change with the point of view, so it is the same for the hydrolysis of ammonium ion, regardless of which point of view is adopted. Thus equation (1) can be obtained by combining the equations for the ionizations of NH_4OH and H_2O

$$H_2O \rightleftharpoons H^+ + OH^-$$
$$\underline{-(NH_4OH \rightleftharpoons NH_4^+ + OH^-)}$$
$$H_2O - NH_4OH \rightleftharpoons H^+ - NH_4^+$$

or $$\qquad H_2O + NH_4^+ \rightleftharpoons NH_4OH + H^+$$

From

$$[H^+][OH^-] = K_w$$

and

$$\frac{[NH_4^+][OH^-]}{[NH_4OH]} = K_B$$

comes

$$\frac{[H^+][OH^-]}{\dfrac{[NH_4^+][OH^-]}{[NH_4OH]}} = \frac{[NH_4OH][H^+]}{[NH_4^+]} = \frac{K_w}{K_B} = K_H = \frac{1.0 \times 10^{-14}}{1.8 \times 10^{-5}} = 5.6 \times 10^{-10}$$

On the other hand, equation (2) can be obtained by combining

$$H_2O \rightleftharpoons H^+ + OH^-$$

and

$$-(NH_3 + H_2O \rightleftharpoons NH_4^+ + OH^-)$$

giving

$$\overline{-NH_3 \rightleftharpoons H^+ - NH_4^+}$$

or

$$NH_4^+ \rightleftharpoons NH_3 + H^+$$

Thus

$$[H^+][OH^-] = K_w$$

and

$$\frac{[NH_4^+][OH^-]}{[NH_3]} = K_B$$

combine

$$\frac{[H^+][OH^-]}{\dfrac{[NH_4^+][OH^-]}{[NH_3]}} = \frac{K_w}{K_B}$$

to give

$$\frac{[NH_3][H^+]}{[NH_4^+]} = \frac{K_w}{K_B} = 5.6 \times 10^{-10} = K_H = K_A \text{ for } NH_4^+.$$

The hydrolysis of metal cations is quite comparable to that of NH_4^+. For example, when a silver salt is dissolved in water, since AgOH (aq) is a weak base ($K_B = 5.0 \times 10^{-3}$), a hydrolysis reaction will take place.

$$Ag^+ + H_2O \rightleftharpoons AgOH \text{ (aq)} + H^+$$

The hydrolysis constant, $K_H = \dfrac{K_w}{K_B}$, as before. Therefore

$$\frac{[AgOH][H^+]}{[Ag^+]} = \frac{10^{-14}}{5.0 \times 10^{-3}} = 2.0 \times 10^{-12}$$

and if

$$[Ag^+] = 1 \ M \quad \text{and} \quad [AgOH] = [H^+]$$

then

$$\frac{X^2}{1} = 2.0 \times 10^{-12}$$

and

$$X = [AgOH] = [H^+] = 1.4 \times 10^{-6} \ M$$

The degree of hydrolysis in this case is very small, being

$$\frac{1.4 \times 10^{-6}}{1} = 0.00014 \text{ percent}$$

With a ferric salt, on the other hand

$$Fe^{+3} + H_2O \rightleftharpoons FeOH^{+2} + H^+$$

which can be seen to involve the *third* ionization of the triacid base $Fe(OH)_3$, which has the relationships

$$Fe(OH)_3 \text{ (s)} \rightleftharpoons Fe(OH)_2{}^+ + OH^- \qquad K_1 = 1 \times 10^{-16}$$
$$Fe(OH)_2{}^+ \rightleftharpoons FeOH^{+2} + OH^- \qquad K_2 = 5.0 \times 10^{-10}$$
$$FeOH^{+2} \rightleftharpoons Fe^{+3} + OH^- \qquad K_3 = 1.3 \times 10^{-12}$$

The first hydrolysis, therefore, will be

$$Fe^{+3} + H_2O \rightleftharpoons FeOH^{+2} + H^+$$

and
$$\frac{[FeOH^{+2}][H^+]}{[Fe^{+3}]} = \frac{K_w}{K_{3'}} = \frac{1 \times 10^{-14}}{1.3 \times 10^{-12}} = 7.7 \times 10^{-3}$$

In a 0.1 molar ferric salt solution then

$$[FeOH^{+2}] = [H^+] = X \quad \text{and} \quad [Fe^{+3}] = 0.1 - X$$

and
$$\frac{X^2}{0.1 - X} = 7.7 \times 10^{-3}$$

so that
$$X = [FeOH^{+2}] = [H^+] = 2.4 \times 10^{-2} \ M.$$

The degree of hydrolysis is thus $2.4 \times 10^{-2}/0.1 = 24$ percent, leaving $[Fe^{+3}] = 7.6 \times 10^{-2} \ M$, and the pH is 1.6, or very strongly acidic.

Hydrolysis may even occur beyond this stage. Considering the second hydrolysis step

$$FeOH^{+2} + H_2O \rightleftharpoons Fe(OH)_2{}^+ + H^+$$

for which

$$\frac{[Fe(OH)_2{}^+][H^+]}{[FeOH^{+2}]} = \frac{K_w}{K_2} = \frac{1 \times 10^{-14}}{5.0 \times 10^{-10}} = 2.0 \times 10^{-5}$$

$$y = [Fe(OH)_2{}^+] \quad \text{and} \quad [FeOH^{+2}] = [H^+] = 2.4 \times 10^{-2}$$

so that
$$y = 2 \times 10^{-5} \ M = [Fe(OH)_2{}^+]$$

Thus 0.02 percent of the total Fe(III) or 0.083 percent of the $FeOH^{+2}$ is hydrolyzed further. Thus the most important species in a 0.1 molar ferric salt solution—such as $Fe(ClO_4)_3$—are Fe^{+3} and $FeOH^{+2}$.

In the case of a cation like Hg^{+2}, where the first and second ionization constants for $Hg(OH)_2$ (aq) are $K_1 = 1 \times 10^{-14}$ and $K_2 = 1.2 \times 10^{-8}$, hydrolysis is even more extensive. For the first step in the hydrolysis of a $1\ M\ Hg^{+2}$ solution, we have

$$Hg^{+2} + H_2O \rightleftharpoons HgOH^+ + H^+$$

$$\frac{[HgOH^+][H^+]}{[Hg^{+2}]} = \frac{K_w}{K_2} = \frac{1 \times 10^{-14}}{1.2 \times 10^{-8}} = 8.3 \times 10^{-7}$$

and if $[HgOH^+] = [H^+] = X$, and $[Hg^{+2}] = 1$

$$\frac{X^2}{1} = 8.3 \times 10^{-7}$$

and

$$X = [HgOH^+] = [H^+] = 9.1 \times 10^{-4}$$

The second step in the hydrolysis is

$$HgOH^+ + H_2O \rightleftharpoons Hg(OH)_2\ (aq) + H^+$$

$$\frac{[Hg(OH)_2][H^+]}{[HgOH^+]^+} = \frac{K_w}{K_1} = \frac{1 \times 10^{-14}}{1 \times 10^{-14}} = 1$$

Therefore, if $[HgOH^+] = [H^+]$, then $Hg(OH)_2$ must be 1 molar, which considering that the solubility of $Hg(OH)_2$ is only 2.3×10^{-4} molar, is impossible, and $Hg(OH)_2$ (s) (or rather HgO) precipitates.

A better attack on this particular problem is the following: The K_{sp} of HgO is 2.7×10^{-26}

$$HgO\ (s) + H_2O \rightleftharpoons Hg^{+2} + 2\ OH^-$$

For the hydrolysis producing a precipitate of HgO, then

$$Hg^{+2} + H_2O \rightleftharpoons HgO\ (s) + 2\ H^+$$

which can be derived from

and

$$2\ H_2O \rightleftharpoons 2\ H^+ + 2\ OH^-$$
$$\underline{-(HgO\ (s) + H_2O \rightleftharpoons Hg^{+2} + 2\ OH^-)}$$
$$H_2O - HgO\ (s) \rightleftharpoons 2\ H^+ - Hg^{+2}$$

or

$$Hg^{+2} + H_2O \rightleftharpoons HgO\ (s) + 2\ H^+$$

Therefore, for the over-all hydrolysis

$$\frac{[H^+]^2[OH^-]^2}{[Hg^{+2}][OH^-]^2} = \frac{[H^+]^2}{[Hg^{+2}]} = \frac{K_w^{\ 2}}{K_{sp}} = \frac{1 \times 10^{-28}}{2.7 \times 10^{-26}} = 3.7 \times 10^{-3}$$

Now if the partial hydrolysis products are ignored, it can be seen that if X moles of Hg^{+2} hydrolyze and precipitate as HgO, $2X$ moles of H^+ are produced, and $(1 - X)$ moles of Hg^{+2} are left in solution. Therefore

$$\frac{(2X)^2}{1 - X} = 3.7 \times 10^{-3}$$

and

$$X = 3.0 \times 10^{-2}\ M, \quad 2X = [H^+] = 6.0 \times 10^{-2}\ M$$

and

$$(1 - X) = [Hg^{+2}] = 0.97\ M$$

so that about 3 percent of the Hg^{+2} has precipitated out as HgO. The $[HgOH^+] = 1.34 \times 10^{-5}$ M from the expression for the first hydrolysis step. Since the concentrations of $HgOH^+$ and $Hg(OH)_2$ $(2.3 \times 10^{-4}$ $M)$ are small in comparison to the concentration of Hg^{+2}, we were justified in ignoring them in our treatment of the problem.

7–4. The Hydrolysis of Cations from the Brønsted Point of View

The cations of the metals in water solution are all more or less solvated. Consequently, when an equation such as $Fe^{+3} + H_2O \rightleftharpoons FeOH^{+2} + H^+$ is written, it must be realized that this is in fact only a shorthand representation for a reaction of the complex cation $Fe(H_2O)_6^{+3}$. A better representation of the reaction would be

$$Fe(H_2O)_6^{+3} \rightleftharpoons Fe(H_2O)_5OH^{+2} + H^+$$

or, from the Brønsted point of view (Section 5–9)

$$Fe(H_2O)_6^{+3} + H_2O \rightleftharpoons Fe(H_2O)_5OH^{+2} + OH_3^+$$

The "hydrolysis" of the cation can thus be seen to be the equivalent of its ionization as an acid. Each cation in aqueous solution then has an acid ionization constant which is the same as the hydrolysis constant. For example

$$Fe(H_2O)_6^{+3} \rightleftharpoons Fe(H_2O)_5OH^{+2} + H^+ \qquad K_1 = 7.7 \times 10^{-3}$$
$$Fe(H_2O)_5OH^{+2} \rightleftharpoons Fe(H_2O)_4(OH)_2^+ + H^+ \qquad K_2 = 2.0 \times 10^{-5}$$
$$Hg(H_2O)_2^{+2} \rightleftharpoons Hg(H_2O)OH^+ + H^+ \qquad K_1 = 8.3 \times 10^{-7}$$
$$Hg(H_2O)OH^+ \rightleftharpoons Hg(OH)_2 \text{ (aq)} + H^+ \qquad K_2 = 1$$
$$Ag(H_2O)_2^+ \rightleftharpoons Ag(H_2O)OH \text{ (aq)} + H^+ \qquad K_1 = 2.0 \times 10^{-11}$$
$$Ag(H_2O)OH \text{ (aq)} \rightleftharpoons Ag(OH)_2^- + H^+ \qquad K_2 = 5.0 \times 10^{-12}$$

7–5. Buffer Solutions

Buffer solutions are solutions containing both a weak acid and its salt, or both a weak base and its salt. These solutions tend to resist (or act as a buffer against) change in pH. Thus if 0.01 mole of HCl is added to a liter of pure water, the pH changes from 7 to 2. On the other hand, if 0.01 mole of HCl is added to a liter of solution containing 0.185 M $NaC_2H_3O_2$ and 10^{-3} M $HC_2H_3O_2$ (which has pH $= 7$), the pH changes only from 7 to 5.9. This is because of the combination of the added H^+ with the $C_2H_3O_2^-$ to produce slightly ionized $HC_2H_3O_2$. Until enough strong acid has been added to transform essentially all of the $C_2H_3O_2^-$ into $HC_2H_3O_2$, the pH of the solution will fall very slowly. After all the $C_2H_3O_2^-$ has been used up, the pH will be essentially equal to that expected from the excess strong acid alone.

The pH of a buffer solution depends on the particular acid-salt (or base-salt) system used and to a first approximation upon the *relative* (not absolute) concentrations of the components. (At high concentrations deviations occur because the activity coefficients deviate significantly from unity, as described in Section 5–7.) The $[H^+]$ can be calculated directly from the acid ionization equilibrium. (This is just a case of common ion effect.) Thus, in the case above

$$\frac{[H^+][Ac^-]}{[HAc]} = \frac{[H^+](0.185)}{10^{-3}} = 1.85 \times 10^{-5}$$

$$[H^+] = 1.0 \times 10^{-7} \, M$$

After 0.01 mole of HCl had been added

$$\begin{array}{cccc} H^+ + & Ac^- & \rightarrow & HAc \\ X & (0.185 - 0.01) & & (0.01 + 0.001) \end{array}$$

$$\frac{[H^+](0.175)}{1.1 \times 10^{-2}} = 1.85 \times 10^{-5}$$

$$[H^+] = 1.16 \times 10^{-6} \, M$$

$$pH = 5.9$$

On the other hand, if 0.2 mole of strong acid is added, essentially all the acetate ion would be used up and $0.2 - 0.185 = 0.015$ mole of free H^+ would be left over, so that

$$\begin{array}{cccc} H^+ & + & C_2H_3O_2^- & \rightarrow & HC_2H_3O_2 \\ (0.015 + X) & & X & & (0.185 + 0.001) \end{array}$$

$$\frac{(0.015 + X)(X)}{0.186} = 1.85 \times 10^{-5}$$

$$X = [C_2H_3O_2^-] = 2.3 \times 10^{-4}$$

The difference between 0.015 and 0.0152 can be neglected, and the hydrogen-ion concentration may be said to be essentially the same as the concentration of excess strong acid.

Since the ionization equilibrium for the weak acid or base and the hydrolysis equilibrium for the salt differ only by the presence or absence of H^+ or OH^-, the hydrolysis equilibrium may be used when more convenient, instead of the ionization equilibrium, for calculations involving buffer solutions. For example, to calculate the $[H^+]$ of a solution containing 0.1 M NH_4OH and 0.05 M NH_4Cl, use of the $NH_4OH \rightleftharpoons NH_4^+ + OH^-$ equilibrium would give $[OH^-]$, and a second calculation would be necessary in order to obtain $[H^+]$. However, from the hydrolysis equilibrium, $[H^+]$ is obtained directly.

$$\frac{[NH_4OH][H^+]}{[NH_4^+]} = \frac{K_w}{K_B}$$

$$\frac{10^{-1}[H^+]}{5 \times 10^{-2}} = \frac{1 \times 10^{-14}}{1.8 \times 10^{-5}}$$

$$[H^+] = 2.8 \times 10^{-10} \, M$$

Likewise, to find [OH⁻] in a solution containing 0.01 M NaHCO₃ and 0.2 M Na₂CO₃

$$\frac{[\text{HCO}_3{}^-][\text{OH}^-]}{[\text{CO}_3{}^{-2}]} = \frac{K_w}{K_2}$$

$$\frac{10^{-2}[\text{OH}^-]}{0.2} = \frac{1 \times 10^{-14}}{4.8 \times 10^{-11}}$$

$$[\text{OH}^-] = 4.2 \times 10^{-3}\ M$$

7–6. The Hydrolysis of the Anions of Polybasic Acids

The anions of polybasic acids hydrolyze in two or more steps. For example, Na₂S, a salt of H₂S undergoes the two successive reactions

$$\text{S}^{-2} + \text{H}_2\text{O} \rightleftharpoons \text{HS}^- + \text{OH}^-$$
and
$$\text{HS}^- + \text{H}_2\text{O} \rightleftharpoons \text{H}_2\text{S} + \text{OH}^-$$

The hydrolysis constants for the two reactions are, respectively

$$\frac{[\text{HS}^-][\text{OH}^-]}{[\text{S}^{-2}]} = \frac{K_w}{K_2} = \frac{1 \times 10^{-14}}{1.3 \times 10^{-13}} = 0.077$$

and
$$\frac{[\text{H}_2\text{S}][\text{OH}^-]}{[\text{HS}^-]} = \frac{K_w}{K_1} = \frac{1 \times 10^{-14}}{1 \times 10^{-7}} = 1 \times 10^{-7}$$

However, since the hydrolysis constant for the first step is so much larger than that for the second, the second step is negligible in comparison to the first, and only the first need be considered. Thus, in calculating the concentration of H₂S (aq) in equilibrium with (say) a 0.01 M Na₂S solution,

$$X = [\text{HS}^-] = [\text{OH}^-], \quad [\text{S}^{-2}] = 0.01 - X$$
and
$$\frac{X^2}{0.01 - X} = 0.077$$

$$X = [\text{HS}^-] = [\text{OH}^-] = 9.0 \times 10^{-3}\ M$$

For the second step, then

$$\frac{[\text{H}_2\text{S}](9.0 \times 10^{-3})}{(9.0 \times 10^{-3})} = 1 \times 10^{-7}\ M = [\text{H}_2\text{S}]$$

From this it can be seen that the second hydrolysis step can be treated in exactly the same way as the second ionization step of a polybasic acid (Section 6–1). The molar concentration of the product of the second hydrolysis step is numerically equal to the second hydrolysis constant.

On the other hand, if the first and second hydrolysis constants are very close together, the second step cannot be ignored. For example, the disodium salt of 3,3'-dihydroxybiphenyl, Na₂C₁₂H₈O₂, for which the free acid has

$K_1 = 1 \times 10^{-10}$ and $K_2 = 2 \times 10^{-11}$, has first and second hydrolysis constants of 5×10^{-4} and 1×10^{-5}. In a 10^{-4} molar solution of the disodium salt, then, if

$$X = [HC_{12}H_8O_2^-] = [OH^-], \quad \text{and} \quad [C_{12}H_8O_2^{-2}] = 10^{-4} - X$$

$$\frac{X^2}{10^{-4} - X} = 5 \times 10^{-4}$$

$$X = [OH^-] = [HC_{12}H_8O_2^-] = 8.5 \times 10^{-5} \, M$$

which is 85 percent. If the molar concentration of the second hydrolysis product, $H_2C_{12}H_8O_2$, now be taken as equal numerically to the second hydrolysis constant, 1×10^{-5}, it can be seen that it will be 12 percent of the $HC_{12}H_8O_2^-$ concentration, and cannot be ignored. The correct solution of this problem is quite the same as that for the ionization of $H_4P_2O_7$, treated in Section 6–11.

7-7. The Hydrolysis of the Salts of Weak Acids and Weak Bases

Salts derived from both a weak acid and a weak base undergo hydrolysis in both their parts. Thus, with the salt $NH_4C_2H_3O_2$

$$NH_4^+ + H_2O \rightleftharpoons NH_4OH + H^+$$

and $$C_2H_3O_2^- + H_2O \rightleftharpoons HC_2H_3O_2 + OH^-$$

or, over-all, $NH_4^+ + C_2H_3O_2^- + H_2O \rightleftharpoons NH_4OH + HC_2H_3O_2$

for which the hydrolysis constant

$$K_H = \frac{[NH_4OH][HAc]}{[NH_4^+][Ac^-]}$$

This is obtained from the individual hydrolysis expressions by multiplying them together

$$\frac{[NH_4OH][H^+]}{[NH_4^+]} \times \frac{[HAc][OH^-]}{[Ac^-]} = \frac{K_w^2}{K_A K_B}$$

and observing that both sides can be divided through by $[H^+][OH^-] = K_w$, to give

$$\frac{[NH_4OH][HAc]}{[NH_4^+][Ac^-]} = \frac{K_w}{K_A K_B} = K_H = 3.0 \times 10^{-5}$$

Provided the concentration of the salt is neither too high nor too low, it can be said in general that the concentration of free weak base and that of free weak acid produced by hydrolysis will be equal. Or, on the other hand, if K_A and K_B are about the same (as they are for NH_4Ac), then the free acid and base concentrations at all salt concentrations will be equal. If this assumption can be made, then an expression for the hydrogen-ion concentration in such a solution can be derived as follows:

If $\qquad [NH_4OH] = [HAc], \quad$ then $\quad [NH_4^+] = [Ac^-]$

and $\qquad \dfrac{[NH_4OH]}{[NH_4^+]} = \dfrac{[HAc]}{[Ac^-]}$

Therefore

$$\frac{[NH_4OH][HAc]}{[NH_4^+][Ac^-]} = \frac{[HAc]^2}{[Ac^-]^2} = \frac{K_w}{K_A K_B}$$

However, from the ionization of HAc

$$\frac{[HAc]}{[Ac^-]} = \frac{[H^+]}{K_A}$$

Therefore

$$\frac{[H^+]^2}{K_A{}^2} = \frac{K_w}{K_A K_B}$$

and $\qquad [H^+] = \sqrt{\dfrac{K_A K_w}{K_B}}$

It can be seen, then, that if the conditions are such that $[HA] \approx [BOH]$ (i.e., the concentration is neither too high nor too low, and K_A and K_B not too greatly different), then the hydrogen-ion concentration is independent of the concentration, and depends only on the values of the constants involved. Thus, for NH_4Ac

$$[H^+] = \sqrt{\frac{1.85 \times 10^{-5} \times 1 \times 10^{-14}}{1.8 \times 10^{-5}}} = 1.0 \times 10^{-7}\ M$$

On the other hand, for NH_4CN

$$[H^+] = \sqrt{\frac{4.0 \times 10^{-10} \times 1 \times 10^{-14}}{1.8 \times 10^{-5}}} = 4.7 \times 10^{-10}\ M$$

A more rigorous treatment of these systems is given in Appendix 2.

7–8. The Insoluble Hydroxide Group

One of the solubility rules cited in Section 1–1 is

> The hydroxides of all the elements except those of the alkali and heavy alkaline earth elements are insoluble.

As you are by now well aware, this rule is only a crude statement of a trend. In actual fact, the solubilities of the hydroxides vary in a more or less regular way from one part of the periodic table to another, and specifically depend on the electronegativity and oxidation state of the cation. It has already been pointed out that the solubilities of the covalent halides (Section 4–3) and chalcogenides (Section 5-1) are a function of the difference in electro-negativity between the metal and the nonmetal involved. The hydroxides of the metals are also sufficiently covalent that their pK_{sp}'s show the same variation with change in electronegativity as do those of the halides and chalcogenides. We find that for

$$MOH, \ pK_{sp} = 36.2 - 18.1\Delta x$$
$$M(OH)_2, \ pK_{sp} = 64.7 - 24.2\Delta x$$
$$M(OH)_3, \ pK_{sp} = 100.8 - 35.3\Delta x$$
$$M(OH)_4, \ pK_{sp} = 133.1 - 43.8\Delta x$$

(For the purposes of these relationships, the electronegativity of the hydroxyl group was taken to be the same as that of oxygen, 3.5.)

Since the electronegativity of the elements decreases generally toward the left in the periodic table, the solubility of both the sulfides and hydroxides increases toward the left. The solubility of the sulfides, however, increases faster than the solubility of the hydroxides. Consequently, whereas the sulfides of the elements to the right of chromium will precipitate in preference to the hydroxides, the reverse is so for the elements to the left of chromium, the hydroxides precipitating in preference to the sulfides in neutral and moderately basic solution. Likewise, as the oxidation state of any given element is raised, the precipitation of the hydroxide tends to be favored over precipitation of the sulfide.

For example, for Bi_2S_3, we calculate

$$pK_{sp} = 235.1 - 171.7(0.7) = 115$$

whereas for $Bi(OH)_3$

$$pK_{sp} = 100.8 - 35.5(1.7) = 40$$

Consequently, the $[Bi^{+3}]$ required to precipitate Bi_2S_3 is very much smaller than that required for $Bi(OH)_3$ and even low sulfide-ion concentrations will precipitate the former without appreciable hydrolysis.

On the other hand, for Y_2S_3

$$pK_{sp} = 235.1 - 171.7(1.3) = 12$$

whereas for $Y(OH)_3$

$$pK_{sp} = 100.8 - 35.5(2.3) = 19$$

Consequently, only the hydroxide can be precipitated from aqueous solution.

Iron(III) is a borderline case. When the $[S^{-2}]/[OH^-]$ ratio is high, Fe_2S_3 precipitates, whereas at low $[S^{-2}]/[OH^-]$ ratios, $Fe(OH)_3$ comes down. (However, in acidic solutions neither reaction takes place, because either the reaction

$$2\ Fe^{+3} + 3\ H_2S \rightarrow 2\ FeS\ (s) + S\ (s) + 6\ H^+$$

or the reaction

$$2\ Fe^{+3} + H_2S \rightarrow 2\ Fe^{+2} + S\ (s) + 2\ H^+$$

takes precedence, depending on the actual acidity.)

In practical analysis, those elements not forming ammine complexes are often precipitated in the absence of sulfide ion as hydroxides with NH_4OH. The hydroxides of the lower oxidation states of many of these elements, however, are too soluble to be completely precipitated by the weak base NH_4OH. Of the hydroxides to be dealt with here, the ones in this class are $Mn(OH)_2$, and $Fe(OH)_2$. These elements will be present in the lower oxidation states due to the reducing action of the H_2S used to precipitate the acid-insoluble sulfide group, as shown above. Because the higher hydroxides are considerably less soluble, it is advisable to oxidize these elements to the less soluble $Fe(OH)_3$ and $Mn(OH)_3$. There is no oxidizing agent *theoretically* capable of oxidizing $Mn(OH)_2$ to $Mn(OH)_3$ without also oxidizing the insoluble $Cr(OH)_3$ to soluble CrO_4^{-2}. However, *in practice* atmospheric oxygen oxidizes $Mn(OH)_2$ and $Fe(OH)_2$ many times more rapidly than it will oxidize $Cr(OH)_3$. Consequently, if the suspension of hydroxides in NH_4OH is shaken for a time in the air, manganese and iron will be oxidized to the less soluble higher hydroxides. (Cobalt will be simultaneously oxidized

$$4\ Co(NH_3)_6^{+2} + O_2\ (g) + 2\ H_2O \rightleftharpoons 4\ Co(NH_3)_6^{+3} + 4\ OH^-$$

but remains in solution as the ammine complex.) After oxidation, the elements in this group are found precipitated as $Al(OH)_3$, $Mn(OH)_3$ (also Mn_3O_4 and MnO_2), and $Cr(OH)_3$.

The insoluble hydroxides are best precipitated from a solution of limited hydroxide-ion concentration in order to prevent the precipitation of $Mg(OH)_2$ which is not very soluble. Limitation of the OH^- concentration is accomplished by buffering the NH_4OH solution with NH_4Cl, the NH_4^+ acting as a weak acid.

$$NH_4^+ + OH^- \rightleftharpoons NH_4OH$$
$$Mg(OH)_2\ (s) + NH_4^+ \rightleftharpoons MgOH^+ + NH_4OH$$

It is because of this intentional limitation of the OH^- concentration that it is especially important to oxidize manganese and iron, since $Mn(OH)_2$ and $Fe(OH)_2$ are only slightly less soluble than $Mg(OH)_2$.

It now must be recognized that, in order to perform the hydroxide precipitation as described, not only is the OH^- concentration of the solution decreased, but the NH_4^+ concentration is increased. Consequently, any element forming an insoluble ammonium salt will precipitate if present in the right oxidation state. Such an element is vanadium, which precipitates with the insoluble hydroxides, but as the slightly soluble ammonium metavanadate, NH_4VO_3. Since NH_4VO_3 is not extremely insoluble, the solution is saturated with NH_4Cl to decrease its solubility.

Advantage is taken of the fact that both vanadium and chromium in their anionic highest oxidation states from insoluble lead salts, $Pb_3(VO_4)_2$ and $PbCrO_4$, and also that they form colored peroxide complexes, to separate these elements from the rest of the group and identify them. In both these respects they are similar to the other elements in this part of the periodic table—Ti, Nb, Mo, Ta, W, and so on.

By virtue of the relationships just discussed, the next groups usually precipitated after the acid-insoluble sulfides are the remaining groups of elements whose sulfides and hydroxides, although not sufficiently insoluble to be precipitated in acid solution, may nevertheless be precipitated from alkaline solution where the concentrations of S^{-2} and OH^- are higher. The elements so precipitated are shown in Table 7–1.

TABLE 7–1. ELEMENTS HAVING SULFIDES* OR HYDROXIDES PRECIPITATING FROM WEAKLY ALKALINE BUT NOT FROM ACIDIC SOLUTION

Be										Al
——	Sc	Ti	V	Cr	**Mn**	**Fe**	**Co**	**Ni**	——	Zn	Ga
——	Y	Zr	Nb	——	——	——	——	——	——	——	In
——	La†	Hf	Ta	——	——	——	——	——	——	——	
——	Ac‡										

* Elements which can be precipitated as sulfides appear in bold face.
† La and the Lanthanides.   ‡ Ac and the Actinides.

7–9. The Elements of the Insoluble Hydroxide Group

The elements which are to be considered in this and the subsequent alkali-insoluble sulfide group are all transition elements except for aluminum (and zinc). The transition elements are characterized by variability of oxidation state, and this plays an important part in the analytical reactions of vanadium, chromium, manganese, iron, and cobalt.

These elements are all abundant, as can be seen by reference to Table 7–2. They all are reactive and are therefore never found native, with the exception of iron and nickel of meteoritic origin.

TABLE 7–2. PHYSICAL PROPERTIES OF ALUMINUM, VANADIUM, CHROMIUM, MANGANESE, AND IRON

	Aluminum	Vanadium	Chromium	Manganese	Iron
Symbol	Al	V	Cr	Mn	Fe
Atomic Number	13	23	24	25	26
Atomic Weight	26.97	50.95	52.01	54.93	55.84
Melting Point (°C)	658	1730	1550	1244	1539
Boiling Point (°C)	2330	3530	2475	2087	2800
Density, 20°C (g/ml)	2.70	5.9	7.1	7.2	7.86
Hardness (Moh)	2–2.9	>9.0*	9.0	5.0	4–5
Abundance in Earth's Crust (%)	8.13	1.7×10^{-4}	0.037	0.10	5.01
Radius of M^{+2} (Å)		0.82	0.80	0.83	0.80
Radius of M^{+3} (Å)	0.57	0.75	0.70		0.67
Standard Electrode Potential for					
$M \to M^{+2} + 2\,e^-$		≈ 1.18	0.91	1.18	0.440
$M \to M^{+3} + 3\,e^-$	1.66	0.87	0.74	0.28	0.036
Electronegativity	1.5	1.4(V(III)) 1.7(V(IV)) 1.9(V(V))	1.4(Cr(II)) 1.6(Cr(III)) 2.2(Cr(VI))	1.4(Mn(II)) 1.5(Mn(III)) 2.5(Mn(VII))	1.45(Fe(II)) 1.8(Fe(III))

* Harder than any other element except diamond.

They are all much less electronegative in their lower oxidation states than most of the elements discussed in Chapters 4 and 5. Consequently, except for such compounds as the hydroxides, sulfides, and the like, they tend to be more ionic, and their solubilities follow more closely the rules for ionic substances. Even when a compound such as $FeCl_3$ is covalent when anhydrous, it tends to become hydrated in water, so that the compound we are dealing with is the salt $[Fe(H_2O)_6]Cl_3$. The solubilities of the compounds of these elements are characteristic of the oxidation state, and compounds of the different elements in the same oxidation state are very similar, as can be seen by referring to Table A11–10.

In particular, it can be seen that the arsenates, carbonates, cyanoferrates(II), fluorides, hydroxides, iodates, oxalates, phosphates, sulfides, and certain double salts of the $+2$ and $+3$ states are sparingly soluble to insoluble, but most of the other compounds are soluble. The $+4$ states are very poorly characterized in acid solution, except for vanadium. The bright-blue vanadyl (VO^{+2}) salts are mostly soluble, except for the fluoride, hydroxide, and phosphate. The only tetravalent* compound of the other elements which can be produced in dilute aqueous acid is MnO_2 (or $MnO(OH)_2$). When this is dissolved in cold aqueous HCl, a brown-green solution is obtained which has been said to contain $MnCl_4$, but actually contains the complex ion $MnCl_6^{-2}$. If this solution is saturated with KCl, the dark-red crystalline compound K_2MnCl_6 precipitates. From 40 percent aqueous HF, by various means, can be obtained the golden-yellow crystalline K_2MnF_6. Several iodate complexes such as $K_2Mn(IO_3)_6$ are known, as well as a cyanide complex which is either $K_2Mn(CN)_6$ or $K_4Mn(CN)_8$. The simple fluoride, MnF_4, is not known. The simple chloride, $MnCl_4$, is known, but only in ether solution.

The two tetrahalides of chromium which are known, CrF_4 and $CrCl_4$, are both decomposed by water, giving a mixture of Cr(III) and Cr(VI) compounds. The fluoride is produced along with CrF_5 when CrF_3 (or other Cr(III) compound) is treated with F_2. The chloride is formed as a gas when $CrCl_3$ is treated with Cl_2 between 600 and 700°C. It can be condensed in liquid air to a solid, but begins to decompose into $CrCl_3$ and Cl_2 above $-80°C$.

The tetravalent states are amphoteric and somewhat more stable under basic conditions. Yellow or brown alkali salts of $VO(OH)_2$, such as $Na_2V_4O_9$, are easily obtained in aqueous solution by treating $VO(OH)_2$ with excess alkali hydroxide. Because $VO(OH)_2$ is such a weak acid, the anion tends to be polymeric, the most characteristic form being $V_4O_9^{-2}$. Likewise, $MnO(OH)_2$ dissolves in concentrated aqueous alkali to give salts of indefinite composition. If alkali hydroxides and MnO_2 are fused together, compounds such as $K_2Mn_2O_5$ are obtained. Salts of tetravalent iron can similarly be prepared under oxidizing conditions. The solution chemistry of Cr(IV), however, seems to be confined almost entirely to the ill-defined CrO_2.

---

* The terms "univalent," "divalent," and so on, are retained to mean "having an oxidation state of one, two, and so on."

The chemistries of the pentavalent states, except for that of pervanadyl ion, VO_2^+, are more properly deferred until Chapter 11, since the solution chemistry of these states is almost entirely that of the anions. The same is true of the $+6$ and $+7$ states.

The oxidation states which are of most concern to us here are Al(III), V(V), Cr(III), Mn(II), and Fe(II and III). The divalent states are basic, the hydroxides showing very little tendency to react with excess base (however, see Chapter 9). Because of the low electronegativities of the $+2$ cations, the hydroxides are fairly soluble, as discussed in Section 7–8. In the case of the trivalent hydroxides, $Al(OH)_3$ and $Cr(OH)_3$ are amphoteric, $Al(OH)_3$ dissolving very easily and $Cr(OH)_3$ somewhat less easily in excess alkali hydroxide, while $V(OH)_3$, $Mn(OH)_3$, and $Fe(OH)_3$ are not appreciably amphoteric (although $Fe(OH)_3$ will dissolve to a very slight extent in very concentrated alkali hydroxide). This allows a separation of these elements into two groups, since, when the mixed precipitated hydroxides are treated with excess alkali hydroxide, the hydroxides of manganese and iron remain unaffected, while the amphoteric hydroxides of aluminum, chromium, and (pentavalent) vanadium go into solution. In practice, this is usually done in the presence of a peroxide, so that chromium is oxidized to Cr(VI), in which state it is very readily soluble in alkali.

These elements are all good complex-ion formers. Advantage is taken of this in their confirmation reactions. The lake used to identify aluminum has already been described (Section 3–9). The peroxide complexes of chromium and vanadium permit both their separation and their identification, because the uniquely characteristic deep-blue complex of chromium(VI) is soluble in, and extractable into, organic solvents such as ether, ethyl acetate, alcohols, and the like, whereas the orange complex of vanadium is not. The chromium complex has been shown by Glasner and Steinberg to be CrO_5 or $CrO_3(H_2O_2)_2$, and has an instability constant of

$$\frac{[H_2O_2]^2[Cr_2O_7^{-2}]^{1/2}[H^+]}{[H_4CrO_7]} = 4.5 \times 10^{-5}$$

The orange vanadium complex is $VO(H_2O_2)^{+3}$, and has been shown by Tolmachev and Serpukhova to have an instability constant of

$$\frac{[VO^{+3}][H_2O_2]}{[H_2VO_3^{+3}]} = 7.8 \times 10^{-5}$$

There is another vanadium peroxide complex, containing more H_2O_2, which is colorless. It is formed with excess H_2O_2. Although the vanadium complex is stable, the chromium complex decomposes very rapidly, especially in water solution and in the presence of acid, according to the equation

$$2\,H_4CrO_7 + 6\,H^+ \rightarrow 2\,Cr^{+3} + 3\,O_2 + H_2O_2 + 6\,H_2O$$

It is considerably more stable when extracted into an organic solvent.

Iron is also frequently identified as its blood-red thiocyanate complex. Although complexes all the way up to $Fe(NCS)_6^{-3}$ have been identified, the species principally responsible for the color is $FeNCS^{+2}$, or more properly, $[Fe(H_2O)_5NCS]^{+2}$. This is a rather weak complex

$$\frac{[Fe^{+3}][NCS^-]}{[FeNCS^{+2}]} = 1.0 \times 10^{-3}$$

but the extreme intensity of its color makes possible detection of minute amounts of iron.

Another complex of iron is the insoluble deep-blue compound known as Prussian blue, and often formulated $Fe_4[Fe(CN)_6]_3$. This also is capable of revealing iron in minute traces. A similar compound, frequently formulated $Fe_3[Fe(CN)_6]_2$, is known as Turnbull's blue. Both of these tend to form exceedingly stable colloidal suspensions and under certain circumstances may be deep green instead of blue. Recent investigation indicates that they are in fact the same compound, which should be formulated $KFe_2(CN)_6 \cdot x\ H_2O$.

Manganese is usually confirmed by oxidation to the deep-purple permanganate ion. This is also a very sensitive test.

7–10. The Elements of the Alkali-Insoluble Sulfide Group

After removal of the insoluble chlorides, the acid-insoluble sulfides, and the NH_4OH-insoluble hydroxides, the only elements besides the alkali and alkaline-earth elements still remaining in solution are cobalt, nickel, and zinc, which form stable complexes with ammonia. These are closely related to the elements just discussed. Nickel is by far the most abundant of them, but none of them is exceedingly rare. They are relatively active metals and consequently are never found native, with the exception of meteoritic nickel. Their physical constants are given in Table 7–3.

TABLE 7–3. PHYSICAL PROPERTIES OF COBALT, NICKEL, AND ZINC

	Cobalt	*Nickel*	*Zinc*
Symbol	Co	Ni	Zn
Atomic Number	27	28	30
Atomic Weight	58.94	58.69	65.38
Melting Point (°C)	1493	1452	419.4
Boiling Point (°C)	3520	2800	907
Density, 20°C (g/ml)	8.9	8.9	7.14
Hardness (Moh)		6.0	2.5
Abundance in Earth's Crust (%)	1×10^{-5}	0.020	4×10^{-5}
Radius of M^{+2} (Å)	0.78	0.74	0.83
Radius of M^{+3} (Å)	0.65	?	Does not exist
Standard Electrode Potential for			
$\quad M \rightleftharpoons M^{+2} + 2\ e^-$	+0.277	+0.25	+0.762
$\quad M^{+2} \rightleftharpoons M^{+3} + 2\ e^-$	−1.84		
Electronegativity	1.5(Co^{+2})	1.5	1.5
	1.9(Co^{+3})		

Like the preceding group of elements, these three in their most characteristic $+2$ oxidation state have relatively low electronegativities. Consequently, except for their hydroxides, sulfides, and certain others, their compounds in water solution have most of the properties expected of ionic substances. Their arsenates, carbonates, cyanoferrates(II), fluorides, hydroxides, iodates, oxalates, phosphates, sulfides, and certain double salts are slightly soluble to insoluble, but most of the other salts are soluble, as can be seen by examining Table A11–11. The +3 state does not exist for zinc and is almost nonexistent for nickel. It is represented by only a handful of simple compounds for cobalt. However, trivalent cobalt in the form of complexes is extremely stable. In fact, trivalent cobalt forms more known complexes than any other element except platinum.

Zinc compounds are almost all colorless. Nickel compounds are green when hydrated or in solution, but yellow to brown when anhydrous. Cobalt(II) compounds are red when hydrated or in solution, but deep "cobalt" blue when anhydrous. This latter color change is taken advantage of in humidity indicators, for at low humidities the hydrated pink or red salts easily lose water to give the blue salts. At higher humidities, the reverse reaction takes place.

The ammine complexes are very characteristic of the water chemistry of these elements, but for the divalent states are rather weak, being considerably weaker than those of such elements as copper, palladium, silver, and so forth. From solutions having a very high NH_3 concentration, solid ammine salts can be obtained (e.g., $Ni(NH_3)_6Br_2$), but they lose ammonia very readily. The stepwise instability constants for the ammine complexes are given in Table 7–4.

TABLE 7–4. STEPWISE INSTABILITY CONSTANTS OF AMMINES OF
COBALT, NICKEL, AND ZINC

	K_1	K_2	K_3	K_4	K_5	K_6	Over-all Constant
Co^{+2}	1.0×10^{-2}	3.1×10^{-2}	1.1×10^{-1}	2.3×10^{-1}	8.7×10^{-1}	5.5	4.1×10^{-5}
Ni^{+2}	2.1×10^{-3}	7.6×10^{-3}	2.5×10^{-2}	8.5×10^{-2}	3.0×10^{-1}	1.2	9.8×10^{-9}
Zn^{+2}	6.6×10^{-3}	5.6×10^{-3}	4.9×10^{-3}	1.1×10^{-2}	——	——	2.0×10^{-9}
Co^{+3}	5.0×10^{-8}	2.0×10^{-7}	8.0×10^{-7}	2.5×10^{-6}	9.0×10^{-6}	3.9×10^{-5}	6.2×10^{-36}

The percentage of the various species present in ammoniacal solutions of $M(II)$ are given in Table 7–5.

TABLE 7–5. PERCENTAGE OF SPECIES IN AMMONIACAL SOLUTIONS OF COBALT(II),
NICKEL(II), AND ZINC(II)

	$1\ M\ NH_3$			$0.1\ M\ NH_3$			$0.01\ M\ NH_3$		
	Co	Ni	Zn	Co	Ni	Zn	Co	Ni	Zn
M^{+2}	0.004	5×10^{-6}	2×10^{-7}	1.3	0.006	0.002	42.6	6.9	6.34
$M(NH_3)^{+2}$	0.04	2×10^{-4}	3×10^{-5}	12.7	0.009	0.027	42.6	32.1	9.51
$M(NH_3)_2^{+2}$	1.5	0.029	0.005	41.0	0.11	0.48	13.3	42.2	17.3
$M(NH_3)_3^{+2}$	12.4	1.16	1.09	34.4	45.8	9.9	1.15	16.9	35.2
$M(NH_3)_4^{+2}$	35.1	13.5	98.9	9.4	53.9	89.6	0.03	2.0	31.7
$M(NH_3)_5^{+2}$	39.9	46.6	——	1.1	0.18	——	4×10^{-4}	0.07	——
$M(NH_3)_6^{+2}$	11.2	38.7	——	0.03	0.02	——	1×10^{-6}	6×10^{-4}	——

It can be seen that even in 1 M NH$_4$OH, the $M(NH_3)_6^{+2}$ species is not the most important one for cobalt and nickel, although they are present in considerable amount. In each case, the $M(NH_3)_5^{+2}$ species is predominant, although run a close second by $Ni(NH_3)_6^{+2}$ and $Co(NH_3)_4^{+2}$. The only important ion of zinc under these conditions is $Zn(NH_3)_4^{+2}$. In 0.1 M NH$_4$OH, the predominant species are $Co(NH_3)_2^{+2}$ and $Ni(NH_3)_4^{+2}$, in each case run a close second by the $M(NH_3)_3^{+2}$ species, and $Zn(NH_3)_4^{+2}$, which is still by far the most important species for zinc. In 0.01 M NH$_4$OH, the most important species are Co^{+2}, $CoNH_3^{+2}$, $Ni(NH_3)_2^{+2}$, and $Zn(NH_3)_3^{+2}$. Also important are $NiNH_3^{+2}$ and (still) $Zn(NH_3)_4^{+2}$. The cobalt complex is so extensively decomposed that $Co(OH)_2$ would precipitate for total cobalt concentrations even as low as 5×10^{-9} molar. Indeed, even in 1 M NH$_4$OH, total concentrations of cobalt above 5×10^{-6} molar will give a precipitate of $Co(OH)_2$. Consequently, very concentrated NH$_4$OH is necessary to dissolve any large amount of a cobalt(II) salt completely as the ammine complex. If ammonium salts are also present, the repression of the OH$^-$ concentration through the equilibrium

$$NH_4^+ + OH^- \rightleftharpoons NH_4OH$$

allows higher cobalt concentrations to be tolerated, and precipitation of the hydroxide, or basic salts, such as Co(OH)Cl may be avoided. In 1 M NH$_4$OH without NH$_4$Cl, total concentrations of zinc in excess of 0.001 molar can be tolerated without precipitation, and of course more in the presence of ammonium salts. On the other hand, $Co(NH_3)_6^{+3}$ can be seen from its instability constant to be extremely stable, and it undergoes very little dissociation. The zinc complexes are colorless. The lower nickel complexes are green, but the higher ones formed in concentrated NH$_4$OH are steel-blue or bluish-violet. The crystalline hexamminenickel salts, such as $Ni(NH_3)_6Br_2$ or $Ni(NH_3)_6(BF_4)_2$, are violet. The cobalt ammines are pink, but their aqueous solutions soon turn brown from reactions such as

$$2\ Co(NH_3)_5^{+2} + O_2 \rightarrow [Co(NH_3)_5OOCo(NH_3)_5]^{+4}$$

The hexamminecobalt(III) ion, $Co(NH_3)_6^{+3}$, which is also formed by oxidation of the Co(II) complex in ammoniacal solution, is orange-yellow. Certain anions are readily incorporated into these complexes if they are in the solution. For example, if the oxidation is carried out in the presence of Cl$^-$, a chloro complex may result.

$$4\ Co(NH_3)_5^{+2} + 4\ Cl^- + O_2 + 2\ H_2O \rightarrow 4\ Co(NH_3)_5Cl^{+2} + 4\ OH^-$$

The role of complexes in the analytical chemistry of these elements extends beyond merely enabling them to be separated from those elements not forming ammines. Many characteristic tests can be cited which involve complexes. Cobalt(II) forms a deep-blue thiocyanate complex, which is too weak, however, to be useful in water solution. (M. Lehne gives $K_1 = 0.001$, $K_2 = 1$, $K_3 = 5$, and $K_4 = 1.1$ for the *stepwise* dissociation constants for CoNCS$^+$, Co(NCS)$_2$, Co(NCS)$_3^-$, and Co(NCS)$_4^{-2}$ in aqueous solution.)

However, in organic solvents the complex is considerably more stable, and the color is much intensified by shaking with a solvent such as acetone. Inasmuch as iron(III) is frequently incompletely separated from this group because of the colloidal nature of its hydroxide, it may interfere with this test by virtue of its blood-red thiocyanate complex. This difficulty may be avoided, however, by adding KF, which forms the very stable, colorless FeF_6^{-3}. Cobalt(II) does not form a fluoro complex.

Another characteristic test for cobalt is the simultaneous oxidation and "complexation" by nitrite ion, NO_2^-

$$Co^{+2} + 7\,NO_2^- + 2\,H^+ \rightleftharpoons Co(NO_2)_6^{-3} + NO\,(g) + H_2O$$

When this is carried out in the presence of NH_4^+ or K^+, the characteristic insoluble yellow salt precipitates out. This reaction is customarily carried out in an acetic acid–ammonium acetate buffer to avoid decomposition due to excess acidity

$$4\,Co(NO_2)_6^{-3} + 20\,H^+ \rightarrow 4\,Co^{+2} + 10\,NO\,(g) + 14\,NO_2\,(g) + 10\,H_2O$$

or excess alkalinity

$$Co(NO_2)_6^{-3} + 3\,OH^- \rightarrow Co(OH)_3\,(s) + 6\,NO_2^-$$

An organic reagent which likewise simultaneously oxidizes and complexes is α–nitroso–β–napthol, which forms "chelate" complexes. (A chelate is a complex in which the complexing agent and the metal atom form a complete ring. The word is from the Greek *chela*, a crab's claw.) The reaction may be

It is carried out in acidic solution and the neutral reddish-purple $Co[C_{10}H_6-(NO)O]_3$ precipitates out. Nickel does not give a reaction with this substance.

Nickel is very seldom detected by any reagent other than dimethyl-glyoxime or some related organic chelating agent. In slightly ammoniacal solution, the scarlet complex precipitates out. Cobalt forms a brown

dimethylglyoxime complex which is even more stable than the nickel com-plex, but is soluble. Cobalt thus reduces the sensitivity of the nickel test, and if it is present, an excess of dimethylglyoxime must be used. The only other element which forms a dimethylglyoxime complex similar in appearance to that of nickel is the very closely related palladium.

Although zinc likewise forms many complexes, the fact that it forms a *white* insoluble sulfide is so characteristic (GeS_2 is the only other one) that this alone is frequently used for its identification. A useful organic chelating agent is diphenylthiocarbazone ("dithizone"),* but this also forms chelates with many other metals. A variation of the cobalt thiocyanatomercuriate test for mercury can be used for zinc. The insoluble $Zn[Hg(NCS)_4]$ is white, but if it is precipitated in the presence of Cu(II) salts, the violet-to-black precipitate of mixed Cu(II) and Zn salts is visible in much smaller amount.

Zinc hexacyanoferrate(II) is one of the less soluble zinc salts. Depending upon conditions, it may precipitate as $Zn_2Fe(CN)_6$ or as $K_2Zn_3(Fe(CN)_6)_2$, both white. If the compound is precipitated in the presence of certain organic dyestuffs, a colored insoluble complex, or lake, is formed. This can be made the basis of a very sensitive test for zinc. The dye known as Orange IV* does not dye $Zn_2Fe(CN)_6$, nor is it oxidized by $Fe(CN)_6^{-3}$ under ordinary conditions. However, in the presence of a zinc salt, the $Fe(CN)_6^{-3}$–$Fe(CN)_6^{-4}$ equilibrium is sufficiently shifted by precipitation of the $Zn_2Fe(CN)_6$ so that the $Fe(CN)_6^{-3}$ oxidizes the Orange IV to a new substance which dyes the precipitate green.

$$2\,Zn^{+2} + Fe(CN)_6^{-3} + dye \rightarrow Zn_2Fe(CN)_6\cdot lake$$

Other dyes can be used in the same way. Diethylaniline† gives a red precipitate. Due to the solubility of $Zn_2Fe(CN)_6$ in both acids and alkalies, control of pH is very important for this reaction.

One other precipitation reaction which may be mentioned is that with potassium cyanocobaltate(III). (See Fernelius, W. C., *Inorganic Syntheses.* New York: McGraw-Hill Book Co, Inc., 1946, Vol. II, p. 225, for the preparation of $K_3Co(CN)_6$.) The colorless $KZn[Co(CN)_6]$ obtained can be ignited to cobalt zincate, $CoZnO_2$, which is known as Rinman's green.

The hydroxides of these three elements are fairly basic, although the salts of zinc appear to be somewhat hydrolyzed in solution. The hydroxides of cobalt and nickel are not amphoteric in the usual sense of the word (but see Section 9–5); but $Zn(OH)_2$ is very easily dissolved in alkali hydroxide solutions. In this respect it is more like the representative elements to the right of it than the transition elements to the left of it in the periodic table. As in the case of $HgCl_2$ and $AuCl_3$, much of the acidity of a $ZnCl_2$ solution is due to such reactions as

$$ZnCl_2 + 2\,H_2O \rightleftharpoons OH_3^+ + ZnCl_2OH^-$$

7–11.   Illustrative Experiments

The following experiments are designed to illustrate some of the relationships discussed above.

(1) Add 10 drops of 0.1 M Ni(NO$_3$)$_2$, 10 drops of 0.1 M MnCl$_2$, and 10 drops of thioacetamide to 1 ml of water. Now add 3 drops of 6 M NaOH, heat the solution in a water bath for 2 minutes, and centrifuge. Decant the centrifugate into another test tube, add 3 drops of 6 M NaOH to this solution, heat the solution, and centrifuge it. Continue to repeat this cycle until five precipitates have been collected.

(a) What are the colors of the precipitates?

(b) Explain the results on the basis of the difference in solubility between NiS and MnS.

(c) Explain the difference in the solubility of the two sulfides by the difference in the electronegativity of the two cations.

(d) From the variation in the electronegativity from the left to the right in the fourth period of the periodic table, should the solubility of the sulfides increase or decrease in this direction?

(2) (a) Add 10 drops of Cr(NO$_3$)$_3$ to 2 ml of 3 M NH$_4$OH, centrifuge, and discard the centrifugate. Add 2.5 ml of water and 10 drops of 6 M acetic acid to the precipitate and stir.

(b) Repeat with Fe(NO$_3$)$_3$ in place of Cr(NO$_3$)$_3$.

(1) Write the equations for the reactions which occurred.

(2) Which hydroxide, Fe(OH)$_3$ or Cr(OH)$_3$, is the more insoluble?

(3) Which is the more electronegative, Fe(III) or Cr(III)?

(3) (a) Add 0.1 M NaOH, dropwise with *shaking*, to 2 ml of water containing 10 drops of 0.1 M ZnSO$_4$. Determine with hydrion paper the pH at which the first permanent precipitate occurs.

(b) Repeat (a) with Hg(NO$_3$)$_2$ in place of ZnSO$_4$.

(1) Write the equations for all the reactions which have taken place.

(2) What was the pH when the Zn(OH)$_2$ began precipitating? When the HgO began precipitating?

(3) Explain from the experimental results which is the more insoluble, Zn(OH)$_2$ or HgO?

(4) The same qualitative results would have been obtained if Hg(OH)$_2$ were stable rather than HgO, since they are about equally insoluble. How do the solubilities of the hydroxides in this family vary as the electronegativity of the cation increases?

(5) Is the trend of the solubilities of the sulfides the same as that for the hydroxides in this family?

(4) (a) Add 10 drops of 6 M NaOH to 10 drops of 0.1 M Mg(NO$_3$)$_2$ in 1 ml of water. To this mixture add 10 drops of thioacetamide and heat the solution for several minutes. Centrifuge the solution and discard the supernate. Add 2 ml of H$_2$O to the precipitate, stir the mixture, centrifuge, and discard the supernate. Add 10 drops of 6 M HCl to the precipitate and heat the solution in a boiling-water bath, with the mouth of the test tube covered with a piece of filter paper saturated with Pb(NO$_3$)$_2$ solution.

(b) Repeat (a) with 0.1 M $FeSO_4$ in place of $Mg(NO_3)_2$.

(1) Write the equations for all the reactions which have taken place.

(2) Which has the sulfide which is more insoluble than the hydroxide, Mg or Fe(II)?

(3) From these results do you expect alkaline sulfide precipitations to produce sulfides or hydroxides for the ions with small electronegativities?

(5) (a) Add 10 drops of 0.1 M $Cr(NO_3)_3$ to 2 ml of H_2O and 10 drops of 6 M NH_4OH. Add 10 drops of thioacetamide to this mixture and heat as usual.

(b) Repeat (a) with $Fe(NO_3)_3$ in place of $Cr(NO_3)_3$ and NaOH instead of NH_4OH.

(1) Look up the colors of the hydroxides and sulfides of Fe(III) and Cr(III). Write the equations for all reactions which took place.

(2) Which has the sulfide which is more insoluble than the hydroxide. Fe(III) or Cr(III)?

(3) Is the trend in the ratio of the solubility product for the sulfides to that for the hydroxides the same as that observed in experiment 4 for the +2 oxidation states?

(4) How do the solubilities of the hydroxides vary as the electronegativity of the cation increases in the fourth period?

(5) Answer (4) for the sulfides.

(6) Which show the greater variation of solubility with change in electronegativity, sulfides or hydroxides?

(7) Explain in a qualitative manner why this should be.

(c) Carry out experiment 5(b) in a less basic medium by adding 10 drops of $Fe(NO_3)_3$ to 10 drops of 6 M NH_4OH and 12 drops of 5 M NH_4Cl in 1.5 ml of water. To this solution add 10 drops of thioacetamide and heat as usual.

(1) Write the equation for the reaction between $Fe(OH)_3$ and HS^- or S^{-2} to give S and the other product you observed.

(2) Explain by Le Châtelier's principle why the oxidation-reduction reaction observed in (c) did not occur in (b).

(6) Add 10 drops of 0.1 M $Cr(NO_3)_3$ to 1 ml of 6 M NaOH. Add 1 ml of 3 percent H_2O_2 to this solution. Heat to boiling and keep hot for several minutes. Neutralize this solution with 12 M HCl and add 6 drops in excess. Add another 1 ml of 3 percent H_2O_2 to this solution, heat to boiling, and keep hot for several minutes. (If the yellow color of CrO_4^{-2} disappears when the HCl is added, the H_2O_2 was probably not completely destroyed by the boiling. If this is the case, make alkaline again and repeat the oxidation.)

(a) What color(s) did you observe for Cr^{+3}? For $Cr_2O_7^{-2}$? For CrO_4^{-2}?

(b) Write the equations for the first reaction between Cr and H_2O_2 and explain by Le Châtelier's rule whether this reaction should proceed better in acidic or basic solutions.

(c) Answer (b) for the second reaction between Cr and H_2O_2.

(d) Write the equation for the equilibrium between $Cr_2O_7^{-2}$ and CrO_4^{-2}, and explain why $Cr_2O_7^{-2}$ is the stable form of Cr(VI) in acid solutions.

(7) To 1 ml of 6 M HNO_3 in a small casserole, add 1 drop of 0.1 M $Mn(NO_3)_2$ solution. Add a pinch or two of solid $NaBiO_3$. Heat if necessary

to obtain a reaction. Pour the solution into a test tube and centrifuge to observe the color of the solution. What reaction has occurred?

(8) To 1 ml of water in a test tube containing 3 drops of 0.1 M Mn(NO$_3$)$_2$, add 6 M NaOH until alkaline and then 3 drops in excess. Now add 5 drops of 3 percent H$_2$O$_2$. What is the precipitate which forms? Centrifuge and transfer the precipitate to a casserole. Add 1 ml of 6 M HNO$_3$ and a pinch of NaBiO$_3$. Heat if necessary, and observe the color of the solution as in experiment 7.

(9) Repeat experiment 8, but shake for 10 minutes with access of air instead of adding H$_2$O$_2$.

(10) To 12 drops of 0.1 M FeSO$_4$ and 12 drops of 0.1 M Zn(NO$_3$)$_2$ in 2 ml of water, add 1 ml of 1 M thioacetamide and make alkaline with 6 M NH$_4$OH. Heat for 10 minutes. Centrifuge and wash the precipitate. To the precipitate transferred to a 10-ml test tube, add 2 ml of saturated Na$_2$SO$_4$ solution and 1 ml of 2 M NaHSO$_4$. Heat and stir. Explain your observations.

(11) Add 1 drop of 0.1 M Fe(NO$_3$)$_3$ to 10 ml of water and mix thoroughly. What is the concentration of Fe(III) in this solution? Now dilute 6 drops of this solution with 3 ml of water. What is the new Fe(III) concentration? To this latter solution, add 1 drop of 3 M HCl and 2 drops of 1 M KNCS. Observe the sensitivity of this reaction.

(12) Put 3 drops of 0.1 M Al(NO$_3$)$_3$ into a 10-ml test tube with 3 ml of water, 3 drops of 3 M NH$_4$C$_2$H$_3$O$_2$, and 4 drops of aluminon reagent. Make the solution alkaline with NH$_4$OH. Centrifuge. Explain your observations.

(13) To 1 ml of 0.1 M K$_2$CrO$_4$ solution, add 0.5 ml 6 M HNO$_3$ and 1 ml amyl alcohol. Now add 10 drops of 3 percent H$_2$O$_2$ and shake quickly twice. Observe the color of the alcohol layer. Now shake vigorously. Observe the colors of both layers. Explain what has happened.

(14) To 3 drops of Na$_3$VO$_4$ in 1 ml of water, add sufficient 6 M HCl to make the solution about 0.3 molar in H$^+$. Add 1 ml of 1 M thioacetamide and heat. Explain your observations. Centrifuge, and divide the supernate into two portions. To one portion, add 1 ml of saturated bromine water. Explain your observations. To the other portion add NH$_4$OH until alkaline, add more thioacetamide, and heat. Now make slightly acidic with 6 M HCl. Explain your observations.

(15) To 3 drops of 0.1 M Na$_3$VO$_4$ in 1 ml of water, add 10 drops of 6 M NH$_4$OH and then 1 ml of 1 M thioacetamide and heat for 10 minutes. Cool and make slightly acidic with HCl. Explain your observations.

(16) To 3 drops of 0.1 M K$_2$CrO$_4$ in 1 ml of water, add sufficient HCl to make the solution about 0.3 molar in H$^+$. Add 1 ml of thioacetamide and heat. Explain your observations.

7–12. Analysis of the Insoluble-Hydroxide and Alkali-Insoluble Sulfide Groups

7–A. Precipitation of the Insoluble Hydroxide Group. Concentrate or dilute the centrifugate from the acid-insoluble sulfide-group precipitation to 1 ml, and add 5 drops of saturated bromine water to destroy H$_2$S and thioacetamide. Continue the addition of bromine until the color persists. Boil to complete the reaction and drive off the excess Br_2. Centrifuge and remove any sulfur which has formed. (Bromine will also oxidize Fe^{+2} to Fe^{+3} and VO^{+2} to $VO_2{}^+$.) Or, if you are analyzing a solution known to/contain only ions of the insoluble-hydroxide and alkali-insoluble sulfide groups, take 1 ml of solution, and omit the bromine treatment. (At this point, if phosphate is present, as determined by prior anion analysis, it must be removed before the addition of NH_4OH. If it were not removed, not only would all the elements of the insoluble-hydroxide and alkali-insoluble sulfide groups precipitate as phosphates, but so also would the alkaline-earth elements (e.g., as $Ba_3(PO_4)_2$, $MgNH_4PO_4$, and so on). To remove the phosphate, add to the acidic solution 0.1 molar zirconyl nitrate, $ZrO(NO_3)_2$, until no further precipitation is observed. Centrifuge off the extremely insoluble $Zr_3(PO_4)_4$ and proceed as usual with the supernate. The excess zirconium will follow iron in the analysis. It will not interfere with the tests for either iron or manganese. Needless to say, if phosphate is present in the original solution, zirconium *must* be absent.)

Now saturate with solid NH_4Cl, make distinctly alkaline with concentrated ammonium hydroxide, heat to boiling, stopper, and shake for 10 minutes, occasionally removing the stopper to allow entrance of more air. (The shaking is necessary to ensure the complete precipitation of manganese, since the initial precipitate, $Mn(OH)_2$, $K_{sp} = 4.6 \times 10^{-14}$, is fairly soluble under these conditions, and shaking with air converts it to the much less soluble $Mn(OH)_3$, $K_{sp} = 1 \times 10^{-36}$, or to other higher hydroxides such as $MnO(OH)_2$.

$$4\ Mn(OH)_2 + O_2 + 2\ H_2O \rightarrow 4\ Mn(OH)_3$$
$$2\ Mn(OH)_2 + O_2 \rightarrow 2\ MnO(OH)_2$$

Ferrous hydroxide, $K_{sp} = 7.9 \times 10^{-15}$, if precipitated, is likewise oxidized to $Fe(OH)_3$, $K_{sp} = 6 \times 10^{-38}$. Simultaneously the $Co(NH_3)_5{}^{+2}$ complex is oxidized to $Co(NH_3)_6{}^{+3}$.

$$4\ Co(NH_3)_5{}^{+2} + O_2 + 4\ NH_3 + 2\ H_2O \rightarrow 4\ Co(NH_3)_6{}^{+3} + 4\ OH^-$$

The hydroxide precipitates, $Al(OH)_3$, $Cr(OH)_3$, $Mn(OH)_3$, and $Fe(OH)_3$, are digested for 5 minutes in the hot-water bath to coagulate them, and then centrifuged. The other elements of the group remain in solution as ammonia complexes, such as $Co(NH_3)_6{}^{+3}$, $Ni(NH_3)_6{}^{+2}$, and $Zn(NH_3)_4{}^{+2}$. This solution should be analyzed by procedure (7–G).

If no precipitate is obtained by the above procedure and if the solution is colored—especially if it became green turning to lavender on heating with NH_4OH—add a few drops of $Al(NO_3)_3$ solution and digest on the hot-water bath. The precipitation of $Al(OH)_3$ causes coprecipitation of the lavender ammonia complex of Cr^{+3} which is formed if chromium is the only element of this group originally present. The precipitate, which will be lavender if chromium is present, should be treated as below, but only chromium should be looked for.

7–B. Separation of the Amphoteric from the Non-Amphoteric Elements. The hydroxide precipitates, separated in (7–A) from the solution of ammonia and washed twice with 3 M NH_4OH, are now treated with 1 ml of 6 M NaOH and 1 ml of 3 percent H_2O_2. Any green color should change completely to yellow. If not, add more H_2O_2 until no green color is detectable. Stir well. Heat. Chromium, vanadium, and aluminum, which form amphoteric hy-

TABLE 7-6. ANALYTICAL SCHEME

Solution: Fe^{+2}, Fe^{+3}, Mn^{+2}, Al^{+3}, Cr^{+3}, VO_2^+, Co^{+2}, Ni^{+2}, Zn^{+2}. Saturate with NH_4Cl. Add 15 M NH_4OH and shake with free access of air. Heat to coagulate the precipitates.

Precipitate: $Fe(OH)_3$, $Mn(OH)_2$, $Al(OH)_3$, $Cr(OH)_3$, and NH_4VO_3. Add 6 M NaOH and 3% H_2O_2. Heat.

Residue: $Fe(OH)_3$; $MnO(OH)_2$. Add 6 M HNO_3 and 3% H_2O_2. Heat. Divide into three portions.

- Add 15 M HNO_3 and $NaBiO_3$. Pink or purple MnO_4^- confirms Mn.
- Add KNCS. Blood-red solution confirms Fe.
- Add $K_4Fe(CN)_6$. Deep-blue (or green) precipitate or solution confirms Fe.

Solution: CrO_4^{-2}, VO_4^{-3}, $Al(OH)_4^-$. Acidulate with HNO_3. Add $Pb(NO_3)_2$.

Precipitate: $Pb_3(VO_4)_2$, $PbCrO_4$. Dissolve in hot 3 M HNO_3. Cool. **Solution:** VO_2^+, $Cr_2O_7^{-2}$. Add amyl alcohol, then 3% H_2O_2. Shake.

- **Alcohol layer:** Deep-blue CrO_5 confirms Cr.
- **Water layer.** Orange $VO(H_2O_2)^{+3}$ confirms V.

Solution: Al^{+3}. Add $(NH_4)_2SO_4$ Discard precipitated $PbSO_4$ and add aluminon reagent. Add NH_4OH. Red precipitate confirms Al.

Solution: $Co(NH_3)_6^{+3}$, $Ni(NH_3)_6^{+2}$, $Zn(NH_3)_4^{+2}$. Add CH_3CSNH_2. Heat.

Precipitate: ZnS, NiS, CoS. Add aqua regia. Evaporate to dryness. **Solution:** Zn^{+2}, Ni^{+2}, Co^{+2}. Dissolve in HNO_3. Divide into five portions.

- Add dimethylglyoxime and NH_4OH. Scarlet precipitate confirms Ni.
- Add HAc and NH_4Ac. Add KNO_2. Yellow $K_3Co(NO_2)_6$ confirms Co.
- Add alcohol and KNCS. Blue color confirms Co.
- Add 6 M NaOH. Heat. Discard precipitated $Co(OH)_2$ and $Ni(OH)_2$. **Solution:** $Zn(OH)_4^{-2}$. Add CH_3CSNH_2. Heat. White precipitate of ZnS confirms Zn.
- Add diethylaniline and $K_3Fe(CN)_6$. Acidulate with HAc. Reddish precipitate confirms Zn.

Solution: Alkali and alkaline-earth ions.

droxides, dissolve, the chromium being simultaneously oxidized. The Cr–V–Al solution is treated according to procedure (7–E).

$$Al(OH)_3 \ (s) + OH^- \rightarrow Al(OH)_4^-$$
$$Cr(OH)_3 \ (s) + OH^- \rightarrow Cr(OH)_4^-$$
$$3 \ H_2O_2 + 2 \ Cr(OH)_4^- + 2 \ OH^- \rightarrow 2 \ CrO_4^{-2} + 8 \ H_2O$$
$$NH_4VO_3 \ (s) + 3 \ OH^- \rightarrow VO_4^{-3} + NH_3 \ (g) + 2 \ H_2O$$

Iron(III) and manganese(III) hydroxides are not amphoteric, and consequently do not dissolve, although the latter is further oxidized.

$$2 \ Mn(OH)_3 + H_2O_2 \rightarrow 2 \ MnO(OH)_2 + 2 \ H_2O$$

Dissolve any residue containing iron and manganese in a few drops of dilute HNO_3 plus 1 or 2 drops of 3 percent H_2O_2 (or more of each if necessary for complete dissolution).

$$MnO(OH)_2 + H_2O_2 + 2 \ H^+ \rightarrow Mn^{+2} + O_2 \ (g) + 3 \ H_2O$$

Heat the solution in the boiling-water bath for at least 5 minutes, or until no more bubbles of oxygen are evolved, to ensure complete decomposition of the H_2O_2.

$$2 \ H_2O_2 \rightarrow 2 \ H_2O + O_2 \ (g)$$

7–C. Detection of Iron. Place 1 drop of the Fe–Mn solution from (7–B) on a spot plate, and add 1 drop of 1 M KNCS solution. A deep-red color proves the presence of iron. A faint-red color is due to traces of iron (a common impurity) and should be ignored or reported as a trace. (It should be noted here that, if the solution contains too high a concentration of HNO_3, oxidation of the NCS^- to thiocyanogen, $(NCS)_2$, may take place. This is almost indistinguishable in color from the iron(III) thiocyanate complex.

$$6 \ NCS^- + 2 \ NO_3^- + 8 \ H^+ \rightarrow 3 \ (NCS)_2 \ (aq) + 2 \ NO \ (g) + 4 \ H_2O)$$

Alternatively, or on a separate portion, may be performed a Prussian-blue test. Put 1 drop of the Fe–Mn solution onto a spot plate and add 1 drop of 0.1 M $K_4Fe(CN)_6$. A deep-blue (or green) precipitate or colloidal solution confirms the presence of iron. Like the thiocyanate test, the Prussian-blue test will reveal small traces of iron.

7–D. Detection of Manganese. Place 1 drop of the Fe–Mn solution on a spot plate and add 1 drop of concentrated HNO_3 and then an excess of $NaBiO_3$. A purple or pink coloration *in the solution* shows the presence of manganese.

7–E. Separation of Chromium and Vanadium from Aluminum. Detection of Aluminum. Heat the NaOH solution from (7–B) containing Al, Cr, and V for 10 minutes in the water bath to ensure complete destruction of the H_2O_2. Now make just neutral with 6 M HNO_3, add just enough excess to dissolve any precipitate that appears, and add 0.5 ml 0.1 M $Pb(NO_3)_2$. Absence of a $PbCrO_4$ or $Pb_3(VO_4)_2$ precipitate indicates the absence of Cr and V. If a precipitate appears, centrifuge, test with $Pb(NO_3)_2$ for completeness of precipitation, and, if complete, remove the supernate containing Al to another test tube. Add 1 ml of 1 M $(NH_4)_2SO_4$. After centrifuging down the $PbSO_4$ formed, add a few more drops of $(NH_4)_2SO_4$ to ensure completeness of precipitation. Remove the supernate, add to it 5 drops of aluminon reagent, and then make alkaline with NH_4OH and mix. Centrifuge. A red precipitate (a lake) which has partially removed the color from the solution shows the presence of Al, if Al has been completely separated from interfering elements such as Mn. Separate the red precipitate from the supernate and wash it with ammonium carbonate solution. If the precipitate remains red, Al is confirmed. (Beryllium is the only other element whose red aluminon lake will remain unchanged.)

7–F. Detection of Chromium and Vanadium. Dissolve the precipitated $Pb_3(VO_4)_2$ and $PbCrO_4$ from (7–E) in hot 3 N HNO_3. Cool completely. Add an equal volume of amyl alcohol and then 10 drops of 3 percent H_2O_2. Quickly shake twice. A deep-blue color (which will gradually fade) in the alcohol layer shows the presence of chromium. A deep-orange color in the water shows the presence of vanadium.

7–G. Analysis of the Co, Ni, Zn Group. Add 1 ml of 1 M thioacetamide solution to the ammoniacal solution containing the complexes of Co, Ni, and Zn obtained in (7–A). Heat in the hot-water bath for 10 minutes, watching the tube carefully. If zinc is present, the first precipitate which appears should be white, becoming gray to black if either cobalt or nickel is also present. Centrifuge and separate from the supernatant solution (which retain for analysis by procedure (3–C) if it contains the ions of the alkali and alkaline-earth groups) and wash with 3 M NH_4OH. Dissolve in a mixture of 1 ml of 6 M HCl and 1 ml of 6 M HNO_3 and evaporate the solution to dryness, first removing any sulfur which may have been produced. Dissolve the residue in a little dilute HNO_3.

7–H. Detection of Nickel. Place a drop of the above solution on a spot plate, make ammoniacal with NH_4OH, and then add an excess of dimethylglyoxime solution. A scarlet precipitate shows the presence of Ni. (A high concentration of cobalt will produce a brown solution. If this is the case, add more dimethylglyoxime.)

7–I. Detection of Cobalt. To a small portion of the Co–Ni–Zn solution add solid NH_4Ac and then 6 M KNO_2 solution. A yellow- or olive-colored precipitate, $K_3Co(NO_3)_6$, indicates the presence of cobalt. (If the solution is too acidic, red-brown fumes of NO_2 will appear. If the solution is too basic, black $Co(OH)_3$ will precipitate.)

To a drop of the Co–Ni–Zn solution on a spot plate, add 2–3 drops of ethyl alcohol and then a crystal of KNCS. A blue color proves the presence of cobalt by formation of $Co(SCN)_4^{-2}$. (If the solution becomes red because of the presence of iron, add a few drops of KF solution to form colorless FeF_6^{-3}, this allows the blue $Co(SCN)_4^{-2}$ to be seen.)

7–J. Detection of Zinc. To a portion of the remaining Co–Ni–Zn solution, add one-half its volume of 6 M NaOH and heat for several minutes to precipitate $Co(OH)_2$ and $Ni(OH)_2$. Centrifuge and remove the supernatant solution for testing for Zn.

To one portion of the supernatant solution, which may contain $Zn(OH)_4^{-2}$, add 1 drop of diethylaniline and 1–2 drops of $K_3Fe(CN)_6$ solution. Add dilute acetic acid until the solution is *barely* acidic. (*Note:* Control of pH is extremely important! Do not overacidify.) Shake the tube and allow it to stand 1 minute or longer. A reddish-colored precipitate shows the presence of zinc.

To another portion of the supernate, add 1 ml of 1 M thioacetamide and heat. The precipitation of white ZnS shows the presence of zinc.

7–13. Questions and Problems

1. Explain why the equilibrium expression for the self-ionization of water is usually written $[H^+][OH^-]$ rather than $\dfrac{[H^+][OH^-]}{[H_2O]}$.

2. When NaCN is dissolved in water, why is $[CN^-]$ not equal to $[Na^+]$?

3. Predict whether aqueous solutions of the following substances will be acidic, basic or neutral:
(a) KCN, (b) NH_4ClO_4, (c) $KClO_4$, (d) NH_4CN, (e) $NH_4C_2H_3O_2$, (f) $AgClO_4$, (g) BaS, (h) $CaCl_2$.

4. Explain why $Al(OH)_3$ and not $Al_2(CO_3)_3$ precipitates when an alkali carbonate is added to an aluminum salt solution.

5. Lanthanum sulfide can be obtained by direct combination of the elements, but cannot be obtained by precipitation from aqueous solution. Explain.

6. Explain why $MgCO_3$ can be precipitated from Na_2CO_3 solution, but not from $(NH_4)_2CO_3$ solution.

7. Using Le Châtelier's principle, explain why the degree of hydrolysis of $Zn(NO_3)_2$ increases with increasing dilution.

8. When 1 mole of HCl is reacted with 1 mole of aniline, $C_6H_5NH_2$, in aqueous solution, the resulting solution is not neutral. Explain.

9. Explain how NH_4^+, Ag^+ and $AuCl_3$ may be similar in their action on water.

10. Compare the classical and Brønsted explanations for why solutions of $Fe(NO_3)_3$ are acidic.

11. What is a buffer? How does it function?

12. Are there any cases in which the second hydrolysis step of a weak electrolyte may not be ignored? Explain.

13. Explain how a solution of a salt, although highly hydrolyzed, may nevertheless be neutral.

14. How is the statement, "The hydroxides of all the elements except those of the alkali and heavy alkaline earth elements are insoluble," inaccurate?

15. Explain the trend of solubilities of metal hydroxides through the periodic table.

16. When ammonium salts are used to limit the OH^- concentration to prevent precipitation of $Mg(OH)_2$, what other problems are created?

17. Is there any correlation between melting point and hardness for the transition elements?

18. Compare the solubilities of the compounds of the various elements in Tables A11–10 and A11–11.

19. Discuss the CrO_4^{-2}–$Cr_2O_7^{-2}$ equilibrium in terms of Le Châtelier's principle.

20. Explain why H_2S and CH_3CSNH_2 are destroyed with bromine before precipitation of the insoluble-hydroxide group.

21. Explain why the H_2O_2 must be destroyed before the solution containing VO_4^{-3} and CrO_4^{-2} is acidified.

22. Explain how reactions normally giving colorless products may be made more sensitive or specific. Give examples.

23. Write ionic equations for the hydrolysis reactions of each of the following substances:
    (a) Potassium cyanide—KCN
    (b) Ammonium perchlorate—NH_4ClO_4
    (c) Phenylammonium or anilinium chloride—$C_6H_5NH_3Cl$
    (d) Sodium hydroperoxide—$NaHO_2$
    (e) Hydroxylammonium chloride—$HONH_3Cl$
    (f) Barium nitrite—$Ba(NO_2)_2$
    (g) Zinc perchlorate—$Zn(ClO_4)_2$
    (h) Ammonium hypochlorite—NH_4ClO
    (i) Trimethyltin(IV) cyanide—$(CH_3)_3SnCN$
    (j) Zinc sulfite—$ZnSO_3$

24. Give the hydrolysis constant for each compound listed in problem 23.

25. Calculate the $[H^+]$ and pH of (a) a 0.1 molar and (b) a 0.01 molar solution of each compound in problem 23.

26. Calculate the degree of hydrolysis in each of the solutions in problem 25.

27. The first ionization constant for germanic acid is 4.0×10^{-10}. Calculate the pH of a 0.1 molar solution of $NaHGeO_3$.

28. Calculate the pH of a liter of solution containing 0.1 gram of $NaC_2H_3O_2$ and 0.4 grams of $HC_2H_3O_2$ (a) using K_A and (b) using K_H.

29. What is the concentration of free HN_3 in a 0.01 molar solution of KN_3?

30. The pH of a 0.1 molar solution of diphenyliodonium nitrate is 4. What is the ionization constant of diphenyliodonium hydroxide, $[(C_6H_5)_2I]OH$?

31. A 0.01 molar solution of hydrazinium iodide is found to be exactly 1 percent hydrolyzed. Calculate K_B for hydrazine.

32. A 0.001 M solution of plutonium chloride, $PuCl_3$, is found to be 2 percent hydrolyzed. What is the third basic ionization constant of $Pu(OH)_3$?

33. The pH of a 0.01 molar solution of erbium chloride, $ErCl_3 \cdot 6 H_2O$, is 5.3. What is the first acid ionization constant of $Er(H_2O)_6^{+3}$?

34. A 0.01 molar solution of $Ga(ClO_4)_3 \cdot 9 H_2O$ is found to be 39 percent hydrolyzed. Calculate the third basic ionization constant of $Ga(OH)_3$.

35. The equilibrium constant for the reaction

$$Fe(CN)_5NO^{-2} + H_2O \rightleftharpoons 2 H^+ + Fe(CN)_5NO_2^{-4}$$

is 7.4×10^{-25}. Calculate the pH of a 0.1 molar solution of $K_4Fe(CN)_5NO_2$.

36. Calculate the pH in each case after the following pairs of solutions are mixed:
    (a) 100 ml 0.1 M HCl and 200 ml 0.05 M $NaC_2H_3O_2$
    (b) 100 ml 0.1 M HCl and 250 ml 0.04 M $NaC_2H_3O_2$
    (c) 100 ml 0.1 M HCN and 400 ml 0.025 M NH_4OH
    (d) 100 ml 0.1 M H_2SO_4 and 50 ml 0.2 M KOH

(e) 100 ml 0.1 M H_2S and 200 ml 0.1 M NaOH

(f) 100 ml 0.1 M HCl and 200 ml 0.2 M $NaC_2H_3O_2$

37. Calculate the ratio of $[HPO_4^{-2}]$ to $[H_2PO_4^-]$ required to buffer solutions at pH (a) 6.0, (b) 7.0, (c) 8.0

38. Calculate (a) the hydrolysis constant, (b) $[H^+]$, (c) the degree of hydrolysis for a 0.1 M $N_2H_6Cl_2$ solution. (Neglect the second hydrolysis step.)

39. Set up all the equations for the hydrolysis of the disodium salt of 3,3′-dihydroxybiphenyl described in Section 7–6 and derive a single equation which describes the system. This equation may easily be solved graphically if desired.

7–14. References

Udy, M. J., *Chemistry of Chromium and Its Compounds,* Vol. I. New York: Reinhold Publishing Corporation, 1956.

Young, R. S., *Cobalt.* New York: Reinhold Publishing Corporation, 1948.

Cobalt thiocyanate complexes: Lehné, M., *Bulletin de la société chimique de France* (1951), p. 76.

CrO_5: Glassner, A., and Steinberg, M., *Journal of the Chemical Society* (London) (1957), p. 2569.

$VO(H_2O_2)^{+3}$: Tolmachev, V. N., and Sherpukhova, L. N., *Zhurnal fizicheskoi khimii,* Vol. 30 (1956), p. 134.

Chapter 8

Simultaneous Equilibria

8–1. Introduction

We have already met some examples of simultaneous equilibria in the chapters on polybasic acids (6) and hydrolysis (7) and qualitatively in the section on the increase in solubility through formation of a weak electrolyte (3–4). In this chapter, we shall consider a number of other examples of simultaneous equilibria. As usual, these may be divided into heterogeneous and homogeneous categories. Since the former are generally the more easily treated (at least where the second phase consists of pure crystalline solids), these will be taken up first.

8–2. Heterogeneous Equilibria Involving Complex Ions and a Common Anion

It frequently happens that an insoluble solid is involved in complex ion equilibria. For example, we have seen (Sections 4–1 and 4–4) that AgCl has a tendency to dissolve in a large excess of hydrochloric acid because of the reaction

$$AgCl\,(s) + Cl^- \rightleftharpoons AgCl_2^-$$

This reaction involves both a complex ion and an insoluble solid. Thus if solid AgCl is added to 0.1 M HCl, AgCl dissolves, forming $AgCl_2^-$ ions until equilibrium is established between the solid and the ions in solution (or until all the solid disappears). *If solid remains when equilibrium is established, then both the equilibrium for the complex ion and the solubility-product equilibrium must be obeyed simultaneously.*

(1) $$[Ag^+][Cl^-] = 1.78 \times 10^{-10}$$

(2) $$\frac{[Ag^+][Cl^-]^2}{[AgCl_2^-]} = 5.6 \times 10^{-6}$$

If equation (1) is divided by equation (2)

(3)
$$\frac{[AgCl_2^-]}{[Cl^-]} = 3.2 \times 10^{-5}$$

which can be seen to be the expression for the equilibrium between AgCl (s) and Cl^- (aq) and $AgCl_2^-$ (aq) in solution. Consequently, in 0.1 M HCl

$$\frac{[AgCl_2^-]}{0.1} = 3.2 \times 10^{-6}$$

and
$$[AgCl_2^-] = 3.2 \times 10^{-5} \; M$$

which represents the solubility of AgCl in 0.1 M HCl. From (2), the $[Ag^+]$ can now be calculated

$$\frac{[Ag^+](0.1)^2}{3.2 \times 10^{-6}} = 5.6 \times 10^{-6}$$

$$[Ag^+] = \frac{(5.6 \times 10^{-6})(3.2 \times 10^{-6})}{10^{-2}} = 1.78 \times 10^{-9} \; M$$

Now it can be seen that

$$[Ag^+][Cl^-] = (1.78 \times 10^{-9})(0.1) = 1.78 \times 10^{-10}$$

as from (1) it must, if solid AgCl is to be in equilibrium with the solution.

Now let us see what will happen if 0.1 mole of $KAg(CN)_2$ is dissolved in 1 liter of water.

$$Ag(CN)_2^- \rightleftharpoons Ag^+ + 2 \, CN^-$$

(4)
$$\frac{[Ag^+][CN^-]^2}{[Ag(CN)_2^-]} = 1.4 \times 10^{-20}$$

From the discussion in Section 4–5, we know that the dissociation of the complex ion will be stepwise, and therefore $[CN^-] \neq 2[Ag^+]$. However, since the stepwise constants are not known, as a first approximation, let us assume that $[CN^-] = 2[Ag^+]$ and see what happens. If $[Ag^+] \doteq X$, then $[CN^-] = 2X$, and

$$\frac{X(2X)^2}{0.1} = 1.4 \times 10^{-20}$$

$$X = 7.0 \times 10^{-8} \; M = [Ag^+]$$

and
$$[CN^-] = 1.40 \times 10^{-7} \; M$$

From the solubility product expression for AgCN

(5)
$$[Ag^+][CN^-] = 1.2 \times 10^{-16}$$

It can be seen that since $(7.0 \times 10^{-8})(1.40 \times 10^{-7}) > 1.2 \times 10^{-16}$, these concentrations are not allowed, but AgCN (s) must precipitate, and equilibria involving solid AgCN must be taken into consideration. Combining (4) and (5) as before, we have

(6)
$$\frac{[Ag(CN)_2{}^-]}{[CN^-]} = \frac{1.2 \times 10^{-16}}{1.4 \times 10^{-20}} = 8.6 \times 10^3$$

Now, if $[Ag(CN)_2{}^-] = 0.1 \ M$, then

$$[CN^-] = \frac{0.1}{8.6 \times 10^3} = 1.17 \times 10^{-5} \ M$$

From (4)
$$\frac{[Ag^+](1.17 \times 10^{-5})^2}{0.1} = 1.4 \times 10^{-20}$$

and
$$[Ag^+] = 1.03 \times 10^{-11} \ M$$

Therefore $[Ag^+][CN^-] = (1.03 \times 10^{-11})(1.17 \times 10^{-5}) = 1.21 \times 10^{-16}$ in conformity with equation (5). As an additional check on the validity of our calculation, from the equation

$$Ag(CN)_2{}^- \rightleftharpoons AgCN \ (s) + CN^-$$

we can say that, since $[CN^-] = 1.17 \times 10^{-5} \ M$, only 1.17×10^{-5} mole of AgCN would have precipitated from 1 liter of solution, and therefore we were justified in assuming that the $[Ag(CN)_2{}^-]$ was not significantly diminished below 0.1 molar by precipitation of AgCN. It can now be seen that the first solution of this problem given above was quite erroneous.

If, instead of 0.1 M Ag(CN)$_2{}^-$, only 1×10^{-7} mole of KAg(CN)$_2$ is dissolved in a liter of water, making the same assumptions as above, we calculate

$$[CN^-] = 1.17 \times 10^{-10} \ M \quad \text{and} \quad [Ag^+] = 1.03 \times 10^{-5} \ M$$

However, since this $[Ag^+]$ is more than the total $[Ag(CN)_2{}^-]$ added, the answer is absurd, and the assumption that AgCN would precipitate is false. This therefore becomes a problem in homogeneous equilibria and will be treated below (Section 8–10).

If instead of the cyano complex, 0.1 mole of KAgCl$_2$ is dissolved in 1 liter of water, the situation is somewhat different. Making the (probably incorrect) assumption that $[Cl^-] = 2 [Ag^+]$, then from equation (2), if $[Ag^+] = X$ and $[Cl^-] = 2X$

$$\frac{4X^3}{0.1} = 5.6 \times 10^{-6}$$

$$X = [Ag^+] = 5.2 \times 10^{-3} \ M$$

and
$$2X = [Cl^-] = 1.04 \times 10^{-2} \ M$$

From this, $[Ag^+][Cl^-] \gg K_{sp}$, and solid AgCl must precipitate. From equation (3)

$$\frac{0.1}{[Cl^-]} = 3.2 \times 10^{-5}$$

and
$$[Cl^-] = 3.3 \times 10^3 \ M$$

which is absurd. It shows, however, that the decomposition of the complex is extensive and must be taken into consideration.

We now observe that for every mole of AgCl which precipitates one mole of free Cl^- is produced. Therefore, for every X moles of AgCl precipitating from 1 liter of solution, $[Cl^-] = X$ and $[AgCl_2^-] = (0.1 - X)$. Then, from equation (3)

$$\frac{[AgCl_2^-]}{[Cl^-]} = \frac{0.1 - X}{X} = 3.2 \times 10^{-5}$$

and
$$X = [Cl^-] = 0.1$$

Since $(0.1 - X)$ can not be distinguished from zero here, we must find the $[AgCl_2^-]$ from equation (2) after obtaining $[Ag^+]$ from equation (1)

$$[Ag^+] = \frac{1.78 \times 10^{-10}}{0.1} = 1.78 \times 10^{-9} \ M$$

$$[AgCl_2^-] = \frac{(1.78 \times 10^{-9})(0.1)^2}{1 \times 10^{-5}} = 1.78 \times 10^{-6} \ M$$

This complex, then, dissociates almost completely into AgCl (s) and Cl^-.

8–3. Heterogeneous Equilibria with No Common Anion

A second type of heterogeneous equilibrium involving complex ions is that in which the complexing agent is different from the anion of the insoluble compound. An example of such an equilibrium is

$$AgCl \ (s) + 2NH_3 \rightleftharpoons Ag(NH_3)_2^+ + Cl^-$$

for which

$$\frac{[Ag(NH_3)_2^+][Cl^-]}{[NH_3]^2} = K$$

It can be seen that this is a combination of the solubility equilibrium for AgCl and the dissociation equilibrium for the complex ion

$$\frac{[Ag^+][Cl^-]}{\dfrac{[Ag^+][NH_3]^2}{[Ag(NH_3)_2^+]}} = \frac{1.78 \times 10^{-10}}{5.9 \times 10^{-8}} = 3.0 \times 10^{-3}$$

Let us calculate the solubility of AgCl in 0.1 M NH$_4$OH. It can be seen from the equation for the reaction that $Ag(NH_3)_2^+$ and Cl^- must be produced in equal amount, so $[Ag(NH_3)_2{}^+] = [Cl^-] = X$. If the $[NH_3]$ is not significantly reduced by formation of the complex ion, then

$$\frac{X^2}{(0.1)^2} = 3.0 \times 10^{-3}$$

and
$$X = [Ag(NH_3)_2{}^+] = [Cl^-] = 5.5 \times 10^{-3} \ M$$

Since two molecules of NH_3 are used up for every $Ag(NH_3)_2{}^+$ formed, the original $0.1 \ M \ NH_3$ will be significantly reduced (by approximately $\frac{0.0110}{0.1}$ or 11 percent), however, so that it is necessary to use $[NH_3] = (0.1 - 2X)$.

$$\frac{X^2}{(0.1 - 2X)^2} = 3.0 \times 10^{-3}$$

Thus
$$X = [Ag(NH_3)_2{}^+] = [Cl^-] = 4.9 \times 10^{-3} \ M$$

which is the amount of AgCl which will dissolve in $0.1 \ M \ NH_4OH$.

Let us consider what will happen if 0.5 mole $Ag(NH_3)_2Cl$ (s) is dissolved in 1 liter of water. If dissociation takes place to such an extent that AgCl precipitates, then $2X$ moles of NH_3 will be liberated for each X moles of AgCl which precipitates, and, therefore, $[NH_3] = 2X$, $[Ag(NH_3)_2{}^+] = [Cl^-] = (0.1 - X)$.

$$\frac{(0.1 - X)^2}{(2X)^2} = 3.0 \times 10^{-3}$$

Then $X = 9.0 \times 10^{-2}$ moles of AgCl (s) precipitating from 1 liter.

$$[Ag(NH_3)_2{}^+] = [Cl^-] = (0.1 - X) = 1.0 \times 10^{-2} \ M$$
$$[NH_3] = 2X = 1.80 \times 10^{-1} \ M$$

8–4. The Solubility of the Salts of Weak Acids in Solutions of Strong Acids

As already noted in Section 3–4, the solubilities of the salts of weak acids are increased in the presence of strong acids

$$MX \, (s) + H^+ \rightleftharpoons M^+ + HX$$

Let us consider the case of LiF in $0.1 \ M$ HCl.

$$[Li^+][F^-] = 3.8 \times 10^{-3}$$

Since LiF is fairly soluble, it may be assumed that an amount of LiF at least equivalent to the HCl will dissolve, due to the formation of an equivalent amount of HF. In addition, more LiF (X moles per liter) will dissolve to give Li^+ and F^-. The total concentration of Li^+ in solution is therefore $(0.1 + X)$ and the free F^- concentration is X. From the K_{sp} expression, then

$$(0.1 + X)(X) = 3.8 \times 10^{-3}$$
$$X = [F^-] = 0.030 \ M$$
$$(0.1 + X) = [Li^+] = 0.130 \ M$$

The amount of LiF which dissolves, then, is 0.130 moles per liter.

With an extremely insoluble salt, on the other hand, the situation is different, even though the acid from which it is derived may be very weak. Let us consider how much AgCN would dissolve in 1 liter of 0.1 M $HClO_4$.

$$AgCN \text{ (s)} + H^+ \rightleftharpoons Ag^+ + HCN$$

Since the total solubility is low, the assumptions made above for LiF cannot be made here. As a first approximation, however, it may be said that $[HCN] = [Ag^+] = X$ and, if X is small, $[H^+] = 0.1$ M. Then, from the solubility and acid ionization equilibria

$$[Ag^+][CN^-] = 1.2 \times 10^{16}$$

$$\frac{[H^+][CN^-]}{[HCN]} = 4.8 \times 10^{-10}$$

$$\frac{[Ag^+][HCN]}{[H^+]} = 2.5 \times 10^{-7}$$

$$\frac{X^2}{0.1} = 2.5 \times 10^{-7}$$

and

$$[Ag^+] = 1.6 \times 10^{-4} \ M$$

The simultaneous equilibria may involve more than one metal ion. For example, AgCl will dissolve in a solution containing Hg^{+2} through formation of chloride complexes of mercury. Let us assume that $HgCl^+$ is the only important mercury complex involved, the reaction being

$$AgCl \text{ (s)} + Hg^{+2} \rightleftharpoons Ag^+ + HgCl^+$$

and ask how much AgCl a liter of 0.1 M solution of $Hg(NO_3)_2$ will dissolve. The equilibria

$$[Ag^+][Cl^-] = 1.81 \times 10^{-10}$$

and

$$\frac{[Hg^{+2}][Cl^-]}{[HgCl^+]} = 1.8 \times 10^{-7}$$

combine to give

$$\frac{[Ag^+][HgCl^+]}{[Hg^{+2}]} = \frac{1.8 \times 10^{-10}}{1.8 \times 10^{-7}} = 1.0 \times 10^{-3}$$

The $[Hg^{+2}]$ will be the "original" mercury concentration minus what has formed $HgCl^+$. Therefore, $[HgCl^+] = X$, $[Ag^+] = X$, and $[Hg^{+2}] = 0.1 - X$.

$$\frac{X \cdot X}{0.1 - X} = 1.0 \times 10^{-3}$$

$$X^2 + (1.0 \times 10^{-3})X - 1.0 \times 10^{-4} = 0$$

$$X = [Ag^+] = \frac{-1.0 \times 10^{-3} \pm \sqrt{1.0 \times 10^{-6} + 4.0 \times 10^{-4}}}{2} = 9.5 \times 10^{-3} \ M$$

Therefore, 0.0095 moles of AgCl will dissolve in 1 liter of this solution. This is quite comparable to the $AgCN-HClO_4$ case.

8–5. The Effect of Hydrolysis on the Solubility of Salts—the Fairly Soluble Case

In Section 3–4, the effect of added strong acid or base on the solubilities of slightly soluble salts derived from weak acids or bases was discussed. For example, it was pointed out that $Ba_3(PO_4)_2$ dissolves in strong acids because of repression of the ionization of the HPO_4^{-2} ion ($H^+ + PO_4^{-3} \rightleftharpoons HPO_4^{-2}$). Since water can also furnish H^+ (or OH^-), it is to be expected that the solubility of salts of weak acids (or bases) may be affected by hydrolysis.

Let us consider the case of CaS, whose $K_{sp} = 5.8 \times 10^{-8}$. If hydrolysis were to be ignored, then $[Ca^{+2}] = [S^{-2}] = X$, so that

$$X^2 = 5.8 \times 10^{-8}$$

$$X = [Ca^{+2}] = [S^{-2}] = 2.4 \times 10^{-4}$$

which would be the same thing as the solubility of the salt.

On the other hand, if hydrolysis be taken into consideration, then from the over-all dissolution reaction

$$CaS\ (s) + H_2O \rightleftharpoons Ca^{+2} + HS^- + OH^-$$

it is apparent that for every HS^- in solution there must be a OH^-. Therefore

$$(1) \qquad\qquad [HS^-] = [OH^-]$$

Also, since one Ca^{+2} goes into solution for every S^{-2} (hydrolyzed or unhydrolyzed), it can be seen that

$$(2) \qquad\qquad [Ca^{+2}] = [HS^-] + [S^{-2}]$$

The individual equilibria involved are

$$CaS\ (s) \rightleftharpoons Ca^{+2} + S^{-2}$$

and
$$S^{-2} + H_2O \rightleftharpoons HS^- + OH^-$$
from which

$$(3) \qquad\qquad [Ca^{+2}][S^{-2}] = K_{sp} = 5.8 \times 10^{-8}$$

and

$$(4) \qquad \frac{[HS^-][OH^-]}{[S^{-2}]} = \frac{K_w}{K_{A2}} = \frac{1 \times 10^{-14}}{1.3 \times 10^{-13}} = 7.7 \times 10^{-2}$$

Eliminating $[OH^-]$ between (1) and (4), we have

$$(5) \qquad\qquad \frac{[HS^-]^2}{[S^{-2}]} = 7.7 \times 10^{-2}$$

A rigorous solution of this system would lead to a fourth-power equation which would be too difficult to solve. However, if it be noted from the solution that ignored hydrolysis that the maximum possible $[S^{-2}] = 2.4 \times 10^{-4} \, M$, it can be seen from equation (5) that hydrolysis will be nearly complete, i.e. $[HS^-] \approx [Ca^{+2}]$. Therefore, let us take

(6) $$[HS^-] = [Ca^{+2}]$$

Now, eliminating $[HS^-]$ between (5) and (6)

(7) $$\frac{[Ca^{+2}]^2}{[S^{-2}]} = 7.7 \times 10^{-2}$$

and eliminating $[S^{-2}]$ between (3) and (7)

(8) $$\frac{[Ca^{+2}]^2}{\dfrac{5.8 \times 10^{-8}}{[Ca^{+2}]}} = 7.7 \times 10^{-2}$$

or $$[Ca^{+2}]^3 = 4.47 \times 10^{-8}$$

and $$[Ca^{+2}] = 1.7 \times 10^{-3} \, M$$

Consequently, the simplification given above was justified, and the solubility is found to be seven times greater than that calculated by ignoring hydrolysis.

In general, systems of this sort will be very difficult to solve rigorously, or (if hydrolysis is less complete) even at all.

8–6. The Effect of Hydrolysis on the Solubility of Salts—the Very Insoluble Case

A much simpler case is that of the sulfides of lower solubility. Let us take, for example, PbS, whose $K_{sp} = 1.3 \times 10^{-28}$. Again, ignoring hydrolysis, $[Pb^{+2}] = [S^{-2}] = X$. Therefore

$$X^2 = 1.3 \times 10^{-28}$$

$$X = [Pb^{+2}] = [S^{-2}] = 1.1 \times 10^{-14} \, M$$

When hydrolysis is taken into consideration, it must be realized that even if the reaction

$$S^{-2} + H_2O \rightleftharpoons HS^- + OH^-$$

goes to completion, this will add only, say, 10^{-12} moles per liter of OH^- to the OH^- concentration, which is already $10^{-7} \, M$ from the ionization of water. This addition is negligible, then, and $[OH^-]$ may be taken as $10^{-7} \, M$. Consequently

$$\frac{[HS^-][OH^-]}{[S^{-2}]} = \frac{[HS^-](10^{-7})}{[S^{-2}]} = 7.7 \times 10^{-2}$$

and $$\frac{[HS^-]}{[S^{-2}]} = 7.7 \times 10^{5}$$

showing that hydrolysis of the sulfide ion is essentially complete. Therefore, it can be seen from the equation

$$PbS\ (s) + H_2O \rightleftharpoons Pb^{+2} + HS^- + OH^-$$

that $$[Pb^{+2}] = [HS^-]$$

$$\frac{[Pb^{+2}]}{\dfrac{1.3 \times 10^{-28}}{[Pb^{+2}]}} = 7.7 \times 10^5$$

$$[Pb^{+2}]^2 = 1.00 \times 10^{-22}$$

and $$[Pb^{+2}] = 1.0 \times 10^{-11}\ M$$

The true solubility, then, is almost a hundredfold greater than that calculated with disregard of hydrolysis. Even this is not quite accurate, however, for small additional increases in solubility should be expected from hydrolysis of Pb^{+2} to $PbOH^+$, and also from the further hydrolysis of HS^- to H_2S. It can be seen that at pH 7

$$\frac{[H_2S][OH^-]}{[HS^-]} = \frac{10^{-14}}{10^{-7}} = \frac{[H_2S](1 \times 10^{-7})}{[HS^-]}$$

$$[H_2S] = [HS^-]$$

A completely rigorous solution of the case is the following

(9) $$[Pb^{+2}][S^{-2}] = 1.3 \times 10^{-28}$$

(10) $$\frac{[HS^-][OH^-]}{[S^{-2}]} = 7.7 \times 10^{-2}$$

but since $[OH^-] = 10^{-7}\ M$ (from the argument given above), this becomes

(10′) $$\frac{[HS^-]}{[S^{-2}]} = 7.7 \times 10^5$$

(11) $$\frac{[H_2S][OH^-]}{[HS^-]} = 1.0 \times 10^{-7}$$

and again

(11′) $$[H_2S] = [HS^-]$$

(12) $$\frac{[PbOH^+][H^+]}{[Pb^{+2}]} = 6.7 \times 10^{-7}$$

but $[H^+]$ also is $10^{-7}\ M$, so

(12′) $$\frac{[PbOH^+]}{[Pb^{+2}]} = 6.7$$

From the fact that the total number of lead atoms and the total number of sulfur atoms in solution must be the same, it follows that

(13) $[Pb^{+2}] + [PbOH^+] = [H_2S] + [HS^-] + [S^{-2}]$

But since $[S^{-2}] \ll [HS^-]$, we can write

(13′) $[Pb^{+2}] + [PbOH^+] = [H_2S] + [HS^-]$

Now combining equations (13′), (12′), and (11′)

(14) $3.85\,[Pb^{+2}] = [HS^-]$

Combining (10′) and (14)

(15) $\dfrac{[Pb^{+2}]}{[S^{-2}]} = 2.0 \times 10^5$

Combining (9) and (15)

(16) $[Pb^{+2}]^2 = 2.6 \times 10^{-23}$

from which $[Pb^{+2}] = 5.1 \times 10^{-12} \; M$

and $[PbOH^+] = 3.5 \times 10^{-11} \; M$

so that the total solubility is $4.0 \times 10^{-11} \; M$.

It can be seen from this that the actual solubility is 4000 times that calculated by ignoring any hydrolysis.

8–7. The Effect of Hydrolysis on the Solubility of Salts—Hydrolysis and Subsequent Precipitation

A third case must also be considered. Let us take the salt trimethyltin(IV) cyanide, $(CH_3)_3SnCN$, for which we estimate

(17) $K_{sp} = 10^{-2} = [(CH_3)_3Sn^+][CN^-]$

If there were no hydrolysis, $[(CH_3)_3Sn^+] = [CN^-] = X$, from which

$$X^2 = 10^{-2}$$

and $X = [CN^-] = [(CH_3)_3Sn^+] = 10^{-1} \; M$

However, in actual fact the CN^- is highly hydrolyzed.

$$CN^- + H_2O \rightleftharpoons HCN + OH^-$$

Since from this

$$[HCN] = [OH^-]$$

and

(18) $\dfrac{[HCN][OH^-]}{[CN^-]} = \dfrac{1 \times 10^{-14}}{4.8 \times 10^{-10}} = 2.1 \times 10^{-5}$

then

(19)
$$\frac{[HCN]^2}{[CN^-]} = 2.1 \times 10^{-5}$$

From (17) it can be seen that $[CN^-]$ must be less than 0.1 M (because of hydrolysis) and $[(CH_3)_3Sn^+] > 0.1$ M. Consequently, from (19)

(20)
$$[HCN]^2 < 2.1 \times 10^{-6}$$

and
$$[HCN] < 1.45 \times 10^{-3} \ M$$

and likewise
$$[OH^-] < 1.45 \times 10^{-3} \ M$$

But now it must be realized that $(CH_3)_3SnOH$ is only slightly soluble, having $K_{sp} = 1.6 \times 10^{-5}$. Since the product of the concentrations of $(CH_3)_3Sn^+$ and OH^- obtained above exceeds this number, $(CH_3)_3SnOH$ must start to precipitate out before the solution is saturated with $(CH_3)_3SnCN$.

$$(CH_3)_3SnCN \ (s) + H_2O \rightleftharpoons (CH_3)_3SnOH \ (s) + HCN$$

Consequently, the $(CH_3)_3SnOH$ solubility equilibrium must also be taken into consideration.

(21)
$$[(CH_3)_3Sn^+][OH^-] = 1.6 \times 10^{-5}$$

Now, combining equations (17), (18), and (21), we have

(22)
$$\frac{[(CH_3)_3Sn^+][CN^-][HCN][OH^-]}{[(CH_3)_3Sn^+][OH^-][CN^-]} = \frac{(10^{-2})(2.1 \times 10^{-5})}{1.6 \times 10^{-5}}$$

from which
$$[HCN] = 1.31 \times 10^{-2} \ M$$

when both solids, $(CH_3)_3SnCN$ and $(CH_3)_3SnOH$, are in equilibrium with the solution.

Now let us note that for charge neutrality it is necessary that

(23)
$$[(CH_3)_3Sn^+] + [H^+] = [CN^-] + [OH^-]$$

but since $[H^+]$ is very small compared to the other terms

(23′)
$$[(CH_3)_3Sn^+] = [CN^-] + [OH^-]$$

Combining (23′) with (17) and (21)

(24) $([CN^-] + [OH^-])[CN^-] = 10^{-2} = [CN^-]^2 + [CN^-][OH^-]$

(25) $([CN^-] + [OH^-])[OH^-] = 1.6 \times 10^{-5} = [OH^-]^2 + [CN^-][OH^-]$

Subtracting (25) from (24)

(26)
$$10^{-2} = [CN^-]^2 - [OH^-]^2$$

Now, noting that dividing (21) by (17) gives

(27) $$\frac{[OH^-]}{[CN^-]} = \frac{1.6 \times 10^{-5}}{10^{-2}} = 1.6 \times 10^{-3}$$

we have, on combining with (26),

(28) $$10^{-2} = \frac{[OH^-]^2}{2.56 \times 10^{-6}} - [OH^-]^2$$

so that

$$[OH^-] = 1.6 \times 10^{-4} \ M$$

From (21)

$$[(CH_3)_3Sn^+] = \frac{1.6 \times 10^{-5}}{1.6 \times 10^{-4}} = 1.0 \times 10^{-1} \ M$$

and from (17)

$$[CN^-] = \frac{10^{-2}}{1.0 \times 10^{-1}} = 1 \times 10^{-1} \ M$$

Consequently, when excess solid $(CH_3)_3SnCN$ is put into pure water a total of 0.1131 moles dissolves in each liter of solution, i.e., $([CN^-] + [HCN])$, of which 0.131 moles reprecipitates as $(CH_3)_3SnOH$, i.e., $([CN^-] + [HCN] - [(CH_3)_3Sn^+])$, the final concentrations being

$$[(CH_3)_3Sn^+] = 1 \times 10^{-1} \ M$$

$$[CN^-] = 1 \times 10^{-1} \ M$$

$$[HCN] = 1.31 \times 10^{-2} \ M$$

$$[OH^-] = 1.6 \times 10^{-4} \ M$$

There are many salts which will undergo hydrolysis to produce precipitates in exactly the same way as $(CH_3)_3SnOH$, because of the fact that, under the conditions of hydrolysis of the anion, the hydroxide (or basic salt) of the metal is less soluble than the salt under consideration. Thus the carbonates of a very wide variety of metals are instantly hydrolyzed in water. This is especially true of the more electronegative $(X > 1.4)$ elements, especially in their higher oxidation states. This makes it impossible in practice to obtain many carbonates. Thus, if Na_2CO_3 is added to an $Al(NO_3)_3$ solution, not the carbonate, but the hydroxide precipitates

$$Al^{+3} + 3 CO_3^{-2} + 3 H_2O \rightleftharpoons Al(OH)_3 \ (s) + 3 HCO_3^{-}$$

Likewise, although $FeCO_3$ can be precipitated

$$Fe^{+2} + CO_3^{-2} \rightleftharpoons FeCO_3 \ (s)$$

it is not possible to obtain $Fe_2(CO_3)_3$, for

$$Fe^{+3} + 3 CO_3^{-2} + 3 H_2O \rightleftharpoons Fe(OH)_3 \ (s) + 3 HCO_3^{-}$$

The sulfides (and selenides and tellurides) of the less electronegative elements (on the left-hand side of the periodic table) are likewise subject to hydrolysis.

$$2 \, Al^{+3} + 3 \, S^{-2} + 6 \, H_2O \rightleftharpoons 2 \, Al(OH)_3 \, (s) + 3 \, H_2S(g)$$

$$Mg^{+2} + S^{-2} + 2 \, H_2O \rightleftharpoons Mg(OH)_2 \, (s) + H_2S \, (g)$$

On the other hand these latter compounds *can* be obtained, because they can easily be prepared in the absence of water by direct combination of the elements.

$$2 \, Al + 3 \, Te \rightleftharpoons Al_2Te_3$$

$$Si + 2 \, S \rightleftharpoons SiS_2$$

$$Al + P \rightleftharpoons AlP$$

These compounds react vigorously with water, producing the metal hydroxide and the volatile hydride

$$La_2Se_3 \, (s) + 6 \, H_2O \rightleftharpoons 2 \, La(OH)_3 \, (s) + 3 \, H_2Se \, (g)$$

$$Mg_3P_2 \, (s) + 6 \, H_2O \rightleftharpoons 3 \, Mg(OH)_2 \, (s) + 2 \, PH_3 \, (g)$$

$$CaC_2 \, (s) + 2 \, H_2O \rightleftharpoons Ca(OH)_2 + C_2H_2 \, (g) \, (acetylene)$$

The mathematics required to solve these cases is much more complicated than that for the simple case of $(CH_3)_3SnCN$.

In the case of the salts of very weak bases, even the hydroxide-ion concentration supplied by the water itself is sufficient to precipitate the weak insoluble base without any hydrolysis of the anion. Thus even the halides of some of the most electronegative metals hydrolyze, as do the halides of the nonmetals. (This was discussed in Section 7–3.) Thus the salts of Hg, Bi, Sn, and Sb, among others, produce precipitates when dissolved in water.

$$HgSO_4 \, (s) + H_2O \rightleftharpoons HgO \, (s) + 2 \, H^+ + SO_4^{-2}$$

$$SnI_4 \, (s) + H_2O \rightleftharpoons SnOI_2 \, (s) + 2 \, H^+ + 2 \, I^-$$

$$BiI_3 \, (s) + H_2O \rightleftharpoons BiOI \, (s) + 2 \, H^+ + 2 \, I^-$$

$$SbI_3 \, (s) + H_2O \rightleftharpoons SbOI \, (s) + 2 \, H^+ + 2 \, I^-$$

These equilibria are all reversed by excess acid, as the equations indicate they should be.

8–8. The Solubility of Metal Hydroxides in Water

If the solubility of a metal hydroxide is fairly high, the K_{sp} equilibrium will predominate over the self-ionization of water. Thus for

$$Cd(OH)_2 \, (s) \rightleftharpoons Cd^{+2} + 2 \, OH^-$$

$$[CdOH^+][OH^-] = 3.0 \times 10^{-10}$$

$$[Cd^{+2}][OH^-]^2 = 2.0 \times 10^{-14}$$

and $$[OH^-] = [CdOH^+] + 2[Cd^{+2}]$$

Combining these equations gives

$$[OH^-] = \frac{3.0 \times 10^{-10}}{[OH^-]} + \frac{4.0 \times 10^{-14}}{[OH^-]^2}$$

and

$$[OH^-]^3 - 3.0 \times 10^{-10}[OH^-] - 4.0 \times 10^{-14} = 0$$

from which

$$[OH^-] = 3.7 \times 10^{-5} \, M$$

$$[CdOH^+] = 8.1 \times 10^{-6} \, M$$

and

$$[Cd^{+2}] = 1.45 \times 10^{-5} \, M$$

giving a total solubility for $Cd(OH)_2$ of $8.1 \times 10^{-6} \, M + 1.45 \times 10^{-5} \, M = 2.26 \times 10^{-5} \, M$.

On the other hand, in the case of a less soluble hydroxide, the self-ionization of water may predominate. Thus, for

$$Pd(OH)_2 \, (s) \rightleftharpoons Pd^{+2} + 2 \, OH^-$$

$$[Pd^{+2}][OH^-]^2 = 1 \times 10^{-31}$$

we can see by inspection that the OH^- contributed by the $Pd(OH)_2$ is much less than $10^{-7} \, M$ and will be negligible in comparison to the $10^{-7} \, M \, OH^-$ from the water itself. Consequently, this becomes

$$[Pd^{+2}](10^{-7})^2 = 1 \times 10^{-31}$$

and

$$[Pd^{+2}] = 1 \times 10^{-17} \, M$$

8–9. Simultaneous Equilibria Involving Two Weak Acids

If two weak acids are present in the same solution, their equilibria cannot be independent because they involve the common hydrogen ion. Consequently, in principle, they must be treated as simultaneous equilibria. In practice, however, if the acids are present in equal concentration, the ionization of the stronger will predominate, unless the ionization constants are very close together. (More accurately stated, the one will predominate for which CK_A is the larger, where C is the concentration of un-ionized acid and K_A its ionization constant.) Consequently, the weaker acid (or the acid for which CK_A is smaller) will be almost completely un-ionized.

For example, in a solution containing $0.1 \, M \, HC_2H_3O_2$ (acetic acid), whose $K_A = 1.85 \times 10^{-5}$, and $0.1 \, M \, HClO$ (hypochlorous acid), whose $K_A = 3.0 \times 10^{-8}$, the hydrogen-ion concentration may be considered to be due entirely to the ionization of the acetic acid, so that

$$[H^+] = [Ac^-] = X$$

$$\frac{X^2}{0.1} = 1.85 \times 10^{-5}$$

and

$$X = [H^+] = 1.36 \times 10^{-3} \, M$$

Then

$$\frac{[H^+][ClO^-]}{[HClO]} = \frac{(1.36 \times 10^{-3})[ClO^-]}{0.1} = 3.0 \times 10^{-8}$$

and

$$[ClO^-] = 2.2 \times 10^{-6} \ M$$

the HClO being only 0.0022 percent ionized.

On the other hand, if the HClO were 1 molar and the HAc only $10^{-6} \ M$, then $(1)(3.0 \times 10^{-8}) > (10^{-6})(1.85 \times 10^{-5})$ and the hypochlorous acid equilibrium would predominate.

$$[H^+] = [ClO^-] = Y$$

$$\frac{[H^+][ClO^-]}{[HClO]} = \frac{Y^2}{1} = 3.0 \times 10^{-8}$$

and

$$Y = [H^+] = 1.73 \times 10^{-4} \ M$$

Then

$$\frac{[H^+][Ac^-]}{[HAc]} = \frac{(1.73 \times 10^{-4})[Ac^-]}{10^{-6}} = 1.85 \times 10^{-5}$$

and

$$[Ac^-] = 1.07 \times 10^{-7} \ M$$

the acetic acid being only 10.7 percent ionized.

Let us consider the case of two acids, HF and HN_3, whose ionization constants are 5.6×10^{-4} and 1.9×10^{-5}, or a factor of only 29 apart.

$$HF + N_3^- \rightleftharpoons F^- + HN_3$$

$$\frac{[F^-][HN_3]}{[HF][N_3^-]} = 29$$

The rigorous treatment of this case results in a cubic equation which, for the system $0.1 \ M$ HF $+ 0.1 \ M$ HN_3, gives the results

$$[F^-] = 5.6 \times 10^{-3} \ M$$

$$[N_3^-] = 2.0 \times 10^{-4} \ M$$

$$[H^+] = 5.8 \times 10^{-3} \ M$$

$$[HN_3] = 9.98 \times 10^{-2} \ M$$

$$[HF] = 9.44 \times 10^{-2} \ M$$

In other words, the ionization of the HF is 6 percent, but the ionization of the HN_3 is a negligible 2 percent. Consequently, even with these closely matched acids the ionization of the stronger predominates. Consequently, only if the constants (or CK_A's) are closer together than this, need the ionization equilibria be treated simultaneously. (The exact treatment of this case is given in Appendix I.)

8–10.   The Dissociation of Complex Ions

At first sight it would seem that when a complex ion dissociates

$$MX_n \rightleftharpoons M + nX$$

it could be said that $[X] = n[M]$. If this assumption were made for the dissociation of 1 M $Cu(CN)_4^{-3}$, then $[Cu^+] = X$, $[CN^-] = 4X$ and

$$\frac{[Cu^+][CN^-]^4}{[Cu(CN)_4^{-3}]} = \frac{(X)(4X)^4}{1} = 2 \times 10^{-27}$$

so that

$$X = [Cu^+] = 1.51 \times 10^{-6} \ M$$

and

$$4X = [CN^-] = 6.0 \times 10^{-6} \ M$$

However, it must be remembered that the dissociation is actually a stepwise process

$$Cu(CN)_4^{-3} \rightleftharpoons Cu(CN)_3^{-2} + CN^-$$

$$Cu(CN)_3^{-2} \rightleftharpoons Cu(CN)_2^- + CN^-$$

$$Cu(CN)_2^- \rightleftharpoons CuCN \ (aq) + CN^-$$

$$CuCN \ (aq) \rightleftharpoons Cu^+ + CN^-$$

and the concentration of products from the later steps is very much less than from the early steps. The constants for this system so far as they are known, are

(1)
$$\frac{[Cu^+][CN^-]^4}{[Cu(CN)_4^{-3}]} = 5 \times 10^{-30}$$

(2)
$$\frac{[Cu^+][CN^-]^3}{[Cu(CN)_3^{-2}]} = 2.5 \times 10^{-29}$$

(3)
$$\frac{[Cu^+][CN^-]^2}{[Cu(CN)_2^-]} = 1.0 \times 10^{-24}$$

From (1) and (2), we have, for the first step of the dissociation

$$\frac{\dfrac{[Cu^+][CN^-]^4}{[Cu(CN)_4^{-3}]}}{\dfrac{[Cu^+][CN^-]^3}{[Cu(CN)_3^{-2}]}} = \frac{[Cu(CN)_3^{-2}][CN^-]}{[Cu(CN)_4^{-3}]} = \frac{5 \times 10^{-30}}{2.5 \times 10^{-29}} = 0.2$$

From this it can be seen that the first dissociation is very extensive. Let us therefore assume as a first approximation that in a 1 M $K_3Cu(CN)_4$ solution $[Cu(CN)_3^{-2}] = [CN^-] = X$. Then

$$\frac{X^2}{1-X} = 0.2$$

and

$$X = 0.36 \ M$$

Consequently, $[Cu(CN)_4{}^{-3}] = 0.64\ M$.

Now, from (2) and (3)

$$\frac{\dfrac{[Cu^+][CN^-]^3}{[Cu(CN)_3{}^{-2}]}}{\dfrac{[Cu^+][CN^-]^2}{[Cu(CN)_2{}^-]}} = \frac{[Cu(CN)_2{}^-][CN^-]}{[Cu(CN)_3{}^{-2}]} = \frac{2.5\times10^{-29}}{1.0\times10^{-24}} = 2.5\times10^{-5}$$

Taking $[Cu(CN)_3{}^{-2}] = [CN^-]$, then $[Cu(CN)_2{}^-] = 2.5\times10^{-5}$. The second dissociation, then, would contribute only 2.5×10^{-5} molar *additional* cyanide-ion concentration. Consequently, our assumption that $[Cu(CN)_3{}^{-2}] = [CN^-]$ was justified. Now, from the over-all equilibrium expression, the $[Cu^+]$ can be calculated.

$$\frac{[Cu^+][CN^-]^4}{[Cu(CN)_4{}^{-3}]} = \frac{[Cu^+](0.36)^4}{0.64} = 5\times10^{-30}$$

$$[Cu^+] = \frac{(5\times10^{-30})(0.64)}{0.01689} = 1.91\times10^{-28}\ M$$

Thus the ratio of $\dfrac{[CN^-]}{[Cu^+]}$ being anything but 4 to 1, is actually 2×10^{27} to 1!

The solubility-product constant for CuCN has been given by Vladimirova and Kakovskii as 3.2×10^{-20}. From this it can be seen that the first treatment of the dissociation of $Cu(CN)_4{}^{-3}$ would give

$$[Cu^+][CN^-] = (4.6\times10^{-7})(1.7\times10^{-6}) = 7.8\times10^{-13}$$

which predicts that CuCN (s) should precipitate from 1 M $Cu(CN)_4{}^{-3}$. From the second treatment, on the other hand

$$[Cu^+][CN^-] = (1.91\times10^{-28})(0.36) = 6.9\times10^{-29}$$

which predicts that no precipitation of CuCN should take place. The observed fact is that precipitation does *not* take place under these conditions.

8–11.   The Hydrolytic Dissociation of Complexes

Let us consider the equilibria in a 0.1 molar solution of the neutral complex $Hg(CN)_2$, now realizing that the hydrolytic reaction

$$CN^- + H_2O \rightleftharpoons HCN + OH^-$$

should be taken into consideration. Combining

$$\frac{[HgCN^+][CN^-]}{[Hg(CN)_2]} = 2.0\times10^{-17}$$

and

$$\frac{[HCN][OH^-]}{[CN^-]} = \frac{1\times10^{-14}}{4.8\times10^{-10}} = 2.1\times10^{-5}$$

we have

$$\frac{[HgCN^+][HCN][OH^-]}{[Hg(CN)_2]} = 4.2 \times 10^{-22}$$

Now assuming that

$$X = [HgCN^+] = [HCN] \text{ and } [OH^-] \approx 10^{-7} \ M$$

$$\frac{10^{-7} X^2}{0.1} = 4.2 \times 10^{-22}$$

$$X = 2.0 \times 10^{-8} \ M$$

This compares to $[HgCN^+] = 1.4 \times 10^{-9} \ M$ if the hydrolysis of CN^- be ignored. However, $[CN^-]$, instead of being $1.4 \times 10^{-9} \ M$, becomes

$$[CN^-] = \frac{(2.0 \times 10^{-8})^2}{2.1 \times 10^{-5}} = 9.8 \times 10^{-11} \ M$$

and $[Hg^{+2}]$, instead of being

$$\frac{[Hg^{+2}][CN^-]}{[HgCN^+]} = [Hg^{+2}] = 1.0 \times 10^{-18} \ M$$

becomes

$$[Hg^{+2}] = \frac{(1.0 \times 10^{-18})[HgCN^+]}{[CN^-]} = \frac{(1.0 \times 10^{-18})(1.4 \times 10^{-9})}{5.8 \times 10^{-11}}$$

$$= 2.0 \times 10^{-16} \ M$$

8–12. The Equilibria of Soluble Ampholytes

When an ampholyte such as $NaHCO_3$ is dissolved in water, it undergoes two reactions, first, ionization as an acid

(1) $$HCO_3^- \rightleftharpoons H^+ + CO_3^{-2}$$

for which $K_{A2} = 4.8 \times 10^{-11}$, and second, hydrolysis

(2) $$HCO_3^- + H_2O \rightleftharpoons H_2CO_3 + OH^-$$

for which

$$K_H = \frac{K_w}{K_{A1}} = \frac{1 \times 10^{-14}}{4.2 \times 10^{-7}}$$

However, the H^+ produced by the first reaction and the OH^- produced by the second reaction must obey the equilibrium restriction

$$[H^+][OH^-] = 1 \times 10^{-14}$$

so that they react with each other, shifting both reactions to the right, or increasing the degree of hydrolysis. Adding equations (1) and (2), and subtracting the equation for the ionization of water, $(H_2O \rightleftharpoons H^+ + OH^-)$, we have

(3) $$2\,HCO_3^- \rightleftharpoons H_2CO_3 + CO_3^{-2}$$

Multiplying the equilibrium expressions for equations (1) and (2), and dividing by the expression for the ionization of water, we have

$$\frac{[H^+][CO_3^{-2}]}{[HCO_3^-]} \times \frac{[H_2CO_3][OH^-]}{[HCO_3^-]} \times \frac{1}{[H^+][OH^-]} = \frac{[H_2CO_3][CO_3^{-2}]}{[HCO_3^-]^2}$$

$$= K_{A2} \times \frac{K_w}{K_{A1}} \times \frac{1}{K_w} = \frac{K_{A2}}{K_{A1}} = \frac{4.8 \times 10^{-11}}{4.2 \times 10^{-7}} = 1.14 \times 10^{-4}$$

or $$\frac{[H_2CO_3][CO_3^{-2}]}{[HCO_3^-]^2} = \frac{K_{A2}}{K_{A1}} = 1.14 \times 10^{-4}$$

which is the equilibrium expression for equation (3).

If K_{A2} and K_w/K_{A1} are not extremely different, and *if the molar concentration of the ampholyte is not much below the numerical value of K_{A2}, then* equation (3) can be interpreted literally to mean that $[H_2CO_3]$ and $[CO_3^{-2}]$ will be produced in equal concentrations: $[H_2CO_3] = [CO_3^{-2}]$. (This is in fact a good approximation under most circumstances.) Also in this particular case, since the values of $K_{A2} = 4.8 \times 10^{-11}$ and $K_w/K_{A1} = 2.4 \times 10^{-8}$ are both small, it can be assumed that the concentration of HCO_3^- will not be appreciably changed, and therefore if we define $X = [H_2CO_3] = [CO_3^{-2}]$, and specify that $[HCO_3^-] = 0.1\,M$, then

$$\frac{X^2}{(0.1)^2} = 1.14 \times 10^{-4}$$

$$X^2 = 1.14 \times 10^{-6}$$

and $$X = [H_2CO_3] = [CO_3^{-2}] = 1.06 \times 10^{-3}\,M$$

Now, from equation (1)

$$\frac{[H^+][CO_3^{-2}]}{[HCO_3^-]} = \frac{[H^+](1.06 \times 10^{-3})}{0.1} = 4.8 \times 10^{-11}$$

and $$[H^+] = 4.5 \times 10^{-9}\,M$$

Thus

$$[OH^-] = \frac{1 \times 10^{-14}}{4.5 \times 10^{-9}} = 2.2 \times 10^{-6}\,M$$

Sodium bicarbonate solutions are consequently basic, as could be predicted from the fact that K_w/K_{A1} is larger than K_{A2}.

A more direct route to the hydrogen-ion concentration also depends upon the assumption that $[H_2CO_3] = [CO_3^{-2}]$, which is valid provided the conditions stated earlier are met. If $[H_2CO_3] \approx [CO_3^{-2}]$, it can be seen that the expression

$$\frac{[H^+]^2[CO_3^{-2}]}{[H_2CO_3]} = K_{A1}K_{A2}$$

reduces to $[H^+]^2 = K_{A1}K_{A2}$, and therefore

$$[H^+] = \sqrt{K_{A1}K_{A2}}$$

This gives $[H^+] = 4.5 \times 10^{-9}$ M, the same as above. It can be seen that, according to this expression, $[H^+]$ in these systems is independent of concentration *provided* the molar concentration is larger numerically than K_{A2}.

This treatment is applicable to most ampholytes. However, a more rigorous treatment is given in Appendix 3.

8–13. Summary

In summary, then, it can be said that in any heterogeneous or homogeneous system, having two or more equilibria involving common substances, it is necessary to realize that these equilibria cannot be independent. Very frequently, however, because of high concentration or because of a large equilibrium constant, one of the equilibria can be seen to dominate the others. Such systems, then, can be treated very simply by calculating the concentrations of the substances involved in the dominant equilibrium as though the other equilibria did not exist. The other equilibria are then examined with the assumption that the concentrations of any substances in common with the dominant equilibrium will be as already found for the dominant equilibrium. On the other hand, when one equilibrium does not clearly dominate the others, it is necessary to treat them mathematically as simultaneous equilibria. Under these circumstances, use must be made of proper conservation equations which define the additive relationships of the concentrations in the particular system under consideration. These conservation equations may arise from the stoichiometry of the substances involved (see Section 8–6, equation 13), or they may arise from considerations of conservation of charge (i.e., the sum of the positive charges in solution must equal the sum of the negative charges; see Section 8–8).

8–14. Questions and Problems

1. It is usually said that whether or not insoluble carbonates can be precipitated from aqueous solution in preference to the metal hydroxide depends on the basic strength of the hydroxide. Yet addition of Na_2CO_3 to a $Hg_2(NO_3)_2$ solution produces Hg_2CO_3, whereas $Hg(NO_3)_2$ gives HgO, despite the fact that Hg_2O and HgO have almost identical base strength (K_{sp}'s $= 7.8 \times 10^{-24}$ and 2.5×10^{-26} for Hg_2O and HgO respectively). Explain.

2. Show that the first basic ionization constant for solid $CdSeO_3$ ($K_{sp} = 1.3 \times 10^{-9}$)
   $$CdSeO_3 \text{ (s)} + H_2O \rightleftharpoons Cd^{+2} + HSeO_3^- + OH^-$$
   is *smaller* than the second.

3. When HCl is added little by little to an aqueous suspension of AgCl, the solubility of the AgCl at first decreases, but then reaches a minimum and then increases again. Explain.

4. The complex ion $Ag(S_2O_3)_2^{-3}$ is in equilibrium in solution with Ag^+ and $S_2O_3^{-2}$ ions

$$Ag(S_2O_3)_2^{-3} \rightleftharpoons Ag^+ + 2\ S_2O_3^{-2}$$

Why may it usually not be said that $[S_2O_3^{-2}] = 2[Ag^+]$? Under what conditions might the statement $[S_2O_3^{-2}] = 2[Ag^+]$ be true?

5. Will $Ag(NH_3)_2^+$ be more completely dissociated in the presence of NO_3^- or Cl^-? Explain. What are the equilibrium constants for the two cases?

6. Explain how the solubility of the salt of a weak acid or a weak base may be affected by pH.

7. Explain how the solubility of AgBr may be affected by addition of (a) $Hg(NO_3)_2$ and (b) NH_4OH.

8. Explain why the solubility of TlCN exceeds the square root of its solubility-product constant.

9. Calculate the PO_4^{-3} and OH^- concentrations in a 0.01 M solution of K_2HPO_4.

10. If $MgCl_2$ is added little by little to a 0.1 M $NaHCO_3$ solution, show by calculation whether $MgCO_3$ or $Mg(OH)_2$ will precipitate first.

11. From the data given in Section 6–3 on the substance AgSH (aq), calculate an equilibrium constant for the reaction AgSH (aq) $\rightleftharpoons Ag^+ + SH^-$. Do the same for $Hg(SH)_2$ (aq).

12. Calculate the molar solubility of LiF in 1 molar HF.

13. Calculate the molar solubility of Cu_2O in water.

14. What is the molar solubility of AgBr in 0.1 M NH_4OH?

15. What is the pH of a solution containing 1 gram SO_2 and 2 grams HCN per 125 ml?

16. When excess of a mixture of TlN_3 and Tl_3PO_4 is shaken with water, the saturated solution is found to contain 4.9×10^{-3} M PO_4^{-3}. If the K_{sp} of TlN_3 is 2.2×10^{-4}, what is the K_{sp} of Tl_3PO_4? (Neglect hydrolysis.)

17. Calculate the molar solubility of $Ni(NH_3)_6(ClO_4)_2$ in 10 M NH_4OH. K_{sp} for $[Ni(NH_3)_6][ClO_4]_2 = 1.4 \times 10^{-6}$.

18. Calculate the molar solubility of $CsHgCl_3$ in 0.1 M HNO_3.

19. Calculate the molar solubility of $CsHgCl_3$ in pure water.

20. (a) The K_{sp} for $AgIO_3$ (s) is 5.3×10^{-8}. The dissociation constant for $AgIO_3$ (aq) is 1.5×10^{-1}. Calculate the molar concentration of *dissolved, undissociated* $AgIO_3$ in a solution saturated with $AgIO_3$.
(b) If the instability constant for the complex $Ag(IO_3)_2^-$ is 1.4×10^{-2}, what is the molar concentration of $AgIO_3$ which would dissolve in 1 M HIO_3 solution? (Assume HIO_3 to be completely ionized.)

21. Calculate what molar concentration of KOH is required to dissolve 2 grams of $PbCrO_4$ in 1 liter of solution.

22. If 0.001 mole of $Pb(OH)_2$ is dissolved completely in 0.1 M KOH, calculate whether it is possible to precipitate $PbCrO_4$ by adding Na_2CrO_4 to this solution. If so, what concentration of Na_2CrO_4 is required?

23. If the first and second ionization constants of $Pb(OH)_2$ (aq) are $K_1 = 9.3 \times 10^{-4}$ and $K_2 = 1.5 \times 10^{-8}$, what is the molar concentration of dissolved un-ionized $Pb(OH)_2$ in a solution saturated with solid $Pb(OH)_2$? What is the concentration of $PbOH^+$?

24. If excess solid KIO_3 is added to a saturated solution of $In(IO_3)_3$ containing excess solid $In(IO_3)_3$, calculate the ratio of $[K^+]$ to $[In^{+3}]$ when equilibrium is reached. K_{sp} for $KIO_3 = 4.8 \times 10^{-2}$. K_{sp} for $In(IO_3)_3 = 3.2 \times 10^{-3}$. (Remember than an equation of the form $x^4 + ax^2 + b = 0$ can be solved for x^2 by the quadratic formula.)

25. A mixture of solid Ag_3PO_4 and solid AgNCS is shaken with insufficient water to dissolve either compound. Calculate the concentrations of $[Ag^+]$, $[NCS^-]$, and $[PO_4^{-3}]$ in the saturated solution.

26. From the following data, calculate the *total* solubility of $PbAc_2$ in 0.1 M $HClO_4$. What are the concentrations of Pb^{+2}, H^+, and HAc?

K_{sp} of solid $PbAc_2 = 1.8 \times 10^{-3}$
K_A for HAc $= 1.85 \times 10^{-5}$
$K_{inst} = 6.9 \times 10^{-3}$ for $PbAc_2$ (aq) $\rightleftharpoons PbAc^+ + Ac^-$
$K_{inst} = 1.8 \times 10^{-1}$ for $PbAc^+ \rightleftharpoons Pb^{+2} + Ac^-$

8–15.   References

Bjerrum, Jannik, Schwarzenbach, Gerold, and Sillén, Lars Gunnar, *Stability Constants*. ("Special Publications Nos. 6 and 7.") London: The Chemical Society, 1957, 1958.

K_{sp} of CuCN: Vladimirova, M. G., and Kakovskii, I. A., *Zhurnal prikladnoi khimii*, Vol. 23 (1950), p. 580.

Chapter 9

Amphoterism.

General Cation Analysis

9–1. Amphoteric Hydroxides in Acids and Bases—Complete or Negligible Reaction

The subject of ampholytes has come up several times in past chapters (Sections 5–10, 6–10, and 8–12), so repetition of the fact that these are substances which act simultaneously as acid and as base is hardly necessary. Most of the ampholytes so far considered have been water-soluble substances such as glycine, $H_2PO_4^-$, $N_2H_5^+$, and so forth. A very important class of ampholytes, however, is that of the insoluble amphoteric metal hydroxides. Thus we find that whereas potassium hydroxide, KOH, invariably acts as a base in water solution and perchloryl hydroxide, $(ClO_3)OH$, (i.e., perchloric acid, $HClO_4$), as an acid, there are many hydroxides which can act as both weak acid and weak base. Thus bismuth hydroxide is described as undergoing the reactions

$$(1) \qquad Bi(OH)_3 \text{ (s)} \rightleftharpoons Bi(OH)_2^+ + OH^- \qquad K_{B1} = 1 \times 10^{-12}$$

$$(2) \qquad Bi(OH)_3 \text{ (s)} \rightleftharpoons BiOH^{+2} + 2\,OH^- \qquad K_{B12} = 1.6 \times 10^{-28}$$

$$(3) \qquad Bi(OH)_3 \text{ (s)} \rightleftharpoons Bi^{+3} + 3\,OH^- \qquad K_{sp} = 3.2 \times 10^{-40}$$

in which it acts as a base. (Note that the K_{sp} of $Bi(OH)_3$ (s) and the over-all basic ionization of $Bi(OH)_3$ (s) are one and the same thing.) Also, we have the reaction

$$(4) \qquad Bi(OH)_3 \text{ (s)} \rightleftharpoons H^+ + H_2BiO_3^- \qquad K_{A1} = 5 \times 10^{-20}$$

in which it acts as an acid. In order to emphasize the acidic nature of substances of this sort, the formula is frequently altered and the reactions written in the manner

(4') $H_3BiO_3 \text{ (s)} \rightleftharpoons H^+ + H_2BiO_3^-$

Since the equilibrium constants for all of these reactions are small, it can be seen that none of the reactions proceeds very far when solid bismuth hydroxide is suspended in water. However, it is easy to see by application of Le Châtelier's principle what will happen if excess strong acid or excess strong base is added. For example, removal of OH^- by addition of strong acid will cause reactions (1), (2), and (3) to shift to the right, with the result that $Bi(OH)_3$ will go into solution as $Bi(OH)_2^+$ (or BiO^+). Likewise, addition of strong base will cause reaction (4) to shift to the right, resulting in $Bi(OH)_3$ going into solution as $H_2BiO_3^-$.

Let us consider a specific example and estimate how much $Bi(OH)_3$ will dissolve in 1 liter of 0.001 M $HClO_4$. From the equation

(5) $Bi(OH)_3 \text{ (s)} + H^+ \rightleftharpoons Bi(OH)_2^+ + H_2O$

it can be seen that, to a first approximation, the H^+ will be consumed, and the $Bi(OH)_2^+$ concentration of the resulting solution will be 0.001 molar. It is of interest to find out what the pH of such a solution would be. Reaction (5) can be seen to be the sum of (1) and the reverse of the ionization of water, $H^+ + OH^- \rightleftharpoons H_2O$. Remembering that the activity of a pure solid is one, and combining the mathematical expressions for (1) and the ionization of water, we have

$$[Bi(OH)_2^+][OH^-] = 1 \times 10^{-12} = K_{B1}$$

$$\frac{1}{[H^+][OH^-]} = 1 \times 10^{14}$$

$$\frac{[Bi(OH)_2^+]}{[H^+]} = 1 \times 10^2$$

Taking $[Bi(OH)_2^+] = 1 \times 10^{-3} M$

$$[H^+] = \frac{[Bi(OH)_2^+]}{1 \times 10^2} = \frac{1 \times 10^{-3}}{1 \times 10^2} = 1 \times 10^{-5} M$$

and pH = 5.0. It can be seen from this example that an insoluble hydroxide acts as a buffer and tends to resist change in pH.

To be certain of the correctness of this procedure, we should check to make sure that the second ionization of $Bi(OH)_3$ does not produce significant amounts of $BiOH^{+2}$ under these conditions. Noting that at pH = 5.0, $[OH^-] = 10^{-9} M$, and from the equilibrium expression for reaction (2)

$$[BiOH^{+2}][OH^-]^2 = 1.6 \times 10^{-28} = K_{B12}$$

$$[BiOH^{+2}] = \frac{1.6 \times 10^{-28}}{(10^{-9})^2} = 1.6 \times 10^{-10} M$$

Therefore we were justified in ignoring the second ionization.

The same approach can be used for basic solutions. Let us find how much $Bi(OH)_3$ will dissolve in 0.001 M KOH.

$$Bi(OH)_3 \text{ (s)} + OH^- \rightleftharpoons H_2BiO_3^- + H_2O$$

Again this can be seen to be the sum of (4′) and the reverse of the ionization of water.

$$[H^+][H_2BiO_3^-] = 5 \times 10^{-20}$$

$$\frac{1}{[H^+][OH^-]} = 1 \times 10^{14}$$

$$\frac{[H_2BiO_3^-]}{[OH^-]} = 5 \times 10^{-6}$$

In this case, the ionization constant of the solid is so small that the ratio $[H_2BiO_3^-]/[OH^-]$ is only 5×10^{-6} to 1. Consequently, only an insignificant fraction of the OH^- will be used up and $[H_2BiO_3^-] = 5 \times 10^{-9}$ M.

The situation could have been quite the reverse. For example, in the case of As_2O_3

$$\tfrac{1}{2} As_2O_3 \text{ (s)} + \tfrac{3}{2} H_2O \rightleftharpoons As(OH)_2^+ + OH^- \qquad K_{B1} = 9.9 \times 10^{-16}$$

$$\tfrac{1}{2} As_2O_3 \text{ (s)} + \tfrac{3}{2} H_2O \rightleftharpoons H^+ + H_2AsO_3^- \qquad K_{A1} = 5.1 \times 10^{-11}$$

from which $\qquad\qquad \dfrac{[As(OH)_2^+]}{[H^+]} = 9.9 \times 10^{-2}$

or $\qquad\qquad\qquad\qquad [H^+] = 10.1[As(OH)_2^+]$

and $\qquad\qquad\qquad \dfrac{[H_2AsO_3^-]}{[OH^-]} = 5.1 \times 10^3$

or $\qquad\qquad\qquad [H_2AsO_3^-] = 5100[OH^-]$

It can easily be seen that the [H+] must always be 10.1 times greater than $[As(OH)_2^+]$ as long as there is excess solid As_2O_3 in equilibrium with the solution, and consequently only an insignificant (barely) fraction (10 percent) of the acid will be used up. For example, in 1 liter of 10^{-3} M $HClO_4$, only 9.9×10^{-5} moles of As_2O_3 (s) will react with the acid to give $As(OH)_2^+$, using up less than 10 percent of the H^+. On the other hand, the $[H_2AsO_3^-]$ must be 5100 times greater than $[OH^-]$. Consequently, As_2O_3 (s) will react with aqueous bases using up essentially all of the OH^-. Thus for the reaction As_2O_3 (s) with 10^{-3} M KOH

$$As_2O_3 \text{ (s)} + OH^- \rightleftharpoons H_2AsO_2^-$$

$[H_2AsO_3^-]$ must be essentially 10^{-3} molar. From the equilibrium expression, then, the $[OH^-]$ has become 2.0×10^{-7} molar.

9–2.   Amphoteric Hydroxides in Acids and Bases—Partial Reaction

A third situation is obviously possible in which it is justified to assume neither that acid (or base) is used up completely nor that the amount used up is insignificant. Such a case is that of the dissolution of $Sn(OH)_2$ (s) in strong base.

$$Sn(OH)_2 \text{ (s)} + OH^- \rightleftharpoons HSnO_2^- + H_2O$$

From the acid ionization constant for the equilibrium

$$Sn(OH)_2 \text{ (s)} \rightleftharpoons H^+ + HSnO_2^-$$

$$[H^+][HSnO_2^-] = 3.7 \times 10^{-15}$$

and the water equilibrium, we have

$$\frac{[HSnO_2^-]}{[OH^-]} = 0.37$$

from which it can be seen that at equilibrium the stannite-ion concentration will be 37 percent of that of the remaining hydroxide ion. Now if we ask how much $Sn(OH)_2$ (s) will dissolve in 1 liter of 10^{-3} M KOH and what will be the $[OH^-]$ in the final solution, we must realize that, since for every $HSnO_2^-$ produced one OH^- must be used up, neither $[OH^-]$ nor $[HSnO_2^-]$ will be 10^{-3} molar, but rather the sum of the two must be 10^{-3} molar.

$$[OH^-] + [HSnO_2^-] = 10^{-3}$$

Consequently

$$\frac{[HSnO_2^-]}{10^{-3} - [HSnO_2^-]} = 0.37$$

$$1.4[HSnO_2^-] = 3.7 \times 10^{-4}$$

$$[HSnO_2^-] = 2.6 \times 10^{-4} \ M$$

and

$$[OH^-] = 7.1 \times 10^{-4} \ M$$

Thus 2.6×10^{-4} moles of $Sn(OH)_2$ will dissolve in 1 liter of 10^{-3} M KOH.

9–3.   Amphoteric Hydroxides with Important Second Ionization Steps

In the examples we have just been considering, we have assumed (and justified) that only the first ionization step of the acid or base need be considered. For homogeneous systems, as we saw in Chapter 6, this is correct unless the successive ionization constants lie very close together. Because with insoluble acids or bases we are combining a heterogeneous first ionization step with a homogeneous second step, however, this assumption may no longer hold (see problem 2, Chapter 8).

Let us consider the dissolution of $Zn(OH)_2$ (s) in 10^{-3} M $HClO_4$ and again in 10^{-3} M KOH. The ionization reactions for $Zn(OH)_2$ (s) are

(6) $Zn(OH)_2$ (s) $\rightleftharpoons ZnOH^+ + OH^-$ $K_{B1} = 1.2 \times 10^{-12}$

(7) $Zn(OH)_2$ (s) $\rightleftharpoons Zn^{+2} + 2\,OH^-$ $K_{sp} = 4.8 \times 10^{-17}$

(8) $Zn(OH)_2$ (s) $\rightleftharpoons HZnO_2^- + H^+$ $K_{A1} = 1.2 \times 10^{-17}$

(9) $Zn(OH)_2$ (s) $\rightleftharpoons ZnO_2^{-2} + 2\,H^+$ $K_{A12} = 2.2 \times 10^{-30}$

From (6) and the ionization of water

$$\frac{[ZnOH^+]}{[H^+]} = 120$$

and therefore if $[ZnOH^+] = 10^{-3}$ M, $[H^+] = 8.3 \times 10^{-6}$ M. However, from (6), (7) and the ionization of water

$$\frac{[Zn^{+2}]}{[ZnOH^+][H^+]} = 4.0 \times 10^9$$

so that the $[Zn^{+2}]$ must be 33200 times greater than $[ZnOH^+]$ if our assumptions were correct, and in any event the value of $[Zn^{+2}]$ which this would give is absurd. It is obvious that here the second ionization cannot be ignored. On the contrary, it would appear that perhaps the first might be ignored and reaction (7) alone be considered, or rather the reaction

$$Zn(OH)_2 \text{ (s)} + 2\,H^+ \rightleftharpoons Zn^{+2} + 2\,H_2O$$

for which

$$\frac{[Zn^{+2}]}{[H^+]^2} = 4.8 \times 10^{11}$$

In this case, if the *initial* $[H^+] = 10^{-3}$ M, then the equilibrium value of $[Zn^{+2}] = 5 \times 10^{-4}$ M. From this

$$\frac{5 \times 10^{-4}}{[H^+]^2} = 4.8 \times 10^{11}$$

$$[H^+] = 3.2 \times 10^{-8} \ M$$

(i.e., a basic solution).
Now from

$$\frac{[ZnOH^+]}{[H\ ]^+} = 120,$$

$$[ZnOH^+] = 3.8 \times 10^{-6} \ M$$

and it can be seen that the first ionization step is indeed unimportant in comparison to the over-all process.

Let us finally examine the system in 10^{-3} M KOH. If it be assumed that in the reaction

$$Zn(OH)_2 \text{ (s)} + OH^- \rightleftharpoons HZnO_2^- + H_2O$$

an insignificant fraction of the $[OH^-]$ is used up (*Note:* $K_{A1} = 1.2 \times 10^{-17}$), then $[OH^-] = 10^{-3}$ M and from

$$\frac{[H^+][HZnO_2^-]}{[H^+][OH^-]} = \frac{1.2 \times 10^{-17}}{1 \times 10^{-14}}$$

(10)
$$\frac{[HZnO_2^-]}{[OH^-]} = 1.2 \times 10^{-3}$$

and
$$[HZnO_2^-] = 1.2 \times 10^{-6} \ M$$

For the second acid ionization

$$\frac{[H^+]^2[ZnO_2^{-2}]}{[H^+]^2[OH^-]^2} = \frac{2.2 \times 10^{-30}}{(1 \times 10^{-14})^2}$$

(11)
$$\frac{[ZnO_2^{-2}]}{[OH^-]^2} = 2.2 \times 10^{-2}$$

and
$$[ZnO_2^{-2}] = 2.2 \times 10^{-8} \ M$$

and we were justified in ignoring the second step.

If, on the other hand, we had examined the dissolution of $Zn(OH)_2$ (s) in 1 M KOH, then from (10)

$$[HZnO_2^-] = 1.2 \times 10^{-3} \ M$$

while from (11)

$$[ZnO_2^{-2}] = 2.2 \times 10^{-2} \ M$$

or $[ZnO_2^{-2}]$ is eighteen times greater than $[HZnO_2^-]$, and once again, just as in acidic solution, the first step has become insignificant in comparison to the over-all process. In neither case is a significant fraction of the $[OH^-]$ used up, the most being 2.3 percent in the last example.

It can be seen from these examples that what species will be of significance in systems such as these depends strongly on both the equilibrium constants and the conditions of the equilibrium.

9–4. Amphoterism and Electronegativity (Qualitative)

There are many hydroxides which are amphoteric. Among them are $Al(OH)_3$, $Sb(OH)_3$, $As(OH)_3$, $Be(OH)_2$, $Cr(OH)_3$, $Ge(OH)_2$, $Au(OH)_3$, IOH, $Pb(OH)_2$, $Pb(OH)_4$, $Mn(OH)_4$, $NpO_2(OH)_2$, $Pt(OH)_4$, $PuO_2(OH)_2$, $Po(OH)_4$, $Te(OH)_4$, $Sn(OH)_2$, $Ti(OH)_4$, $UO_2(OH)_2$, $V(OH)_4$, $Zn(OH)_2$. As will be seen below, these substances have for the most part a difference of electro-negativity too small for them to be strong bases, but yet too large for them to be strong acids. Consequently, they are neither strongly basic nor strongly acidic, but rather a little bit of each.

Let us consider a simplified picture of what changing the difference of electronegativity in a hydroxide does in three typical cases. In the compound CsOH, the difference in electronegativity between cesium and oxygen is $3.5 - 0.7 = 2.8$, so large that the electrons will be concentrated almost entirely around the oxygen

$$Cs^+ \underset{\longrightarrow}{\longrightarrow} : \overset{..}{\underset{..}{O}} : \overset{-}{H}$$

Thus the substance consists essentially of Cs^+ and OH^- ions, and is a strong base. In the compound ClOH, however, the difference in electronegativity is very small, $3.5 - 3.0 = 0.5$. Consequently, the chlorine atom pulls very strongly on the electrons shared with the oxygen, which in turn pulls strongly on the electrons it shares with the hydrogen.

$$: \overset{..}{\underset{..}{Cl}} : \overset{\leftharpoonup}{O} : \overset{\leftharpoonup}{H}$$

Therefore, the hydrogen goes very readily to anything else such as a water molecule, which will give it a better share of electrons than the ClO^- group will, and ClOH is consequently an acid (hypochlorous acid).

$$ClO \cdots H + OH_2 \rightleftharpoons ClO^- + OH_3{}^+$$

In AgOH, on the other hand, the difference in electronegativity is intermediate between the other two cases ($3.5 - 1.8 = 1.7$) and AgOH is intermediate in nature. The silver atom attracts the oxygen's electrons strongly enough so that the OH^- ion is not lost very easily as such, but not strongly enough to cause H^+ to be liberated easily. However, if AgOH is treated with a strong acid, the Ag^+ attracts the OH^- less strongly than the proton of an oxonium ion, $OH_3{}^+$, does, and consequently the AgOH acts as a base.

$$AgOH + OH_3{}^+ \rightleftharpoons Ag^+ + 2 H_2O$$

On the other hand, if AgOH is treated with a strong base, the AgO^- ion attracts the proton of the AgOH less strongly than the free OH^- does, and consequently AgOH acts as an acid.

$$AgOH + OH^- \rightleftharpoons AgO^- + H_2O$$

Silver hydroxide is thus an ampholyte.

9–5. The Criterion of Amphoterism

In Table 9–1 will be found listed the acidic and basic ionization constants of a number of amphoteric oxides and hydroxides. It will be noticed that there are constants given for many which were not listed above as amphoteric hydroxides and are not ordinarily considered to be amphoteric, despite the fact that they have measurable acid ionization constants. On what basis, then, do we ordinarily decide whether to call a hydroxide amphoteric? Let us consider the cases of $Mn(OH)_2$ and $Ni(OH)_2$, which are not considered to be amphoteric, of $Cu(OH)_2$, which is a borderline case, and of $Sn(OH)_2$, which is definitely amphoteric. Let us find out what concentration of each of these will dissolve in 0.01 M strong base. Using the constants from Table 9–1, and observing that when $[OH^-] = 0.01$ M $[H^+] = 1 \times 10^{-12}$ M

$$[HMnO_2^-] = \frac{1 \times 10^{-19}}{1 \times 10^{-12}} = 1 \times 10^{-7} \ M$$

$$[HNiO_2^-] = \frac{6 \times 10^{-19}}{1 \times 10^{-12}} = 6 \times 10^{-7} \ M$$

$$[HCuO_2^-] = \frac{1.6 \times 10^{-16}}{1 \times 10^{-12}} = 1.6 \times 10^{-4} \ M$$

(At the same time

$$[CuO_2^{-2}] = \frac{5.0 \times 10^{-29}}{(1 \times 10^{-12})^2} = 5 \times 10^{-5} \ M$$

giving a total solubility of $Cu(OH)_2$ equal to

$$1.6 \times 10^{-4} + 5 \times 10^{-5} = 2.1 \times 10^{-4} \ M)$$

In the case of $Sn(OH)_2$ we cannot neglect the amount of OH^- which is used up, so let us write

$$\frac{[H^+][HSnO_2^-]}{[H^+][OH^-]} = \frac{2.7 \times 10^{-15}}{1 \times 10^{-14}}$$

$$\frac{[HSnO_2^-]}{[OH^-]} = 2.7 \times 10^{-1}$$

If X moles of $HSnO_2^-$ goes into solution, then $10^{-2} - X$ moles of OH^- will remain, so that

$$\frac{X}{0.01 - X} = 0.27$$

$$1.27X = 2.7 \times 10^{-3}$$

and $$X = 2.1 \times 10^{-3} \ M = [HSnO_2^-]$$

It can be seen, then, that the amounts of $Mn(OH)_2$ and $Ni(OH)_2$ dissolving in fairly concentrated alkali are negligible, and the concentration of $HCuO_2^- + CuO_2^{-2}$ is on the lower limit of the concentrations of solutions usually used in the laboratory. The concentration of $HSnO_2^-$, on the other hand, is well within the range of concentrations commonly used. The division of substances into the categories *amphoteric* and *non-amphoteric* can now be seen to be a practical, rather than a strictly theoretical one.

TABLE 9–1. IONIZATION CONSTANTS (I.E., pK'S) FOR SOLID AMPHOLYTES

$$pK_{Bn}: M(OH)_x \rightleftharpoons M(OH)_{x-n}^{+n} + nOH^-$$

$$pK_{An}: M(OH)_x \rightleftharpoons nH^+ + H_{x-n}MO_x^{-n}$$

Solid Ampholyte	pK_{B1234}	pK_{B123}	pK_{B12}	pK_{B1}	pK_{A1}	pK_{A12}	pK_{A123}
½ Ag₂O				7.7	17.5	30.5	
Al(OH)₃		31.59	22.32		12.56		
½ As₂O₃			15.02		10.29	22.42	35.8
Au(OH)₃		53.0			17.28	30.64	>42.7
Be(OH)₂			17.7	8.0	16.49	30.70	
Bi(OH)₃		39.5	27.8	12.0	19.30		
Cd(OH)₂			13.70	9.53	18.68	>33.1	
Co(OH)₂			15.60	11.0	19.10		
Cr(OH)₃		30.3	20.2	12.5	14.4		
Cu(OH)₂			18.8	11.8	15.80	28.30	
Fe(OH)₂			14.10	8.54	18.43	33.54	
Ga(OH)₃		35.3	24.31	13.6	15.0	25.3	37.0
Ge(OH)₄	57.0				8.76	12.7	
HgO			25.60	14.50	18.40		
In(OH)₃		33.3	23.4	13.5	18.6		
Mn(OH)₂			13.34	9.44	19.0		
Ni(OH)₂			15.55	10.58	18.22		
Pb(OH)₂			14.40	6.59	15.13		
PbO₂	65.49*					32.46	
PuO₂(OH)₂			20.5	12.2	13.63		
½ Sb₂O₃		41.4		17.11	16.06		
SnO			25.70	13.84	14.57		
Sn(OH)₄	57.0					22.0	
Te(OH)₄	53.52			11.89	2.75	10.49	
Th(OH)₄	44.5	34.5	23.26	12.49	19.80	33.80	
U(OH)₄	45.0	31.7			17.8		
UO₂(OH)₂			22.0	12.54	17.60	31.77	
VO(OH)₂			22.13	13.5	10.3†		
½ V₂O₅		40.0‡		14.8	7.8	9.52	
Zn(OH)₂			16.32	11.92	16.92	29.66	
Zr(OH)₄	55.8	42.1	28.6	15.7	17.4		

* Pb(OH)₄
† $[H^+][HV_2O_5^-]$
‡ ½ V₂O₅ (s) + ⅗ H₂O $\rightleftharpoons$ VO^{+3} + 3 OH$^-$

9–6. Amphoteric Hydroxides in Water—One Constant Negligible in Comparison to the Other

In the examples given above, the specification of a high hydrogen-ion or hydroxide-ion concentration made it possible to select either the basic ionization equilibrium (in acidic solution) or the acidic ionization equilibrium (in basic solution) as being predominant and to ignore the other. In neutral solution, on the other hand, the system must be carefully examined to see which equilibrium will predominate. For example, if solid lead hydroxide is suspended in pure water, the acid and basic equilibria must simultaneously be obeyed.

$$Pb(OH)_2 \text{ (s)} \rightleftharpoons PbOH^+ + OH^-$$

(12) $$[PbOH^+][OH^-] = K_B = 2.6 \times 10^{-7}$$

$$Pb(OH)_2 \text{ (s)} \rightleftharpoons HPbO_2^- + H^+$$

(13) $$[H^+][HPbO_2^-] = K_A = 7.4 \times 10^{-16}$$

Estimating by sight the concentrations of the ions involved, it can be seen that $[PbOH^+] = [OH^-] \approx 10^{-4}$ M, whereas $[H^+] = [HPbO_2^-] \approx 10^{-8}$ M. (It can immediately be seen that even the ionization of water produces more H^+ than the latter equilibrium, however, and the estimation of the concentration of $HPbO_2^-$ should take this into account. Setting $[H^+] = 10^{-7}$, then $[HPbO_2^-] = 7.4 \times 10^{-9}$ M.) Thus the basic ionization strongly predominates over the acidic, and, to a first approximation, the acidic ionization can be ignored. Then from (12), setting $[PbOH^+] = [OH^-] = X$

$$X^2 = 2.6 \times 10^{-7}$$

$$X = 5.1 \times 10^{-4} \ M = [PbOH^+] = [OH^-]$$

Now from the water equilibrium

$$[H^+] = \frac{1 \times 10^{-14}}{2.0 \times 10^{-4}} = 5.1 \times 10^{-11} \ M$$

and from (13)

$$[HPbO_2^-] = \frac{7.4 \times 10^{-16}}{2.0 \times 10^{-11}} = 3.7 \times 10^{-5} M$$

or 7.4 percent as much as the $[PbOH^+]$. For the further ionization,

$$PbOH^+ \rightleftharpoons Pb^{+2} + OH^-$$

$$\frac{[Pb^{+2}][OH^-]}{[PbOH^+]} = 1.5 \times 10^{-8}$$

since $$[OH^-] = [PbOH^+] = 5.1 \times 10^{-4} \ M$$

$$[Pb^{+2}] = 1.5 \times 10^{-8} \ M$$

it can be seen that we were justified in ignoring the effect of this on the first basic ionization. Nevertheless, Pb^{+2} is almost as important a species in solution as $HPbO_2^-$.

In the case of VO_2OH the situation is just reversed.

$$VO_2OH \text{ (s)} \rightleftharpoons VO_2^+ + OH^-$$

$$[VO_2^+][OH^-] = 1.6 \times 10^{-15}$$

$$VO_2OH \text{ (s)} + H_2O \rightleftharpoons H^+ + H_2VO_4^-$$

$$[H^+][H_2VO_4^-] = 1.6 \times 10^{-8}$$

It can be seen by inspection that the acidic ionization will predominate over the basic, giving

$$[H^+] = [H_2VO_4^-] = \sqrt{1.6 \times 10^{-8}} = 1.3 \times 10^{-4} \ M$$

$$[OH^-] = \frac{1 \times 10^{-14}}{1.3 \times 10^{-4}} = 7.7 \times 10^{-11} \ M$$

and
$$[VO_2^+] = \frac{1.6 \times 10^{-15}}{7.7 \times 10^{-11}} = 2.1 \times 10^{-5} \ M$$

9–7. Amphoteric Hydroxides in Water—Neither Constant Negligible

If the ionization constants are too large the approximation used above may not be good enough. For example, in the case of tellurous acid we have

$$H_2TeO_3 \ (s) \rightleftharpoons H^+ + HTeO_3^-$$

(14)
$$[H^+][HTeO_3^-] = 1.8 \times 10^{-3}$$

$$H_2TeO_3 \ (s) \rightleftharpoons TeO_2H^+ + OH^-$$

(15)
$$[TeO_2H^+][OH^-] = 1.3 \times 10^{-12}$$

If we now assume as before that the basic ionization is of minor importance and therefore $[H^+] = [HTeO_3^-]$, then $[H^+] = [HTeO_3^-] = \sqrt{1.8 \times 10^{-3}}$ $= 4.2 \times 10^{-2} \ M$. From this

$$[OH^-] = \frac{1 \times 10^{-14}}{4.2 \times 10^{-2}} = 2.4 \times 10^{-13} \ M$$

and
$$[TeO_2H^+] = \frac{1.3 \times 10^{-12}}{2.4 \times 10^{-13}} = 5.4 \ M$$

which is absurd. Consequently, this system must be handled as one of simultaneous equilibria. To this end, we must establish one more relationship in the form of a conservation equation. Since the sums of the positive and negative charges in the system must be equal in order to maintain over-all neutrality,

(16)
$$[H^+] + [TeO_2H^+] = [OH^-] + [HTeO_3^-]$$

Equation (15) and the water equation give

(17)
$$\frac{[TeO_3H^+]}{[H^+]} = 1.3 \times 10^2$$

Combining (14), (15), and the water equation, we have

(18)
$$[TeO_2H^+][HTeO_3^-] = 2.34 \times 10^{-1}$$

Now substituting (17), (15), and (18) into (16), we have

(19)
$$\frac{[TeO_2H^+]}{1.3 \times 10^2} + [TeO_2H^+] = \frac{1.3 \times 10^{-12}}{[TeO_2H^+]} + \frac{2.34 \times 10^{-1}}{[TeO_2H^+]}$$

Clearing of fractions gives us

(20) $[TeO_2H^+]^2 + 1.3 \times 10^2[TeO_2H^+]^2 = 1.69 \times 10^{-10} + 30.42$

of which the third term is negligible, giving

(20') $131[TeO_2H^+]^2 = 30.42$

and $[TeO_2H^+] = 0.482 \ M$

From (18)

$$[HTeO_3^-] = \frac{0.234}{0.482} = 0.485 \ M$$

From (14)

$$[H^+] = \frac{1.8 \times 10^{-3}}{0.485} = 3.7 \times 10^{-3} \ M$$

and $[OH^-] = 2.7 \times 10^{-12} \ M$

Thus the acidic ionization strongly predominates in the sense that the solution has a low pH (2.43), but not in the sense that $[HTeO_3^-]$ is much greater than $[TeO_2H^+]$.

Another approach to this problem would have been to use the same type of approximation as was used for the HCO_3^- case (Section 6–7), i.e.

$$[TeO_2H^+] = [HTeO_3^-]$$

Then from (18)

$$[TeO_2H^+] = [HTeO_3^-] = \sqrt{2.34 \times 10^{-1}} = 0.484 \ \text{molar}$$

Then from (17)

$$[H^+] = \frac{[TeO_2H^+]}{1.3 \times 10^2} = 3.7 \times 10^{-3} \ M$$

and $OH^- = 2.7 \times 10^{-12} \ M$

Or again it may happen that the acidic and basic ionizations of an amphoteric hydroxide, although both small, are almost equally important. In this case, the equilibria must once more be considered simultaneously. Furthermore, if the hydrogen and hydroxide ion concentrations contributed by the ionization of water are large in comparison to those coming from the ampholyte, then this source also must be considered. A case of this sort is that of gallium hydroxide suspended in pure water. The equilibria involved are

$$Ga(OH)_3 \ (s) \rightleftharpoons Ga(OH)_2^+ + OH^-$$
$$Ga(OH)_3 \ (s) \rightleftharpoons H_2GaO_3^- + H^+$$
$$H_2O \rightleftharpoons H^+ + OH^-$$

for which we have the equilibrium expressions

(21) $[Ga(OH)_2^+][OH^-] = 2.5 \times 10^{-14}$

(22) $[H^+][H_2GaO_3^-] = 1 \times 10^{-15}$

(23) $[H^+][OH^-] = 1 \times 10^{-14}$

Since the sum of positive charges in solution must equal the sum of the negative charges, then

(24) $[Ga(OH)_2{}^+]+[H^+] = [H_2GaO_3{}^-] + [OH^-]$

if the second and third ionizations as acid and base can be ignored.

Combining equations (21) and (23)

(25) $[Ga(OH)_2{}^+] = 2.5\,[H^+]$

Combining equations (23) and (24)

(26) $[H^+][H_2GaO_3{}^-]+1 \times 10^{-14} = [H^+][Ga(OH)_2{}^+]+[H^+]^2$

Combining equations (22) and (26)

(27) $1 \times 10^{-15}+1 \times 10^{-14} = 1.1 \times 10^{-14} = [H^+][Ga(OH)_2{}^+]+[H^+]^2$

Combining equations (25) and (27)

(28) $1.1 \times 10^{-14} = 2.5\,[H^+]^2+[H^+]^2 = 3.5\,[H^+]^2$

Therefore

$$[H^+] = 5.6 \times 10^{-8}\ M$$

$$[OH^-] = \frac{1 \times 10^{-14}}{5.6 \times 10^{-8}} = 1.80 \times 10^{-7}\ M$$

$$[Ga(OH)_2{}^+] = \frac{2.5 \times 10^{-15}}{1.8 \times 10^{-7}} = 1.4 \times 10^{-7}$$

$$[H_2GaO_3{}^-] = \frac{1 \times 10^{-15}}{5.6 \times 10^{-8}} = 1.80 \times 10^{-8}\ M$$

These values can be seen to satisfy the conservation equation (24). From the second basic ionization expression for $Ga(OH)_2$ (s)

$$[GaOH^{+2}][OH^-]^2 = 5.0 \times 10^{-25}$$

$$[GaOH^{+2}] = \frac{5.0 \times 10^{-25}}{[OH^-]^2} = \frac{5.0 \times 10^{-25}}{3.24 \times 10^{-14}} = 1.5 \times 10^{-13}\ M$$

and it can be seen that we were justified in ignoring the second ionization.

9–8.   The Variation of Acidity (and Basicity) with Oxidation State

In the preceding section, it was pointed out that whether a substance such as CsOH, AgOH, or ClOH is basic, amphoteric, or acidic depends upon the difference in electronegativity between the hydroxyl group and the other element. Since, for a given element, the electronegativity increases as the oxidation state increases, it follows, then, that the hydroxides of the element will become less basic and more acidic as the oxidation state is increased. This fact is exemplified in Table 9–2 for the hydroxides of manganese.

TABLE 9–2. VARIATION OF ACIDITY (OR BASICITY) WITH OXIDATION STATE

Valence	Hydroxide	Electro- negativity	Description
+2	$Mn(OH)_2$	1.4	Fairly strong base ($pK_{sp} = 13.34$)
+3	$Mn(OH)_3$	1.5	Weak base ($pK_{sp} = 36$)
+4	$Mn(OH)_4$	1.75	Amphoteric ($pK_{sp} = 56$)
+5	$H_3MnO_4 = (MnO(OH)_3$	2.0	Weak acid ($pK_A \approx 8$)
+6	$H_2MnO_4 = MnO_2(OH)_2$	2.25	Moderately strong acid ($pK_A \approx 1$)
+7	$HMnO_4 = MnO_3OH$	2.5	Very strong acid ($pK_A = -2.25$)

With the nonmetals, which are much more electronegative to begin with, so that the hydroxides of even the lowest states are acidic, only a variation in acidity is seen; the acidity increasing with rise in oxidation state as before. This effect is shown for chlorine in Table 9–3.

TABLE 9–3. THE ACIDITIES OF THE HYDROXIDES OF CHLORINE

Oxidation State	Hydroxide	Acid Ionization Constant
+1	$HClO = ClOH$	3.0×10^{-8}
+3	$HClO_2 = ClOOH$	1.1×10^{-2}
+5	$HClO_3 = ClO_2OH$	$5.0 \times 10^{+2}$
+7	$HClO_4 = ClO_3OH$	$2.0 \times 10^{+7}$

9–9.   The Effect of the Number of Oxygen Atoms on Acidity

There is at least one other factor, however, which affects the strength of an oxy acid, and that is the relative number of hydrogen and oxygen atoms in it. Thus we find for an acid of a nonmetal of formula $(HO)_mXO_n$, if $n = 0$, $K_A = 10^{-7}$ or smaller. If $n = 1$, $K_A \approx 10^{-2}$. If $n = 2$, $K_A \approx 10^{+3}$. If $n = 3$, $K_A \approx 10^{+8}$. Thus the addition of one oxygen atom increases the K_A by a factor of about 10^5. This can be seen by reference to Table 9–3. Other examples are given in Table 9–4.

TABLE 9–4. IONIZATION CONSTANTS OF OXY ACIDS OF THE NONMETALS

Class ($n = 3$)		Class ($n = 1$) (cont.)	
$HClO_4$	$2 \times 10^{+7}$	H_2SeO_3	2.7×10^{-3}
		H_2TeO_3	2.7×10^{-3}
Class ($n = 2$)		HNO_2	5.1×10^{-4}
H_2SeO_4	$\approx 10^{+3}$	$H(CH)O_2$	2.6×10^{-4}
$HClO_3$	$5 \times 10^{+2}$	H_2CO_3	1.5×10^{-4}
H_2SO_4	$1 \times 10^{+2}$		
HNO_3	22	Class ($n = 0$)	
HIO_3	0.164	$H_2N_2O_2$	8.9×10^{-8}
		$HClO$	3.0×10^{-8}
Class ($n = 1$)		H_6TeO_6	2.5×10^{-8}
$H(PH_2)O_2$	8.5×10^{-2}	$HBrO$	2.5×10^{-9}
H_5IO_6	2.3×10^{-2}	H_3AsO_3	6.0×10^{-10}
H_2SO_3	1.8×10^{-2}	H_3BO_3	5.7×10^{-10}
$HClO_2$	1.1×10^{-2}	H_4GeO_4	4.0×10^{-10}
$H_2(PH)O_3$	1.0×10^{-2}	H_4SiO_4	1.6×10^{-10}
H_3PO_4	7.6×10^{-3}	HIO	4×10^{-11}
H_3AsO_4	$.0 \times 10^{-3}$	H_2O_2	1.8×10^{-12}

The acids of the transition elements seem to be uniformly weaker by a factor of about 10^4 than those of the nonmetals of the same class, but otherwise much the same rules can be applied. Some measured and estimated constants are given in Table 9–5.

TABLE 9–5. IONIZATION CONSTANTS OF OXY ACIDS OF THE TRANSITION METALS

Class ($n = 3$)			Class ($n = 1$)		
				K_1	K_2
$HMnO_4$	$1.8 \times 10^{+2}$		H_3VO_4 (s)	1.6×10^{-8}	3.0×10^{-10}
$HTcO_4$	$\approx 10^{+2}*$		H_3MnO_4 (s)	$\approx 10^{-8}*$	
$HReO_4$	$1.8 \times 10^{+1}$				

Class ($n = 2$)			Class ($n = 0$)	
	K_1	K_2		
H_2CrO_4	0.18	3.2×10^{-7}	H_4ZrO_4 (aq)	5×10^{-14}
H_2MnO_4	$\approx 10^{-1}$	$\geqslant 10^{-7}$		
H_2FeO_4	$\approx 10^{-1}$	$\geqslant 10^{-7}$		
H_2MoO_4	1.6×10^{-2}	8×10^{-5}		

* Estimated value.

From these relationships, it can be seen that if the value of n for the excess of oxygen atoms over hydroxyl groups for any reason were not to increase as the oxidation state of the central atom increases, the acidity might not increase as one would expect. We see in Table 9–6 some examples for which no increase in acidity, or even a decrease in acidity, with increasing oxidation state is observed.

TABLE 9–6. CHANGE IN IONIZATION CONSTANTS OF OXY ACIDS WITH
CHANGE IN OXIDATION STATE

$H(CH)O_2$	2.6×10^{-4}	HIO_3	1.64×10^{-1}
H_2CO_3	1.5×10^{-4}	H_5IO_6	2.3×10^{-2}
$H(PH_2)O_2$	8.5×10^{-2}	H_2TeO_3	2.7×10^{-3}
$H_2(PH)O_3$	1.0×10^{-2}	H_6TeO_6	2.5×10^{-8}
H_3PO_4	7.6×10^{-3}		

Even for the same oxidation state, the acidity is found to change as the excess of oxygen over hydrogen atoms (per central atom) changes, as can be seen in Table 9–7.

TABLE 9–7. CHANGE OF IONIZATION CONSTANTS OF OXY ACIDS $(HO)_m X_l O_n$
AS A FUNCTION OF n/l

Acid	n/l	K_A
H_3PO_4	1	7.6×10^{-3}
$H_4P_2O_6$	1	$>6.3 \times 10^{-3}$
$H_4P_2O_7$	3/2	0.14
$H_5P_3O_{10}$	5/3	≈ 0.4
$H_3P_3O_9$	2	Large ($K_3 = 9 \times 10^{-3}$)
H_2CrO_4	2	0.18
$H_2Cr_2O_7$	5/2	25
H_3BO_3	0	5.7×10^{-10}
$H_5B_3O_7$	2/3	1.65×10^{-7}
$H_6B_4O_9$	3/4	1.2×10^{-7}
$H_2B_4O_7$	5/4	1.8×10^{-4}

Since salts of both H_5IO_6 and HIO_4 are known, it is quite probable that these acids are another case of this sort. The K_A for HIO_4 is probably about 10^{+8}, whereas that for H_5IO_6 is 2.3×10^{-2}.

9–10.   Successive Ionization Constants

We have seen that, as the number of oxygen atoms changes, the K_A changes by a factor of about 10^5 for each oxygen atom. This same factor applies also to the successive ionizations of polybasic acids having only one central atom, as shown in Table 9–8.

TABLE 9–8. SUCCESSIVE IONIZATION CONSTANTS OF OXY ACIDS

Acid	K_1	K_2	K_3	K_4
H_2SO_4	102	1.26×10^{-2}		
H_3PO_4	7.6×10^{-3}	6.2×10^{-8}	1×10^{-12}	
H_3AsO_4	5.0×10^{-4}	9.3×10^{-8}	3.0×10^{-12}	
$H_2(PH)O_3$	1.0×10^{-2}	2.0×10^{-7}		
H_2SeO_3	2.7×10^{-3}	4.8×10^{-9}		
H_2SO_3	1.72×10^{-2}	6.2×10^{-8}		
H_2TeO_3	2.7×10^{-3}	1.8×10^{-8}		
H_5IO_6	2.9×10^{-2}	4.4×10^{-9}	1.05×10^{-15}	$<10^{-15}$

In the case of acids having more than one central atom, however, the ratio is much less, and in extreme cases may approach the theoretical minimum factor of 4 (for example, with sebacic acid).

TABLE 9–9. SUCCESSIVE IONIZATION CONSTANTS OF POLYNUCLEAR ACIDS

	K_1	K_2	K_3	K_4
$H_2B_4O_7$	1.7×10^{-7}	1.5×10^{-5}		
$H_2C_2O_4$	3.8×10^{-2}	5.0×10^{-5}		
$H_2C_{10}H_{16}O_4*$	2.8×10^{-5}	3.0×10^{-6}		
$H_2N_2O_2$	8.9×10^{-8}	1.0×10^{-11}		
$H_4P_2O_6$	6.3×10^{-3}	1.5×10^{-3}	5.4×10^{-8}	9.3×10^{-11}
$H_4P_2O_7$	1.4×10^{-1}	1.1×10^{-2}	2.9×10^{-7}	3.5×10^{-9}
$H_5P_3O_{10}$	≈ 0.4	5×10^{-2}	1×10^{-2}	7.9×10^{-7}
				$7.6 \times 10^{-10}(K_5)$
$H_2S_2O_6$	1.6	4×10^{-4}		

* Sebacic acid.

The factor of 10^5 also does not apply to acids of types different from the ones we have been discussing. In particular, if both hydrogen atoms are to be ionized off the same atom, the ratio of K_1 to K_2 may be much greater than 10^5, as for example with H_2S, H_2Se, and H_2Te. Examples of this sort are given in Table 9–10.

TABLE 9–10. SUCCESSIVE IONIZATION CONSTANTS OF ACIDS

	K_1	K_2
H_2O	1.0×10^{-14}	$<10^{-36}$
H_2S	1.0×10^{-7}	1.3×10^{-13}
H_2Se	1.3×10^{-4}	1.0×10^{-11}
H_2Te	2.3×10^{-3}	$10^{-11}(?)$
H_2O_2	1.8×10^{-12}	$\approx 10^{-25}$
$N_2H_6^{+2}$	0.76	1.15×10^{-8}

The ions of the very electronegative nonmetals are almost exclusively anions. For example, chlorine occurs in water solution as Cl^-, ClO_2^-, ClO_3^-, and ClO_4^-. The ions of the metals having very low electronegativity and only low oxidation states occur exclusively as cations. For example, the alkali metals occur in water solution as Li^+, Na^+, K^+, Rb^+, Cs^+, and Fr^+. The occurrence of the elements of intermediate electronegativity as cations or as anions, however, will depend on both the oxidation state of the element and the pH of the solution. Thus in acidic solution we have Ag^+, Cu^{+2}, Zn^{+2}, Cr^{+3}, Au^{+3}, Sn^{+4}, VO^{+2}, VO_2^+, and UO_2^{+2}, whereas these same elements occur in basic solution as AgO^-, $HCuO_2^-$, $HZnO_2^-$, CrO_2^-, AuO_2^-, SnO_3^{-2}, $HV_2O_5^-$, VO_4^{-3}, and $U_2O_7^{-2}$. On the other hand, in acidic solution we have Cr^{+2}, Cr^{+3}, Mn^{+2}, and Re^{+3}, but also in acidic solution we have $Cr_2O_7^{-2}$, MnO_4^-, and ReO_4^-, where the occurrence of the element as a cation or as an anion depends upon the oxidation state.

9-11. The Dehydration of Amphoteric Hydroxides

If just enough alkali hydroxide is added to the solution of the salts of certain heavy metals, the oxide, rather than the hydroxide, precipitates. (Or the hydroxide may precipitate first—but dehydrates on standing, even in contact with water.) For example, if a $Hg(NO_3)_2$ solution is made neutral, HgO (not $Hg(OH)_2$) precipitates. If a $AgNO_3$ solution is made alkaline, yellow $AgOH$ precipitates, and immediately dehydrates to black Ag_2O. If a $CuSO_4$ solution is made alkaline, blue $Cu(OH)_2$ precipitates, but on standing, especially if heated or if some H_2O_2 catalyst is added, dehydration to black CuO takes place.

$$Hg^{+2} + 2\,OH^- \rightleftharpoons HgO\,(s) + H_2O$$

$$2\,Ag^+ + 2\,OH^- \rightleftharpoons 2\,AgOH\,(s) \rightleftharpoons Ag_2O\,(s) + H_2O$$

$$Cu^{+2} + 2\,OH^- \rightleftharpoons Cu(OH)_2\,(s); \quad Cu(OH)_2\,(s) \xrightarrow[H_2O_2]{\Delta\ or} CuO + H_2O$$

On the other hand, magnesium hydroxide, $Mg(OH)_2$, does not dehydrate in contact with water. Whether a hydroxide may dehydrate in contact with water depends on its K_A and K_B. If both of these are high, dehydration is likely. The specific relationship for a monohydroxide like $AgOH$ can easily be derived from the acid and basic equilibrium expressions, taking the concentration of soluble, un-ionized hydroxide into consideration.

(1) $$\frac{[Ag^+][OH^-]}{[AgOH]} = 5.0 \times 10^{-3}$$

(2) $$\frac{[H^+][AgO^-]}{[AgOH]} = 8 \times 10^{-13}$$

Multiplying these together

(3)
$$\frac{[Ag^+][AgO^-][H^+][OH^-]}{[AgOH]^2} = 4.0 \times 10^{-15}$$

But since $[H^+][OH^-] = 1 \times 10^{-14}$ then

(4)
$$[Ag^+][AgO^-] = 0.40[AgOH]^2$$

in this particular case. (In general $\dfrac{[M^+][MO^-]}{[MOH]^2} = \dfrac{K_A K_B}{K_w}$.)

Since from

$$[Ag^+][OH^-] = 2 \times 10^{-8}$$

and
$$[H^+][AgO^-] = 3.2 \times 10^{-18}$$

which are the expressions for the heterogeneous equilibria, it can be shown that in a saturated solution

(5)
$$[Ag^+][AgO^-] = 6.4 \times 10^{-12}$$

it follows that

(6)
$$[AgOH]^2 = 1.6 \times 10^{-11}$$

and
$$[AgOH] = 4 \times 10^{-6} \, M$$

That is, in a saturated solution, there is 4×10^{-6} molar *un-ionized* AgOH. Any AgOH present in excess of this equilibrium concentration must precipitate as Ag_2O.

$$Ag^+ + AgO^- \rightleftharpoons Ag_2O \, (s)$$

This principle applies not only to oxides which precipitate, but also to oxides which remain in solution. Thus the system

$$2 \, HCrO_4^- \rightleftharpoons Cr_2O_7^{-2} + H_2O$$

should be considered in the same light as

$$2 \, AgOH \, (aq) \rightleftharpoons Ag_2O \, (s) + H_2O$$

However, since there is no "K_{sp}" (i.e., $[Ag^+][AgO^-]$) which must be exceeded in this case, there will be no upper limiting value of concentration of $HCrO_4^-$ which must be exceeded before oxide formation will take place (as there is for AgOH), but rather there will be a homogeneous equilibrium condition which is obeyed at all concentrations, namely

$$[HCrO_4^-]^2/[Cr_2O_7^{-2}] = 2.3 \times 10^{-2}$$

as described in Section 6-8.

TABLE 9–11. pK_{eq}'s FOR THE REACTION $M_n(OH)_2$ (s OR aq) $\rightleftharpoons M_nO$ (s OR aq) $+ H_2O$ (l)

Hydroxide	pK_{eq}	Hydroxide	pK_{eq}
RbOH (s)	35.2	HClO$_4$ (aq)	0.07
CsOH (s)	34.1	H$_2$SO$_3$ (aq)	0.07
KOH (s)	33.8	H$_2$CO$_3$ (aq)	0.00
NaOH (s)	24.6	AlOOH (s)	0.00
H$_2$SO$_4$ (aq)	23.5	Al(OH)$_3$ (s) (hydragillite)	−0.07
HNO$_3$ (aq)	20.6	Pd(OH)$_2$ (s)	−0.07
Ba(OH)$_2$ (s)	15.9	Ni(OH)$_2$ (s)	−0.07
LiOH (s)	15.5	Zn(OH)$_2$ (s)	−0.15
Sr(OH)$_2$ (s)	12.7	Be(OH)$_2$ (s)	−0.15
Ca(OH)$_2$ (s)	9.6	CH$_3$OH (aq)	−0.44
H$_2$WO$_4$ (s)	7.7*	Sn(OH)$_2$ (s)	−0.44
ZrO(OH)$_2$ (s)	7.6	Fe(OH)$_2$ (s)	−0.73
HfO(OH)$_2$ (s)	7.3	Mn(OH)$_3$ (s)	−1.10
La(OH)$_3$ (s)	7.0	Cu(OH)$_2$ (s)	−1.32
H$_2$MoO$_4$ (s)	5.9	HAsO$_2$ (aq)	−1.39
Mg(OH)$_2$ (s)	5.4	H$_2$GeO$_3$ (aq)	−1.5
Cr(OH)$_3$ (s) (anh)	4.8	In(OH)$_3$ (s)	−1.6
H$_3$AsO$_4$ (s)	3.2	Cr(OH)$_3$ (s) (hydrated)	−2.3
HClO (aq)	2.9	H$_2$SiO$_3$ (s)	−3.0
H$_2$SeO$_3$ (aq)	2.6	HCO$_2$H (aq)	−3.2
Mn(OH)$_2$ (s)	2.5	Sn(OH)$_4$ (s)	−3.6
Co(OH)$_2$ (s)	2.4	Ga(OH)$_3$ (s)	−3.7
UO$_2$(OH)$_2$ (s)	2.2	Hg(OH)$_2$ (aq)	−3.7
HNO$_2$ (aq) $\rightleftharpoons$ N$_2$O$_3$ (aq)	2.05*	Co(OH)$_3$ (s)	−3.7
Au(OH)$_3$ (s)	1.9	Fe(OH)$_3$ (s)	−3.7
B(OH)$_3$ (s)	1.8	H$_2$TeO$_3$ (s)	−4.1
Cd(OH)$_2$ (s)	1.8	Th(OH)$_4$ (s)	−4.8
Zr(OH)$_4$ (s) $\rightleftharpoons$ ZrO(OH)$_2$ (s)	1.5	TiO(OH)$_2$ (s)	−5.9
TlOH (s)	1.3	U(OH)$_4$ (s)	−6.6
HNO$_2$ (aq) $\rightleftharpoons$ N$_2$O$_3$ (g)	1.1	HSbO$_2$ (aq)	−7.9
BiOOH (s)	1.0	H$_2$N$_2$O$_2$ (aq)	−29.7
H$_2$SiO$_3$ (s) $\rightleftharpoons$ H$_2$Si$_2$O$_7$	0.5*		

* Very approximate (from *heats* of hydration).

9–12.   Other Ampholytic Systems

The ionization of an amphoteric hydroxide can just as easily be written as the ionization of an oxide with water. For example, the series of reactions

$$Zn^{+2} + 2\,OH^- \rightleftharpoons Zn(OH)_2\,(s) \rightleftharpoons 2\,H^+ + ZnO_2^{-2}$$

could be written

$$Zn^{+2} + 2\,OH^- \rightleftharpoons ZnO\,(s) + H_2O \rightleftharpoons 2\,H^+ + ZnO_2^{-2}$$

Therefore, although $Zn(OH)_2$ and ZnO are distinct chemical substances, it can be seen that the oxide should do the same things that the hydroxide does, and the oxide can thus also be described as amphoteric. It should be expected, then, that ZnO will dissolve in excess of either strong acid or of strong base, just as the hydroxide does, and this in fact is the case.

$$ZnO\ (s) +\ 2\ H^+ \rightleftharpoons Zn^{+2} + H_2O$$

$$ZnO\ (s) + 2\ OH^- \rightleftharpoons ZnO_2^{-2} + H_2O$$

These reactions are quite comparable to those which have already been described for the sulfides of the more electronegative elements (Sections 5–2 and 6–3).

$$HgS\ (s) + 2\ H^+ \rightleftharpoons Hg^{+2} + H_2S$$

$$HgS\ (s) + 2\ SH^- \rightleftharpoons HgS_2^{-2} + H_2S$$

Likewise comparable are the reactions

$$AgCl\ (s) \rightleftharpoons Ag^+ + Cl^-$$

$$AgCl\ (s) + Cl^- \rightleftharpoons AgCl_2^-$$

or a closer parallel would be

$$BeF_2\ (s) + 2\ H^+ \rightleftharpoons Be^{+2} + 2\ HF$$

$$BeF_2\ (s) + 2\ HF_2^- \rightleftharpoons BeF_4^{-2} + 2\ HF$$

Thus it can be seen that what has earlier been called the formation of complex ions may likewise be described in terms of amphoterism.

$$Zn^{+2} + 2\ OH^- \rightleftharpoons Zn(OH)_2 \rightleftharpoons ZnO_2^{-2} + 2\ H^+$$

$$Zn^{+2} + 2\ OH^- \rightleftharpoons ZnO + H_2O \rightleftharpoons ZnO_2^{-2} + 2\ H^+$$

$$Hg^{+2} + 2\ SH^- \rightleftharpoons HgS + H_2S \rightleftharpoons HgS_2^{-2} + 2\ H^+$$

$$Be^{+2} + 2\ HF_2^- \rightleftharpoons BeF_2 + 2\ HF \rightleftharpoons BeF_4^{-2} + 2\ H^+$$

$$Ag^+ + \text{``}HCl_2^{-}\text{''} \rightleftharpoons AgCl + HCl \rightleftharpoons AgCl_2^- + H^+$$

The concept of amphoterism, then, can be extended to cover many other classes of compounds besides the hydroxides (see also Sections 5–10, 6–10, and 8–12).

9–13. The Hydroxy Complexes

In exactly the same way as the substances producing complex (thio, fluoro, chloro, and the like) anions may be considered ampholytes, so the oxides and hydroxides which are normally called ampholytes may be considered to produce "oxy" complex anions. For example, the anion HgO_2^{-2} might be called "oxymercurate", to emphasize its relationship to HgS_2^{-2}, "thiomercurate". It is found, however, that if solid salts containing these "oxyanions" are prepared from water solution, they almost invariably contain "water of crystallization." Examples are $Na_2SnO_3 \cdot 3\ H_2O$, $Na_2PtO_3 \cdot 3\ H_2O$,

$Na_2PbO_3·3 H_2O$, $NaAuO_2·2 H_2O$, $NaSbO_3·3 H_2O$, $NaIO_4·2 H_2O$, $Na_2TeO_4·2 H_2O$, and $K_2SnS_3·3 H_2O$. Examination of the structures of these substances by X-ray techniques has shown, however, that they are really better described by such formulas as $Na_2Sn(OH)_6$, $Na_2Pt(OH)_6$, $NaAu(OH)_4$, $NaSb(OH)_6$, $NaIO_2(OH)_4$, $Na_2TeO_2(OH)_4$, and $K_2Sn(SH)_3(OH)_3$. They are therefore in reality *hydroxy* complexes rather than oxy complexes and quite comparable to the fluoro and chloro complexes. For example, when $Zn(OH)_2$ dissolves in base, the reaction is more properly described as the formation of a hydroxy complex.

$$Zn(OH)_2 \text{ (s)} + OH^- \rightleftharpoons Zn(OH)_3^-$$

$$Zn(OH)_3^- + OH^- \rightleftharpoons Zn(OH)_4^{-2}$$

and
$$Zn(OH)_2 \text{ (s)} + 2 OH^- \rightleftharpoons Zn(OH)_4^{-2}$$

Since there will also be the complex ion $ZnOH^+$ (see Table 9–1), it can be seen that this system is in every way comparable to those of complex ions we have already considered. Just as we have the series Hg^{+2}, $HgCl^+$, $HgCl_2$, $HgCl_3^-$, and $HgCl_4^{-2}$, we also have the series Zn^{+2}, $ZnOH^+$, $Zn(OH)_2$, $Zn(OH)_3^-$, and $Zn(OH)_4^{-2}$.

As with other complex ions, although the over-all or cumulative constant for a series may be known, the stepwise constants have frequently not been determined.

The relationship between the instability constants for the hydroxy complex ions and the acid-ionization constants for amphoteric hydroxides is easily determined. As an example, for

$$Al(OH)_3 \text{ (s)} \rightleftharpoons H^+ + H_2AlO_3^-$$

we have

$$[H^+][H_2AlO_3^-] = 2.8 \times 10^{-13}$$

whereas, for the dissociation of the complex ion to the hydroxide

$$Al(OH)_4^- \rightleftharpoons Al(OH)_3 \text{ (s)} + OH^-$$

we have

$$\frac{[OH^-]}{[Al(OH)_4^-]} = K_{inst}$$

Recognizing that $H_2AlO_3^-$ and $Al(OH)_4^-$ are merely different ways of writing the same thing (i.e., $Al(OH)_4^- = H_2AlO_3^-·H_2O$) it can be seen that the two equilibria must be related through the water equilibrium, and thus

$$\frac{[H^+][OH^-]}{[H^+][Al(OH)_4^-]} = \frac{1 \times 10^{-14}}{2.8 \times 10^{-13}}$$

and
$$\frac{[OH^-]}{[Al(OH)_4^-]} = 3.6 \times 10^{-2} = K_{inst}$$

Furthermore, this expression is related to the cumulative equilibrium expression for complete dissociation of the complex ion

$$Al(OH)_4^- \rightleftharpoons Al^{+3} + 4\,OH^-$$

through the solubility-product expression for $Al(OH)_3$

$$[Al^{+3}][OH^-]^3 = 2.5 \times 10^{-32}$$

giving

$$[Al^{+3}][OH^-]^3 \cdot \frac{[OH^-]}{[Al(OH)_4^-]} = \frac{[Al^{+3}][OH^-]^4}{[Al(OH)_4^-]}$$

$$= 2.5 \times 10^{-32} \times 3.6 \times 10^{-2} = 9.0 \times 10^{-34}$$

The treatment of the hydroxy complexes is the same as that for other complexes. It must be remembered, however, that they are unique in involving an ion derived from the solvent (water) itself. There are times when this fact cannot be ignored.

9–14.   Neutral Hydroxy Complexes (or Soluble Un-ionized Hydroxides)

One additional point which can be observed from examination of Table 9–12 is that there are many cases known for which the un-ionized hydroxide has an appreciable solubility, and therefore the neutral hydroxy complex must be considered along with the charged species. Substances of this sort, for which quantitative data are available, are AgOH, AsOOH, $Cd(OH)_2$, $Co(OH)_2$, $Cu(OH)_2$, $Fe(OH)_2$, $Fe(OH)_3$, $Hg(OH)_2$, IOH, LiOH, NaOH, $Ni(OH)_2$, $Pb(OH)_2$, $PuO(OH)_2$, $Sn(OH)_2$, $Sb(OH)_3$, $Te(OH)_4$, $UO_2(OH)_2$, $Zn(OH)_2$, and $Zr(OH)_4$. These may be compared with the similar cases of complex halides (see Table 4–2). The instability equilibrium for the neutral complex is related to the solubility-product equilibrium through the concentration of neutral complex present in a saturated solution of the insoluble hydroxide. Thus for $Hg(OH)_2$

$$K_{inst} = \frac{[Hg^{+2}][OH^-]^2}{[Hg(OH)_2]} = 1.07 \times 10^{-22}$$

and

$$K_{sp} = [Hg^{+2}][OH^-]^2 = 2.5 \times 10^{-26}$$

Therefore the concentration of *un-ionized* $Hg(OH)_2$ in a saturated solution of HgO is

$$[Hg(OH)_2] = 2.3 \times 10^{-4}\,M$$

In calculating the total solubility of a metallic hydroxide, it may be necessary to take this into account. For example, in the case of the solubility of $Pb(OH)_2$, treated in Section 9–6, the solubility, ignoring the contribution of un-ionized $Pb(OH)_2$ (aq), was found to be

$$[PbOH^+] + [Pb(OH)_3^-] = 1.14 \times 10^{-4} + 8.4 \times 10^{-6} = 1.22 \times 10^{-4}\,M$$

TABLE 9-12. CUMULATIVE pK_{inst}'s OF HYDROXY COMPLEXES

Complex	pK_{inst}	Complex	pK_{inst}	Complex	pK_{inst}	Complex	pK_{inst}	Complex	pK_{inst}	Complex	pK_{inst}
AgOH (aq)	2.30	$Ag(OH)_2^-$	4.2	$Ag(OH)_3^{-2}$	5.2						
$AlOH^{+2}$	9.27	$Al(OH)_2^+$	?	$Al(OH)_3$ (aq)	?	$Al(OH)_4^-$	33.03				
AsOOH (aq)	14.33	$AsO(OH)_2^-$	18.73	$AsO(OH)_3^{-2}$	20.60	$AsO(OH)_4^{-3}$	21.2				
$BaOH^+$	0.85										
$BeOH^+$	9.7	$Be(OH)_2$ (aq)	?	$Be(OH)_3^-$	15.21	$Be(OH)_4^{-2}$	15.0				
$BiOH^{+2}$	12.7	$Bi(OH)_2^+$	15.8	$Bi(OH)_3$ (aq)	?	$Bi(OH)_4^-$	35.2				
$CaOH^+$	1.46										
$CdOH^+$	4.17	$Cd(OH)_2$ (aq)	8.33	$Cd(OH)_3^-$	9.02	$Cd(OH)_4^{-2}$	< 8.6				
$CeOH^{+2}$	4.6										
$CeOH^{+3}$	13.28	$Ce(OH)_2^{+2}$	27.06								
$CoOH^+$	4.6	$Co(OH)_2$ (aq)	4.6	$Co(OH)_3^-$	10.5						
$CrOH^{+2}$	10.1	$Cr(OH)_2^+$	17.8	$Cr(OH)_3$ (aq)	?	$Cr(OH)_4^-$	29.9				
$CuOH^+$	7.0	$Cu(OH)_2$ (aq)	13.68	$Cu(OH)_3^-$	17.0	$Cu(OH)_4^{-2}$	18.5				
$DyOH^{+2}$	5.2										
$ErOH^{+2}$	5.4										
$FeOH^+$	5.56	$Fe(OH)_2$ (aq)	9.77	$Fe(OH)_3^-$	9.67	$Fe(OH)_4^{-2}$	8.56				
$FeOH^{+2}$	11.87	$Fe(OH)_2^+$	21.17	$Fe(OH)_3$ (aq)	30.67						
$GaOH^{+2}$	11.0	$Ga(OH)_2^+$	21.7	$Ga(OH)_3$ (aq)	?	$Ga(OH)_4^-$	34.3	$Ga(OH)_5^{-2}$	38.0	$Ga(OH)_6^{-3}$	40.3
$GdOH^{+2}$	4.60										
$GeOH^{+3}$	?	$Ge(OH)_2^{+2}$	?	$Ge(OH)_3^+$	?	$Ge(OH)_4$ (aq)	?	$Ge(OH)_5^-$	62.2	$Ge(OH)_6^{-2}$	72.3
Hg_2OH^{+2}	9.0										
$HgOH^+$	11.10	$Hg(OH)_2$ (aq)	21.97	$Hg(OH)_3^-$	21.20						
IOH (aq)	9.49	$I(OH)_2^-$	11.14								
$InOH^{+2}$	9.9	$In(OH)_2^+$	19.8	$In(OH)_3$ (aq)	?	$In(OH)_4^-$	28.7				
$LaOH^{+2}$	4.0										
LiOH (aq)	0.14										
$LuOH^{+2}$	6.6										
$MgOH^+$	2.58										

Species	pK	Species	pK	Species	pK	Species	pK	Species	pK	Species	pK
$MnOH^+$	3.90	$Mn(OH)_2$ (aq)	?	$Mn(OH)_3^-$	8.3						
$NaOH$ (aq)	−0.70										
$NdOH^{+2}$	5.5										
$NiOH^+$	4.97	$Ni(OH)_2$ (aq)	8.55	$Ni(OH)_3^-$	11.33						
$PbOH^+$	7.82	$Pb(OH)_2$ (aq)	10.85	$Pb(OH)_3^-$	14.58						
$PbOH^{+3}$	?	$Pb(OH)_2^{+2}$	?	$Pb(OH)_3^+$	?	$Pb(OH)_4$ (aq)	?	$Pb(OH)_5^-$	?	$Pb(OH)_6^{-2}$	61.0
								$Po(OH)_5^-$	?	$Po(OH)_6^{-2}$	4.06*
$PrOH^{+2}$	4.30										
$PuOH^{+2}$	7.0										
$PuOH^{+3}$	12.39										
PuO_2OH^+	8.3	$PuO_2(OH)_2$ (aq)	16.6	$PuO_2(OH)_3^-$	20.87						
$SbOH^{+2}$	?	$Sb(OH)_2^+$	24.3	$Sb(OH)_3$ (aq)	36.7	$Sb(OH)_4^-$	38.3				
$ScOH^{+2}$	8.9										
$SmOH^{+2}$	4.8										
$SnOH^+$	11.86	$Sn(OH)_2$ (aq)	20.64	$Sn(OH)_3^-$	25.13						
$SnOH^{+3}$	?	$Sn(OH)_2^{+2}$	?	$Sn(OH)_3^+$	?	$Sn(OH)_4$ (aq)	?	$Sn(OH)_5^-$	?	$Sn(OH)_6^{-2}$	63.0
$TeOH^{+3}$	?	$Te(OH)_2^{+2}$	?	$Te(OH)_3^+$	41.6	$Te(OH)_4$ (aq)	53.0	$Te(OH)_5^-$	64.8	$Te(OH)_6^{-2}$	71.0
$ThOH^{+3}$	10.0	$Th(OH)_2^{+2}$	21.2	$Th(OH)_3^+$	32.0	$Th(OH)_4$ (aq)	?	$Th(OH)_5^-$	38.7	$Th(OH)_6^{-2}$	38.7
$TlOH$ (aq)	0.83										
$TlOH^{+2}$	12.86	$Tl(OH)_2^+$	25.37								
UOH^{+3}	13.3	$U(OH)_2^{+2}$	?	$U(OH)_3^+$	?	$U(OH)_4$ (aq)	?	$U(OH)_5^-$	41.2		
UO_2OH^+	9.5	$UO_2(OH)_2$ (aq)	22.80	$UO_2(OH)_3^-$	18.40	$UO_2(OH)_4^{-2}$	32.40				
VOH^{+2}	11.1	$V(OH)_2^+$	21.6								
$VOOH^+$	8.6	$VO(OH)_2$ (aq)	?	$V_2O_4(OH)^-$							
$VOOH^{+2}$	?	$VO(OH)_2^+$	25.2	$VO(OH)_3$ (aq)	25.8	$VO(OH)_4^-$	46.2	$VO(OH)_5^{-2}$	58.5		
YOH^{+2}	5.0										
$ZnOH^+$	4.40	$Zn(OH)_2$ (aq)	11.3	$Zn(OH)_3^-$	13.14	$Zn(OH)_4^{-2}$	14.66				
$ZrOH^{+3}$	13.8	$Zr(OH)_2^{+2}$	27.2	$Zr(OH)_3^+$	40.1	$Zr(OH)_4$ (aq)	52.9	$Zr(OH)_5^-$	52.4		

* For $Po(OH)_6^{-2} \rightleftharpoons PoO_2 (s) + 2\,OH^- + 2\,H_2O$.

However, from the K_{sp} relationship and

$$K_{inst} = \frac{[Pb^{+2}][OH^-]^2}{[Pb(OH)_2]} = 2.9 \times 10^{-10}$$

$$[Pb(OH)_2] = 4.5 \times 10^{-3}$$

so that the *total* solubility of $Pb(OH)_2$, ionized and un-ionized, is

$$1.2 \times 10^{-4} + 4.5 \times 10^{-3} = 4.6 \times 10^{-3} \ M$$

and the *un-ionized* $Pb(OH)_2$ is seen to contribute by far the most important part (98 percent).

9–15. Electronegativity and Amphoterism (Quantitative)

In conformity with what we have said about the fact that, in general, acidity varies with electronegativity, it is found that the correspondence of K_A for the amphoteric hydroxides and the electronegativity of the metal is fairly good. Thus for $M(OH)_2$, where M is from the first transition series, we have

	$Mn(OH)_2$	$Fe(OH)_2$	$Co(OH)_2$	$Ni(OH)_2$	$Cu(OH)_2$	$Zn(OH)_2$
pK_A	19.0	18.4	19.1	18.2	15.8	16.9
Electronegativity	1.4	1.45	1.5	1.5	1.7	1.5

The pK_{sp}'s of the hydroxides have already (Section 7–9) been shown to vary according to the electronegativity of the metal

	$Mn(OH)_2$	$Fe(OH)_2$	$Co(OH)_2$	$Ni(OH)_2$	$Cu(OH)_2$	$Zn(OH)_2$
pK_{sp}	13.34	14.10	15.60	15.55	18.8	16.32
Electronegativity	1.4	1.45	1.5	1.5	1.7	1.5

Now when these are combined, it is found that the cumulative pK_{inst}'s also follow the electronegativity correlation just as the pK_A's and pK_{sp}'s do.

	$Mn(OH)_3^-$	$Fe(OH)_3^-$	$Co(OH)_3^-$	$Ni(OH)_3^-$	$Cu(OH)_3^-$	$Zn(OH)_3^-$
pK_{inst}	8.3	9.7	10.5	11.3	17.0	13.1
Electronegativity	1.4	1.45	1.5	1.5	1.7	1.5

9–16. The Brønsted Approach to Amphoterism

In the preceding sections we have considered the formation of hydroxy complexes to be merely the addition of OH^- ions from solution to the metal ion. For example

$$Zn^{+2} + OH^- \rightleftharpoons ZnOH^+$$

$$Zn^{+2} + 2\,OH^- \rightleftharpoons Zn(OH)_2 \ (aq)$$

$$Zn^{+2} + 3\,OH^- \rightleftharpoons Zn(OH)_3^-$$

$$Zn^{+2} + 4\,OH^- \rightleftharpoons Zn(OH)_4^{-2}$$

and so forth.

However, as already discussed in Sections 5–9 and 7–4, metal cations are actually present in solution as aquo complexes. These are capable of ionizing-off hydrogen ions either to water

$$Zn(H_2O)_4^{+2} + H_2O \rightleftharpoons Zn(H_2O)_3OH^+ + OH_3^+$$

or at higher pH to hydroxide ion

$$Zn(H_2O)_4^{+2} + {}^*OH^- \rightleftharpoons Zn(H_2O)_3OH^+ + H_2O^*$$

or of exchanging a water molecule for a hydroxide ion from solution

$$Zn(H_2O)_4^{+2} + {}^*OH^- \rightleftharpoons Zn(H_2O)_3{}^*OH^+ + H_2O$$

where the asterisk serves to distinguish a particular oxygen atom. However, since in general there is no practical way of distinguishing one water molecule from another, these last two processes, for all practical purposes of equilibrium, are equivalent. The first of these processes will be characterized by an acid-ionization constant or a hydrolysis constant, which are identical, as discussed in Section 7–4.

$$\frac{[Zn(H_2O)_3OH^+][OH_3^+]}{[Zn(H_2O)_4^{+2}]} = K_A = K_{hyd} = 2.5 \times 10^{-10}$$

The second (or third) reaction above is the reverse of the reaction for the dissociation of the complex ion, $ZnOH^+$, which is characterized by a dissociation constant, K_{inst}, and which is identical with the basic ionization constant, K_B

$$\frac{[Zn^{+2}][OH^-]}{[ZnOH^+]} = K_{inst} = K_B = 4.0 \times 10^{-5}$$

These two constants are related to each other through the water constant

$$K_A K_B = K_{hyd} K_{inst} = (2.5 \times 10^{-10})(4 \times 10^{-5}) = 1 \times 10^{-14} = K_w$$

The constant for the second (or third) reaction above *as written* is, of course

$$\frac{[Zn(H_2O)_3OH^+]}{[Zn(H_2O)_4^{+2}][OH^-]} = \frac{1}{K_{inst}} = \frac{1}{4 \times 10^{-5}} = 2.5 \times 10^4$$

As the pH is gradually raised, the successive reactions taking place are

$$Zn(H_2O)_3OH^+ + OH^- \rightleftharpoons Zn(H_2O)_2(OH)_2 \ (aq)\dagger + H_2O$$

$$Zn(H_2O)_2(OH)_2 \ (aq) + OH^- \rightleftharpoons Zn(H_2O)(OH)_3^- + H_2O$$

$$Zn(H_2O)(OH)_3^- + OH^- \rightleftharpoons Zn(OH)_4^{-2} + H_2O$$

The formation of hydroxy complexes may therefore be considered to be merely another way of looking at the ionization of the hydrated ions as Brønsted acids.

† Or if the concentration is high enough (i.e., $>1 \times 10^{-5} \ M$), $Zn(H_2O)_2(OH)_2 \ (s)$.

9–17. Illustrative Experiments

The Variation of Acidity (and Basicity) with Oxidation State. The variation of basicity, or acidity, with change in oxidation state can be demonstrated *in principle* with the compounds of a single element. For example, $Cr(OH)_2$ is basic, $Cr(OH)_3$ is amphoteric, and H_2CrO_4 is acidic; $Mn(OH)_2$ and $Mn(OH)_3$ are basic, $MnO(OH)_2$ is amphoteric, and H_3MnO_4, H_2MnO_4, and $HMnO_4$ are increasingly acidic. However, *in practice*, there is no one element with which all three qualities (i.e., basicity, amphoterism, and acidity) can easily be demonstrated in the laboratory. For example, although $Cr(OH)_3$ and H_2CrO_4 are easily obtained, $Cr(OH)_2$ is such a powerful reducing agent that it rapidly reduces water

$$2\ Cr(OH)_2\ (s) + 2\ H_2O \rightleftharpoons 2\ Cr(OH)_3\ (s) + H_2$$

and cannot be kept long enough to be examined. On the other hand, although $Mn(OH)_2$, $MnO(OH)_2$, and $HMnO_4$ can all be easily obtained, both the acidic and the basic properties of $MnO(OH)_2$ are so weak that they cannot be easily demonstrated (i.e., the solubility of $MnO(OH)_2$ in either acidic or basic solution, in the absence of complexing agents (e.g., Cl^-), is too small to observe). Consequently, it will be necessary to demonstrate this principle with examples of two different elements.

(1) You have already used the amphoteric and acidic properties of chromium to separate it from iron and manganese. However, in order to observe definitely the amphoteric nature of $Cr(OH)_3$, put 10 drops of $Cr(NO_3)_3$ into a test tube and add 6 M NaOH, *dropwise* with stirring, until *two* distinct reactions have occurred. DO NOT HEAT. Now add concentrated HNO_3, *dropwise* with stirring, until again two reactions have occurred. Explain.

(2) In order to demonstrate the acidic nature of chromium in the $+6$ state, add 5 drops of 1 M K_2CrO_4 solution to 1 ml of 1 M HNO_3 (made by diluting 1 volume of 6 M HNO_3 with 5 volumes of water) and add $Hg_2(NO_3)_2$ solution dropwise until a reaction occurs. What has happened? How does this show the acidic nature of $+6$ chromium?

(3) To 5 drops of 0.3 M Na_3VO_4 solution, add an equal volume of 6 M NaOH. Does $VO(OH)_3$ show acidic properties?

(4) To 10 drops of 0.3 M Na_3VO_4 solution add, *dropwise* with shaking, 12 M HCl until two distinct reactions have taken place. Save the solution. Does H_3VO_4 show basic properties?

(5) To the solution saved from (4) add a small amount of Al metal and as the metal is used up, continue to add more until the following color changes have taken place: The original yellow solution (VO_2^+) becomes green (a mixture of VO_2^+ and VO^{+2}), then blue (VO^{+2}), and then green (V^{+3}). If too much Al has been added the solution may become purple (V^{+2}). When the V^{+3} (or V^{+2}) stage has been reached, and all the Al dissolved, add an excess of 6 M NaOH and centrifuge. Does $V(OH)_3$ (or $V(OH)_2$) show any acidic properties?

Neutral Hydroxy Complexes. The total concentration of ions of mercury (principally $HgOH^+$) in a solution saturated with HgO is somewhat less than 10^{-8} molar. (Calculate the concentrations to check this point.) If this were entirely precipitated from 3 ml of solution by addition of S^{-2}, the quantity of HgS obtained would be far too small to be observed. As calculated in Section 9–5, however, the concentration of un-ionized $Hg(OH)_2$ in such a solution is 2.3×10^{-4} molar, which will give an easily observed precipitate with sulfide ion.

In the same way, concentrations of Hg^{+2} and OH^- which should easily give a precipitate of HgO do not because of the formation of un-ionized $Hg(OH)_2$ in solution.

(6) Shake a pinch of HgO with 3 ml of distilled water in a 3-ml centrifuge tube for five minutes. Centrifuge thoroughly (the supernate should be absolutely clear and colorless), transfer the supernate to another tube, add one drop of 6 M HCl and 5 drops of thioacetamide solution, and heat for 5 minutes in a boiling-water bath. Centrifuge and carefully observe the bottom of the tube. Explain.

(7) Into 20 ml of distilled water with stirring, add dropwise 0.1 M $Hg(NO_3)_2$ until a definite permanent effect is observed. In the light of the discussion above, explain your observations.

(8) Weigh a clean, dry 3-ml test tube on the balance and record the tare weight. Now weigh into the test tube a small amount of ZnO—not less than 0.1 gram. Record the total weight of tube + ZnO. With a clean, dry spatula, add the ZnO with shaking in very small increments to 10 ml of 0.1 M $Zn(NO_3)_2$ solution. Take care not to lose any ZnO. At the first sign of cloudiness in the $Zn(NO_3)_2$ solution, reweigh the ZnO tube. How much ZnO was dissolved in the $Zn(NO_3)_2$? Explain.

(9) Precipitate in each of two test tubes HgS from 2 drops of 0.1 M $Hg(NO_3)_2$ diluted with a little water. Wash the precipitates once with water. Add 0.5 ml of water to each. To one of the tubes add 6 M KOH, dropwise with stirring, until the HgS has just barely dissolved. Write an equation for the reaction. Now with stirring add exactly the same number of drops of 6 M NaOH to the other tube. Explain the difference.

9–18.   General Cation Analysis

As pointed out in Chapter 1, the general analysis of the metallic elements depends upon the successive precipitation of ever-widening groups in the periodic table by reagents of successively decreasing selectivity. The groups are dictated by the trends of solubility and complex-formation in the periodic table and the conditions of precipitation. Each group is then split into subgroups and finally into the individual elements for identification. In the usual schemes, the few elements having insoluble chlorides (and tungsten) are separated first; then, those with the most insoluble (acid-insoluble) sulfides; then those with alkali-insoluble hydroxides (along with vanadium, whose salt NH_4VO_3 is only slightly soluble) and alkali-insoluble sulfides; then those with insoluble carbonates; and finally those most of whose compounds are soluble. It goes without saying that the elements of each group must be completely removed before separation of those of the next group is attempted. In general, the group precipitations in a general unknown are carried out exactly as already described for the individual groups. However, certain additional comments must be made. The schematic outline of the group separations is given in Table 9–13. Again it is emphasized, however, that this is not the only possible scheme which can be devised, and it will be to the student's benefit to attempt to devise others.

For a sample in solution which is to be analyzed only for cations, the preliminary examination of the sample is simple—consisting merely of determining the pH and examining the color. If the solution is apparently colorless, colored ions may be present only in low concentration. However, it must be remembered that the concentration of an ion which imparts an observable color to a solution varies greatly, depending upon the intensity of color of the ion under consideration. Thus the intensely purple MnO_4^- ion can be seen at a dilution of two parts per million. The intensely green $CrCl^{+2}$ and $CrCl_2^+$ ions are also detectable at a very low concentration. On the other hand, the very pale pink Mn^{+2} is not observable until the concentration is quite high. Most of the other common colored ions are detectable at intermediate concentrations. If only one colored ion is present, the color of the solution may be an excellent clue to the identity of one component of the solution. It should be pointed out here, however, as discussed in Section 4–10, that the presence of certain colorless anions may drastically change the color of some of the cations. Thus $Cr(H_2O)_6^{+3}$ is lavender or blue, depending on whether it is viewed by transmitted or reflected light, whereas in chloride or sulfate solutions, it is green because of the presence of $CrCl^{+2}$ and $CrCl_2^+$ or $CrSO_4^+$. Likewise, in HNO_3 or $HClO_4$ solution, $Fe(H_2O)_6^{+2}$ is very pale lavender, whereas in the presence of Cl^-, it is yellow because of the presence of $FeCl^{+2}$ and $FeCl_2^+$. In the presence of NCS^-, the blood-red $FeNCS^{+2}$ or $Fe(NCS)_2^+$ is formed. Also at pH's approaching 7, iron(III) solutions are red-brown due to the presence of $FeOH^{+2}$ and $Fe(OH)_2^+$. In the case of copper(II), blue $Cu(H_2O)_4^{+2}$ exists in HNO_3, $HClO_4$, or in H_2SO_4 solutions, blue $CuSO_4$ (aq) of about the same hue, whereas HCl solutions contain green-to-brownish yellow $CuCl^+$, $CuCl_2$ (aq), $CuCl_3^-$, and so on. It should also be noted that, in particular cases of mixtures of ions of complementary colors, the solutions may appear to be colorless despite the actual presence of colored ions. For example, just the right proportions of red Co^{+2} and green Ni^{+2} or of pink Nd^{+3} and green Pr^{+3} give solutions which are quite colorless (or slightly grayish) to the eye. (Review Section 4–10.)

The pH of the solution is also a clue as to what may be present. If the solution is acidic, tungsten(VI) must be absent—as well as silicon(IV). If the solution is neutral, the easily hydrolyzed cations such as Hg^{+2}, Bi^{+3}, Sb^{+3}, and the like, must be absent, unless there are large quantities of halide, cyanide, or other complexing substances which may prevent precipitation of oxides or hydroxides through formation of such ions as $Hg(CN)_4^{-2}$, $Bi(NCS)_4^-$, $SbCl_4^-$, and so on. In alkaline solution in which no ammonia can be detected, NH_4^+ and the cations of the nonamphoteric metals must be absent, except for those with soluble hydroxides, such as Na^+, K^+, Ba^{+2}, and Tl^+. If the solution is alkaline and ammoniacal, the absence of a precipitate shows the absence of those elements which do not form ammine complexes, but which do have insoluble hydroxides—e.g., Al and Cr(III). If, after the test for NH_4^+, large quantities are found to be present, then V(V) must be absent.

TABLE 9–13. SCHEMATIC OUTLINE FOR THE SEPARATION OF GROUPS

Ions for all groups. Add HCl.		Test for NH_4^+ on separate portion.		
Precipitate: AgCl, Hg_2Cl_2, H_2WO_4, $PbCl_2$, TlCl.	Solution: Hg, Pb, Bi, Cu, Cd, Mo, As, Sb, Sn, Fe, Mn, Cr, Al, Co, Ni, Zn, V, Ba, Sr, Ca, Mg, K, Na. Make $[H^+]$ 0.3 M, add H_2O_2, add NH_4I, add CH_3CSNH_2, and heat.			
	Precipitate: HgS, PbS, Bi_2S_3, CdS, CuS; MoS_3, As_2S_3, Sb_2S_3, SnS_2.	Solution: Fe, Mn, Cr, Al, V, Co, Ni, Zn, Ba, Sr, Ca, Mg, K, Na. Add NH_4OH and shake with air.		
		Precipitate: $Fe(OH)_3$, $Mn(OH)_3$, $Cr(OH)_3$, $Al(OH)_3$, NH_4VO_3.	Solution: $Co(NH_3)_6^{+3}$, $Ni(NH_3)_6^{+2}$, $Zn(NH_3)_4^{+2}$, Ba^{+2}, Sr^{+2}, Ca^{+2}, Mg^{+2}, Na^+, K^+. Add CH_3CSNH_2 and heat.	
			Precipitate: CoS, NiS, ZnS.	Solution: Ba^{+2}, Sr^{+2}, Ca^{+2}, Mg^{+2}, Na^+, K^+. Add $(NH_4)_2CO_3$.
			Precipitate: $BaCO_3$, $SrCO_3$, $CaCO_3$.	Solution: Mg^{+2}, Na^+, K^+.

9–A. The Ammonium Ion. Having completed the preliminary examination described above, analyze a portion of the sample for NH_4^+ as in Section 3–13.

9–B. Precipitation of the Insoluble Chloride Group. Take a second portion (3 ml) of the original solution for the systematic analysis for all the other metallic elements. If the solution is alkaline, add 6 M HNO_3 until just neutral (certain basic salts may precipitate) and then 1 drop of 6 M HCl. Or, if the solution is initially neutral or acidic, add 1 drop of HCl directly. If no precipitate appears, proceed directly to the analysis of the acid-insoluble sulfide group. If a precipitate forms, add 4 more drops of 6 M HCl, stir well, and centrifuge. Test for completeness of precipitation by adding 1 drop more of HCl to the clear supernate. If a precipitate appears, stir and centrifuge again. Repeat the process until no further precipitation takes place. When precipitation is complete, remove the supernate and retain it for the analysis of subsequent groups (9–C). Wash the precipitate with 1 ml of 1.5 M HCl, centrifuge, and add the wash solution to the original supernate. Wash the precipitate once again with 1 ml of 1.5 M HCl, but this time *discard* the wash solution. Analyze the precipitate for elements of the insoluble chloride group according to the procedures in Section 4–12.

9–C. *Precipitation of the Acid-Insoluble Sulfide Group.* Adjust the [H^+] of the supernate from (9–B) to 0.3 molar with HCl or NH_4OH by means of methyl violet paper. Carry out the additions of H_2O_2 and NH_4I, described in Section 5–15, and then proceed with the precipitation with CH_3CSNH_2, *first making certain* that the [H^+] is 0.3 molar. If no precipitate is obtained, proceed to the precipitation of the insoluble hydroxide group as in (9–D). If a precipitate is obtained upon heating with CH_3CSNH_2, centrifuge, readjust the [H^+] to 0.3 molar, add a few drops more of CH_3CSNH_2, and heat again to ensure complete precipitation and centrifuge. (Be careful at this point not to make the solution alkaline, for this may cause irreversible precipitation of NiS or CoS.) Remove the supernate and retain it for the analysis of subsequent groups (9–D). Wash the precipitate with 2 ml of water, washing down the sides of the centrifuge tube if necessary. Centrifuge. Add the wash liquid to the supernate retained from the group precipitation. Wash twice more with water, discarding the washes. Proceed with the analysis of the sulfide precipitate as in Section 5–15.

9–D. *Removal of Interfering Anions.* If certain polyvalent anions, such as PO_4^{-3}, AsO_4^{-3}, $C_2O_4^{-2}$, AsO_3^{-3}, and so on, are present in the solution (as $H_2PO_4^-$, $H_2AsO_4^-$, $HC_2O_4^-$, AsO^+, and so on, at low pH) and if such cations as those of the alkaline-earth metals, Fe^{+3}, Cr^{+3}, and the like, are present, insoluble salts of these ions will precipitate when the pH is raised by adding NH_4OH to precipitate the insoluble hydroxide. Of course, no harm is done by precipitating $FePO_4$ or $CrPO_4$, instead of $Fe(OH)_3$ or $Cr(OH)_3$, but the precipitation of $Ba_3(PO_4)_2$ or CaC_2O_4, for example, would bring the alkaline-earth elements down in the wrong group. Consequently, if interfering anions are suspected of being present, they must be removed before the solution is made alkaline. (If the original solution was alkaline and contained no precipitate, it must be obvious that either the cations or the anions in question must be absent and there can be no need for this procedure. An exception is $CrPO_4$ which dissolves in alkaline solution. However, the presence of Cr(III) should be obvious from its color.) Of the anions listed, AsO_4^{-3} and AsO_3^{-3} will already have been removed as As_2S_3 in the acid-insoluble sulfide precipitation. Molybdate ion, which might also cause interference, will likewise have been removed as MoS_3. Phosphate and oxalate ions are most easily removed as their insoluble zirconium salts. Zirconyl phosphate, $ZrO(H_2PO_4)_2$, is so extremely insoluble that it precipitates even from concentrated HCl solution. Zirconium oxalate, $Zr(C_2O_4)_2$, is also insoluble, but dissolves in the presence of an excess of oxalate ion, forming the complex ion $Zr(C_2O_4)_4^{-4}$. Any excess zirconium over that required to precipitate PO_4^{-3} and $C_2O_4^{-2}$ will precipitate with the insoluble hydroxides as white $ZrO(OH)_2$ or $Zr(OH)_4$ and, not being amphoteric, will follow iron and manganese in the subdivision of the insoluble-hydroxide group. Since it neither is oxidized by $NaBiO_3$ nor forms a color with NCS^-, it does not interfere with the tests for iron and manganese. (If zirconium is a possible element in the original solution and phosphate is found to be present, it must be reasoned that there could in fact have been no zirconium in the original solution.)

In order to remove PO_4^{-3} and $C_2O_4^{-2}$, add to the supernate from the acid-insoluble sulfide-group precipitation 1 drop of 0.1 M $ZrO(NO_3)_2$ solution. *Without stirring,* observe whether a precipitate has formed. If it has, add 5 more drops of ZrO^{+2} solution, stir, and centrifuge. (If the solution were stirred after the addition of the first drop of ZrO^{+2} solution, and if a large quantity of $C_2O_4^{-2}$ were present, the excess oxalate would form $Zr(C_2O_4)_2^{-4}$, and no precipitate would form. When the ZrO^{+2} solution is added without stirring, there should be a *local* excess of ZrO^{+2}, so that $Zr(C_2O_4)_2$ can precipitate.) Test for completeness of precipitation by adding 1 drop more of ZrO^{+2} solution. Add more if necessary, stir, centrifuge, remove the supernate for subsequent analysis (9–E), and discard the zirconium salt precipitate.

9–E. *Precipitation of the Insoluble Hydroxides.* To the supernate from the acid-insoluble sulfide precipitation (9–C)—or if PO_4^{-3} or $C_2O_4^{-2}$ was present, to the supernate from the zirconium salt precipitation (9–D)—after heating in the water bath for 15 minutes to remove as much of the H_2S as possible, add 5 drops of saturated bromine water. One of the functions of the bromine is to remove the remaining CH_3CSNH_2 and H_2S

$$H_2S + Br_2 \rightleftharpoons S\,(s) + 2\,H^+ + 2\,Br^-$$

$$CH_3CSNH_2 + Br_2 + H_2O \rightleftharpoons CH_3CONH_2 + S\,(s) + 2\,H^+ + 2\,Br^-$$

Another important function, however, is to restore several elements to oxidation states which are easy to handle, since they had been reduced to lower states by the acidic H_2S (or CH_3CSNH_2) used to precipitate acid-insoluble sulfides

$$2\,Fe^{+3} + H_2S \rightleftharpoons S\,(s) + 2\,H^+ + 2\,Fe^{+2}$$

$$2\,Fe^{+2} + Br_2 \rightleftharpoons 2\,Fe^{+3} + 2\,Br^-$$

$$2\,VO_2^+ + H_2S \rightleftharpoons S\,(s) + H_2O + 2\,VO^{+2}$$

$$2\,VO^{+2} + Br_2 + H_2O \rightleftharpoons 2\,VO_2^+ + 2\,H^+ + 2\,Br^-$$

(It should be recognized that, under the conditions of precipitation of the acid-insoluble sulfides, the MnO_4^- and $Cr_2O_7^{-2}$ ions will also be reduced.

$$2\,MnO_4^- + 5\,H_2S + 6\,H^+ \rightarrow 2\,Mn^{+2} + 5\,S\,(s) + 8\,H_2O$$

$$Cr_2O_7^{-2} + 3\,H_2S + 8\,H^+ \rightarrow 2\,Cr^{+3} + 3\,S\,(s) + 7\,H_2O$$

However, Mn^{+2} and Cr^{+3} are not oxidized by bromine water.) Any free sulfur which results from the bromine-water treatment should be removed on the end of a clean stirring rod. The addition of bromine water should be continued until the color of the bromine persists. Now heat the solution in the hot-water bath until all the excess bromine is driven off (*use the hood!*), and continue to heat until the volume is about 2 ml.

Cool the solution and add NH_4OH and NH_4Cl; carry out the NH_4OH precipitation as described in Section 7–12. Save the supernate for subsequent analysis. Wash the precipitate once with 6 M NH_4OH saturated with NH_4Cl, adding the wash solution to the supernate from the NH_4OH precipitation. Wash twice more with 6 M NH_4OH saturated with NH_4Cl, discarding the wash solutions. Analyze the washed precipitate for the elements of the insoluble-hydroxide group, as described in Section 7–12. Remember that, if zirconium salts were added to remove phosphate and oxalate, a white precipitate of $ZrO(OH)_2$ or $Zr(OH)_4$ will occur along with the $Mn(OH)_3$ and $Fe(OH)_3$ precipitates.

9–F. Precipitation of the Alkali-Insoluble Sulfides. To the ammoniacal supernate from the precipitation of the insoluble-hydroxide group, add thioacetamide, as described in Section 7–12, and proceed with the precipitation of CoS, NiS, and ZnS, carefully watching for an initial precipitate of white ZnS. Test for completeness of precipitation. Remove the supernate and retain for further analysis. Wash the precipitate once with water and add the washes to the supernate (9–*G*). Wash once more and discard the wash liquor. Analyze the precipitate for Co, Ni, and Zn, as described in Section 7–12.

If thallium was found in the insoluble-chloride group, an additional step is necessary at this point to separate thallium, which is never completely precipitated as TlCl and precipitates here as Tl_2S, from Co, Ni, and Zn. Dissolve the sulfide precipitate in aqua regia, as described in Section 7–12, evaporate *almost* to dryness and make distinctly alkaline with Na_2CO_3. The insoluble $CoCO_3$, $NiCO_3$, and $ZnCO_3$ will precipitate, while Tl_2CO_3 remains in solution. Wash the precipitate twice with Na_2CO_3 solution, discarding the washes. Dissolve the carbonate in dilute HCl and proceed with the analysis for Co, Ni, and Zn.

9–G. Precipitation of the Alkaline-Earth Group. If the supernate from the alkali-insoluble sulfide precipitation (9–*F*) contains *any* color, it may contain suspended or dissolved MoS_3, V_2S_5, or NiS. In this event, make it acidic with acetic acid and boil. The weak acetic acid will destroy any thio anions, such as MoS_4^{-2} or VS_4^{-3}, and coagulate colloidal NiS without causing the insoluble sulfides to dissolve through loss of H_2S.

$$MoS_4^{-2} + 2\ HAc \rightleftharpoons MoS_3\ (s) + H_2S\ (g) + 2\ Ac^-$$

but *not*

$$NiS\ (s) + 2\ HAc \rightleftharpoons Ni^{+2} + H_2S\ (g) + 2\ Ac^-$$

Centrifuge down and discard any dark precipitate. Now evaporate the solution (the supernate from the alkali-insoluble sulfide precipitation if no color was observed; the acetic acid solution if Mo, V, or Ni had to be removed) to about 3 ml in a casserole. Add an equal volume of 15 *M* HNO_3, and evaporate to dryness (HOOD !). Add 3 ml of 15 *M* HNO_3 and evaporate to dryness again. This procedure is necessary to destroy the large amounts of ammonium salts present which may prevent precipitation of the alkaline-earth carbonates. Dissolve the residue from the nitric acid treatment in 1 ml of distilled water and add an equal volume of 5 *M* NH_4Cl and 5 drops of 15 *M* NH_4OH. Heat in a boiling-water bath, but do not allow the solution itself to boil. With constant stirring add 1 ml of $(NH_4)_2CO_3$ reagent. (The alkaline-earth carbonates form slimy, colloidal precipitates in the cold. Heating greatly assists their coagulation.) Allow the mixture to stand for a few minutes and centrifuge. Test for completeness of precipitation. When precipitation is complete, centrifuge and remove the supernate, retaining it for further analyses. Wash the carbonate precipitate twice with warm water, discarding the washings. Analyze the precipitate for Ba, Sr, and Ca, and the supernate for Mg, Na, and K, as described in Section 3–13.

9–19. Questions and Problems

1. Predict whether the following substances will be acidic, basic, or amphoteric in water solution: (a) CrO_2, (b) $Ac(OH)_3$, (c) BrO_2OH, (d) GeO, (e) H_5AtO_6, (f) FrOH, (g) $TeO_2(OH)_2$, (h) Ag_2O_3.

2. Explain by what criterion a substance is classified as acidic, basic, or amphoteric.

3. (a) Write equations showing the amphoteric nature of $Al(OH)_3$ in water.
   (b) Write equations starting with $Al(H_2O)_6^{+3}$ showing the amphoteric nature of Al(III) from the Brønsted point of view.

4. Just as water ionizes slightly, according to the equation
$$2 H_2O \rightleftharpoons OH_3^+ + OH^-$$
so liquid ammonia ionizes slightly according to the equation
$$2 NH_3 \rightleftharpoons NH_4^+ + NH_2^-$$
   (a) Would the following substances be acidic, basic, or amphoteric in liquid ammonia: NH_4Cl, HNO_3, KNH_2, NH_4ClO_4, $Zn(NH_2)_2$, $Ba(NH_2)_2$?
   (b) The substance $AgNH_2$ is amphoteric in liquid ammonia. Write equations showing its reaction *as* an acid and *as* a base, and *with* an acid and *with* a base, in liquid ammonia.
   (c) The ion $Cr(NH_3)_6^{+3}$ in liquid ammonia is the counterpart of $Cr(H_2O)_6^{+3}$ in water. Using appropriate equations, describe the amphoterism of Cr(III) in liquid ammonia from the Brønsted point of view.

5. Will the presence of a relatively high concentration of un-ionized $Cd(OH)_2$ (aq) in a saturated cadmium hydroxide solution invalidate the K_{sp} relationship? Explain.

6. Explain why the concentration of AsO^+ in a saturated solution of As_2O_3 in water is much higher than you would calculate directly from the K_{sp} relationship $[AsO^+][OH^-] = K_{sp}$.

7. Explain why the acidic or basic character of an element usually changes as its oxidation state changes.

8. Predict the acid-ionization constants for the following substances: (a) $HBrO_2$, (b) H_5AtO_6, (c) H_6PoO_6, (d) $H_4AtO_6^-$, (e) $H(GeH)O_2$, (f) $HBrO_4$, (g) $HRuO_4$, (h) H_2MoO_4, (i) H_3CrO_4.

9. From the data given in Table 9–11, predict whether the following hydroxides can spontaneously dehydrate in contact with water: (a) $Co(OH)_2$, (b) $Co(OH)_3$, (c) $TlOH$, (d) $HClO_4$, (e) $In(OH)_3$, (f) $AlOOH$.

10. Explain when the concentration of un-ionized $Pb(OH)_2$ (aq) in solution must be taken into account when calculating the concentrations of the various Pb(II) ions in solution.

11. Describe amphoterism from the point of view of hydroxy complexes.

12. What is the relationship of K_{inst}, K_B, K_A, and K_{hyd} for an amphoteric substance?

13. Calculate the concentration of $PuO_2(OH)_2$ which will dissolve in 0.1 M KOH.

14. Calculate the concentration of $Te(OH)_4$ which will dissolve in 0.01 M $HClO_4$.

15. Calculate the concentration of $UO_2(OH)_2$ which will dissolve in 0.1 M $HClO_4$.

16. Calculate the molar concentrations of Pb^{+2} and $HPbO_2^-$ in a solution saturated with solid $Pb(OH)_2$.

17. Calculate the solubility of VO_2OH (s) in pure water as a set of simultaneous equilibria, and show how much the solution differs from that calculated in Section 9–6.

18. Calculate the concentrations of Ag^+, $Ag(OH)$ (aq), $Ag(OH)_2^-$, and $Ag(OH)_3^{-2}$ in a saturated aqueous solution of Ag_2O.

19. Calculate the concentrations of $As(OH)_2^+$, $As(OH)_3$ (aq), $As(OH)_4^-$, $As(OH)_5^{-2}$, and $As(OH)_6^{-3}$ in a saturated aqueous solution of As_2O_3.

20. Calculate the concentrations of Hg^{+2}, $HgOH^+$, $Hg(OH)_2$ (aq), and $Hg(OH)_3^-$ in a saturated aqueous solution of HgO.

21. Nitrous acid is an amphoteric substance having, for the basic ionization, HNO_2 (aq) $\rightleftharpoons NO^+ + OH^-$, $K_B = 7 \times 10^{-19}$. In common with other strongly ampholytic substances of this sort, it also undergoes spontaneous dehydration to the oxide, the constant for the reaction, $2\,HNO_2$ (aq) $\rightleftharpoons N_2O_3$ (aq) $+ H_2O$ (l), being 9×10^{-3}. If exactly 0.01 mole of N_2O_3 be dissolved in 500 ml of water what are the molar concentrations of N_2O_3, HNO_2, NO^+, NO_2^-, H^+, and OH^- in the solution?

22. Some of the constants for the system $AgNO_2$ in water are

$$AgNO_2 \text{ (s)} \rightleftharpoons AgNO_2 \text{ (aq)} \qquad 10^{-1.92}$$
$$AgNO_2 \text{ (s)} \rightleftharpoons Ag^+ + NO_2^- \qquad 10^{-3.80}$$
$$Ag(NO_2)_2^- \rightleftharpoons Ag^+ + 2\,NO_2^- \qquad 10^{-2.83}$$

Using these and the values for other appropriate constants given elsewhere in this text, calculate the molar concentrations of Ag^+, $AgOH$ (aq), $AgNO_2$ (aq), $Ag(NO_2)_2^-$, NO^+, HNO_2, NO_2^-, H^+, and OH^- in a saturated $AgNO_2$ solution in water.

9–20. References

Feigl, F., *Qualitative Analysis by Spot Tests*, 5th ed. New York: Elsevier Publishing Company, Inc., 1958.

McAlpine, R. K., Soule, B. A., *Prescott and Johnson's Qualitative Analysis*, 2d ed. New York: D. Van Nostrand Company, Inc., 1933.

Johnson, W. C., ed., *Organic Reagents for Metals*. New York: Chemical Publishing Company, Inc., 1955.

Wenger, P. E., and Duckert, R., eds., *Reagents for Qualitative Inorganic Analysis*. New York: Elsevier Publishing Company, Inc., 1948.

Prodinger, W., *Organic Reagents Used in Quantitative Inorganic Analysis*. New York: Elsevier Publishing Company, Inc., 1940.

Sandell, E. B., *Colorimetric Determination of Traces of Metals*. New York: Interscience Publishers, Inc., 1950.

Vogel, A., *Macro and Semimicro Qualitative Inorganic Analysis*. New York: Longmans, Green and Company, 1954.

Snell, F. D., and Snell, C. T., *Colorimetric Methods of Analysis*, 3d ed. Vol. II. New York: D. Van Nostrand, Company, Inc., 1949.

Treadwell, F. P., and Hall, W. T., *Analytical Chemistry*, 9th ed., Vol. I. New York: John Wiley and Sons, Inc., 1937.

Yoe, J. H., and Sarver, L. A., *Organic Analytical Reagents*. New York: John Wiley and Sons, Inc., 1941.

Chapter 10

The Quantized Atom and the Structure

of Molecules and Complex Ions

10–1. The Structure of the Atom as Revealed by Spectroscopy

The atom has already been described as consisting of a positively charged nucleus around which "revolve planetary electrons." That most of the mass of the atom is contained in the positively charged nucleus, whose radius is only 0.001 percent of the total radius of the atom, was demonstrated by Ernest Rutherford in 1911. By bombarding very thin gold foil with alpha particles (He^{+2} ions), which would be repelled and deflected by the positive nuclei but not by the negative electrons, he was able to show that the radius of an atomic nucleus is on the order of 10^{-13} cm. This compares with a total radius for a small atom complete with electrons of about 10^{-8} cm. Thus the nucleus occupies only 10^{-15} of the total volume of the atom, the rest being mostly empty space containing a few electrons. These electrons, however, are not distributed at random in a formless cloud within the volume of the atom, but rather have an orderly arrangement.

The arrangement of the electrons within the atom was deduced from the study of spectral lines. If atoms are exposed to sources of energy, such as electric arcs or sparks, or hot flames, they absorb energy and become "excited." Upon leaving the source of energy, the energy is lost again in the form of electromagnetic radiation (visible and ultraviolet light). The light, however, is not emitted with all possible wave lengths, but rather a few very distinct wave lengths. The number of wave lengths depends upon the number of electrons in the atom and also on the amount of energy used to excite it. Because the usual spectrograph focuses the light to be studied through a narrow slit, whose image is a line, the distinct wave lengths show up as a series of lines of different characteristic wave length—or a "line spectrum." Examples of these are shown in Fig. 10–1. Each distinct wave length corresponds to a loss by the atom of a discrete amount of energy, which is radiated when an electron falls from an excited energy level to a lower level. The relationship between the wave length of the light emitted and the energy difference between the levels between which the electron falls is

$$E = \frac{hc}{\lambda} = h\nu$$

where E is the energy in ergs, λ is the wave length in centimeters, ν, the frequency, is the number of waves per second (i.e., ν is the frequency in

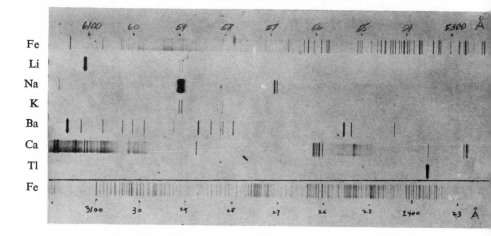

Fig. 10–1. Representative Spectra. Note the yellow sodium "D lines" at 5890 and 5896Å which also appear in all the other spectra because of sodium impurity; the red line of lithium (6130Å); the green line of barium (5535Å); and the green line of thallium (5350Å). Note the absence of strong lines for potassium in this part of the spectrum.

reciprocal seconds or in cycles per second), c is the velocity of light in centimeters per second and h is a constant of proportionality (Planck's constant) whose value is 6.624×10^{-27} erg-seconds. Since the spectral lines from any element are characteristic of that element, it can be seen that there must be only certain energy levels in the atoms of any given element between which the electrons may fall. These energy levels in the simplest case, the hydrogen atom, are related to each other approximately according to the expression

$$E = \frac{-13.54Z^2}{n^2}$$

volts per unit charge, where Z is the charge on the nucleus (1 in this case) and n (which is called the *quantum number*) is any *integer* from 1 to ∞.

Close study of the spectral lines reveals that, to describe all the possible energy states of an atom, four quantum numbers are required. These are

n = principal quantum number
l = radial or angular momentum quantum number
m = magnetic quantum number
s = spin quantum number

There are certain restrictions on the values the quantum numbers may have. They are

$$l = 0, \cdots (n-1)$$
$$m = -l, \cdots 0, \cdots +l$$
$$s = \pm\tfrac{1}{2}$$

Each quantum number m corresponds to an "orbital." The quantum number l describes the kind of orbital: All orbitals for which $l = 0$ are spherically symmetrical around the nucleus (Fig. 10–2a). Such orbitals are known as s orbitals (from the spectral designation for *sharp* lines. Note

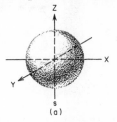

Fig. 10–2 (a). Shapes of Orbitals, $l=0$.

that the letter s is used to represent two different things: (1) the spin quantum number, and (2) the orbitals for which $l = 0$.) Since, when $l = 0$, m can be only 0, there is only one s orbital in each principal quantum level. All orbitals for which $l = 1$ are dumbbell-shaped and extend along the three

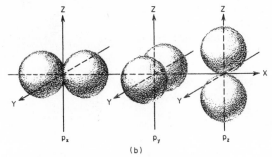

Fig. 10–2 (b). Shapes of Orbitals, $l=1$.

Cartesian axes, as shown in Fig. 10–2b. There are three of these orbitals corresponding to $m = -1$, $m = 0$, and $m = +1$. They are known as p orbitals (from the spectral designation for *principal* lines). The orbitals for which $l = 2$ have the shape of a double dumbbell (i.e., two dumbbells

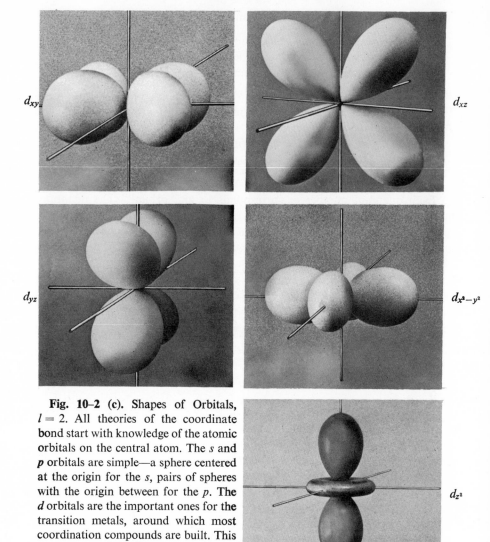

Fig. 10–2 (c). Shapes of Orbitals, $l = 2$. All theories of the coordinate bond start with knowledge of the atomic orbitals on the central atom. The s and p orbitals are simple—a sphere centered at the origin for the s, pairs of spheres with the origin between for the p. The d orbitals are the important ones for the transition metals, around which most coordination compounds are built. This is because the transition elements, by definition, do not have enough electrons to fill all these orbitals.

The d orbitals consist basically of four lobes around the origin. The d_{xy}, d_{xz}, and d_{yz} align the lobes at 45° between the axes. Of the three that are aligned on the axes, only two are allowed, to make the full complement of 10 d electrons. Any of the three axial orbitals could be chosen. Ordinarily, the $d_{x^2-y^2}$ and a hybrid of the other two, called d_{z^2}, are used. The models pictured here are of unperturbed orbitals, such as would exist in the gas phase in the absence of ligands.

Source: Ralph G. Pearson, "Crystal Field Explains Inorganic Behavior," *Chemical and Engineering News* (June 29, 1959), p. 72.

crossing in the middle) or a four-bladed propeller (Fig. 10–2c). (The one exception is the d_{z^2} orbital.) There are five of them in each principal quantum level above $n = 2$ (for $m = -2$, $m = -1$, $m = 0$, $m = +1$, and $m = +2$). They are called d orbitals (from the spectral designation for *diffuse* lines). Orbitals for which $l = 3$ are more complicated yet. Since m may now have the values -3, -2, -1, 0, $+1$, $+2$, and $+3$, there are seven such f orbitals (so-called from the spectral designation for *fundamental* lines). The f orbitals are the last (i.e., highest values of l) used in the ground state of any atom of an element of the known periodic table. Higher values of l may be observed in excited atoms, however. These are given alphabetic designations in order from f, i.e., g, h, and so on. In the same manner, the principal quantum levels are sometimes designated alphabetically. Thus for the K-shell, $n = 1$, for the L-shell, $n = 2$, for the M-shell, $n = 3$, and so on. In general, the principal quantum levels will be designated by numbers in this book. However, occasionally it is more convenient to refer to "the L-electrons" than to "the electrons in the second principal quantum level" or to "the electrons for which $n = 2$."

Orbitals must *not* be considered to be orbits or paths along which the electrons travel like planets around the sun. Rather they are regions in space (three-dimensional surfaces) where electrons of specified energy have the highest *probability* of being. The term "planetary electrons" is therefore based on a very poor analogy and should not be used.

It can be seen that when n is specified, l may then have any of n possible different values. When l is specified, m may then have any of $2l + 1$ possible different values. The number of values which s may have is limited to two, $-\frac{1}{2}$ and $+\frac{1}{2}$. In an unexcited atom, the electrons will be found distributed in the lowest available energy levels. There is one further restriction on the energy distribution of the electrons in an atom to be considered before a detailed picture of atomic structure can be developed. This is the Pauli exclusion principle, which states that *no two electrons in any atom may have all four quantum numbers the same.*

10–2 Building the Atom—the First Three Periods

To demonstrate the principle, let us build up the electronic structures of several atoms. The hydrogen atom, $Z = 1$, has one electron in the lowest available level, $n = 1$. When $n = 1$, l can be only 0, $m = 0$, and $s = -\frac{1}{2}$ or $+\frac{1}{2}$. Let us arbitrarily place electrons first in the spin state $s = -\frac{1}{2}$, rather than $s = +\frac{1}{2}$. The electron in the ground state of the hydrogen atom will thus have the quantum numbers $n = 1$, $l = 0$, $m = 0$, $s = -\frac{1}{2}$, and can be designated as $1s^1$. In the helium atom ($Z = 2$) there is one electron with quantum numbers the same as for hydrogen and one with quantum numbers $n = 1$, $l = 0$, $m = 0$, $s = +\frac{1}{2}$. The electron configuration of the helium atom may be designated as $1s^2$. For lithium ($Z = 3$), however, it is no longer possible to put all of the electrons in the level $n = 1$ without having all four quantum numbers the same for two of the three electrons, which is forbidden by the Pauli exclusion principle. Consequently, the third electron must go into the next lowest available orbital, which is the $2s$ orbital, for which $n = 2$, $l = 0$, $m = 0$, and $s = -\frac{1}{2}$. The ground state of the lithium atom may thus be designated as $1s^2\, 2s^1$. For beryllium ($Z = 4$), the electron

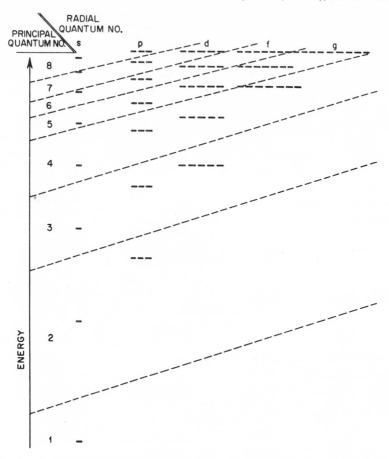

Fig. 10–3. Relationship of Electronic Energy Levels.

configuration is $1s^2\, 2s^2$. For boron ($Z = 5$), it is no longer possible to put electrons into the $2s$ level without violating the Pauli exclusion principle, so the fifth electron goes into the level $n = 2$, $l = 1$, $m = -1$, $s = -\frac{1}{2}$. The configuration of boron is $1s^2\, 2s^2\, 2p^1$. In carbon ($Z = 6$) there is a choice between putting the sixth electron into the orbital $m = 0$, $s = -\frac{1}{2}$, and putting it into the orbital $m = -1$, $s = +\frac{1}{2}$. Since single electrons in the orbitals having different values of m are "degenerate," i.e., have the same energy, whereas pairing electrons in the same orbital results in a state of higher energy, the lower energy state will be $m = 0$, $s = -\frac{1}{2}$. If the different p

orbitals be designated as p_x, p_y, p_z, the configuration of the carbon atom in its ground state, then, will be $1s^2\ 2s^2\ 2p_x{}^1\ 2p_y{}^1$, which, if it be recognized that as long as there are available orbitals having the same values of n and l the electrons will remain unpaired, may be shortened to $1s^2\ 2s^2\ 2p^2$.

It will perhaps be easier to see the relationships of the energy levels from the diagram in Fig. 10–3.

From this Figure, it can be seen that as the shells acquire more sublevels the energy range of one shell may overlap the energy range of the next. For example, the $3d$ orbitals lie higher in energy than the $4s$ orbital. The $4f$ orbitals lie higher than even the $6s$! The consequences of this can be seen in the following examples.

10–3. The Transition Elements and the Fourth and Fifth Periods

In argon, the last electron is put into the $3p$ level, giving the structure $1s^2\ 2s^2\ 2p^6\ 3s^2\ 3p^6$. From Fig. 10–3, it can be seen that the next available orbital is the $4s$, into which one electron is put to form the potassium atom, giving the structure $1s^2\ 2s^2\ 2p^6\ 3s^2\ 3p^6\ 3d^0\ 4s^1$. Calcium has a second electron in the $4s$ orbital. Let us represent this diagrammatically as

		Third quantum level	Fourth quantum level
		d	s	p
(Calcium)	Argon Core	☐ ☐ ☐ ☐ ☐	⇵	☐ ☐ ☐

According to Fig. 10–3, the next available level is now the $3d$, so the elements scandium and titanium will have the structures

		$3d$	$4s$	$4p$
(Scandium)	Argon Core	↓ ☐ ☐ ☐ ☐	⇵	☐ ☐ ☐

		$3d$	$4s$	$4p$
(Titanium)	Argon Core	↓ ↓ ☐ ☐ ☐	⇵	☐ ☐ ☐

Scandium begins the *first transition series*. A transition element was defined in general chemistry as "one in which electrons were being added to the shell below the valence shell." The reason for these elements can now be seen. With certain irregularities, which will be discussed in Chapter 16, the electrons are put one at a time into the $3d$ orbitals until manganese is reached, which has the structure

Pairing of electrons in the $3d$ level now occurs until zinc is reached, with the structure

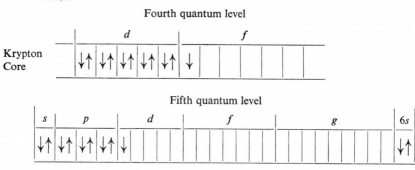

Now the next available level is the $4p$, whose orbitals are occupied singly in gallium, germanium, and arsenic, and with pairing in selenium, bromine, and krypton. Now the next available level is the $5s$, into which one electron is put in rubidium.

10–4. The Rare-Earth Elements and Beyond

The process is now repeated in essentially the same manner through the fifth period (containing the second transition series) and on into the sixth period, where the third transition series begins with lanthanum (krypton core, $4d^{10} 5s^2 5p^6 5d^1 6s^2$). Electrons in the $5d$ and $4f$ levels are almost identical in energy. After lanthanum, the $4f$ is favored over the $5d$, so that cerium has the structure

Cerium thus begins the first transition series *of the second type*, or the first *rare-earth* series. This is also known as the lanthanide series. After the fourteen-member lanthanide series, the third transition series (of the first type) is resumed, and is completed with mercury. In the seventh period a second "rare-earth" series, the actinide series, begins with protoactinium, in which the $5f$ level is filled.

The order in which the sublevels are completed (although not necessarily the order in which they are begun) can be determined by following the arrows from the top down in Fig. 10–4. Each time the vertical line between the *s*-

and *p*-level columns is crossed, a new period begins. From this diagram, it can be seen that no electrons will be found in the *g* levels in the ground state of any existing element.

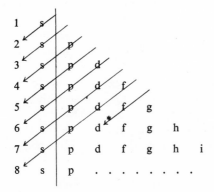

Fig. 10–4. Order of Completion of Atomic Sublevels.

* Extent of completion in heaviest known element.

The electronic structures of the elements in their ground states are shown in Appendix 8. The configurations of the 5*f* and 6*d* electrons for the elements above curium ($Z = 96$) are still in doubt. The structures given seem reasonable on the basis of available evidence and by analogy with the lanthanide series. Elements 103–104 were first made in 1959. Number 103 finishes the actinide series. Element 104 should be a congener of hafnium.

10–5.   Electronic Structure and the Periodic Table

The reason for the periodicity of the properties of the elements as expressed in the periodic table now becomes apparent. Each period of the periodic table begins when a single electron occurs in an *s* orbital at a time when the *d* orbitals of the preceding principal quantum level are completely vacant. Since the first element in each period has this feature in common with each of the others, they are all similar in chemical and physical properties, constituting the family of very similar alkali metals. (Hydrogen, having no electrons at all in the quantum level below its valence level—since a lower level does not exist—is quite different in its properties from the first members of the later periods.)

Likewise, each time an element has the *p* orbitals filled, the three pairs of *p* electrons are found to constitute a closed symmetrical shell of eight (an octet) with the pair of *s* electrons of the same principal quantum level, and a noble gas, terminating the period, results.

In short, each time a particular arrangement of outer electrons recurs, the properties which result from it recur in modified form—periodic properties such as valence, crystal structure, melting point, boiling point, electronegativity, and so on. The recurrence of these and other properties were the original basis of the periodic classification of the elements and are reflections of the existence of naturally related groups or families of elements.

Nonperiodic properties are those which are the result of gradual changes of the inner structure of the atom. These include atomic weight, atomic number, K-electron spectrum, and so on. The first two of these are the result of adding neutrons and protons to the nucleus, increasing its mass and charge. The K-electron spectrum moves gradually to shorter wave lengths as one goes from hydrogen to the heaviest elements. This is also the result of the increase in positive charge in the nucleus which results in ever stronger attraction of the K- (and also the other) electrons.

There are also certain periodic functions of the nucleus such as nuclear spin. However, these are beyond the scope of this book.

10–6.   The Chemist's Atom. Hybrid s-p Orbitals

Electronic structure as we have been discussing it above is the structure of isolated atoms in the gaseous state where each atom is beyond the influence of any other atom. The atoms with which the chemist deals, however, are almost invariably associated with other atoms in compounds. This fact drastically modifies their electronic structure.

For example, although it is possible for the carbon atom ($1s^2\,2s^2\,2p_x{}^1 2p_y{}^1$) to react using only its p electrons, and leaving the electrons in the completed $2s^2$ level unshared (as in CO, CH_3NC, and so on), this is an unusual situation. In general, under the influence of the coulombic fields of the neighboring atoms, the carbon atom's $2s$, $2p_x$, $2p_y$, and $2p_z$ orbitals are transformed into four identical (degenerate) orbitals which, because they are no longer either s or p orbitals but have some of the character of both, are called *hybrid* orbitals, and in this case are given the designation sp^3 to indicate the number of each type of original orbital which went into their make-up. Since there were four original orbitals, there are four hybrid orbitals. Since the hybrid orbitals are identical they must be oriented symmetrically in space. The most symmetrical orientation of four objects around a fifth one in space is at the corners of a regular tetrahedron. Consequently, when the carbon atom forms a molecule with four other identical atoms, the four are found at the corners of a regular tetrahedron, with the carbon atom at the center, as shown for CF_4 in Fig. 10–5a. The actual bond structure of the same molecule is shown in Fig. 10–5b, where the solid lines stand for the pairs of electrons forming the bonds, and the three unshared pairs of electrons on each fluorine atom are omitted for the sake of simplicity. The inner angle ($\angle FCF$) of such a structure is $109° \, 28'$.

When the four groups attached to the carbon atom are not the same (so that the electron pairs are not all concentrated at the same distance from the carbon atom), the bond angles will change somewhat so that the tetrahedron becomes irregular. For example, in the compound CH_2F_2, the fluorine atoms are more electronegative than the hydrogen atoms and pull the bonding electrons farther away from the carbon than the hydrogens do. Therefore, the electron pairs in the C-F bonds repel each other less than the electron pairs in the C-H bonds, so that the FCF angle collapses to something

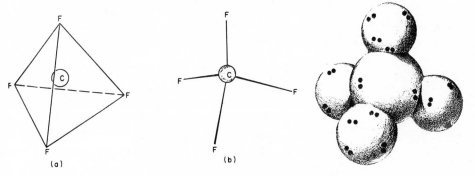

Fig. 10–5. Three Representations of the CF_4 Molecule.

less than 109° 28'. If one of the electron pairs is not attached to anything, it nevertheless repels the other electron pairs, and consequently an irregularly 109° 28' structure is retained with respect to the location of the electron pairs around the central atom. Since the unshared electron pair is pulled less (i.e., not at all) away from the carbon atom, it will lie closest to it and will repel each of the bonding pairs more than they do each other. Consequently the angles between the bonds will always be less than tetrahedral when there is an unshared pair of electrons on a carbon atom to which three other atoms are attached. Such an example would be the methide ion, CH_3^-, which is

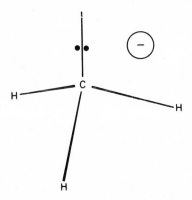

The tetrahedral configuration is not unique to carbon. On the contrary, whenever four pairs of electrons (bonding or unshared) are found in s and p orbitals having the same principal quantum number, if these are the only orbitals forming bonds, then the structure will be tetrahedral. Thus the ammonium ion, NH_4^+, and the hydroborate ion, BH_4^-, are isostructural with (i.e., have the same structure as) methane, CH_4, and are regular tetra-hedra. Ammonia, NH_3, and oxonium ion, OH_3^+, are isostructural with methide ion, CH_3^-, and are distorted tetrahedra with *HNH* and *HOH* angles of 108°. Likewise, the oxygen atom in water has two unshared pairs of electrons and two bonds to hydrogen with an angle of 105°, and is pre-sumably isostructural with NH_2^- and FH_2^+.

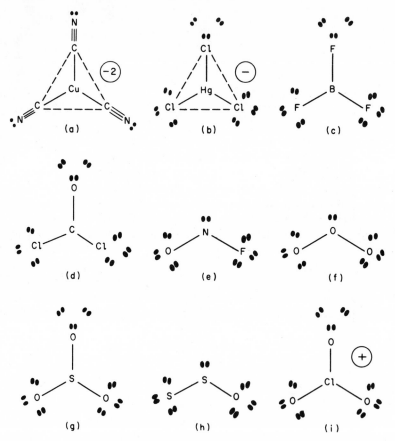

Fig. 10–6 (a)–(i). Various Triangular Molecules.

To emphasize that any sp^3 hybrid, regardless of the principal quantum number, will be tetrahedral, let us note that the *CCuC* angles in $Cu(CN)_4^{-3}$, the *ClHgCl* angles in $HgCl_4^{-2}$, *HGaH* angles in GaH_4^-, the *ISnI* angles in SnI_4, the *CAsC* angles in $(CH_3)_4As^+$, the *OSO* angles in SO_4^{-2}, and the *OClO* angles in ClO_4^- are all 109° 28'. When all four pairs of electrons on the central atom are not in the same environment, as in $HgI_2(OH)_2^{-2}$, $B(OH)_3F^-$, $(CH_3)_3SiBr$, BiH_3, SO_2Cl_2, ClO_2^-, ClO_3^-, or ClO_3F, the structure will no longer be regular, but is still, nevertheless, tetrahedral.

When only three pairs of electrons, unshared or forming bonds, surround an atom in s and p orbitals, they arrange themselves in three sp^2 hybrid orbitals directed toward the corners of a plane triangle. Such an arrangement is found in $Cu(CN)_3^{-2}$, $HgCl_3^{-2}$, BF_3, $COCl_2$, NOF, O_3, SO_3, S_2O, and ClO_2^+ (see Fig. 10-6). When the three pairs of electrons are identical, as in examples a, b, c, g, and i, the triangle will be regular and the bond angle at the central atom will be $120°$. When the electron pairs are not identical, as in examples d, e, f, and h, the triangle will be irregular and the bond angles will deviate somewhat from $120°$. The molecule will still be planar, however.

When only two pairs of electrons are in the s and p orbitals, either unshared or in bonds, the arrangement is linear ($180°$ angle) with sp hybridization. Such an arrangement is found in $AgCl_2^-$, $HgBr_2$, Hg_2Br_2, $TlCl$ (g), CO, HCN, CO_2, NO^+, SO_2^{+2}, and so forth.

$$: \overset{..}{\underset{..}{Cl}} - Ag - \overset{..}{\underset{..}{Cl}} :^{\;-} \qquad : \overset{..}{\underset{..}{Br}} - Hg - \overset{..}{\underset{..}{Br}} : \qquad : \overset{..}{\underset{..}{Br}} - Hg - Hg - \overset{..}{\underset{..}{Br}} : \qquad : \overset{..}{\underset{..}{Tl}} - \overset{..}{\underset{..}{Cl}} :$$
$$\qquad\quad a \qquad\qquad\qquad\qquad b \qquad\qquad\qquad\qquad c \qquad\qquad\qquad\qquad d$$

$$: C - \overset{..}{\underset{..}{O}} : \qquad H : C - \overset{..}{N} : \qquad : \overset{..}{\underset{..}{O}} - C - \overset{..}{\underset{..}{O}} : \qquad : N - \overset{..}{\underset{..}{O}} :^{\;+} \qquad : \overset{..}{\underset{..}{O}} - S - \overset{..}{\underset{..}{O}} :^{\;+2}$$
$$\quad e \qquad\qquad f \qquad\qquad\quad g \qquad\qquad\qquad h \qquad\qquad\qquad i$$

Fig. 10-7. Various Linear Molecules.

10-7.   Multiple Bonds

Many of the molecules discussed in Section 10-3 have been discussed in unfamiliar terms. For example, CO_2 is usually described as having two double bonds, $O{=}C{=}O$, rather than two single bonds, as shown in Fig. 10-7g. Likewise $COCl_2$ and NOF are usually described as having double bonds between oxygen and carbon or oxygen and nitrogen,

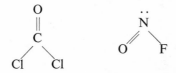

rather than single bonds as shown in Fig. 10-6d and e. Also the bonds in CO, HCN, and NO^+ are usually described as triple bonds, $: C{\equiv}O:$, $: C{\equiv}N:^-$, and $: N{\equiv}O:^+$, rather than as in Fig. 10-7e, f, and h. It therefore becomes necessary to decide what a multiple (double or triple) bond is.

Let us take the $COCl_2$ molecule as an example. If the three bonds from carbon to chlorine and oxygen are described as sp^2 hybrid bonds, then there will be one remaining p orbital of the carbon atom not involved in bonding. This will be symmetrically disposed with respect to the plane of the sp^2 hybrid bonds and therefore perpendicular to them, as shown in Fig. 10-8a. Since the oxygen atom also has p orbitals, it can be seen from Fig. 10-8b that there will be *sidewise* overlap of the p orbital of the carbon atom and a p

orbital of the oxygen atom. Since the *p* orbital of the oxygen atom contains a pair of electrons, the pair must consequently occupy the *p* orbital of the carbon atom at least part of the time. This sharing of electrons through *sidewise* overlapping of orbitals is known as π(pi)-bonding. In contrast, the

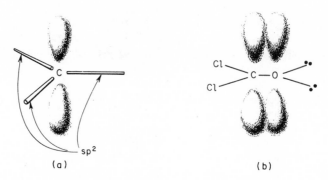

(a)   (b)

Fig. 10–8. The Arrangement of One pi and Three sigma Bonds about a Carbon Atom – (a) Generalized, (b) in $COCl_2$.

sharing of electrons by *endwise* overlapping of orbitals as in the bonds formed by the sp^2 hybrid orbitals is known as σ(sigma)-bonding. *The geometry of the molecule is determined almost entirely by the sigma bonds and unshared pairs of electrons.* The pi bonds have only a secondary effect on structure.

In the same way as a double bond consists of one sigma and one pi bond, a triple bond consists of one sigma and two pi bonds, as is shown for HCN in Fig. 10–9. The overlap of orbitals in CO_2 is also shown.

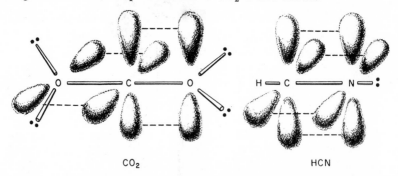

CO_2 HCN

Fig. 10–9. The Bond Structure in CO_2 and HCN.

Thus it can be seen why Cl—Hg—Cl, O=C=O, O=S=O^{+2}, and H—C≡N are all linear, since each has only two sigma bonds. Likewise

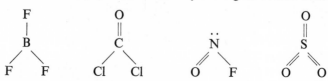

having only three sigma bonds (including unshared pairs), are plane triangles and

$$
\underset{F}{\overset{F}{\underset{\diagup\ \diagdown}{\overset{|}{C}}}}\ \ \ \ \ \ \ \ \underset{O}{\overset{\cdot\cdot}{\underset{\diagup\!\!\!/\ \diagdown}{Cl}}}^{-} \ \ \ \ \ \ \ \ \underset{O}{\overset{\cdot\cdot}{\underset{\diagup\!\!\!/\ \diagdown}{Cl\cdot}}}^{-} \ \ \ \ \ \ \ \ \underset{O}{\overset{Cl}{\underset{Cl\diagup\!\!\!/\ \diagdown}{S}}}
$$

having four sigma bonds (or unshared pairs) each, are tetrahedra. The CF_4 molecule is a *regular* tetrahedron, since all four electron pairs are in identical situations. The structures of ClO_2^-, ClO_3^-, and SO_2Cl_2, however, are irregular tetrahedra because the four pairs of electrons are not identical.

10–8.   The Use of d Orbitals in Bonding

In the third quantum level, d orbitals become available for the first time. Although no valence electrons are found in the $3d$ orbitals in the ground states of the atoms until after element 20 (calcium), in the fourth period, nevertheless, these orbitals may be used for bond formation under some circumstances. We saw in Section 10–3 that, although the ground state of the carbon atom has the electronic configuration $1s^2\ 2s^2\ 2p_x^1\ 2p_y^1$, the state of primary concern to the chemist is the excited state $1s^2\ 2s^1\ 2p_x^1\ 2p_y^1\ 2p_z^1$. This is the state from which most of the compounds of carbon may be considered to have been formed, although in certain cases (CO, CN^-, CH_3^-, and so on) the ground-state configuration may be considered to have been used.

In the case of phosphorus, arsenic, antimony, and bismuth, the ground state is $ns^2\ np_x^1\ np_y^1\ np_z^1$ (where the levels below the valence level have been omitted, and n is the principal quantum number of the valence level in each case). An excited state is $ns^1\ np_x^1\ np_y^1\ np_z^1\ nd^1$.

In contrast to carbon, these elements form many compounds from the ground-state configuration (leaving the s electrons paired). Such compounds are

$$
\underset{H}{\overset{\cdot\cdot}{\underset{H\diagup\ \diagdown Cl}{P}}} \ \ \ \ \ \ \underset{I}{\overset{\cdot\cdot}{\underset{I\diagup\ \diagdown I}{As}}} \ \ \ \ \ \ \underset{CH_3}{\overset{\cdot\cdot}{\underset{CH_3\diagup\ \diagdown Br}{Sb}}} \ \ \ \ \ \ \underset{H}{\overset{\cdot\cdot}{\underset{H\diagup\ \diagdown H}{Bi}}}
$$

On the other hand, substances formed from the excited state indicated include BiF_6^-, H_3AsO_4, SbF_3Cl_2, and PF_5. In the case of H_3AsO_4,

$$
HO-\overset{\overset{\textstyle O}{\|}}{\underset{\underset{\textstyle HO}{|}}{As}}-OH
$$

the molecule is tetrahedral, because although the d orbital of the arsenic atom is used for *pi*-bonding, there are only four *sigma* bonds, which use sp^3

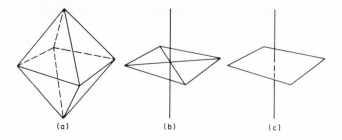

Fig. 10–10. Three Representations of a Regular Octahedron.

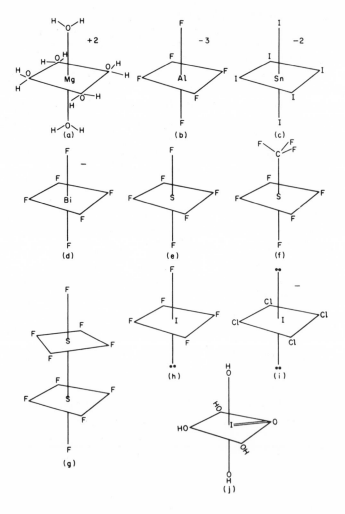

Fig. 10–11. Various Octahedral Molecules.

hybrid orbitals. Other examples of tetrahedral substances using d orbitals for pi-bonding are SO_2Cl_2, ClO_3^-, ClO_2^-, and so forth. In BiF_6^-, there is a total of six *sigma* bonds. This requires all the s and p orbitals and also two of the d orbitals. Six hybrid orbitals are formed which are described as sp^3d^2. The six sp^3d^2 hybrid bonds are directed toward the six corners of a regular octahedron if all six electron pairs are in identical situations, or an irregular octahedron if they are not identical. Various representations of an octahedron are shown in Fig. 10–10. Drawing a is of a geometrical regular octahedron, b shows the orientation of bonds inside the octahedron, and c is a conventionalized figure which retains the three-dimensional impression of a without having quite such a clutter of lines. Representation c will be used for illustrations. The structures of BiF_6^- and several other substances having the same electronic configuration are shown in Fig. 10–11. The substances 10–11 a, b, c, d, and e are regular octahedra. Substances f, g, h,

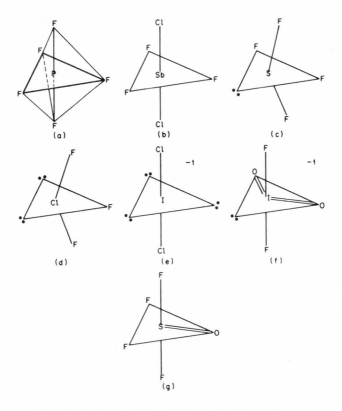

Fig. 10–12. Various Trigonal Bipyramidal Molecules.

i, and j, which have more than one kind of group around the central atom are irregular octahedra. The S_2F_{10} molecule has two interlocking octahedra, each sulfur atom occupying the center of one and a corner of the other. In the H_5IO_6 molecule, a third d orbital is required for the pi bond between iodine and the lone oxygen atom.

In the case of SbF_3Cl_2 and PF_5, five *sigma* bonds are formed, requiring *one* d orbital. The hybridization is sp^3d. There is no regular polyhedron having five corners. The next best thing is the trigonal bipyramid, which may be considered to be two triangular (trigonal) pyramids joined base to base. In this case the two atoms at the apices of the bipyramid are designated as *apical* and the three at the corners of the common base as *equatorial*. The central atom lies in the center of the common base. If all five groups are not the same this structure will be distorted somewhat. Examples of this structure are shown in Fig. 10–12. The PF_5 molecule is a "regular" trigonal bipyramid. The others are all distorted in some degree. In $IO_2F_2{}^-$, two additional d orbitals are required for pi-bonding of the oxygen atoms to the iodine; in SOF_4, one additional d orbital is needed for pi-bonding oxygen to sulfur.

When seven, eight, or nine groups are attached to a central atom, an appropriately larger number of d orbitals is required. The seven-coordinate structure may be described as that of an octahedron one face of which has been expanded to accommodate the seventh atom. Examples of this are IF_7 and $PoI_6{}^{-2}$. A schematic representation is shown in Fig. 10–13.

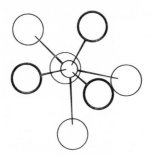

Fig. 10–13. An Example of Seven-coordination.

10–9. Complexes of the Transition Elements

The transition elements are characterized by having d orbitals in the principal quantum level below the valence level partially filled with electrons. These d orbitals vary in energy from somewhat above to slightly below the energy of the s orbital of the valence level (or, more pertinently, of the sp^3 hybrid orbitals of the valence level). The exact relationship of the d orbitals with the s (or sp^3) orbitals will depend upon several factors, such as the atomic number, the oxidation state, and so forth. Just as the elements discussed in Section 10–8 make use of the d orbitals overlying the valence level, so the transition elements may make use of the d orbitals underlying it. (The transition elements may also use the d orbitals overlying the valence level. This matter will be more fully discussed below.)

If a transition metal is to use its underlying d orbitals for bonding, the number it can use will depend on the number of nonbonding valence electrons which the d orbitals must accommodate. For example, the Zn^{+2}–cyanide complex is derived from Zn^{+2}, which has the electronic structure

		3d				4s	4p	
Argon Core	↓↑	↓↑	↓↑	↓↑	↓↑			

All the d orbitals are required for nonbonding electrons, leaving only the s and p orbitals for accepting electron pairs from the cyanide ions ($:C: : :N:^-$); consequently sp^3 hybrid bonds result and $Zn(CN)_4^{-2}$ is tetrahedral.

In the neutral (zero-valent) nickel atom, the electronic structure is

		3d				4s	4p	
Argon Core	↓↑	↓↑	↓↑	↓	↓	↓↑		

The excited state

		3d				4s	4p	
Argon Core	↓↑	↓↑	↓↑	↓↑	↓↑			

would be isoelectronic with Zn^{+2}, leaving four sp^3 hybrid orbitals for bonding, resulting in tetrahedral configurations for $Ni(CO)_4$, $Ni(CN)_4^{-4}$, and so on.

The Cr^{+3}–cyanide complex on the other hand, is derived from Cr^{+3}, with an electronic structure

		3d				4s	4p	
Argon Core	↓	↓	↓					

This leaves six orbitals available for formation of *sigma* bonds, giving rise to d^2sp^3 hybrid orbitals. The d^2sp^3 hybrids, like the sp^3d^2 hybrids, are directed toward the corners of an octahedron. The $Cr(CN)_6^{-3}$ complex is therefore an octahedral complex. The possibility suggests itself that the structure

		3d				4s	4p	
Argon Core	↓↑	↓						

might be realized, freeing seven orbitals for bond formation. This is not done for the reason to be discussed in Section 10–11.

Likewise in the Cr^{+2} cyanide complex, the Cr^{+2} ion has the configuration

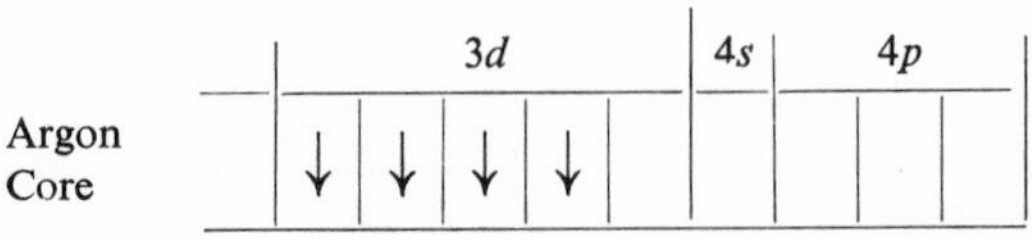

An excited state would be

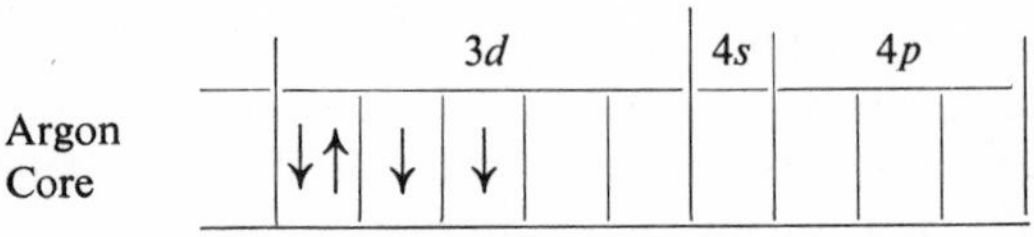

which frees six orbitals for d^2sp^3 hybrid bond formation and $Cr(CN)_6^{-4}$ is octahedral.

The carbonyl of chromium(0) is derived from the neutral chromium atom, which has the configuration

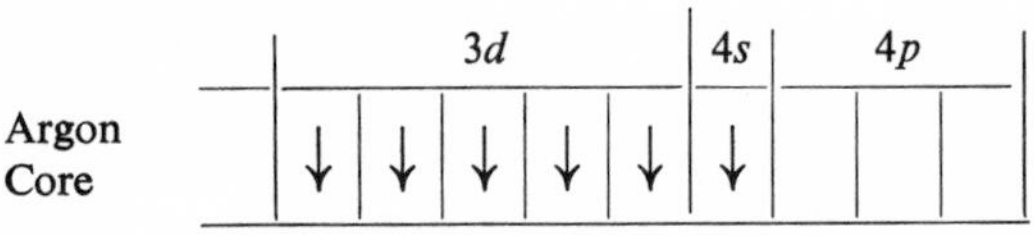

An excited state would be

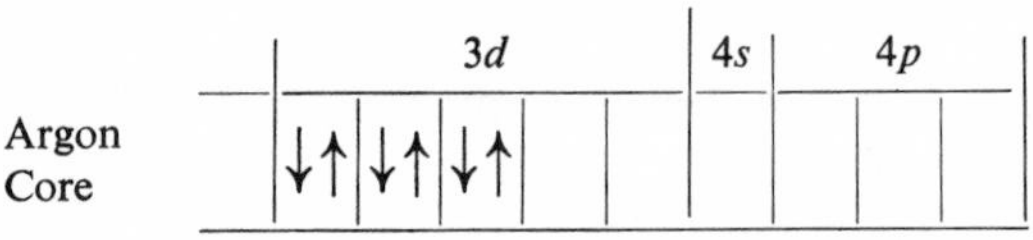

again leaving six orbitals for d^2sp^3 hybridization. The $Cr(CO)_6$ molecule is likewise octahedral.

When only one d orbital can be made available, the complex or molecule cannot attain a coordination number of six. Thus in the Ni^{+2}–cyanide complex, the electronic configuration of the simple Ni^{+2} ion would be

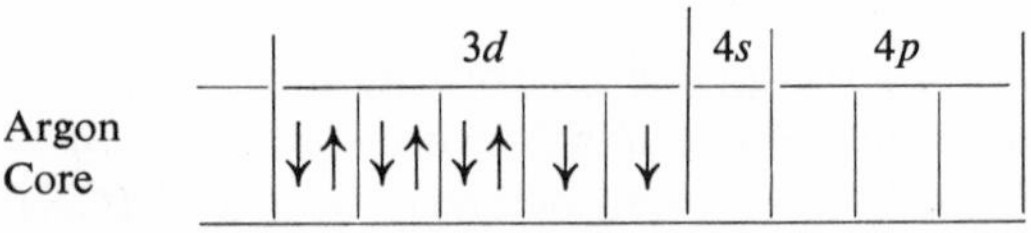

An excited state would be

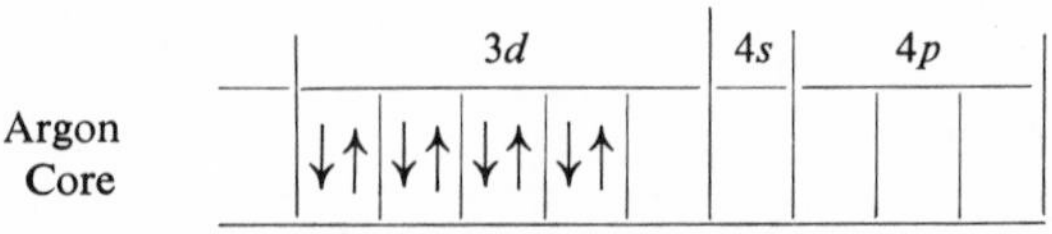

The first would provide only four orbitals of sp^3 hybridization. The second would provide five orbitals with one d orbital included in the hybridization For complexes of the type we are discussing it is generally found that the more d character there is in the hybrid orbitals, the stronger are the bonds. Consequently the Ni(II)–cyanide complex is found to be derived from the excited state in which the d orbital is incorporated into the hybridization. It is found, however, that in most complex ions of this type, for which the oxidation state of the central atom is greater than zero, only four of the orbitals available are used, the hybridization being dsp^2.

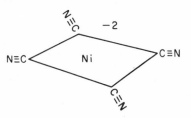

Fig. 10–14. The Structure of the $Ni(CN)_4^{-2}$ Ion.

This results in a square planar geometry for the complex. The $Ni(CN)_4^{-2}$ ion thus has the four CN groups at the corners of a square in the center of which is the nickel atom, as shown in Figure 10–14. In addition to these strong bonds, much weaker ones can be formed in the two empty octahedral positions above and below the plane of the complex. For example, in very concentrated alkali cyanide solution, the reaction $Ni(CN)_4^{-2} + CN^- \rightleftharpoons Ni(CN)_5^{-2}$ takes place. The similar $PtCl_4^{-2}$ ion is shown in Fig. 10–15 as it occurs in crystalline K_2PtCl_4.

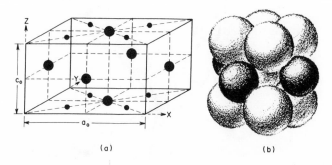

(a)   (b)

Fig. 10–15. The Crystal Structure of K_2PtCl_4.

The case of cupric complexes is peculiar in that despite the fact that in the Cu^{+2} ion all the d orbitals are occupied,

	3d				4s	4p	
Argon Core	↓↑	↓↑	↓↑	↓↑	↓		

it nevertheless forms square complexes, apparently by promotion of the single electron to an excited state (according to one explanation), such as

	3d		4s	4p	
Argon Core	↓↑ ↓↑ ↓↑ ↓↑				↓

The hybridization in the $Cu(NH_3)_4^{+2}$ ion therefore is dsp^2. As in the case of other square complexes, these can also form additional weak bonds in the vacant octahedral positions. Thus in very concentrated aqueous ammonia the reaction

$$Cu(NH_3)_4^{+2} + NH_3 \rightleftharpoons Cu(NH_3)_5^{+2}$$

takes place. The equilibrium constant for this reaction, however, is only 0.40, compared to a constant of $1.1 \times 10^{+12}$ for the reaction

$$Cu^{+2} + 4\,NH_3 \rightleftharpoons Cu(NH_3)_4^{+2}$$

When four of the d orbitals are available for bonding, it is sometimes possible for eight covalent bonds to be formed. Such a situation is found in the ions $Mo(CN)_8^{-4}$, $Mo(CN)_8^{-3}$, $W(CN)_8^{-4}$, and $W(CN)_8^{-3}$. As mentioned in the previous section, eight-coordination (d^4sp^3-hybridization) gives rise to the distorted dodecahedral structure shown in Fig. 10–16.

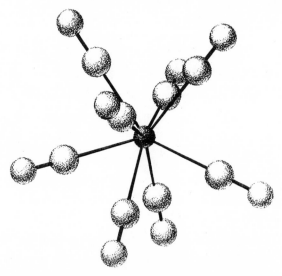

Fig. 10–16. The Structure of the Octacyanomolybdate, -tungstate, and -rhenate Ions.

The availability of underlying d orbitals can now be seen to place an upper limit on the coordination number of the complexes for which these orbitals are used. This is well exemplified by the cyanide complexes, all of which are "inner" or "penetration" complexes, as this type is called. Fig. 10–17 shows most of the known cyanide complexes in relationship to the

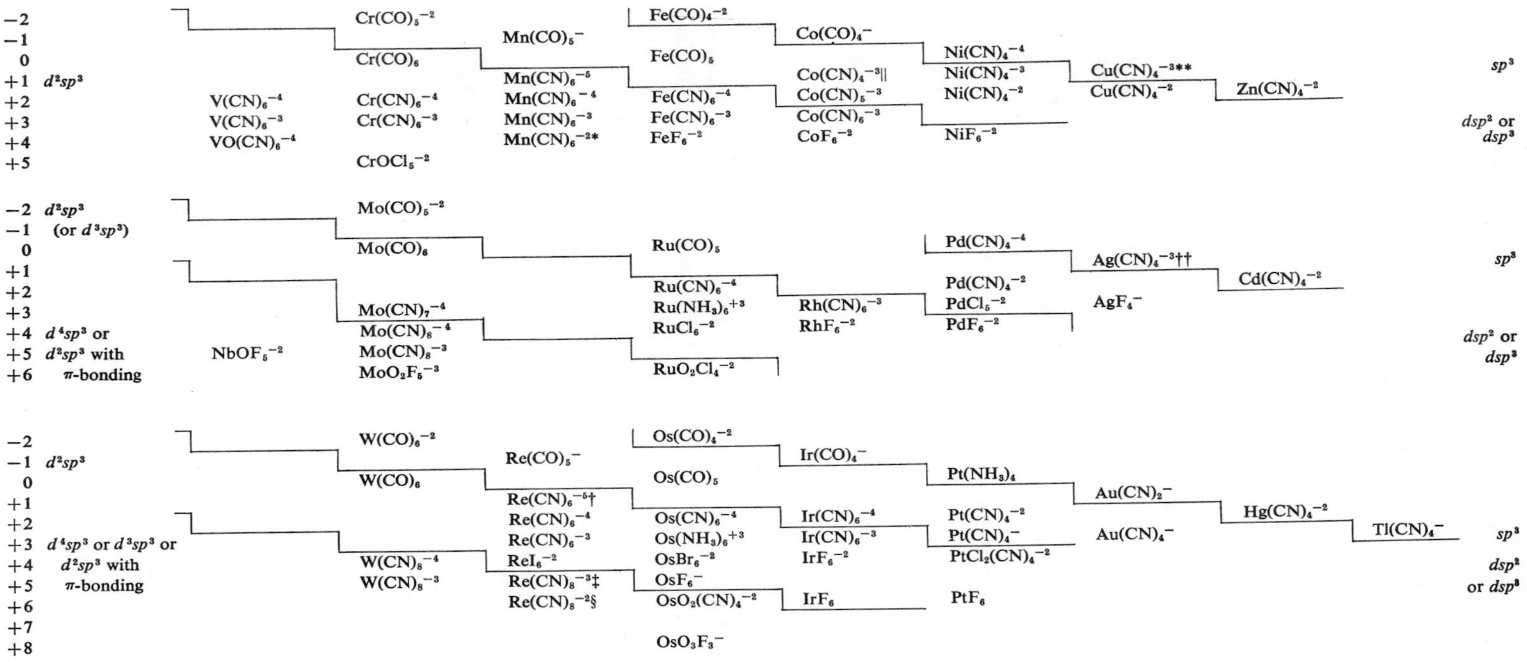

* Or $Mn(CN)_8^{-4}$. † Also $Re(CO)_4(CN)_2^-$. ‡ Also $ReO_2(CN)_4^{-3}$. § Also $ReOCl_6^{-2}$. || Also $Co(CN)_3CO^{-2}$. ¶ Also $Ni_2(CN)_6^{-4}$.
** Also $Cu(CN)_3^{-2}$ and $Cu(CN)_2^-$. †† Also $Ag(CN)_3^{-2}$ and $Ag(CN)_2^-$.

Fig. 10–17. The Relationship of Electronic Structure and Coordination Number: the Cyano Complexes.

central element's oxidation state and position in the periodic table. The decrease in coordination number with decreasing number of available d orbitals, as one goes to the right in the periodic table, is noteworthy. Some additional complexes have been included to round out the picture.

10-10. Inner and Outer Complexes

The coordination number of the Ni(II)–cyanide complex is four, or at most five, as discussed in the previous section. In this complex, all the electrons are paired; that is, for every electron of spin $-\frac{1}{2}$, there is a spin $+\frac{1}{2}$ and the complex is diamagnetic; that is to say, it tends to move away from a magnetic field. On the other hand, the coordination number of the Ni(II)–ammonia complex may be as high as six, as discussed in Section 7–10. In this complex, all of the electrons are not paired, as is attested by the fact that it is paramagnetic, tending to move into a magnetic field. The electronic structure of the nickel atom in this case is

	3d	4s	4p	4d
Argon Core	↓↑ ↓↑ ↓↑ ↓ ↓			

and according to one (Pauling's) explanation, two of the d orbitals in the valence level are hybridized with the s and p orbitals to give six octahedral sp^3d^2 orbitals. (It should be noted, however, that molecular orbital and ligand field theories give a different explanation.) The complexes such as $Ni(CN)_4^{-2}$, which utilize the *inner d* orbitals, are known as "inner" or "penetration" complexes. Those in which the *outer d* orbitals are used are known as "outer" complexes. Whether a complex will be inner or outer undoubtedly depends upon the relationship of several factors. However, *as a rule of thumb*, it can be said that if the difference in electronegativity between the central atom and the coordinated group is less than 1.8, the complex will be *inner*; whereas if the electronegativity difference is greater than 1.9, it will be *outer*. Thus FeF_6^{-3}, with an electronegativity difference of $4.0-1.8 = 2.2$, is a paramagnetic outer complex; whereas AuF_4^{-}, with a difference of $4.0-2.3 = 1.7$, is a diamagnetic inner complex. The fluoro complex of Cu(III), which is less electronegative than Au(III) (probably about 1.85), is a paramagnetic outer complex, $CuF_6^{-3} (4.0-1.85 = 2.15)$; whereas the fluoro complex of Ag(III) (probably about 2.2) is a diamagnetic inner complex $(4.0-2.1 = 1.8)$. It should be pointed out that only in special cases can the magnetic properties be used as a criterion of bond type. The coordination numbers of the inner complexes are limited by the number of available orbitals. The coordination numbers of the outer complexes are limited by the radius ratio effect.

10–11. The Radius Ratio Effect

If identical rigid spheres are packed around another sphere of different size, so that the outer spheres are all in contact with the central one, it is found that the maximum number of spheres which can surround the central one can be exactly predicted from the ratio of the radii, i.e.,

$$\frac{\text{Radius of central sphere}}{\text{Radius of surrounding spheres}} = \text{radius ratio}$$

The radius ratio limits for given coordination numbers are shown in Table 10–1.

TABLE 10–1. MINIMUM RADIUS RATIOS FOR GIVEN COORDINATION NUMBER

Configuration	Coordination Number	Radius Ratio
Linear	2	up to 0.15
Triangular	3	0.15–0.22
Tetrahedral	4	0.22–0.41
Octahedral*	6	0.41–0.59
†	7	0.59–0.645
Square antiprism	8	0.645–0.73
Cube	8	0.73–1.00
Cubo-octahedron	12	1.00–

* Or square.   † (See Fig. 10–13) or octahedral.

Although atoms cannot be considered to be completely rigid, nevertheless radius ratios are a reasonably good guide to the geometrical limitations to coordination number.

In the case of outer complexes, where the availability of bonding orbitals is usually not a limitation, the coordination number will be limited by the radius ratio. Thus the very small beryllium atom can coordinate only four fluorine atoms in BeF_4^{-2}, even though fluorine atoms are relatively small (radius ratio = 0.23), whereas the larger aluminum atom coordinates six in AlF_6^{-3} (radius ratio = 0.42). On the other hand, aluminum can coordinate only four chlorine atoms in $AlCl_4^-$ (radius ratio = 0.315).

It can now be seen why, in the case of the complexes of Cr(III), the coordination number was only six, despite the fact that seven orbitals could be made available—the relatively small size of the chromium atom results in a radius ratio which limits the coordination number to six. It can also be seen why, when the number of available orbitals it not a limitation on the coordination number of Ni(II), it goes up to six (as in $Ni(NH_3)_6^{+2}$). In the case of the larger molybdenum and tungsten atoms, if the coordinating groups are small enough, coordination numbers up to eight may result. Thus with the small fluorine atom or the long, thin cyano groups, we have MoF_8^{-2}, $Mo(CN)_8^{-3}$, and $Mo(CN)_8^{-4}$. On the other hand, with the larger chlorine atom, six is the maximum coordination number, as in $MoCl_6^{-2}$, even though eight orbitals could be made available.

It can now be seen that there are at least two factors which limit the coordination number of a complex—the number of available orbitals (for inner complexes) and the radius ratio. The factor which imposes the lower coordination number will govern the form of the complex.

With respect to almost all of the common elements, especially those of the first transition series and Al, Zn, Cd, Sn, Sb, and so on, the coordination number is limited by the radius-ratio effect to six. Higher coordination numbers for these elements almost never occur. Lower coordination numbers may occur, however, as a result either of the number of bonding orbitals available or as a result of the charge effect.

10–12.   The Charge Effect

The foregoing discussion explains satisfactorily most of the observed coordination numbers. Remaining to be explained, however, are the very low coordination numbers of such complexes as $Cu(CN)_2{}^-$ and $Ag(NH_3)_2{}^+$.

Let us consider first the cyano complexes of Cu(I). As we proceed from $Cu(CN)_2{}^-$ to $Cu(CN)_3{}^{-2}$ to $Cu(CN)_4{}^{-3}$, more and more electrical charge is being placed on a relatively small ion. The consequent repulsion of like negative charges will tend to expel negative groups to lower the charge as much as possible. Accordingly, in order to reduce the charge on the complex ion, $Cu(CN)_4{}^{-3}$ will very easily lose CN^- to give $Cu(CN)_3{}^{-2}$, this will also tend to lose CN^- to give $Cu(CN)_2{}^-$. This will, of course, be opposed by the strength of the bonds between Cu and CN.

Let us now recall the statement made in Section 10–9 (in reference to the $Ni(CN)_4{}^{-2}$ complex) that the more d character in a bond the stronger it will be. Pauling gives the relative bond strengths cited in Table 10–2. These apply only when the principal quantum number is constant, and when the coordinating groups are the same. It can be seen that, *other things being equal,* a complex such as $Co(CN)_4{}^{-3}$ should have considerably stronger metal-to-cyanide bonds than the complex $Cu(CN)_4{}^{-3}$, because the former has dsp^2 hybridization, whereas the latter has only sp^3.

TABLE 10–2. RELATIVE BOND STRENGTHS AS A FUNCTION OF HYBRIDIZATION
(AFTER PAULING)

Bond Type	Relative Strength	Bond Type	Relative Strength
s	1.000	dsp^2	2.694
p	1.732	d^2sp^3	2.923
sp	1.932	d^4sp	2.983
sp^2	1.991	d^4sp^3	<3.000
sp^3	2.000	d^5sp^3	3.000
d	2.236		

From this it can be seen that the bonds in the $Co(CN)_4{}^{-3}$ complex should be 1.347 times stronger than those in $Cu(CN)_4{}^{-3}$, and therefore should be much more able to resist the disruptive influence of the -3 charge.

As the bonds gain more d character, the magnitude of the negative charge which can be tolerated should increase. In fact, it is found that for d^2sp^3 hybridization charges even as great as five in $Mn(CN)_6^{-5}$ are possible.

Although at first sight, the discussion above offers a reasonable explanation for why the cuprous cyanide complex does not normally attain its maximum possible coordination number of four, it still apparently does not explain the fact that the highest complex between Ag^+ and NH_3 which is known is $Ag(NH_3)_2^+$ (whereas $Ag(CN)_4^{-3}$ is known). In order to understand this, it is necessary to take a more detailed look at the structure of the complex. A silver atom is neutral when it carries one electron above the completed $4d$ level. When one electron is lost, as in Ag^+, the silver atom carries one positive charge. If another group, such as $:NH_3$ is covalently bonded to the silver ion, Ag^+, each of the bonded atoms may be considered as owning one electron of the bonding pair, as in Fig. 10-18a.

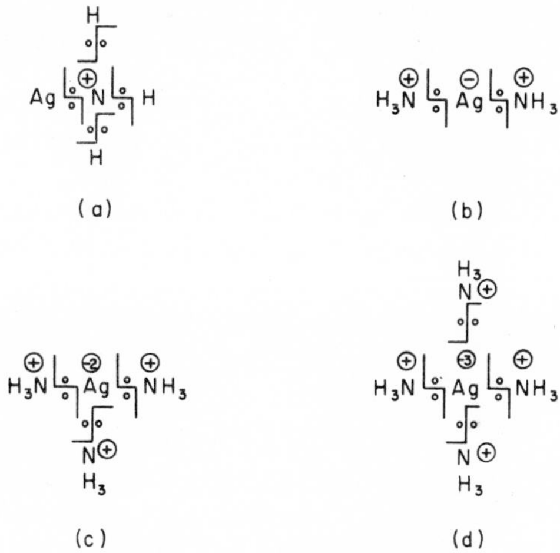

Fig. 10-18. The Charge Effect.

This gives the silver atom the one electron it needs to be neutral, and the nitrogen atom (needing five electrons to be neutral and having four) bears a positive charge. With $Ag(NH_3)_2^+$, the silver atom will have gained one more electron than it needs to be neutral, and is thus negative. (Fig. 10-18b). Since silver is fairly electronegative, a single negative charge can be tolerated. However, when we come to $Ag(NH_3)_3^+$ the excess negative change which the silver atom would have to bear militates against this combination and the coordination number of Ag(I) toward NH_3 is limited to two. As in the case of the cyano complexes, however, higher coordination numbers are realized when stronger bonds are possible. Thus $Cu(NH_3)_4^{+2}$, with dsp^2 bonding, and $Co(NH_3)_6^{+3}$, with d^2sp^3 bonding, are stable despite the -2 charge on the Cu atom and the -3 charge on the Co atom. (Examination of the argument given for $Ag(NH_3)_2{}^+$ will reveal that it can also be applied to the negative complexes such as $Cu(CN)_2{}^-$ and $AgCl_2{}^-$.)

10–13. Mixed Complexes and Isomerism

So far we have discussed in detail only complexes having one kind of coordinated group or ligand. It is quite possible to have complexes with more than one kind of ligand attached to the central atom, just as in the case of simple molecules. For example, when we talk of such complexes as

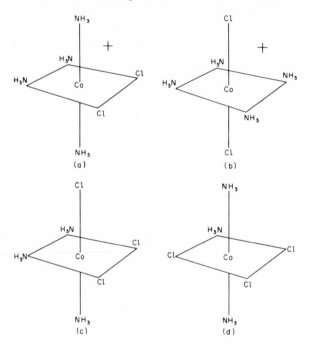

Fig. 10–19. Cis and Trans Isomers of Cobalt Complexes.

$NiNH_3{}^{+2}$, $Ni(NH_3)_2{}^{+2}$, and so on, what we really mean is $Ni(H_2O)_5NH_3{}^{+2}$, $Ni(H_2O)_4(NH_3)_2{}^{+2}$, and so forth. The "outer" nickel mixed complexes are not sufficiently stable to isolate in the form of salts (although such salts as $Ni(H_2O)_6Br_2$ and $Ni(NH_3)_6Br_2$ can be obtained). The "inner" cobalt complexes, however, are very stable, and hundreds of mixed complexes are known. For example, we have the whole series of complexes of Co(III) with NH_3 and $NO_2{}^-$: $Co(NH_3)_6{}^{+3}$, $Co(NH_3)_5NO_2{}^{+2}$, $Co(NH_3)_4(NO_2)_2{}^+$, $Co(NH_3)_3(NO_2)_3$ (a neutral molecule), $Co(NH_3)_2(NO_2)_4{}^-$, $Co(NH_3)$-$(NO_2)_5{}^{-2}$, and $Co(NO_2)_6{}^{-3}$. One of the earliest clues to the existence of mixed complexes and to the constancy of coordination number was Werner's observation that in the series $CoCl_3 \cdot 6\ NH_3$, $CoCl_3 \cdot 5\ NH_3$, $CoCl_3 \cdot 4\ NH_3$, $CoCl_3 \cdot 3\ NH_3$, the first compound had the same electrolytic characteristics as $AlCl_3$, and all of its chlorine was immediately precipitated by $AgNO_3$; the second acted like $BaCl_2$, and only two-thirds of its chlorine was immediately precipitated by $AgNO_3$; the third acted like NaCl, and only one-third of its chlorine was immediately precipitated by $AgNO_3$; whereas the last was not an electrolyte at all, and gave no precipitate with $AgNO_3$. Werner came to the conclusion that the compounds were actually

$$[Co(NH_3)_6]Cl_3, \quad [Co(NH_3)_5Cl]Cl_2, \quad [Co(NH_3)_4Cl_2]Cl, \quad \text{and} \quad [Co(NH_3)_3Cl_3]$$

with a constant coordination number of six. The first two of these have only one possible orientation of ligands around the central atom. With the last two, however, different arrangements are possible, as are shown in Fig. 10–19. The arrangements with like ligands on the same side of the central atom are known as *cis* (Latin prefix *cis*, meaning "on this side of"), and those having the ligands on opposite sides are *trans* (Latin preposition or prefix meaning "across" or "on the other side of"). The various different structural arrangements having the same empirical chemical formula are called *isomers*.

Cis and trans isomers are also possible with the four-coordinate planar complexes as shown in Fig. 10–20, but not with tetrahedral complexes.

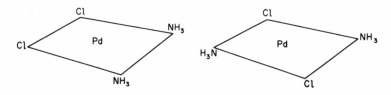

Fig. 10–20. Cis and Trans Isomers of Palladium Complexes.

Cis and trans isomers may be quite different in both physical and chemical properties.

There are also other kinds of isomerism besides the geometrical (or cis-trans) variety. Only one need be mentioned here. Besides the two compounds shown above, two others which may have the empirical formula $Pd(NH_3)_2Cl_2$ are

$$[Pd(NH_3)_3Cl^+][Pd(NH_3)Cl_3^-] \quad \text{and} \quad [Pd(NH_3)_4^{+2}][PdCl_4^{-2}]$$

10–14. Homoatomic Complex Ions

When elemental sulfur is added to a solution of Na_2S, it dissolves, and the solution is found to contain a complicated mixture of anions ranging from S_2^{-2} and S_3^{-2} up to at least S_6^{-2}. These are the polysulfide ions, S_x^{-2}, or specifically disulfide, trisulfide, and so on. Structurally they are merely chains of sulfur atoms carrying two extra electrons

$$\overset{-}{\underset{\cdot\cdot}{:}S:\overset{\cdot\cdot}{\underset{\cdot\cdot}{S}}:\overset{-}{}\,, \quad \overset{-}{\underset{\cdot\cdot}{:}S:}\overset{\cdot\cdot}{\underset{\cdot\cdot}{S}}:\overset{\cdot\cdot}{\underset{\cdot\cdot}{S}}:\overset{-}{}\,, \quad \overset{-}{\underset{\cdot\cdot}{:}S:}\overset{\cdot\cdot}{\underset{\cdot\cdot}{S}}:\overset{\cdot\cdot}{\underset{\cdot\cdot}{S}}:\overset{\cdot\cdot}{\underset{\cdot\cdot}{S}}:\overset{-}{}$$

and so on.

The polysulfide ions are mild oxidizing agents, since they are capable of being reduced to S^{-2}, e.g.

$$S_2^{-2} + 2\,e^- \rightleftharpoons 2\,S^{-2}$$

Consequently, if ammonium polysulfide is used to dissolve the arsenic subgroups out of the acid-insoluble sulfide precipitate, it is not necessary to carry out the oxidation of tin(II) with H_2O_2 before the group precipitation, since the polysulfide ions will oxidize SnS, as is shown, using S_2^{-2} for simplicity

$$SnS\ (s) + S_2^{-2} \rightleftharpoons SnS_3^{-2}$$

Polyselenide, Se_x^{-2}, and polytelluride, Te_x^{-2}, ions are also known (as well as mixed ions of the same type, SSe^{-2}, and so on). The peroxide ion, O_2^{-2}, the superoxide ion, O_2^-, and the ozonide ion, O_3^-, of course, also belong to this group. In the same manner, polyhalide ions exist. For example, free iodine is very soluble in solutions of alkali iodides, and from them salts such as KI_3, RbI_5, CsI_7, and so on, can be isolated. Again, mixed complexes, such as ICl_2^-, $IBrCl^-$, and so on, are possible. The ions Br_3^- and Cl_3^- are also known, but are much less stable than I_3^-. Equilibrium constants for some of these ions are given in Table 10–3.

TABLE 10–3. INSTABILITY CONSTANTS FOR INTERHALOGEN AND HOMOATOMIC IONS

$Cl_3^- \rightleftharpoons Cl_2\,(aq) + Cl^-$	$10^{+0.72}$	$I_3^- \rightleftharpoons I_2\,(aq) + I^-$	$10^{-2.89}$
$Br_2Cl^- \rightleftharpoons Br_2\,(aq) + Cl^-$	$10^{-0.08}$	$I_6^{-2} \rightleftharpoons 2\,I_2\,(aq) + 2\,I^-$	$10^{-5.79}$
$ICl_2^- \rightleftharpoons ICl\,(aq) + Cl^-$	$10^{-2.22}$	$I_{14}^{-2} \rightleftharpoons 6\,I_2\,(aq) + 2\,I^-$	$10^{-18.4}$
$IBrCl^- \rightleftharpoons IBr\,(aq) + Cl^-$	$10^{-1.64}$	$S_2^{-2} \rightleftharpoons S\,(s) + S^{-2}$	$10^{-0.23}$
$I_2Cl^- \rightleftharpoons I_2\,(aq) + Cl^-$	$10^{-0.54}$	$S_3^{-2} \rightleftharpoons 2\,S\,(s) + S^{-2}$	$10^{-0.75}$
$Br_3^- \rightleftharpoons Br_2\,(aq) + Br^-$	$10^{-1.20}$	$S_4^{-2} \rightleftharpoons 3\,S\,(s) + S^{-2}$	$10^{-1.87}$
$Br_5^- \rightleftharpoons 2\,Br_2\,(aq) + Br^-$	$10^{-1.30}$	$S_2O_3^{-2} \rightleftharpoons S\,(s) + SO_3^{-2}$	$10^{-5.57}$
$IBr_2^- \rightleftharpoons IBr\,(aq) + Br^-$	$10^{-2.57}$	$Te_2^{-2} \rightleftharpoons Te\,(s) + Te^{-2}$	$10^{-2.60}$
$I_2Br^- \rightleftharpoons I_2\,(aq) + Br^-$	$10^{-1.10}$		

10–15. Questions and Problems

1. Why are alpha particles repelled by atomic nuclei but not by "planetary" electrons?

2. The radius of a helium atom is approximately 1 Ångstrom unit (10^{-8} cm). What volume would 1 cc of liquid helium occupy if all the electrons were taken away, and the remaining matter were compressed until all the nuclei were in contact with one another?

3. What is the origin of spectral "lines"?

4. What is the maximum number of electrons which can occupy the fourth quantum level?

5. What is the maximum number of electrons which can be put into the fifth quantum level without any being in the sixth?

6. What is the maximum number of electrons which can be put into the fourth quantum level before the third is filled to completion?

7. Give the four quantum numbers of the last electron in the ground state of C, Mg, Ti, Co, La.

8. Define "transition series of the first type" and "transition series of the second type." What other names are applied to the two known transition series of the second type?

9. Explain the periodicity of chemical and physical properties of the elements.

10. Are atomic number and atomic weight periodic properties? Explain.

11. How does the chemist's carbon atom differ from the spectroscopist's?

12. How does the shape of the CH_2F_2 molecule differ from that of CF_4? Explain.

13. How does the shape of the OF_2 molecule differ from that of H_2O? Explain.

14. Explain the difference between *sigma* and *pi* bonds. Describe the role these play in determining the shape of the molecule.

15. What is the difference between "inner" and "outer" complexes of the transition metals? What property can frequently be used to decide whether a complex is inner or outer?

16. Predict whether the following will be inner or outer complexes: (a) $Fe(H_2O)_6^{+2}$, (b) PtS_3^{-2}, (c) $Mn(CN)_6^{-4}$, (d) CrF_6^{-3}, (e) PdF_6^{-2}, (f) $Co(NH_3)_6^{+2}$ (note that here

$$\text{H}$$
$$\overset{..}{}$$

you are dealing with a substituted ammonium ion, $Co : \overset{..}{\underset{..}{N^+}} : H$, and the electro-

$$\text{H}$$

negativity involved is that of N^+, which is 3.3, rather than that of N^0, which is 3.0.), (g) $Pt(NH_3)_4^{+2}$, (h) $CuCl_4^{-2}$.

17. Explain why the cyano and fluoro complexes of Fe(III) are $Fe(CN)_6^{-3}$ and FeF_6^{-3}, whereas the chloro complex is $FeCl_4^{-}$.

18. Discuss whether there is any fundamental difference in bonding between $Fe(CO)_4^{-2}$, $Ni(CO)_4$, and $Zn(CN)_4^{-2}$. What is the formal oxidation state of the central atom in each case?

19. Discuss the difference and similarities between "valence bonds," as exemplified by those in $HgCl_2$, and "coordinate bonds," as exemplified by those in $HgCl_4^{-2}$ or $Hg(NH_3)_4^{+2}$.

20. (a) The following hypothetical reactions may be thought of as producing co-ordinate bonds, on the one hand (1 and 3), and covalent bonds on the other (2). Discuss.

   (1) $C^{+4} + 4 H^- \rightarrow CH_4$

   (2) $C + 4 H \rightarrow CH_4$

   (3) $C^{-4} + 4H^+ \rightarrow CH_4$

   (b) Discuss the difference between the C—C bond in CH_3CH_3 and the B—N bond in BH_3NH_3.

21. Offer an explanation for the fact that iron carbonyl is pentacoordinate, $Fe(CO)_5$, whereas the cyanonickel(II) ion with the same number of nonbonding electrons, is only tetracoordinate, $Ni(CN)_4^{-2}$.

22. The solubility of I_2 in water is 1.12×10^{-3} moles per liter. What is the equilibrium constant for the reaction $I_3^- \rightleftharpoons I_2 (s) + I^-$?

23. Calculate the molar solubility of sulfur in 0.01 M Na_2S.

24. Calculate the molar solubility of iodine in 0.01 M KI.

25. The solubility of bromine in water at 25° is 0.224 molar. Calculate the molar solubility of bromine in 0.1 M KBr and in 1 M KBr.

26. What is the geometrical structure of the complex ion, and electronic structure of the manganese atom, in the Mn(IV)–OH⁻ complex?

27. What would be the geometrical structure of the complex ion and the electronic structure of the cobalt atom in the Co(V)–F⁻ complex?

28. In the iron-complex heme, a complex with an iron(III) atom surrounded only by four nitrogen atoms which are constrained to a plane by the structure of the organic part of the molecule, what is the electronic structure of the iron atom?

29. The equilibrium constant for the reaction

$$Cl_2 \text{ (g)} \rightleftharpoons Cl_2 \text{ (aq)}$$

is 5.9×10^{-2}, where the pressure of Cl_2 (g) is measured in atmospheres. Calculate the solubility of chlorine in 1 M KCl when the pressure of Cl_2 (g) over the solution is 0.75 atm.

10–16.   References

Herzberg, Gerhard, *Atomic Spectra and Atomic Structure*, 2d rev. ed. New York: Dover Publications, 1944.

Pauling, Linus, *The Nature of the Chemical Bond*, 2d ed. Ithaca, New York: Cornell University Press, 1945.

Gould, E. S., *Inorganic Reactions and Structure*. New York: Henry Holt and Company, 1955.

Gilreath, E. S., *Fundamental Concepts of Inorganic Chemistry*. New York: McGraw Hill Book Company, Inc., 1958.

Brown, F. I., *A Simple Guide to Modern Valency Theory*. New York: Longmans, Green and Company, 1953.

Cartmell, E., and Fowles, G. W. A., *Valency and Molecular Structure*. London: Butterworths Scientific Publications, 1956.

Fano, U., and Fano, L., *Basic Physics of Atoms and Molecules*. New York: John Wiley and Sons, Inc., 1959.

Bailar, John C., ed., *The Chemistry of the Coordination Compounds*. New York: Reinhold Publishing Corporation, 1956.

Martell, A. E., and Calvin, M., *Chemistry of Metal Chelate Compounds*. Englewood Cliffs, N.J.: Prentice-Hall, Inc., 1952.

Pearson, R. G., "Crystal Field Explains Inorganic Behavior," *Chemical and Engineering News*, June 19, 1959, p. 72.

Chapter 11

The Reducible Elements. Anions

11–1. Elements Reducible to Negative Oxidation States

As discussed in Section 1–9, electronegativity is the ability of an element in a molecule to attract bonding electrons. It should be expected, then, that the more electronegative an element is the more easily it can be reduced, since, after all, being reduced is merely a matter of attracting electrons. Thus we find that the most electronegative of the elements (outside of the noble gases)—fluorine—has the greatest tendency of all to exist in the lowest possible oxidation state (-1) and rarely exists in any other. Of all the elements, it is the only one which cannot be described as even having a positive oxidation state, and even the zero oxidation state (F_2) avidly grabs electrons to give fluorides, such as HF or F^-.

The elements near fluorine in the periodic table are also highly electronegative and have strong tendencies to go to negative states. Positive states for these elements are possible now, but still are less stable than the negative ones, for the elements closest to fluorine. As we proceed farther away from fluorine in the periodic table, the electronegativity decreases in a more or less regular fashion, and the stability of the negative states decreases, while the stability of the positive states increases, to match. The further we go from fluorine, the more difficult it becomes, therefore, to reduce an element to a negative oxidation state, so that in practice there is only a small group of

TABLE 11–1. ELEMENTS REDUCIBLE TO NEGATIVE OXIDATION
STATES IN AQUEOUS SOLUTION

——	C	N	O	F
——	——	P	S	Cl
——	——	As	Se	Br
——	——	Sb	Te	I
——	——	——	Po	At

elements, as shown in Table 11–1, that can be reduced in aqueous solution to hydride or negative ions, such as Cl^-, H_2S, S^{-2}, AsH_3, CH_4, and so on. The other elements on the fringes of this group also form (unstable) hydrogen compounds, but they are not easily obtained by reduction of higher states in aqueous solution. Examples of these are B_2H_6, SiH_4, GeH_4, SnH_4, PbH_4, and BiH_3.

Analytical use of these negative oxidation states has already been met. Thus in either acidic or alkaline solution, arsenic compounds (except AsO_4^{-3} in alkaline solution) are easily reduced by active reducing agents, such as zinc or aluminum metal, to gaseous arsine, AsH_3. As has already been pointed out in Section 5–13, if antimony is present it will likewise be reduced in acidic solution to stibine, SbH_3. Reflecting the lesser ease of reduction of antimony, however, is the fact that, in alkaline solution in which AsH_3 *is* produced, SbH_3 fails to be produced. This difference in ease of reduction can be used to separate arsenic and antimony. Bismuthine, BiH_3, cannot be produced by this means in either acidic or alkaline solution, thus carrying the trend to its logical conclusion.

11–2. Elements Reducible to the Free State

In like manner, the nonmetals and also the more electronegative metals are easily reduced from positive oxidation states to the zero state (free element), and again the trend in ease of reduction parallels fairly closely the trend in electronegativity. Accordingly, among the metals, the compounds of gold are the most easily reduced to the metal, and gold is the most electronegative of the metals. Platinum compounds are next most easily reduced to the metal, and platinum stands next to gold in electronegativity. As one moves away from gold in any direction in the periodic table, as we now know it, electronegativity and ease of reduction both decrease until the rise in electronegativity among the nonmetals on the right-hand side of the periodic table is encountered. At this point, the ease of reduction to the free element also increases, and the closer we come to fluorine *in general*, the greater the ease of reduction of the positive oxidation states to the free element. Thus, as mentioned earlier, we find that arsenite, AsO_3^{-3}, requires a fairly good reducing agent to be reduced to elemental arsenic; selenite, SeO_3^{-2}, is easily reduced to free selenium by moderately good reducing agents; and bromate is reduced to free bromine by very weak reducing agents indeed (e.g., by bromide ion).

TABLE 11–2. ELEMENTS EASILY REDUCED TO THE FREE STATE
FROM AQUEOUS SOLUTION

									C	N	O	F
											S	Cl
——	Cr	Mn	Fe	Co	Ni	Cu	Zn	Ga	Ge	As	Se	Br
——	Mo	Tc	Ru	Rh	Pd	Ag	Cd	In	Sn	Sb	Te	I
——	W	Re	Os	Ir	Pt	Au	Hg	Tl	Pb	Bi	Po	At

The elements that are easily reduced from positive states to the free element are shown in Table 11–2. Those which, from an equilibrium point of view, are more easily reduced than H^+ is reduced to H_2, are shown in bold-face type. Other elements which in practice can easily be reduced to the free element from aqueous solution are shown in ordinary type.

Practical use may be made of the difference in reducibility in separating one element from another. Thus platinum can be separated from Pd, Rh, Ru, Ir, and Os by reduction with hydrazine, N_2H_4, which reduces only the Pt. (This would not be a separation from gold which is also reduced.) You have already made use of the relative reducibilities of copper and cadmium in the separation of these two by reduction of Cu by sodium dithionite, which leaves Cd^{+2} in solution. Two other elements which are regularly reduced to the zero oxidation state in the course of the qualitative analytical procedure are mercury and bismuth. The latter is reduced in the confirmatory test for bismuth by alkaline stannite. The former is reduced, both in the confirmatory test for mercury itself and also in the confirmatory test for tin by acidic stannous ion. In addition, the reduction of antimony to the metal takes place as an incidental reaction during the confirmatory procedure for tin. The reduction of silver to the metal is familiar to you from general chemistry. Silver is also reduced to the metal by arsine in the test for arsenic.

$$6 \, Ag^+ + AsH_3 \, (g) + 3 \, H_2O \rightarrow 6 \, Ag \, (s) + H_3AsO_3 + 6 \, H^+$$

Among the nonmetals, the sulfites are easily reduced to free sulfur, for example by H_2S

$$SO_3^{-2} + 2 \, H^+ + 2 \, H_2S \rightarrow 3 \, S \, (s) + 3 \, H_2O$$

Selenites are even more easily reduced, for example by SO_2

$$SeO_3^{-2} + 2 \, SO_2 + H_2O \rightarrow Se \, (s) + 2 \, SO_4^{-2} + 2 \, H^+$$

11–3. Elements Reducible from One Positive Oxidation State to Another

In addition, there are many elements which are easily reduced from one positive oxidation state to another. This occurs with most of the elements which have stable high-oxidation states and which are good oxidizing agents in 1 molar acid. They are shown in Table 11–3 in the form in which they exist in acidic solution. Oxidation states which are good oxidizing agents when put into 1 molar acid, and which are frequently found as anions in solid salts, are shown in Table 11–4 in the anionic form. From this it can be seen that many anions which are frequently encountered are good oxidizing agents. Table 11–5 lists the more common anions in decreasing order of the oxidizing power of the species, which results when they are dissolved in 1 molar acid.

The oxidizing power of these high oxidation states is very characteristic of them. It exhibits well defined trends, especially in the horizontal rows of

TABLE 11–3. OXIDIZING STATES IN THE FORM IN WHICH THEY ARE STABLE IN 1 MOLAR SOLUTIONS OF NON-COMPLEXING ACIDS

—	—	—	—	—	—	—	—	—	—	NO_3^-, HNO_2	O_3, H_2O_2	—
—	—	—	—	—	—	—	—	—	—	—	H_2SO_3	ClO_4^-, ClO_3^-
VO_2^+	$Cr_2O_7^{-2}$	MnO_4^-	—	—	—	—	—	—	—	H_3AsO_4	$HSeO_4^-$, H_2SeO_3	BrO_3^-
—	—	TcO_4^-	RuO_4	RhO_2	PdO_2, Pd^{+2}	—	—	—	—	Sb_2O_5	H_6TeO_6, TeO_2H^+	H_5IO_6, HIO_3
—	—	ReO_4^-	OsO_4	IrO_2	PtO_2, Pt^{+2}	Au^{+3}	Hg^{+2}, Hg_2^{+2}	Tl^{+3}	PbO_2	Bi_2O_5	H_6PoO_6, PoO_2	$H_5AtO_6(?)$, $HAtO_3$

TABLE 11–4. OXIDIZING ANIONS COMMONLY FOUND IN SALTS

—	—	—	—	—	—	—	—	—	—	NO_3^-, NO_2^-	O_2^-, O_2^{-2}	—
—	—	—	—	—	—	—	—	—	—	—	$S_2O_8^{-2}$, SO_3^{-2}	ClO_4^-, ClO_3^-, ClO_2^-, ClO^-
VO_4^{-3} (or VO_3^-)	CrO_4^{-2} (or $Cr_2O_7^{-2}$)	MnO_4^-, MnO_4^{-2}	FeO_4^{-2}	—	—	—	—	—	—	AsO_4^{-3}	SeO_4^{-2}, SeO_3^{-2}	BrO_3^-
—	—	TcO_4^-	RuO_4^-, RuO_4^{-2}	$RhCl_6^{-3}$	$PdCl_6^{-2}$, $PdCl_4^{-2}$	—	—	—	—	$Sb(OH)_6^-$	$H_4TeO_6^{-2}$, TeO_3^{-2}	IO_4^-, IO_3^-
—	—	ReO_4^-	OsO_4^{-2}	$IrCl_6^{-2}$, $IrCl_6^{-3}$	$PtCl_6^{-2}$, $PtCl_4^{-2}$	$AuCl_4^-$	—	—	$Pb(OH)_6^{-2}$	BiO_3^-	—	—

TABLE 11–5. ORDER OF DECREASING OXIDIZING POWER IN 1 MOLAR ACID

$F_2 (\to HF)$	$HNO_2 (\to NO)$
$O_3 (\to O_2 + H_2O)$	$NO_3^- (\to NO)$
$S_2O_8^{-2} (\to SO_4^{-2})$	$NO_3^- (\to HNO_2)$
$Ag^{+2} (\to Ag^+)$	$OsO_4 (\to Os)$
$Co^{+3} (\to Co^{+2})$	$Hg^{+2} (\to Hg_2^{+2})$
$H_2O_2 (\to H_2O)$	$Hg^{+2} (\to Hg)$
$H_5IO_6 (\to IO_3^-)$	$NO_3^- (\to N_2O_4)$
$PbO_2 (\to PbSO_4)$	$Ag^+ (\to Ag)$
$Ce^{+4} (\to Ce^{+3})$	$Fe^{+3} (\to Fe^{+2})$
$Bi_2O_5 (\to BiO^+)$	$H_2SeO_3 (\to Se)$
$HClO_2 (\to Cl^-)$	$PtCl_4^{-2} (\to Pt)$
$MnO_4^- (\to Mn^{+2})$	$IrCl_6^{-3} (\to Ir)$
$Mn^{+3} (\to Mn^{+2})$	$PtCl_6^{-2} (\to PtCl_4^{-2})$
$HClO (\to Cl^-)$	$O_2 (\to H_2O_2)$
$PbO_2 (\to Pb^{+2})$	$Sb_2O_5 (\to SbO^+)$
$ClO_3^- (\to Cl^-)$	$PdCl_4^{-2} (\to Pd)$
$BrO_3^- (\to Br^-)$	$TeO_2H^+ (\to Te)$
$Au^{+3} (\to Au)$	$H_3AsO_4 (\to HAsO_2)$
$Cr_2O_7^{-2} (\to Cr^{+3})$	$I_2 (\to I^-)$
$Cl_2 (\to Cl^-)$	$H_2SO_3 (\to S)$
$O_2 (\to H_2O)$	$Fe(CN)_6^{-3} (\to Fe(CN)_6^{-4})$
$PdCl_6^{-2} (\to PdCl_4^{-2})$	$Cu^{+2} (\to Cu)$
$Tl^{+3} (\to Tl^+)$	$BiO^+ (\to Bi)$
$MnO_2 (\to Mn^{+2})$	$VO^{+2} (\to V^{+3})$
$SeO_4^{-2} (\to H_2SeO_3)$	$HAsO_2 (\to As)$
$Br_2 (\to Br^-)$	$SbO^+ (\to Sb)$
$IO_3^- (\to I^-)$	$SO_4^{-2} (\to H_2SO_3)$
$IrCl_6^{-2} (\to IrCl_6^{-3})$	$Sn^{+4} (\to Sn^{+2})$
$H_6TeO_6 (\to TeO_2)$	$ReO_4^- (\to Re)$
$AuCl_4^- (\to Au)$	$S (\to H_2S)$
$VO_2^+ (\to VO^{+2})$	

the periodic table. For example, we find oxidizing power in 1 molar acid increasing in the following series:

$$Ti(IV) < V(V) < Cr(VI) < Mn(VII)$$

$$Cr(VI) < Mn(VI) < Fe(VI)$$

$$Ge(IV) < As(V) < Se(VI) < Br(VII)$$

$$Hg(II) < Tl(III) < Pb(IV) < Bi(V) < Po(VI) < At(VII)$$

$$Hf(IV) < Ta(V) < W(VI) < Re(VII) < Os(VIII)$$

Referring to Table 11–5, it can be seen that the only common oxidizing agents capable of oxidizing Mn^{+2} to MnO_4^- in $1 M$ H^+ are $S_2O_8^{-2}$, H_5IO_6, PbO_2 (in H_2SO_4), Bi_2O_5 (or $NaBiO_3$), and $HClO_2$. You have used $NaBiO_3$ for this purpose in the confirmatory test for manganese. Periodic acid and ammonium or potassium peroxydisulfate (with Ag^+ catalyst) are also frequently used for this purpose.

On the other hand, every oxidizing agent listed in Table 11–5 is capable of oxidizing H_2S to free sulfur, provided precipitation of an insoluble sulfide does not take precedence (e.g., $2 Ag^+ + H_2S (g) \rightarrow Ag_2S (s) + 2 H^+$). Thus it is observed that, after the precipitation of the acid-insoluble sulfide group, many of the elements left in solution are in a reduced state (e.g., Ce^{+3}, Mn^{+2}, Cr^{+3}, VO^{+2}, Fe^{+2}, $Fe(CN)_6^{-4}$, and so on). Likewise, when the supernate from the precipitation of the insoluble hydroxide group, which contains $Co(NH_3)_6^{+3}$, is treated with H_2S to precipitate the alkali-insoluble sulfides, reduction of Co(III) takes place.

$$2 Co(NH_3)_6^{+3} + 3 H_2S (g) + 6 H^+ \rightarrow 2 CoS (s) + S (s) + 12 NH_4^+$$

11–4. The Oxidizing and Reducing Power of Anions

In the elimination tests for anions, the oxidation of Mn^{+2} to $MnCl_6^{-3}$ in concentrated hydrochloric acid is used to detect the presence of the more powerful anionic oxidants (the cationic oxidants having previously been precipitated as carbonates or hydroxides). Due to the fact that $MnCl_6^{-3}$ is a much poorer oxidizing agent than Mn^{+3} (the Mn(III) has been stabilized by complex formation), more oxidants than those above Mn^{+3} ($\rightarrow Mn^{+2}$) in Table 11–5 will oxidize Mn^{+2} under these conditions. Oxidants at least down as far as NO_3^- ($\rightarrow NO$) and perhaps somewhat farther are capable of oxidizing Mn^{+2} under these conditions. Solutions of $MnCl_2$ in concentrated HCl turn brown or black ($MnCl_6^{-3}$) when treated with solutions containing the anions $S_2O_8^{-2}$, $H_4IO_6^-$, MnO_4^-, ClO_3^-, BrO_3^-, CrO_4^{-2} (or $Cr_2O_7^{-2}$), SeO_4^{-2}, IO_3^-, VO_4^{-3} (or VO_3^-), NO_2^-, and NO_3^-, to mention the more common ones.

At the opposite end of the scale, of course, are those anions which are derived from low oxidation states and are easily oxidized. Table 11–6 shows the more common of these reducing agents (along with reducing agents of other types) arranged in order of decreasing reducing power. The order of reducing agents in Table 11–6 may be continued by reading Table 11–5 up

TABLE 11–6. ORDER OF DECREASING REDUCING POWER IN 1 MOLAR ACID

Zn ($\rightarrow Zn^{+2}$)	Tl ($\rightarrow Tl^+$)	Pb ($\rightarrow Pb^{+2}$)
H_2Te ($\rightarrow Te$)	P ($\rightarrow HPH_2O_2$)	PH_3 ($\rightarrow P$)
HPH_2O_2 ($\rightarrow H_2PHO_3$)	Co ($\rightarrow Co^{+2}$)	H_2 ($\rightarrow H^+$)
$H_2C_2O_4$ ($\rightarrow CO_2$)	Ni ($\rightarrow Ni^{+2}$)	Ti^{+3} ($\rightarrow TiO^{+2}$)
Cr^{+2} ($\rightarrow Cr^{+3}$)	H_2PHO_3 ($\rightarrow H_3PO_4$)	H_2S ($\rightarrow S$)
Cd ($\rightarrow Cd^{+2}$)	Sn ($\rightarrow Sn^{+2}$)	

from the bottom and interchanging products and reactants. For example Sn^{+4} ($\rightarrow Sn^{+2}$) becomes Sn^{+2} ($\rightarrow Sn^{+4}$), SO_4^{-2} ($\rightarrow H_2SO_3$) becomes H_2SO_3 ($\rightarrow SO_4^{-2}$), and so forth. The better reducing agents can be detected through reduction of Fe^{+3} which, in the presence of $Fe(CN)_6^{-3}$, gives Prussian blue. The formation of Prussian blue makes Fe^{+3} a somewhat better oxidizing agent than is indicated by its position in Table 11–5 (the precipitation of the very stable Prussian blue provides driving force for the reaction, i.e., shifts the equilibrium, e.g., with I^-,

$$2 Fe^{+3} + 2 Fe(CN)_6^{-3} + 2 I^- + 2 K^+ \rightarrow 2 KFe[Fe(CN)_6] (s) + I_2)$$

but, as a rule of thumb, those anions which are better reducing agents than Fe^{+2} will give this test. Thus the turning blue of a $FeCl_3$–$K_3Fe(CN)_6$ mixture by a solution from which all reducing cations have been removed, indicates one or more of S^{-2}, SO_3^{-2}, I^-, AsO_2^-, and also NO_2^-. Some others whose positions in the Tables indicate that they should react, such as $C_2O_4^{-2}$, do not, at least at room temperature, because they react so sluggishly. Oxalate reacts at an appreciable rate, even with the much more powerful oxidant MnO_4^-, only in hot solution. This characteristic is frequently used in the detection of oxalate.

11–5. The Coexistence of Oxidants and Reductants

The mere fact that the order of oxidizing power predicts that one ion should oxidize another does not prove that the reaction will take place under ordinary conditions, for certain substances are very sluggish in their reactions. We have already seen that the reaction

$$5 H_2C_2O_4 + 2 MnO_4^- + 6 H^+ \rightarrow 10 CO_2 (g) + 2 Mn^{+2} + 8 H_2O$$

proceeds very slowly at room temperature, because of the sluggishness of oxalic acid as a reducing agent. (This is presumably because of the drastic rearrangement of bonds which must be made in going from

$$
\begin{array}{ccc}
HO & & OH \\
\diagdown & & \diagup \\
 & C\!-\!C & \\
\diagup & & \diagdown \\
O & & O
\end{array}
$$

to $O=C=O$. Likewise, Fe^{+3} and $PH_2O_2^-$ can exist in the same solution, as can also Fe^{+2} and ClO_4^-, because of the sluggishness of $PH_2O_2^-$ as a reducing agent and of ClO_4^- as an oxidizing agent. (That is, their activation energies—Section 2–2—are high.) As a matter of fact solid $Fe(PH_2O_2)_3$ and $Fe(ClO_4)_2 \cdot 6 H_2O$ are easily obtained. Both of these substances decompose on heating, however, as might be expected. Substances which contain within themselves parts which are potentially capable of oxidizing and reducing each other are frequently explosives. The ammonium ion, which can be oxidized to free nitrogen, or N_2O, when combined with oxidizing anions frequently gives potential explosives. You have already utilized the oxidation of NH_4^+ by NO_3^- to get rid of NH_4^+ and you know that solid NH_4NO_3 decomposes when heated according to the equation

$$NH_4NO_3 (s) \xrightarrow{\;\Delta\;} N_2O (g) + 2H_2O (g)$$

Under certain conditions, this reaction can be explosive, and NH_4NO_3 is an important ingredient in certain high explosives such as amatol. Ammonium perchlorate is also in this category. When finely divided $(NH_4)_2Cr_2O_7$ is heated, a decomposition reaction takes place which generates enough heat to make the reaction self-sustaining. The glowing reaction spreads through the entire mass while a green ash is violently thrown out by the vigorous evolution of nitrogen.

$$(NH_4)_2Cr_2O_7 \text{ (s)} \longrightarrow N_2 \text{ (g)} + 4 \text{ } H_2O \text{ (g)} + Cr_2O_3 \text{ (s)}$$

This reaction is frequently used to make artificial volcanoes.

On the other hand, in the case of the majority of the oxidants and reductants listed in Tables 11–5 and 11–6, reaction is fairly rapid and a knowledge of their relative oxidizing and reducing power can be used to predict what combinations are not possible in solution. Thus S^{-2}, SO_3^{-2}, Fe^{+2}, I^-, and so on, cannot be present in solutions containing ClO_3^-, Ce^{+4}, $Cr_2O_7^{-2}$, MnO_4^-, NO_2^-, NO_3^-, and the like—and vice-versa—for more or less rapid reaction will take place in each case. It should be remembered, however, that if formation of a very insoluble precipitate or a very stable complex ion is possible, the redox reaction may be prevented (as mentioned in Section 11–3). Accordingly, although S^{-2} is apparently capable of reducing Ag^+, the extremely insoluble Ag_2S is formed, instead. Likewise, AsO_4^{-3} should be capable of oxidizing Fe^{+2}, but instead the insoluble $Fe_3(AsO_4)_2 \cdot 6 \text{ } H_2O$ is formed. In the same manner, thiosulfate ion, $S_2O_3^{-2}$, should be capable of reducing Ag^+ and I^- should be capable of reducing Hg^{+2}, but the formation of the very stable complex ions $Ag(S_2O_3)_2^{-3}$ and HgI_4^{-2} prevents this.

Nevertheless, even with all the exceptions due to high activation energies and formation of precipitates and complex ions, a knowledge of oxidizing and reducing powers is a valuable guide to what reactions will or will not take place.

11-6. The Balancing of Oxidation-Reduction Equations

An oxidation-reduction reaction may be considered to consist of two parts—the oxidation "half-reaction" and the reduction "half-reaction"—neither of which can occur by itself. Since the oxidation half-reaction uses up electrons and the reduction half-reaction gives up electrons, the stoichiometry of the over-all reaction is determined by the relative number of electrons involved in each half-reaction, since the total number of electrons gained and lost must be the same.

Let us consider the reaction between Sn^{+2} and Fe^{+3}. The half-reactions are

(1) $$Sn^{+2} \rightarrow Sn^{+4} + 2 \text{ } e^-$$

and (2) $$Fe^{+3} + e^- \rightarrow Fe^{+2}$$

In order for the electrons gained to equal those lost, we must write instead of equation (2)

(3) $2\,Fe^{+3} + 2\,e^{-} \rightarrow 2\,Fe^{+2}$

Now when we add (1) and (3),

$$Sn^{+2} \rightarrow Sn^{+4} + 2\,e^{-}$$

$$2\,Fe^{+3} + 2\,e^{-} \rightarrow 2\,Fe^{+2}$$

(4) $Sn^{+2} + 2\,Fe^{+3} \rightarrow Sn^{+4} + 2\,Fe^{+2}$

we obtain (4), the balanced over-all equation.

In the case of the reaction of Pb^{+4} with bismuth metal we have

(5) $Bi \rightarrow Bi^{+3} + 3\,e^{-}$

and (6) $Pb^{+4} + 2\,e^{-} \rightarrow Pb^{+2}$

It is now necessary to multiply (5) by $\dfrac{2 \times 3}{3} = 2$ and (6) by $\dfrac{3 \times 2}{2} = 3$ in order that the number of electrons gained and lost be equal.

(7) $2\,Bi \rightarrow 2\,Bi^{+3} + 6\,e^{-}$

(8) $3\,Pb^{+4} + 6\,e^{-} \rightarrow 3\,Pb^{+2}$

(9) $2\,Bi + 3\,Pb^{+4} \rightarrow 2\,Bi^{+3} + 3\,Pb^{+2}$

Most reactions are not so simple, but also involve water and H^{+} or OH^{-}. For example, in the reaction between permanganate and chromium(II) in acidic solution

(10) $Cr^{+2} \rightarrow Cr^{+3} + e^{-}$

but for conservation of atoms and charge in the reaction

(11) $MnO_4^{-} + 8\,H^{+} + 5\,e^{-} \rightarrow Mn^{+2} + 4\,H_2O$

H_2O and H^{+} must be included. Now multiplying (10) by 5

(12) $5\,Cr^{+2} \rightarrow 5\,Cr^{+3} + 5\,e^{-}$

(11) $MnO_4^{-} + 8\,H^{+} + 5\,e^{-} \rightarrow Mn^{+2} + 4\,H_2O$

(13) $5\,Cr^{+2} + MnO_4^{-} + 8\,H^{+} \rightarrow 5\,Cr^{+3} + Mn^{+2} + 4\,H_2O$

The half-reaction method is very useful because of the fact that a knowledge of the standard oxidation potentials of the half-reactions will give information on whether the over-all reaction can go as written. (This matter will be taken up quantitatively in Chapter 13.)

An alternative method for balancing redox equations uses the half-reactions only by implication. Let us consider the reaction between Ce^{+4}

and AsO^+ in acidic solution. Without attempting to balance the equation, the reaction will be

$$(14) \qquad Ce^{+4} + AsO^+ \rightarrow Ce^{+3} + H_3AsO_4$$

The oxidation number of the cerium changes by one (i.e., one electron is gained) and that of the arsenic changes by two (i.e., two electrons are lost), so we may write

$$(15) \qquad Ce^{+4} \;+\; AsO^+ \rightarrow Ce^{+3} + H_3AsO_4$$
$$\qquad\qquad \underset{\longrightarrow}{|+1\,e^-} \quad \underset{\longrightarrow}{|-2\,e^-}$$

Consequently, in order to make the number of electrons gained and lost equal, it is necessary to take $2\,Ce^{+4}$ (and, of course, $2\,Ce^{+3}$)

$$(16) \qquad 2\,Ce^{+4} + AsO^+ \rightarrow 2\,Ce^{+3} + H_3AsO_4$$

Now it can be seen that, whereas there are four oxygen atoms on the right, there is only one on the left. Since the reaction is run in aqueous solution, the extra oxygens will be derived from water, and the reaction may be written

$$(17) \qquad 2\,Ce^{+4} + AsO^+ + 3\,H_2O \rightarrow 2\,Ce^{+3} + H_3AsO_4 + 3\,H^+$$

the hydrogens in excess of those required to form H_3AsO_4 appearing as H^+. Since it is not possible to create or destroy charge, a check on the correctness of equation (17) is to see that the algebraic sum of the charges on the left equals that on the right. Since $2(+4)+(+1) = 2(+3)+(+3)$, the equation must be correctly balanced.

Let us consider the reaction in acidic solution between MnO_4^- and Sn^{+2}

$$(18) \qquad MnO_4^- \;+\; Sn^{+2} \rightarrow Mn^{+2} + Sn^{+4}$$
$$\qquad\qquad \underset{\longrightarrow}{|+5\,e^-} \quad \underset{\longrightarrow}{|-2\,e^-}$$

Therefore

$$(19) \qquad 2\,MnO_4^- + 5\,Sn^{+2} \rightarrow 2\,Mn^{+2} + 5\,Sn^{+4}$$

Now there are eight oxygens on the left and none on the right. The addition of $8\,H_2O$ to the right will balance these and will require the use of $16\,H^+$ on the left.

$$(20) \qquad 2\,MnO_4^- + 5\,Sn^{+2} + 16\,H^+ \rightarrow 2\,Mn^{+2} + 5\,Sn^{+4} + 8\,H_2O$$

Now the charge balance is $2(-1)+5(+2)+16(+1) = 2(+2)+5(+4)$, and the equation is balanced.

In cases like that of dichromate oxidations, it is the total change of oxidation state per ion which must be considered rather than the change per atom. Thus for $Cr_2O_7^{-2}$ going to Cr^{+3}, the total gain of electrons per $Cr_2O_7^{-2}$ ion is six, with production of two Cr^{+3} ions

$$(21) \qquad Cr_2O_7^{-2} \;+\; Sn^{+2} \rightarrow 2\,Cr^{+3} + Sn^{+4}$$
$$\qquad\qquad \underset{\longrightarrow}{|+6\,e^-} \quad \underset{\longrightarrow}{|-2\,e^-}$$

Therefore

(22) $\qquad Cr_2O_7^{-2} + 3\,Sn^{+2} + 14\,H^+ \rightarrow 2\,Cr^{+3} + 3\,Sn^{+4} + 7\,H_2O$

and $\qquad -2 + 3(+2) + 14(+1) = 2(+3) + 3(+4)$

The balancing of equations for basic solutions or equations involving peroxides is more difficult. After determining the relative number of molecules of oxidant and reductant, these are best balanced by equalizing the charges. The final check is then made by means of the hydrogen atoms. Thus, for the oxidation of $Fe(OH)_3$ by ClO^-

(23) $\qquad Fe(OH)_3 + ClO^- \rightarrow FeO_4^{-2} + Cl^-$
$$\underset{\longrightarrow}{|-3\,e^-} \qquad \underset{\longrightarrow}{|+2\,e^-}$$

and

(24) $\qquad 2\,Fe(OH)_3 + 3\,ClO^- \rightarrow 2\,FeO_4^{-2} + 3\,Cl^-$

There are now three negative charges on the left and seven on the right. In order to equalize them (since this is an *alkaline* solution), we shall add $4\,OH^-$ to the left. This gives a total of thirteen oxygens on the left compared with eight on the right, so now five H_2O's must be added to the right to balance.

(25) $\qquad 2\,Fe(OH)_3 + 3\,ClO^- + 4\,OH^- \rightarrow 2\,FeO_4^{-2} + 3\,Cl^- + 5\,H_2O$

The check shows ten hydrogen atoms on each side.

Again let us consider the reaction between Ti^{+3} and H_2O_2 in acidic solution. (The oxidation state of each oxygen in H_2O_2 is taken to be -1. Observe from Tables 11–5 and 11–6 that Ti^{+3} is a better reducing agent than H_2O_2.)

(26) $\qquad Ti^{+3} \quad + \quad H_2O_2 \quad \rightarrow TiO^{+2} + H_2O$
$$\underset{\longrightarrow}{|-1\,e^-} \qquad \underset{\longrightarrow}{|+2\,e^-}$$

(27) $\qquad 2\,Ti^{+3} + H_2O_2 \rightarrow 2\,TiO^{+2} + H_2O$

Since there are two oxygens on the left and three on the right, we must add $1\,H_2O$ to the left (or subtract it from the right). This requires $2\,H^+$ on the right to balance the charges, giving

(28) $\qquad 2\,Ti^{+3} + H_2O_2 + H_2O \rightarrow 2\,TiO^{+2} + H_2O + 2\,H^+$

or (28') $\qquad 2\,Ti^{+3} + H_2O_2 \rightarrow 2\,TiO^{+2} + 2\,H^+$

Since there are now two hydrogen atoms on each side in (28'), the equation is balanced.

Let us consider the reaction between $Cr_2O_7^{-2}$ and H_2O_2 in acidic solution. (Observe from Table 11–5 that H_2O_2 is a better reducing agent than Cr^{+3}.)

(29)
$$Cr_2O_7^{-2} + H_2O_2 \rightarrow Cr^{+3} + O_2$$
$$\overset{\longrightarrow}{\underset{2x(+3\,e^-)}{\rule{0pt}{0pt}}} \quad \overset{\longrightarrow}{\underset{-2\,e^-}{\rule{0pt}{0pt}}}$$

(30)
$$Cr_2O_7^{-2} + 3\,H_2O_2 \rightarrow 2\,Cr^{+3} + 3\,O_2$$

There are thirteen oxygens on the left and six on the right, therefore

(31)
$$Cr_2O_7^{-2} + 3\,H_2O_2 \rightarrow 2\,Cr^{+3} + 3\,O_2 + 7\,H_2O$$

This requires the addition of eight positive charges to the left (as H^+)

(32)
$$Cr_2O_7^{-2} + 3\,H_2O_2 + 8\,H^+ \rightarrow 2\,Cr^{+3} + 3\,O_2 + 7\,H_2O$$

There are now fourteen hydrogen atoms on each side and the equation is balanced.

Finally, let us consider the reaction in alkaline solution of $Cr(OH)_4^-$ and H_2O_2.

(33)
$$Cr(OH)_4^- + H_2O_2 \rightarrow CrO_4^{-2} + H_2O$$
$$\overset{\longrightarrow}{\underset{-3\,e^-}{\rule{0pt}{0pt}}} \quad \overset{\longrightarrow}{\underset{+2\,e^-}{\rule{0pt}{0pt}}}$$

(34)
$$2\,Cr(OH)_4^- + 3\,H_2O_2 \rightarrow 2\,CrO_4^{-2} + ?\,H_2O$$

There are now two negative charges on the left and four on the right, so we must add 2 OH^- to balance the charges.

(35)
$$2\,Cr(OH)_4^- + 3\,H_2O_2 + 2\,OH^- \rightarrow 2\,CrO_4^{-2} + ?\,H_2O$$

Now there are sixteen oxygens on the left and eight on the right—excluding the ($?\,H_2O$). Putting eight H_2O's on the right would balance the oxygens.

(36)
$$2\,Cr(OH)_4^- + 3\,H_2O_2 + 2\,OH^- \rightarrow 2\,CrO_4^{-2} + 8\,H_2O$$

Now there are sixteen hydrogens on each side and the equation is balanced.

11–7. The Effect of Anionic Size, Charge, and Shape on the Solubilities of Salts

This subject has been fairly well covered in Chapter 3. However, it is appropriate to expand the discussion a little here.

It is to be expected that the solubilities of the salts whose anions have similar sizes, charges, and *shapes* will be similar. The effect of size can clearly be seen in the pK_{sp}'s of the series

	K_2PtF_6	K_2PtCl_6	K_2PtBr_6
	4.54	5.85	4.2
and	K_2SiF_6	K_2GeF_6	K_2SnF_6
	4.4	4.52	2.22

where the solubility passes through a minimum as the anionic size increases. Other examples could be cited, but this would merely repeat what was said in Chapter 3. Some examples of the effect of anionic charge are seen in the relative *molar solubilities* of the following substances:

KPF_6 K_2SiF_6 K_3AlF_6

0.495   0.022   0.0056

$K_3Fe(CN)_6$ $K_4Fe(CN)_6$ $K_5Mn(CN)_6$

1.34   0.54   0.066

K_2IrCl_6 K_3IrCl_6

0.025   0.26

The shape of the anion will also have an effect on the solubility of its salts. For example, for several pairs of anions having about the same radius, but having different shapes, we find that the octahedral anions (in these cases) give less soluble salts than the square anions. The potassium salts of the following anions have pK_{sp}'s

$PtCl_4^{-2}$ $PtCl_6^{-2}$ $PdCl_4^{-2}$ $PdCl_6^{-2}$ $PtBr_4^{-2}$ $PtBr_6^{-2}$

2.1   5.85   4.9   5.2   2.4   4.2

It is probable that a difference would also be found between the salt of a square anion, such as $K_2Pt(CN)_4$ or K_2PtCl_4, and that of a tetrahedral anion of the same size, such as $K_2Hg(CN)_4$ or K_2HgCl_4; however, there are no data available for comparison.

A possible example of the effect of change of shape from planar to pyramidal can be seen in the pK_{sp}'s of the series

$MgCO_3$ $MgSO_3$ $MgSeO_3$

4.4   2.5   4.9

That the increase in the solubility of $MgSO_3$ over that of $MgCO_3$ is not entirely due to the increase in the size of SO_3^{-2} over that of CO_3^{-2} is shown by the fact that with the even larger SeO_3^{-2} the solubility once more decreases. It is reasonable, therefore, to attribute the change in solubility to the change in the shape of the anion. It is true, of course, that the solid sulfite is $MgSO_3 \cdot 6\ H_2O$, while the carbonate is $MgCO_3 \cdot 3\ H_2O$, but this difference is itself probably attributable to the difference in the shapes of the anions.

In the case of CO_3^{-2} and $C_2O_4^{-2}$, despite the differences in size and shape the solubilities of their salts are very similar in neutral or alkaline solution. In acidic solution, the oxalates are uniformly less soluble because oxalic acid is a considerably stronger acid (second constant) than carbonic (K_A for $HCO_3^- = 4.8 \times 10^{-11}$, for $HC_2O_4^- = 5.0 \times 10^{-5}$).

TABLE 11–7. COMPARATIVE pK_{sp}'S FOR CARBONATES AND OXALATES

	Mg^{+2}	Ca^{+2}	Sr^{+2}	Ba^{+2}	Mn^{+2}	Fe^{+2}	Co^{+2}	Ni^{+2}	Cu^{+2}
CO_3^{-2}	4.4	8.3	9.0	8.3	10.7	10.5	12.1	8.2	9.6
$C_2O_4^{-2}$	4.1	8.8	7.2	7.0	15.0	6.7	7.4	9.4	7.5

	Zn^{+2}	Cd^{+2}	Hg_2^{+2}	Pb^{+2}	Ag^+	La^{+3}	Ce^{+3}
CO_3^{-2}	10.8	11.3	16.1	13.0	11.1		
$C_2O_4^{-2}$	8.8	7.8	13.0	11.1	11.0	25.4	28.6

There are data, however, to show that when size and charge are kept constant, but the anion is made less symmetrical by substituting another atom for one of the oxygens, the solubility increases, but the relative solubilities remain the same. Thus, the salts of the fluorosulfonate ion, SO_3F^-, are uniformly more soluble than the corresponding perchlorates, while the difluorophosphates, $PO_2F_2^-$, also isomorphous, are even more soluble. Likewise, the monofluorophosphates, PO_3F^{-2}, are more soluble than the corresponding sulfates, as are also the thiosulfates, SO_3S^{-2}. Table 11–8 shows the pK_{sp}'s of some comparative series

TABLE 11–8. pK_{sp}'S OF SOME ISOMORPHOUS SALTS

	K^+	Cs^+
ClO_4^-	1.95	2.4
SO_3F^-	0.60	2.0

	Ca^{+2}	Sr^{+2}	Ba^{+2}	Pb^{+2}	Hg_2^{+2}	Ag^+	Tl^+
SO_4^{-2}	4.63	6.49	10.06	7.80	6.17	4.77	2.4
PO_3F^{-2}	2.4	2.5	6.4	7.0	6.5	3.05	
SO_3S^{-2}	v.sol.	0.5	4.2	3.2	34.7	sl.sol.	6.70

The unexpectedly low solubilities of $Hg_2S_2O_3$ and $Tl_2S_2O_3$ are undoubtedly due to specific covalent interaction between the heavy metal and the external sulfur atom.

In summary, then, it can be said that the salts of anions having the same charge and approximately the same size and shape will have very similar solubilities. Some examples of these are collected in Table 11–9.

TABLE 11–9. pK_{sp}'S OF SALTS OF FORM MXO_4

	Na^+	K^+	Rb^+	Cs^+	Tl^+	Ag^+
BH_4^-	−4.15	2.9	3.6	6.6		
BF_4^-		2.7	3.0	4.7		
$B(C_6H_5)_4^-$	1.67	7.65				
ClO_4^-	−2.8	1.95	2.3	2.4	2.4	
IO_4^-	2.5	3.08	3.26	2.36		
MnO_4^-		1.25	2.54	4.08		2.79
ReO_4^-		2.72	3.02	3.40	4.92	4.10

	Ca^{+2}	Sr^{+2}	Ba^{+2}	Ra^{+2}	Pb^{+2}	Hg^{+2}	Hg_2^{+2}	Ag^+	Tl^+
SO_4^{-2}	4.63	6.49	10.06	14.38	7.80	1.43	6.17	4.77	2.4
SeO_4^{-2}	0.3		10.55		6.84			7.25	3.3
FeO_4^{-2}			insol.		insol.				
MnO_4^{-2}			9.61		insol.				
CrO_4^{-2}	3.15	4.44	9.93		13.75		8.70	11.89	12.01
MoO_4^{-2}		6.7	7.40		5.4			10.55	
WO_4^{-2}	8.06	9.77	14.6		6.35		16.96	11.26	

	Al^{+3}	Fe^{+3}	Cr^{+3}	Bi^{+3}
PO_4^{-3}	18.24	21.89	22.62	22.89
AsO_4^{-3}	15.80	20.24	20.11	9.36(?)

11-8. The Nature of Acid Anhydrides

The hydroxides which are bases and the oxy acids may both be considered to be derived from oxides by the addition of water.

$$Na_2O + H_2O \rightarrow 2\,NaOH$$

$$SO_3 + H_2O \rightarrow H_2SO_4$$

$$N_2O_5 + H_2O \rightarrow 2\,HNO_3$$

If an anion is derived from a weak acid, the salt will give the free weak acid when dissolved in a solution of low pH. If then, the K_A and K_B of the acid are both relatively high (see Section 9–11), dehydration of the acid to the anhydride may result. If this happens, the nature of the anhydride will have an important bearing on the stability of the solution. For example, when a germanate is acidified with a non-complexing acid, the solid germanic anhydride (i.e., germanium dioxide, GeO_2), precipitates out of solution.

$$GeO_3^{-2} + 2\,H^+ \rightarrow GeO_2\,(s) + H_2O$$

When a carbonate is acidified, gaseous carbonic anhydride (carbon dioxide, CO_2) is evolved.

$$CO_3^{-2} + 2\,H^+ \rightarrow CO_2\,(g) + H_2O$$

If the anhydride were liquid and insoluble in water, it would separate as a separate liquid phase. A case of this sort is that of benzenediazoic acid, $C_6H_5N_2OH$. As an acid, this substance has an ionization constant of $10^{-4.92}$, while as a base (benzenediazonium hydroxide), its ionization constant is $10^{-2.92}$. Consequently, when an alkali diazotate is carefully acidified an (explosive) insoluble oil separates as a second liquid phase.

$$2\,C_6H_5N_2O^- + 2\,H^+ \rightarrow (C_6H_5N_2)_2O(l) + H_2O$$

If, on the other hand, the anhydride is soluble in water, and nonvolatile, everything stays in solution. This would be the case in the acidification of a dilute (but not concentrated) nitrite solution, in which soluble N_2O_3 (aq) is produced.

$$2\,NO_2^- + 2\,H^+ \rightarrow N_2O_3\,(aq) + H_2O$$

If the solution is too concentrated, however, evolution of gaseous N_2O_3 or decomposition of the N_2O_3 into gaseous products takes place and the solution is unstable.

$$2 NO_2^- + 2 H^+ \rightarrow NO\ (g) + NO_2\ (g) + H_2O$$

In the same way, when alkali arsenite solutions which are less than 0.1 molar are acidified, the arsenious acid formed is unstable with respect to dehydration to the oxide, but the oxide is soluble as such to the extent of 0.1 molar and therefore does not precipitate. The solution is stable.

$$2 AsO_2^- + 2 H^+ \rightarrow As_2O_3\ (aq) + H_2O$$

In order to understand the reasons for the differences among the various acid anhydrides, it is necessary first of all to understand their structures. We have already seen (Section 10–7) that most of the elements on the right-hand side of the periodic table are capable of forming multiple bonds. The nature of these multiple bonds changes, however, from one part of the periodic table to another. The elements near fluorine can use p orbitals to form pi-bonds, but this ability falls off rapidly away from fluorine, especially going *down* in the periodic table. Table 11–10 shows the elements which can use p orbitals for pi-bonding. Those which are especially good at it are in bold-faced type.

TABLE 11–10. ELEMENTS USING p ORBITALS FOR PI-BONDING

B	**C**	**N**	**O**	**F**
		P	**S**	(Cl)
			Se	(Br)
			(Te)	

Elements which only seldom use p orbitals for pi-bonding are enclosed in parentheses. The use of p orbitals for pi-bonding by the halogens is restricted by their univalency and high electronegativity. An example of multiple bonding of this sort in the case of fluorine and boron is

$$\begin{array}{c} F \\ \diagdown \\ \quad \overset{(-)\ (+)}{B = F} \\ \diagup \\ F \end{array}$$

of chlorine

$$\begin{array}{c} Cl \\ \diagdown \\ \quad \overset{(-)\ (+)}{B = Cl} \\ \diagup \\ Cl \end{array}$$

where, however, it takes place to a much lesser extent than in BF_3; of sulfur,

$$S\!=\!C\!=\!S \qquad \text{and} \qquad \overset{\displaystyle \cdot\cdot}{\underset{O \quad O}{S}}$$

(where a d orbital is also used) and

$$\underset{O \quad O}{\overset{O}{\underset{\|}{S}}}$$

and of selenium and tellurium in $Se\!=\!C\!=\!Se$, $S\!=\!C\!=\!Se$, $S\!=\!C\!=\!Te$, and certain other similar compounds. (Very occasionally, phosphorus and arsenic form multiple bonds using p orbitals in such compounds as

and a corresponding compound with a second arsenic atom replacing the nitrogen.) This means that in many of their compounds, such as the oxides, these elements need be bonded to only two or three other atoms and consequently *these compounds may exist as simple molecules* which are volatile. In Table 11–11 are listed the oxides which are gaseous (or fairly volatile) at room temperature. Those in bold-face type are derived from weak acids and therefore would be liberated upon addition of a strong acid to a solution of the appropriate salt. Consequently, when acid is added to a solution of one of these salts, the evolution of a gas of particular chemical and physical characteristics is indicative of the presence of a particular anion.

(1) $CO_3^{-2} + 2\,H^+ \rightarrow H_2O + CO_2$ (g) (colorless, odorless)
$CO_2 + Ba^{+2} + 2\,OH^- \rightarrow H_2O + BaCO_3$ (s) (white)

(2) $2\,NO_2^- + 2\,H^+ \rightarrow H_2O + NO$ (g) (colorless) $+ NO_2$ (g) (red-brown, suffocating)
$2\,NO$ (g) $+ O_2$ (g) $\rightarrow 2\,NO_2$ (g)

TABLE 11–11. BOILING POINTS (°C) OF OXIDES VOLATILE
AT ROOM TEMPERATURE

CO_2	-78.5*	N_2O_5	47, dec.	$(O_3$	$-112)$	$(F_2O$	$-144.8)$
CO†	-190	N_2O_4	21.3‡	$(O_2$	$-183.0)$		
		N_2O_3	3.5, dec.				
		NO	-151.8				
		N_2O§	-88.5				

		SO_3	44.8	Cl_2O_7	82
		SO_2	-10.0	Cl_2O_6	
		S_2O	?	ClO_2	9.9
				Cl_2O	3.8
				Br_2O_6	
				BrO_2	
				Br_2O	

* Sublimes.

† Liberation of CO from formic acid ($HCHO_2$) requires strongly dehydrating conditions, such as concentrated H_2SO_4.

‡ Decomposes into NO_2.

§ Liberation of N_2O from $H_2N_2O_2$ is very slow.

(3) $2\,O_2^{-2} + 4\,H^+ \rightarrow 2\,H_2O_2 \xrightarrow{\text{slow}} 2\,H_2O + O_2$ (g) (colorless, odorless)

(4) $SO_3^{-2} + 2\,H^+ \rightarrow H_2O + SO_2$ (g) (colorless, acrid)

$SO_2 + Ba^{+2} + Br_2$ (aq) $+ 2\,H_2O \rightarrow 2\,Br^- + 4\,H^+ + BaSO_4$ (s) (white)

(5) $6\,ClO_2^- + 6\,H^+ \rightarrow 3\,H_2O + Cl_2O$ (g) (yellow-red, suffocating)
$+ 4\,ClO_2$ (g) (red-yellow, suffocating)

(6) $2\,ClO^- + 2\,H^+ \rightarrow H_2O + Cl_2O$ (g)

(7) $4\,BrO_3^- + 4\,H^+ \rightarrow 2\,H_2O + 3\,O_2$ (g) $+ 2\,Br_2$ (l or g) (red, suffocating)

The evolution of some of these anhydrides may not necessarily mean that the corresponding anion is present in simple form, for it may be present in a complex. Thus CO_2 will be generated when acid is added to a solution containing the tricarbonatouranate(VI) ion, $UO_2(CO_3)_3^{-4}$. Oxides of nitrogen are produced from acidified solutions containing hexanitrocobaltate(III) ion, $Co(NO_2)_6^{-3}$. Complexes containing CO, NO, O_2, and SO_3^{-2} groups may also decompose under appropriate circumstances producing the corresponding gases. One especially important case is that of thiosulfate, $S_2O_3^{-2}$, which gives the reaction

$$S_2O_3^{-2} + 2\,H^+ \rightarrow S\ (s) + SO_2\ (g) + H_2O$$

Quite similar is the selenosulfate ion which decomposes even more readily.

$$SeSO_3^{-2} + 2\,H^+ \rightarrow Se\ (s) + SO_2\ (g) + H_2O$$

For the elements outside of the bold-face group in Table 11–10 generally, and almost always for elements not listed in the table, only d orbitals can be used for forming multiple bonds. This means that there must always be *four sigma* bonds (sp^3) (or *sigma* orbitals occupied by unshared pairs of electrons) for these elements. Consequently, their compounds with polyvalent elements like oxygen are always three-dimensional, usually being high polymers, but at least having large molecules. Accordingly, SiO_2 is an infinite polymer of silicon and oxygen atoms (see Section 1–4). Even P_2O_5 in its simplest form is, in reality, a fairly large molecule, P_4O_{10}, with each phosphorus surrounded tetrahedrally by four oxygen atoms. It may also exist as a high polymer. Compounds with structures of this sort are much less volatile (P_4O_{10}) or quite nonvolatile (SiO_2) at room temperature.

11–9.   Volatile Weak Acids

In addition to the weak acids having volatile anhydrides which are evolved on acidification, there are the weak acids which are themselves volatile and which are evolved when solutions of their salts are acidified. These are generally binary compounds of hydrogen. Besides the ones which give definitely acidic solutions in water (shown in Table 11–12 in bold-face type) are those (shown in Table 11–12 in ordinary type) which are too

TABLE 11–12. BOILING POINTS (°C) OF VOLATILE WEAK ACIDS*

B_2H_6†‡	−92.5	C_2H_2	−83.6§	**HN_3** 37	———	**HF** 19.4
		CH_4‡	−161.5	**HCN** 26		
				NH_3 −33.35		
SiH_4†‡	−111.8			**PH_3**‡ −87.4	**H_2S** −61.80	——— ‖
GeH_4‡	−90.0			**AsH_3** −55	**H_2Se** −42	——— ‖
				SbH_3 −17	**H_2Te** −4	——— ‖

* Acids in bold-faced type are liberated by strong acids; others by water alone.

† Decomposed by water and spontaneously flammable in air.

‡ Produced along with other products such as B_4H_{10}, B_5H_9, B_5H_{11}, etc.; C_3H_4; Si_2H_6, Si_3H_8, etc.; Ge_2H_6, Ge_3H_8, etc.; P_2H_4.

§ Sublimes.

‖ HCl, HBr, and HI are too strongly acidic to be liberated except by concentrated strong acids.

weakly acidic to act as acids in water, but which, nevertheless, do form binary compounds with less electronegative elements. These latter compounds are hydrolyzed by water alone, giving the volatile weak acid directly. None of this latter class is more than slightly soluble in water, although some (e.g., B_2H_6) react with water (e.g., to give H_2 and H_3BO_3). Typical reactions are

$$Mg_3P_2 \text{ (s)} + 6 \ H_2O \text{ (l)} \rightarrow 3 \ Mg(OH)_2 \text{ (s)} + 2 \ PH_3 \text{ (g)}$$

$$AlN \text{ (s)} + 3 \ H_2O \text{ (l)} \rightarrow Al(OH)_3 \text{ (s)} + NH_3 \text{ (g)}$$

All of these substances are colorless. Many of them have characteristic odors. Hydrogen fluoride is acrid. Hydrogen sulfide smells like rotten eggs, H_2Se like rotten garlic, and H_2Te even worse. Hydrogen sulfide is about as poisonous as HCN; H_2Se and H_2Te are considerably more so. Hydrogen cyanide smells like bitter almonds. Hydrazoic acid is very explosive and poisonous, attacking the mucous membranes. Phosphine is poisonous and has a very objectionable smell, like a bad case of halitosis. Arsine and stibine are also very poisonous and have unpleasant smells. Methane is odorless and nontoxic, as is also acetylene. (The odor usually associated with acetylene, produced by the reaction

$$CaC_2 \text{ (s)} + 2 \ H_2O \text{ (l)} \rightarrow Ca(OH)_2 \text{ (s)} + C_2H_2 \text{ (g)}$$

is actually the result of traces of H_2S and PH_3.)

The generation of many of these volatile compounds does not necessarily mean that the corresponding anions are present in simple form. For example, when solutions containing such complexes as $Ni(CN)_4^{-2}$, $Zn(CN)_4^{-2}$, and so on, but not the more stable $Fe(CN)_6^{-3}$, $Fe(CN)_6^{-4}$, and $Co(CN)_6^{-3}$, are acidified, HCN is liberated. In addition, there is the selenocyanate ion, NCSe, which decomposes according to the equation

$$NCSe^- + H^+ \rightarrow Se \text{ (s)} + HCN \text{ (g)}$$

(Thiocyanate ion, on the other hand, is too stable to undergo this reaction. Acidification of a thiocyanate solution merely gives the free acid.) The same is true of complexes of N_3^- and C_2H^-, such as $Cr(N_3)_6^{-3}$ and $Cr(C_2H)_6^{-3}$. We have already seen (Section 5–2) how complexes of S^{-2} (or SH^-) decompose in acid with liberation of H_2S.

11–10.   Other Volatile Ansolvides

The possibility of existence of solvent systems other than the water system was discussed in Section 9–12. Two examples will be cited of anions derived from such systems which give rise to volatile products when acidified. The first is the trithiocarbonate ion, CS_3^{-2}, which upon acidification slowly gives H_2S and the volatile liquid, CS_2.

$$CS_3^{-2} + 2 \ H^+ \rightarrow H_2CS_3 \rightarrow CS_2 \text{ (l)} + H_2S \text{ (g)}$$

The second is the fluorosilicate ion, which, upon strong acidification, gives HF and gaseous SiF_4.

$$SiF_6^{-2} + 2 \ H^+ \rightarrow 2 \ HF \text{ (aq)} + SiF_4 \text{ (g)}$$

11–11.   Insoluble Acid Anhydrides

As has been pointed out in Section 4–7 and again in Section 11–8, when the solution of a salt of certain weak acids is acidified, the insoluble free acid may precipitate, and this may be subject to spontaneous dehydration Thus the ions shown in Table 11–13 precipitate free acid on moderate acidification with noncomplexing acids (see, however, the discussion in Section 4–7). In general, these are only partially dehydrated, retaining much of their water. Many of the precipitates are amphoteric, dissolving in excess strong acid. The precipitates from Ti, Zr, Hf, and V fall in this category.

TABLE 11–13

TiO_3^{-2}	VO_3^-	
ZrO_3^{-2}	NbO_3^-	MoO_4^{-2}
HfO_3^{-2}	TaO_3^-	WO_4^{-2}

On the other side of the periodic table, the anions shown in Table 11–14 produce precipitates when moderately acidified. Spontaneous dehydration gives GeO_2, PbO_2, Bi_2O_5, TeO_2, and PoO_2.

TABLE 11–14.

$Be(OH)_4^{-2}$	$B(OH)_4^-$			
	$Al(OH)_4^-$	SiO_3^{-2}		
$Zn(OH)_2^{-2}$		GeO_3^{-2}		
		$Sn(OH)_6^{-2}$	$Sb(OH)_4^-$ and $Sb(OH)_6^-$	TeO_3^{-2}
$Pt(OH)_6^{-2}$ $Au(OH)_4^-$		$Pb(OH)_6^{-2}$	$Bi(OH)_6^-$	PoO_3^{-2}

Almost all of these dissolve in excess of the usual complexing acids, except for silicic acid (which, however, dissolves in HF). The more powerful oxidants, (PbO_2, Bi_2O_5) may be reduced.

$$HSb(OH)_6 + 5\,H^+ + 6\,Cl^- \rightarrow SbCl_6^- + 6\,H_2O$$
$$H_2SiO_3\,(s) + 6\,HF \rightarrow 2\,H^+ + SiF_6^{-2} + 3\,H_2O$$
$$\begin{cases} PbO_2\,(s) + 4\,H^+ + 6\,Cl^- \rightarrow PbCl_6^{-2} + 2\,H_2O \\ PbCl_6^{-2} \rightarrow PbCl_2\,(s) + Cl_2\,(g) + 2\,Cl^- \end{cases}$$
$$Bi_2O_5\,(s) + 10\,H^+ + 12\,Cl^- \rightarrow 2\,BiCl_4^- + 2\,Cl_2\,(g) + 5\,H_2O$$

Only those of lower oxidation state (or lower electronegativity) dissolve in non-complexing acids. Thus H_2SnO_3, PbO_2, H_2PtO_3, $HSb(OH)_6$, and Bi_2O_5 do not dissolve in HNO_3 or $HClO_4$.

11–12.   Anions as Bases and Complexing Agents

One further characteristic of anions which must be kept in mind is that they are bases (see Sections 7–2 and 7–6). Anions derived from strong acids such as $HClO_4$, HSO_3F, HBF_4, HNO_3, and so forth, are very weak bases and will have little or no effect on the pH of the solution. The weaker the acid from which the anion is derived, however, the stronger a base it will be. This follows from the fact that the basic ionization constant, K_B, and the hydrolysis constant, K_H ,are the same thing.

$$K_B = K_H = \frac{K_W}{K_A}$$

The presence of anions of weak acids therefore has considerable effect on the pH of the solution.

In general, the anions of weak acids are also good complexing agents and may prevent precipitation of cations which otherwise would precipitate as hydroxides when the pH is high (as it will be in the presence of the free anions of weak acids). In this way, such ions as Ag^+, Pb^{+2}, Pu^{+4}, and so on, remain in solution at pH's above 7, when acetate ion is present, through formation of $Ag(C_2H_3O_2)_2{}^-$, $Pb(C_2H_3O_2)_3{}^-$, and so on.

11–13. Illustrative Experiments on Variations of Oxidizing and Reducing Power

The following experiments are designed to demonstrate variations of oxidizing and reducing power within certain families (columns) of the periodic table.

(1) (a) To 10 drops of $Cd(NO_3)_2$ in 1 ml of H_2O add 5 drops of $SnCl_2$ Repeat with $Hg(NO_2)_2$ in the place of $Cd(NO_3)_2$.

(b) Add 10 drops of $Cd(NO_3)_2$ to 1 ml of water in a test tube and add a pinch of Zn metal to this solution. In another test tube, perform a control experiment by doing the same experiment with $Zn(NO_3)_2$ in place of $Cd(NO_3)_2$. Now heat both test tubes in a boiling-water bath for 5 minutes. Examine the Zn metal in the two tubes to determine if the Zn metal in the first tube is a different color from that in the control tube.

(1) Write the ionic equations for any reactions which you observed.

(2) $SnCl_2$ is a fair reducing agent (better than Cu, but poorer than Fe), so it certainly would reduce any substance which is easily reduced. Would you say Cd^{+2} would fall in one of the two blocks of elements on the periodic table which are easily reduced?

(3) Of Zn^{+2}, Cd^{+2}, and Hg^{+2}, which is the best oxidizing agent from the experimental results?

(4) Is it the most or least electronegative?

(5) Of Zn, Cd, and Hg, which is the best reducing agent from the experimental results?

(2) Place 1–2 cm of Cu wire in a solution of 10 drops of $AgNO_3$ in 1 ml of water.

(1) Write the ionic equation for the reaction observed. (Note that metals in a finely divided state often appear black even if the color for large crystals of the metal is different from black.)

(2) Considering the variation in electronegativities and the results of the first experiment, would you expect Au to react with $AgNO_3$?

(3) All three elements, Cu, Ag, and Au, are very poor reducing agents since their positive ions are good oxidizing agents. Which of the three elements is expected to be the poorest reducing agent from the above experimental results?

(4) Is this element the most or least electronegative?

(5) Is it at the top or bottom of the group?

(3) (a) To 10 drops of H_3AsO_3 and 4 drops of 6 M HCl, add a few granules of Zn metal. Insert a wad of cotton into the mouth of the tube. Cover the mouth with a piece of filter paper saturated with $AgNO_3$ and heat the solution gently. Repeat with $SbCl_3$ and with $Bi(NO_3)_3$ in place of H_3AsO_3.

(1) Write the ionic equations for any reactions which you observed to occur. (BiH_3 would react with $AgNO_3$ in the same manner as SbH_3.)

(b) Place 1 ml of concentrated NH_4OH in a test tube and a piece of filter paper saturated with $AgNO_3$ over the mouth of the tube. Heat the solution gently. The following equilibrium is shifted to the right by the heating:

$$NH_4^+ + OH^- \rightleftharpoons NH_3 \text{ (aq)} \rightleftharpoons NH_3 \text{ (g)}$$

The NH_3 gas is then absorbed by the $AgNO_3$ solution.

(2) Between the $+3$ oxidation states of As and Bi, which is the best oxidizing agent when the -3 state is the product?

(3) Is this element the most or least electronegative?

(4) Is it easier to oxidize NH_3 or AsH_3 to the elemental form?

(5) Considering the electronegativities in the fifth family, which would you expect to be the best reducing agent, NH_3, PH_3, AsH_3, SbH_3, or BiH_3?

The following experiments are designed to demonstrate the variation of oxidizing and reducing power within each period.

(4) (a) Add 4 drops of 6 M H_2SO_4 and 10 drops of KBr to 10 drops of 0.1 M $KBrO_3$ solution. Note any color change. Repeat with 0.1 M H_2SeO_3 instead of $KBrO_3$.

(b) Add 10 drops of 0.1 M H_3AsO_3 to 5 drops of 6 M H_2SO_4 in 2 ml of water. To this solution, add 15 drops of 0.1 M Na_2SO_3 and heat in a water bath for 2 minutes. Repeat the experiment with 0.1 M H_2SeO_3 instead of H_3AsO_3. (*Note:* Elemental Se is either red or black.)

(1) Write ionic equations for all reactions which occurred.

(2) Which is the best oxidizing agent, BrO_3^-, H_2SeO_3, or H_3AsO_3?

(3) Does this substance contain the most or least electronegative element (Br, Se, or As)?

(5) Cooperate with another student in doing this experiment *in the hood.* Add 30 ml of concentrated NH_4OH to the 250 ml Erlenmeyer flask, in the apparatus shown in Fig. 11-1. Plug up one hole of your No. 6 rubber stopper with a stirring rod and attach a rubber hose to a piece of glass tubing inserted in the other hole. Insert a piece of glass tubing about 20 cm long into the other end of the rubber hose and insert the free end of the glass tubing to the bottom of a 6-inch Pyrex test tube containing CuO (rods if possible). Ask your instructor to make sure you do not have a closed system. Then heat the CuO *very strongly* with your Bunsen burner, and continue heating as you heat the NH_4OH gently with a second burner. Continue this procedure until a visible change occurs in the CuO.

(1) Write the balanced equation for the reaction of NH_3 (not NH_4OH) with the CuO to give N_2 as one of the products.

(2) Considering the electronegativities of N and C, is CH_4 likely to affect CuO in the same manner as NH_3?

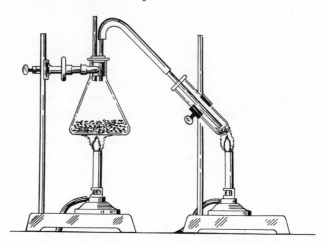

Fig. 11–1. Apparatus for Generation of Ammonia and Reaction with CuO.

(3) Considering the electronegativities of C, N, and O, which should be the easiest to reduce, C, N_2, or O_2 to CH_4, NH_3, or H_2O, respectively?

(4) Write the following sentence in your laboratory notebook, using the correct word in each parenthesis: The more electronegative elements tend to be (a) the (better or poorer) oxidizing agents, (b) the (better or poorer) reducing agents, (c) the (more or less) easily reduced, and (d) the (more or less) easily oxidized.

11–14. Preparation of the Solution for Anion Analysis

In order to carry out many of the tests for anions it is necessary first to remove any possible interfering cations (see procedure 7–A).

11–A. *Removal of Interfering Cations.* Test the pH of the solution. If it is acidic, add 6 M NaOH, dropwise with stirring, to 10 ml of the solution until it is just alkaline or until a precipitate appears. To this solution, or to the original solution if it was found to be alkaline, add 1 drop of sulfate-free 1.5 M Na_2CO_3 solution. If no precipitate is formed by either NaOH or Na_2CO_3, proceed directly to the anion analysis.

If a precipitate forms, add 2 ml of Na_2CO_3 solution to the solution in a casserole and boil for ten minutes. Cover the casserole with a watch glass to prevent spattering. Do not allow to go dry; add water from time to time to make up for evaporation losses. (The vapors can be examined for the presence of NH_3 at this time.) Cool and centrifuge out the precipitate. Adjust the volume of the solution to about 10 ml with water. The solution is now ready for analysis for anions.

The above treatment should convert all insoluble salts except silicates, phosphates, arsenates, most sulfides, certain cyanides, and the halides and thiocyanate of silver into soluble sodium salts and insoluble carbonates or hydroxides. The solubility of the residue should be tested in 3 M $HC_2H_3O_2$ If there has been incomplete conversion to carbonates, this residue will not dissolve completely. It should be washed with water and set aside for detection of phosphate, and so forth. For the salts which are not converted into soluble form by the carbonate treatment, it is necessary to carry out certain procedures to liberate the anions to make them available for analysis. These are discussed in procedures (11–B) and those following.

It is possible to estimate from the K_{sp}'s the extent of conversion of an insoluble compound to soluble form. For example, for the case of $BaCrO_4$, we have

$$BaCrO_4 \text{ (s)} + CO_3^{-2} \rightleftharpoons BaCO_3 \text{ (s)} + CrO_4^{-2}$$

The K_{sp} relationships are

$$[Ba^{+2}][CrO_4^{-2}] = 8.5 \times 10^{-11}$$

and $$[Ba^{+2}][CO_3^{-2}] = 1.6 \times 10^{-9}$$

or $$\frac{[Ba^{+2}][CrO_4^{-2}]}{[Ba^{+2}][CO_3^{-2}]} = \frac{[CrO_4^{-2}]}{[CO_3^{-2}]} = \frac{8.5 \times 10^{-11}}{1.6 \times 10^{-9}} = 0.053$$

Therefore, if $[CO_3^{-2}] = 1.5$ M, then $[CrO_4^{-2}] = 0.08$ M, which is the maximum concentration possible, but is a perfectly adequate concentration to detect. With $BaSO_4$, the maximum concentration of sulfate ion obtainable is about the same, but still adequate for detection. With AgCl, we have

$$2 \text{ AgCl (s)} + CO_3^{-2} \rightleftharpoons Ag_2CO_3 \text{ (s)} + 2 \text{ Cl}^-$$

The K_{sp} relationships are

$$[Ag^+][Cl^-] = 2.8 \times 10^{-10}$$

and $$[Ag^+]^2[CO_3^{-2}] = 8.2 \times 10^{-12}$$

or $$\frac{[Ag^+]^2[Cl^-]^2}{[Ag^+]^2[CO_3^{-2}]} = \frac{[Cl^-]^2}{[CO_3^{-2}]} = \frac{(2.8 \times 10^{-10})^2}{8.2 \times 10^{-12}} = 9.6 \times 10^{-9}$$

Now if $[CO_3^{-2}] = 1.5$ M, $[Cl^-] = 1.2 \times 10^{-4}$ M, which is a little difficult to detect with certainty. With AgI, by the same argument, $[I^-]$ would be 3.0×10^{-11} M, which it would be out of the question to detect.

If the unknown sample is a solid which is not completely soluble in water, it should be ground very fine with mortar and pestle. Put about 1.5 g of the pulverized sample into a casserole and boil for 10 minutes with 2 ml of 1.5 M Na_2CO_3. Replenish the water as necessary to prevent the sample from going dry. Cool, transfer the solution to a test tube, and centrifuge. After washing with water, test the residue with 3 M $HC_2H_3O_2$. If it consists only of carbonates, it will dissolve completely. If it is not completely soluble, wash with water, discarding the washes, and repeat the carbonate treatment. Add this carbonate solution to the previous one. If the residue is not now completely soluble in 3 M $HC_2H_3O_2$, wash it and set it aside for examination for phosphate, and so on (11–B).

11–B. Treatment of the Residue from the Carbonate Treatment. (1) *Sulfide Ion.* Put about 5 mg of the residue from the carbonate treatment into a small test tube and mix it with a small amount of granulated zinc. Add 1 ml of 3 M HCl and hold tightly over the mouth of the test tube a piece of filter paper which has been moistened with 0.2 M Pb(C$_2$H$_3$O$_2$)$_2$ solution. Development of a black spot of PbS on the paper shows the presence of sulfide ion. Even highly insoluble sulfides will undergo reaction with zinc and HCl, according to the equation

$$MS \text{ (s)} + Zn \text{ (s)} + 2 H^+ \rightleftharpoons M \text{ (s)} + Zn^{+2} + H_2S \text{ (g)}$$

(2) *Phosphate and Arsenate Ions.* To a few milligrams of the residue from the carbonate treatment add 1 ml of 3 M HNO$_3$ and heat to boiling. Centrifuge. Any residue may be silver halides or pseudohalides (i.e., cyanide, thiocyanate, and so on) and may be used in the test for these substances. Add to the separated supernate several drops of 1 M NH$_4$I and heat; then, add CH$_3$CSNH$_2$ and heat for ten minutes in the hot-water bath. A yellow precipitate may be either free sulfur or As$_2$S$_3$. Remove the precipitate, and dissolve it in 2 ml 6 M NaOH. Have available a small wad of cotton and a piece of filter paper wetted with 0.1 M AgNO$_3$ solution. Add to the test tube a few aluminum pellets (do not use powder) and immediately plug the mouth of the tube with cotton wad and cover the mouth tightly with the AgNO$_3$ paper. Development of a black spot of metallic silver on the paper shows the presence of arsenic, which must have been present as AsO$_4^{-3}$ (see procedure 5–J).

To the supernatant solution from the nitric acid treatment, add Br$_2$ until the color persists, boil off the excess, centrifuge and then add 3 drops of 0.1 M (NH$_4$)$_2$MoO$_4$ solution and heat in a water bath. DO NOT BOIL. A yellow precipitate of ammonium molybdophosphate shows the presence of PO$_4^{-3}$. (If arsenate has not been removed by the CH$_3$CSNH$_2$ treatment, this may be ammonium molybdoarsenate.) Centrifuge and wash the precipitate to make sure it is really yellow.

$$PO_4^{-3} + 3 NH_4^+ + 12 MoO_4^{-2} + 24 H^+ \rightarrow (NH_4)_3PMo_{12}O_{40} \text{ (s)} + 12 H_2O$$

(3) *Halides and Pseudohalides of Silver.* To a few milligrams of the residue from the carbonate treatment, add 1 ml 3 M HNO$_3$ and boil—or take the residue from the nitric acid treatment for phosphate and arsenate ions (see above). Centrifuge. Put the residue from the HNO$_3$ treatment into a small test tube, add 10 drops of CH$_3$CSNH$_2$ solution and 5 drops of 6 M NH$_4$OH, and heat in the water bath. The silver salts will be metathesized to Ag$_2$S allowing the halide and pseudohalide ions to go into solution.

$$2 AgX \text{ (s)} + S^{-2} \rightarrow Ag_2S \text{ (s)} + 2 X^-$$

The analysis of this solution for halide and pseudohalide is described in procedure 11–Q.

11–15.   Elimination Tests and Systematic Analysis for Anions

These tests are designed to show the presence of members of certain groups of anions or the complete absence of those groups. This knowledge will simplify the systematic anion analysis later.

11–*C*. *Color.* Examine the residue from the carbonate treatment, or the original solution if the carbonate treatment produced no precipitate, for color. Colored anions which may be encountered are MnO$_4^-$ (purple), MnO$_4^{-2}$ (green), Cr$_2$O$_7^{-2}$ (orange), CrO$_4^{-2}$ (yellow), Fe(CN)$_6^{-3}$ (red), Fe(CN)$_6^{-4}$ (yellow), and so forth.

The vanadate ion, (VO$_3^-$)$_x$ or VO$_4^{-3}$ is colorless, but in the acidic solution before Na_2CO_3 treatment there may be VO_2^+ (yellow). The absence of any color in the original solution (if acidic) eliminates all of these ions. The absence of any color in the original solution (if basic) or in the supernate from the carbonate treatment eliminates MnO_4^-, MnO_4^{-2}, CrO_4^{-2}, $Cr_2O_7^{-2}$, $Fe(CN)_6^{-3}$, and $Fe(CN)_6^{-4}$. If an original purple color in neutral or acidic solution becomes green after Na_2CO_3 treatment, permanganate is indicated in the original solution.

$$4 MnO_4^- + 4 CO_3^{-2} + 2 H_2O \rightarrow 4 MnO_4^{-2} + O_2 + 4 HCO_3^-$$

On reacidification, the green solution will revert to purple and simultaneously a brown-to-black solid will precipitate

$$3 MnO_4^{-2} + 4 H^+ \rightarrow 2 MnO_4^- + MnO(OH)_2 \text{ (s)} + H_2O$$

or if the solution is fairly strongly acidified no precipitate will appear

$$4 MnO_4^{-2} + 8 H^+ \rightarrow 4 MnO_4^- + Mn^{+2} + 4 H_2O$$

An original orange color in a solid sample or in acidic solution which becomes yellow on treatment with carbonate shows the presence of $Cr_2O_7^{-2}$.

$$Cr_2O_7^{-2} + 2 CO_3^{-2} + H_2O \rightarrow 2 CrO_4^{-2} + 2 HCO_3^-$$

An original lemon-yellow color in the solid or in alkaline solution unchanged by the carbonate treatment may be CrO_4^{-2} or $Fe(CN)_6^{-4}$. An original lemon-yellow color in acidic solution unchanged by the carbonate treatment may be $Fe(CN)_6^{-4}$. An original red color in acidic or neutral solution unchanged by the carbonate treatment may be $Fe(CN)_6^{-3}$. (If the carbonate treatment is prolonged, the $Fe(CN)_6^{-3}$ may be partially decomposed to red-brown insoluble $Fe(OH)_3$ and CN^-. The CN^- will then be detected as such. Consequently, CN^- found in the presence of $Fe(CN)_6^{-3}$ or of Fe^{+3}—from the cation analysis—must be suspected to have come from the decomposition of $Fe(CN)_6^{-3}$

$$Fe(CN)_6^{-3} + 3 CO_3^{-2} + 3 H_2O \rightarrow Fe(OH)_3 \text{ (s)} + 3 HCO_3^- + 6 CN^-)$$

11–D. *Volatile Acids and Anhydrides.* This test must be performed on the original solution before any Na_2CO_3 is added. Put 5 drops of the unknown solution, or a little of the solid suspended in 5 drops of water, into a small test tube and heat gently *without boiling*. Hold the test tube to the light and observe whether there is any effervescence when 2 drops of 3 M H_2SO_4 are added. If no gas is evolved, none of the anions of volatile acids or anhydrides (CO_3^{-2}, S^{-2}, SO_3^{-2}, NO_2^-, and so on) are present. (Evolution of NO_2 from acidified NO_2^- may be slow. Consequently NO_2^- should be tested for even in the absence of effervescence.) If a precipitate forms, centrifuge it out and discard it. Retain the solution for tests to detect the presence of ions forming insoluble silver salts (11–Q).

11–E. *Insoluble Calcium Salts.* To 10 drops of the solution from the carbonate treatment (10 drops of the original solution if the carbonate treatment was found to be unnecessary), add 10 drops of water and then 3 M $HC_2H_3O_2$, dropwise with stirring and counting the drops, until the evolution of CO_2 becomes less brisk. Test the pH by withdrawing a droplet of solution on the end of the stirring rod and touching it to blue litmus paper. It should still be alkaline. Continue the dropwise addition of $HC_2H_3O_2$, testing the pH after addition of each drop, until the solution is exactly neutral. Now add just as many drops more of $HC_2H_3O_2$ as it took to neutralize the solution. Warm until effervescence ceases. Now add 4 drops of 0.1 M $Ca(NO_3)_2$ solution. If

TABLE 11-15. SCHEMATIC OUTLINE FOR THE ANALYSIS OF ANIONS
(Original solution or supernate from the carbonate treatment)

Solution: CO_3^{-2}, $C_2O_4^{-2}$, F^-, SO_3^{-2}, AsO_2^-, AsO_4^{-3}, PO_4^{-3}, CrO_4^{-2}, SO_4^{-2}, S^{-2}, $Fe(CN)_6^{-4}$, $Fe(CN)_6^{-3}$, Cl^-, Br^-, I^-, NCS^-, ClO_3^-, NO_2^-, NO_3^-, MnO_4^-, (CN^-, VO_4^{-3}, MoO_4^{-2}, WO_4^{-2}).
Add HAc; add $Ca(NO_3)_2$.

Precipitate: CaF_2, CaC_2O_4.

Add H_2SO_4 and $KMnO_4$; heat.

- Decolorization: $C_2O_4^{-2}$.
- Solution: F^-. Add $ZrO(NO_3)_2$ and alizarin. Decolorization: F^-.

Solution: SO_3^{-2}, AsO_2^-, AsO_4^{-3}, PO_4^{-3}, CrO_4^{-2}, SO_4^{-2}, S^{-2}, $Fe(CN)_6^{-4}$, $Fe(CN)_6^{-3}$, Cl^-, Br^-, I^-, NCS^-, ClO_3^-, NO_2^-, NO_3^-, MnO_4^-, (CN^-, VO_4^{-3}, MoO_4^{-2}, WO_4^{-2}).
Add $Ba(NO_3)_2$.

Precipitate: $BaCrO_4$, $BaSO_4$. Add HCl.

- Residue: $BaSO_4$.
- Solution: CrO_4^{-2}. Add NaAc. Precipitate: $BaCrO_4$.

Solution: SO_3^{-2}, AsO_2^-, AsO_4^{-3}, PO_4^{-3}, S^{-2}, $Fe(CN)_6^{-4}$, $Fe(CN)_6^{-3}$, Cl^-, Br^-, I^-, NCS^-, ClO_3^-, NO_2^-, NO_3^-, MnO_4^-, (CN^-, VO_4^{-3}, MoO_4^{-2}, WO_4^{-2}).
Add $Zn(NO_3)_2$.

Precipitate: ZnS, $Zn(CN)_2$, $Zn_3K_2[Fe(CN)_6]_2$, $Zn_3[Fe(CN)_6]_2$. Divide precipitate into four parts and test individually for each anion.

Solution: SO_3^{-2}, AsO_2^-, AsO_4^{-3}, PO_4^{-3}, Cl^-, Br^-, I^-, NCS^-, ClO_3^-, NO_2^-, NO_3^-, MnO_4^-, (VO_4^{-3}, MoO_4^{-2}, WO_4^{-2}). Add Br_2-water.

Precipitate: $BaSO_4$: SO_3^{-2}.

Solution: AsO_2^-, AsO_4^{-3}, PO_4^{-3}, Cl^-, Br^-, I^-, NCS^-, ClO_3^-, NO_2^-, NO_3^-, MnO_4^-, (VO_4^{-3}, MoO_4^{-2}, WO_4^{-2}). Heat till effervescence (CO_2) ceases. Make ammonical.

Precipitate: $Ba(AsO_2)_2$, $Ba_3(AsO_4)_2$, $Ba_3(PO_4)_2$, ($Ba_3(VO_4)_2$, $BaMoO_4$, $BaWO_4$). Do individual tests.

Solution: Cl^-, Br^-, I^-, NCS^-, ClO_3^-, NO_2^-, NO_3^-, MnO_4^-. Add $AgNO_3$.

Precipitate: $AgCl$, $AgBr$, AgI, $AgNCS$.

Solution: ClO_3^-, NO_2^-, NO_3^-, MnO_4^-.

no precipitate forms, F^- and $C_2O_4^{-2}$ are absent. If a precipitate does form, separate it, wash it well with dilute $HC_2H_3O_2$, and set it aside to test it for F^- and $C_2O_4^{-2}$ (11–M).

11–F. Insoluble Barium Salts. To the supernate from the calcium salt precipitation, add 2 drops of 0.1 M $Ba(NO_3)_2$ solution. If no precipitate is formed, CrO_4^{-2} and SO_4^{-2} are absent. If a yellow precipitate forms, CrO_4^{-2} must be present. Retain the precipitate to test for SO_4^{-2} and CrO_4^{-2} (11–N). If the precipitate is white, CrO_4^{-2} must be absent, but SO_4^{-2} is confirmed. Add a little more $Ba(NO_3)_2$ to ensure complete precipitation.

Unless SO_3^{-2} was definitely shown to be absent in the test for volatile acids and anhydrides, add, to a small portion of the separated supernate from the barium salt precipitate, bromine water dropwise with stirring until the color of bromine persists. Any white precipitate which appears is $BaSO_4$, showing the presence of SO_3^{-2}. (If CrO_4^{-2} is present, SO_3^{-2} obviously will not be.)

$$SO_3^{-2} + Br_2 (aq) + H_2O \rightarrow SO_4^{-2} + 2 Br^- + 2 H^+$$

11–G. Insoluble Zinc Salts. To the rest of the supernate from the precipitation of the acid-insoluble barium salts, add a few drops of 0.5 M $Zn(NO_3)_2$ solution. If no precipitate appears, S^{-2}, CN^-, $Fe(CN)_6^{-4}$, and $Fe(CN)_6^{-3}$ must be absent. If a precipitate appears, add enough $Zn(NO_3)_2$ for complete precipitation, centrifuge, separate, and retain both precipitate and supernate for further tests (11–O and 11–H). It should be apparent that both S^{-2} and $Fe(CN)_6^{-3}$ could not be in this precipitate (see Tables 11–5 and 11–6).

11–H. Alkali-Insoluble Barium Salts. To the supernate from the zinc salt precipitation, add 5 drops of 15 M HNO_3 and boil to expel any CO_2 or SO_2. Then add sufficient concentrated NH_4OH to make the solution strongly alkaline. The absence of a precipitate at this point indicates the absence of AsO_2^-, AsO_4^{-3}, PO_4^{-3}, VO_4^{-3}, and WO_4^{-2}. If precipitation occurs, add a little more $Ba(NO_3)_2$ to ensure complete precipitation, centrifuge, and retain the precipitate for future tests (11–P). If the precipitate is yellow, VO_4^{-3} is indicated. Save the supernate (11–I).

11–I. Insoluble Silver Salts. Acidify with HNO_3 the supernate from the precipitation of the alkali-insoluble barium salts and add 5 drops of 0.1 M $AgNO_3$. If no precipitate forms, Cl^-, Br^-, I^-, and NCS^- are absent. If a yellow precipitate forms, I^- is probably present. If there is a precipitate, separate it and wash it. Set it aside for further analysis (11–Q). Also retain the supernate for analysis (11–R).

11–J. Oxidants. To 5 drops of the solution from the carbonate treatment (11–A) add dropwise 20 drops of a saturated solution of $MnCl_2$ in 12 M HCl and heat to boiling. If no brown or black color develops, oxidizing anions must be absent. These include MnO_4^- (or MnO_4^{-2}), CrO_4^{-2}, VO_4^{-3}, NO_2^-, or NO_3^-.

11–K. Reducing Agents. To 5 drops of the solution from the carbonate treatment add 1.5 ml of water, 3 drops of 6 M HCl, 3 drops of $FeCl_3$, and 2 drops of *freshly prepared* $K_3Fe(CN)_6$ solution. Allow the mixture to stand for a few minutes. If a deep-blue solution does not form, I^-, S^{-2}, SO_3^{-2}, NO_2^-, and $Fe(CN)_6^{-4}$ are absent. If *both* (11–J) and (11–K) give positive results, NO_2^- *must* be present. (Explain.)

11–L. Detection of Anions of Volatile Acids or Anhydrides. (1) *Carbonate.* Add to a $\frac{1}{2}$ ml portion of the *original* unknown solution, or to a few milligrams of solid unknown suspended in water, 5 drops of 3 (percent) H_2O_2 to oxidize any SO_3^{-2} which may be present. (Omit if 11–*F* showed SO_3^{-2} to be absent.) Fill the bulb of a gas-absorption pipet with saturated $Ba(OH)_2$ solution or put 5 ml of the saturated $Ba(OH)_2$ into a test tube. Acidify the sample with dilute HCl and by means of rubber tube or stopper immediately attach a gas absorption pipet or a bent glass tube leading into the $Ba(OH)_2$ solution in the test tube. Warm the HCl solution gently. Development of cloudiness or a precipitate in the $Ba(OH)_2$ solution indicates the presence of CO_3^{-2}.

(2) *Sulfite*. Repeat the test for carbonate, omitting the H_2O_2, and replacing the $Ba(OH)_2$ solution with a mixture of 0.1 M $Ba(NO_3)_2$ and a few drops of bromine water. A white precipitate of $BaSO_4$ shows the presence of SO_3^{-2}.

(3) *Sulfide*. Repeat the test for sulfite, replacing the gas absorption pipet with a strip of filter paper moistened with $Pb(C_2H_3O_2)_2$ solution. A black spot of PbS on the filter paper shows the presence of S^{-2}.

11–*M*. *The Insoluble Calcium Salts*. (1) *Oxalate*. To the well-washed precipitate obtained in (11–*E*) add a few drops of dilute H_2SO_4, heat, and add 1 small drop of 0.01 M $KMnO_4$. If the color of MnO_4^- is discharged, $C_2O_4^{-2}$ is present.

(2) *Fluoride*. If oxalate is present, continue to add $KMnO_4$ until the MnO_4^- color persists.

$$2\ MnO_4^- + 5\ C_2O_4^{-2} + 16\ H^+ \rightarrow 2\ Mn^{+2} + 10\ CO_2\ (g) + 8\ H_2O$$

Now add just sufficient 3 percent H_2O_2 to discharge the MnO_4^- color. On a spot plate prepare some zirconium-alizarin lake by mixing one drop of 0.003 M $ZrO(NO_3)_2$ solution with 2 drops of 2 percent alizarin S solution. Finally add a drop of the solution which has been treated with $KMnO_4$. If the red lake becomes light yellow or straw-colored, F^- is present. (This test depends upon the great tendency of F^- to complex the less electronegative metals

$$Zr(OH)_4 + 6\ F^- + 4\ H^+ \rightleftharpoons ZrF_6^{-2} + 4\ H_2O)$$

11–*N*. *Acid Insoluble Barium Salts*. (1) *Sulfate and Chromate*. If the precipitate obtained in (11–*F*) was yellow, wash it well with water and add sufficient dilute HCl to remove all yellow color from the precipitate, or to dissolve it completely. If it dissolves completely, sulfate is absent. If a white residue is left, SO_4^{-2} is present. To the dilute HCl solution, add 2 M $NaC_2H_3O_2$ solution until the orange color has become yellow. A yellow precipitate of $BaCrO_4$ shows the presence of CrO_4^{-2}.

11–*O*. *Insoluble Zinc Salts*. (1) *Sulfide*. Sulfide will already have been detected in (11–*L*), so the test need not be repeated here.

(2) *Cyanide*. Cyanide will not purposely be added to your unknown samples; however, as noted in procedure (11–*B*), it may result from decomposition of $Fe(CN)_6^{-3}$, and therefore a test for it is included here.

Transfer a portion of the precipitate obtained in (11–*G*), well washed with $Zn(NO_3)_2$ solution, to a small flask, add 5 ml of water, and shake to form a suspension. Acidify the suspension with dilute HCl and place over the mouth of the flask a piece of filter paper which has been wetted with NaOH solution. Heat the flask to boiling and continue to heat for half a minute. Now add to the filter paper 2 drops of freshly prepared $FeSO_4$ solution, and acidify the spot with 1 drop of 12 M HCl. Then add 1 drop of $FeCl_3$ solution and 1 drop of KCl solution. A blue color shows the presence of CN^-.

$$6\ CN^- + Fe(OH)_2\ (s) \rightarrow Fe(CN)_6^{-4} + 2\ OH^-$$
$$K^+ + Fe^{+3} + Fe(CN)_6^{-4} \rightarrow KFe[Fe(CN)_6]\ (s)$$

(3) *Hexacyanoferrate(II)*. Transfer a portion of the precipitate obtained in (11–*G*) to a spot plate, acidify with dilute HCl, and add a drop of FeCl$_3$ and 1 drop of KCl. A blue color (Prussian blue) shows the presence of Fe(CN)$_6^{-4}$.

(4) *Hexacyanoferrate(III)*. Acidify another portion of the precipitate from (11–*G*) with dilute HCl and add a drop of freshly prepared FeSO$_4$ solution and one drop of KCl. Development of a blue color (Turnbull's blue) shows the presence of Fe(CN)$_6^{-3}$.

11–*P. Alkali-Insoluble Barium Salts.* (1) *Arsenite.* To a portion of the precipitate obtained in (11–*H*), in a test tube, add 0.5 ml 6 *N* NaOH. Put in a few aluminum pellets and immediately plug the mouth of the tube with a wad of cotton; put a piece of filter paper over the end of the tube. A blackening of the filter paper shows the presence of AsO$_2^-$. (Recall the discussion in Section 5–13).

(2) *Tungstate.* When no more arsine can be detected coming from the test tube (add more aluminum if necessary), make the solution acidic with HCl. If a white precipitate appears, separate and wash it. Suspend it in concentrated HCl, add a few drops of SnCl$_2$ solution, and heat to boiling. Development of a blue color ("tungsten blue") indicates the presence of WO$_4^{-2}$.

(3) *Arsenate.* To the supernate from the tungstic acid precipitation add a few pieces of mossy zinc and repeat the test for arsine. A black spot on the AgNO$_3$ paper shows the presence of AsO$_4^{-3}$. The two tests for arsenic (arsenite and arsenate) will serve to determine the oxidation state of the arsenic in the original solution. (Of course, both *may* be present unless there are other oxidizing or reducing ions which rule out one of them.)

(4) *Molybdate and Vanadate.* These ions (and tungstate) will be detected in the analysis for cations. They are mentioned here because, if present, they form precipitates with Ba^{+2} in alkaline solution, and also produce color changes during the tests for arsenic. (Tungstate and molybdate will give "tungsten blue" or "molybdenum blue," and vanadate will give colors changing from an original yellow or orange through green to blue to green, and finally to purple, as the vanadium is reduced from VO$_2^+$ (yellow) to VO^{+2} (blue) to V^{+3} (green) to V^{+2} (purple). These ions may be tested for here, using the tests employed in cation analysis. Note, however, that molybdenum and tungsten must be removed before the peroxide test for vanadium can be carried out, because molybdenum and tungsten likewise form yellow-to-orange peroxy complexes.

(5) *Phosphate.* If arsenate has been completely reduced to arsine by the above, it should be possible to test immediately for phosphate (after re-oxidizing any V, Mo, or W with bromine water). However, if any arsenate remains, it will give the same test as a phosphate. Consequently, it is best to carry out the procedure given in (11–*B*) before testing for phosphate.

11–*Q. Insoluble Silver Salts.* (1) *Thiocyanate.* Put a portion of the silver salt precipitate obtained in (11–*I*) into a test tube, add a few drops of water, and then a drop or two of 1 *M* FeCl$_3$ solution. Development of the red color of the FeNCS^{+2} complex ion in the supernate shows the presence of NCS$^-$.

(2) *Chloride.* Put a second portion of the silver salt precipitate obtained in (11–*I*) into a test tube and treat with 5 drops of ammoniacal AgNO$_3$ (Miller's reagent). This has just enough free Ag$^+$ in it so that it will dissolve AgCl, but not AgNCS, AgBr, or AgI. Stir. If all the precipitate dissolves, only chloride is present. If a residue remains, centrifuge and make the supernate acidic with

HNO_3. The precipitation of white AgCl confirms the presence of Cl^-. (A faint precipitate may be due to traces of NCS^- or Br^- or to chance contamination by Cl^-.)

(3) *Preparation of the Sample for the Detection of Bromide and Iodide.* Suspend the rest of the silver-salt precipitate obtained in (11–*I*) in 1 ml of water. Add 3 drops of 6 M HNO_3 and 1 ml of CH_3CSNH_2. Heat in a water bath for 10 minutes. Remove the supernate, which now should contain any or all of Cl^-, Br^-, I^-, and NCS^-, and also excess CH_3CSNH_2. Add to the supernate 5 drops of 0.1 M $Cd(NO_3)_2$ solution, and heat again on the water bath for ten minutes. If no yellow precipitate of CdS appears, all the CH_3CSNH_2 was hydrolyzed and the H_2S driven off in the first heating. If CdS precipitates, centrifuge, add 5 drops more of 0.1 M $Cd(NO_3)_2$ to the supernate, and heat again. Continue this procedure until no more CdS is produced. Centrifuge off the CdS, and remove the supernate for analysis.

(4) *Iodide.* To a 2-drop portion of the supernate from the CdS treatment add NH_4OH until basic. Now add a few drops of carbon tetrachloride and then a few drops of NaClO solution. Finally, add acetic acid dropwise, shaking the mixture at intervals. If the CCl_4 layer becomes purple (with extracted I_2), iodide ion is present. Continue the addition of NaClO with shaking until the purple color is discharged.

$$2\ I^- + ClO^- + 2\ HC_2H_3O_2 \rightarrow I_2\ (\text{in } CCl_4) + Cl^- + 2\ C_2H_3O_2^- + H_2O$$
$$I_2\ (\text{in } CCl_4) + 5\ ClO^- + H_2O \rightarrow 2\ IO_3^- + 5\ Cl^- + 2\ H^+$$

(5) *Bromide.* To the same tube, add 2 drops of 6 M H_2SO_4 and continue the addition of NaClO. If bromide ion is present, a brown-to-red color will develop in the CCl_4 layer.

$$2\ Br^- + ClO^- + 2\ H^+ \rightarrow Br_2\ (\text{in } CCl_4) + Cl^- + H_2O$$

11–*R*. *The Soluble Group.* (1) *Preparation.* Before analyzing for the ions of this group, it is first necessary to remove the various metallic ions that have been added for the precipitation of the anion groups. To the supernate from the silver-salt precipitation (11–*I*), add solid Na_2CO_3 until the solution is alkaline. Heat to boiling and evaporate in a casserole to small volume. Centrifuge and remove the supernate for analysis of the ions of the soluble group.

(2) *Chlorate and Permanganate.* Permanganate will be conspicuous by the survival of the purple color (or green in alkaline solution—see procedure 11–*B*) through the precipitation of the silver salts. It is the only colored ion which can do this (except for the very similar TcO_4^-). The addition of $NaNO_2$ to reduce ClO_3^- to Cl^-, however, will reduce MnO_4^- to Mn^{+2}. As in cation analysis, the Mn^{+2} may be reoxidized to MnO_4^- as a check. (Permanganate is reduced by H_2S and appears in the cation analysis as Mn^{+2}.)

To a portion of the carbonate solution obtained above, add 6 M H_2SO_4 until the solution is slightly acidic, add a few crystals of $NaNO_2$, and heat to boiling. Any MnO_4^- will be reduced to Mn^{+2}, and any ClO_3^- to Cl^-.

$$2\ MnO_4^- + 5\ NO_2^- + 6\ H^+ \rightarrow 2\ Mn^{+2} + 5\ NO_3^- + 3\ H_2O$$
$$ClO_3^- + 3\ NO_2^- \rightarrow Cl^- + 3\ NO_3^-$$

To the boiled solution, add 2 drops 15 M HNO_3 and 2 drops 0.1 M $AgNO_3$. A white precipitate of AgCl shows the presence of ClO_3^-.

(3) *Nitrite.* On a spot plate, place a few drops of the carbonate solution and a crystal of $FeSO_4$. Add acetic acid until acidic. A brown color shows the

presence of NO_2^-. (Acetic acid is not sufficiently acidic to bring about the corresponding reaction with NO_3^-.)

$$2 \, Fe^{+2} + NO_2^- + 2 \, H^+ \rightarrow FeNO^{+2} + Fe^{+3} + H_2O$$

$$(4 \, Fe^{+2} + NO_3^- + 4 \, H^+ \rightarrow FeNO^{+2} + 3 \, Fe^{+3} + 2 \, H_2O)$$

(4) *Nitrate.* This test is run on a portion of the original carbonate-treated solution (11–*A*). Put 1 ml of this solution into a casserole and add 10 drops of 0.1 *M* KI and 2 drops of concentrated H_2SO_4. Heat until most of the color of free iodine disappears. Add 6 *M* NaOH until the solution is basic, and add 5 drops more. Warm the solution gently until the vapors coming off do not affect red litmus. Transfer the solution to a *dry* test tube with a pipet, making sure none of the liquid touches the upper part of the tube. Now add a few pellets of aluminum metal. Push a loose wad of cotton part way down the tube, but far enough above the liquid so it does not get wet. Suspend in the upper part of the tube, not touching the cotton, a piece of moist red litmus paper. Cover the test tube with a 10-ml beaker and warm the tube until a vigorous reaction takes place. Take care that the cotton wad is not wetted. Let the tube stand and cool. By the end of about 5 minutes, the litmus paper should have turned generally blue, beginning at the bottom, if NO_3^- was present.

$$2 \, NO_2^- + 2 \, I^- + 4 \, H^+ \rightarrow 2 \, NO \, (g) + I_2 \, (g) + 2 \, H_2O$$

$$3 \, NO_3^- + 8 \, Al \, (s) + 5 \, OH^- + 18 \, H_2O \rightarrow 3 \, NH_3 \, (g) + 8 \, Al(OH)_4^-$$

11–16. Questions and Problems

1. Explain the correlation between electronegativity and the stability of negative oxidation states.

2. If a sample of element 111 could be obtained, predict whether it would be more or less easily reduced than gold from the $+3$ state to the free metal.

3. Predict whether element 117 will be more easily reduced to the -1 state than astatine.

4. Predict whether or not the $+7$ state of element 107 will be a better oxidizing agent than ReO_4^-.

5. Is it ever possible for an oxidant and a reductant to exist in the same solution together? If so, explain when. (There are at least three possibilities.)

6. Explain the difference in physical properties between CO_2 and SiO_2.

7. Predict which of the following substances might form the same type of crystals (a) as $BaSO_4$: $KClO_4$, $CaSO_4$, $CdBeF_4$, $TlBF_4$, $TlPF_6$, $LaAsO_4$, $RbSO_3F$, $TlInBr_4$, K_2PbCl_6, $CsPO_2F_2$; (b) as CaF_2: PbF_2, LaH_2, $HgCl_2$, $KLaF_4$, KBF_4.

8. Balance the following equations:
   (a) $MnO_4^- + Fe^{+2} \rightarrow Mn^{+2} + Fe^{+3}$ in acid
   (b) $H_2S + I_2 \rightarrow S + I^-$ in acid
   (c) $S_2O_3^{-2} + I_2 \rightarrow S_4O_6^{-2} + I^-$
   (d) $NO_3^- + Zn \rightarrow NH_4^+ + Zn^{+2}$ in acid
   (e) $MnO_4^- + C_2O_4^{-2} \rightarrow Mn^{+2} + CO_2$ in acid
   (f) $Cr_2O_7^{-2} + Fe^{+2} \rightarrow Cr^{+3} + Fe^{+3}$ in acid

(g) $Cr_2O_7^{-2} + Sn^{+2} \rightarrow Cr^{+3} + Sn^{+4}$ in acid

(h) $Hg_2S + S_2^{-2} \rightarrow HgS_2^{-2} + S$

(i) $CeO_2 + I^- \rightarrow Ce^{+3} + I_2$ in acid

(j) $NO_3^- + Cl^- \rightarrow NOCl + Cl_2$ in acid

(k) $Cu^{+2} + CN^- \rightarrow Cu(CN)_2^- + (CN)_2$

(l) $CrO_4^{-2} + Sn(OH)_3^- \rightarrow Cr(OH)_4^- + Sn(OH)_6^{-2}$ in base

(m) $Cr(OH)_4^- + ClO^- \rightarrow CrO_4^{-2} + Cl^-$ in base

(n) $CN^- + MnO_4^{-2} \rightarrow NCO^- + MnO_2$ in base

(o) $CN^- + Fe(CN)_6^{-3} \rightarrow NCO^- + Fe(CN)_6^{-4}$ in base

(p) $Cl_2 \rightarrow Cl^- + ClO_3^-$ in base

(q) $P \rightarrow PH_3 + PH_2O_2^-$ in base

(r) $Cr(OH)_4^- + H_2O_2 \rightarrow CrO_4^{-2}$ in base

(s) $Cr_2O_7^{-2} + H_2O_2 \rightarrow Cr^{+3}$ in acid

(t) $PbO_2 + Pb \rightarrow PbSO_4$

(u) $Ag^+ + SbH_3 \rightarrow Ag_3Sb$

(v) $Ag^+ + AsH_3 \rightarrow Ag + H_3AsO_3$

(w) $Sn^{+2} + H_2O_2 \rightarrow Sn^{+4}$ in acid

(x) $S_2O_3^{-2} + H_2O_2 \rightarrow S_4O_6^{-2}$ in acid

(y) $S^{-2} + SO_3^{-2} \rightarrow S$ in acid

9. Calculate the concentration of (a) PO_4^{-3} and (b) AsO_4^{-3} in solution after treatment of (a) $Ba_3(PO_4)_2$ and (b) $Ba_3(AsO_4)_2$ with 1.5 M Na_2CO_3; $K_{sp}(Ba_3(PO_4)_2) = 6.0 \times 10^{-39}$; $K_{sp}(Ba_3(AsO_4)_2) = 1.1 \times 10^{-13}$.

10. Find the equilibrium constants for the reactions of Zn and HCl with (a) HgS, (b) Bi_2S_3, (c) PdS. (See Chapter 12).

11–17. References

Boltz, D. F., ed., *Colorimetric Determination of Nonmetals.* New York: Interscience Publishers, Inc., 1958.

The Chemistry of the Ferrocyanides. New York: American Cyanamid Company, 1953.

Bromine. Michigan Chemical Corporation.

Iodine, Its Properties and Technical Applications. New York: Chilean Iodine Educational Bureau, Inc., 1951.

Yost, D. M., and Russell, Jr., H., *Systematic Inorganic Chemistry (N, P, O, S, Se, Te).* New York: Prentice-Hall, Inc., 1946.

Beckham, L. J., Fessler, W. A., and Kise, M. A., "Nitrosyl Chloride," *Chemical Reviews,* Vol. 48 (1951), p. 320.

Gray, P., *The Chemistry of Dinitrogen Tetroxide.* London: Royal Institute of Chemistry, 1958.

Maxted, E. B., *Modern Advances in Inorganic Chemistry.* Oxford: Oxford University Press, 1947, chap. III.

Van Wazer, J. R., *Phosphorus and Its Compounds.* New York: Interscience Publishers, Inc., 1958.

Recent Aspects of the Inorganic Chemistry of Nitrogen. London: The Chemical Society, Special Publication No. 10, 1957.

Haszeldine, R. N., and Sharpe, A. G., *Fluorine and Its Compounds.* New York: John Wiley and Sons, Inc., New York, 1951.

Simons, J. H., ed., *Fluorine Chemistry* (2 vols.). New York: Academic Press, Inc., 1950, 1954.

Morgan, G. T., *Organic Compounds of Arsenic and Antimony.* New York: Longmans, Green and Company, 1918.

Mann, F. G., *The Heterocyclic Derivatives of Phosphorus, Arsenic, Antimony, Bismuth and Silicon.* New York: Interscience Publishers, Inc., 1950.

Chapter 12

Redox Equilibria. The General Unknown

12–1. Redox Equilibria and Half-Reactions

So far we have considered oxidation-reduction (redox) reactions only from the qualitative point of view. In this and the next chapter, we shall take up some of the quantitative aspects of redox reactions.

Like any other type of reaction, redox reactions are subject to the laws of chemical equilibrium. Thus, for reactions such as

$$Fe^{+2} + Cr^{+3} \rightleftharpoons Fe^{+3} + Cr^{+2}$$

or $\quad MnO_4^- + 5\,VO^{+2} + H_2O \rightleftharpoons Mn^{+2} + 5\,VO_2^+ + 2\,H^+$

or $\qquad Hg_2Cl_2\,(s) + 2\,NH_3 \rightleftharpoons Hg\,(l) + HgNH_2Cl\,(s) + NH_4^+ + Cl^-$

there are equilibrium expressions of the usual type, each characterized by its own equilibrium constant.

$$\frac{[Fe^{+3}][Cr^{+2}]}{[Fe^{+2}][Cr^{+3}]} = K_1$$

$$\frac{[Mn^{+2}][VO_2^+]^5[H^+]^2}{[MnO_4^-][VO^{+2}]^5} = K_2$$

$$\frac{[NH_4^+][Cl^-]}{[NH_3]^2} = K_3$$

It would, of course, be possible in theory to make tables containing the constant for every conceivable redox reaction. However, considering the number of possible combinations of oxidizing and reducing agents among the more than one hundred elements in the periodic table, such a compilation would be impossible in practice, besides being completely unwieldy if it could be done. Even a compilation of the more important redox reactions would be very large indeed.

In Section 11–6, the use of half-reactions to balance redox equations was discussed. If it were possible to determine an equilibrium constant for each of these half-reactions, it would be possible to make a far smaller compilation of equilibrium constants, which could then be combined to give all the constants for complete reactions required.

In theory, it should be possible to take a half-reaction such as

$$Ag\,(s) \rightleftharpoons Ag^+ + e^-$$

or

$$Ce^{+3} \rightleftharpoons Ce^{+4} + e^-$$

and determine equilibrium constants

$$[Ag^+][e^-] = K_1$$

or

$$\frac{[Ce^{+4}][e^-]}{[Ce^{+3}]} = K_2$$

In practice, of course, the concentration of free electrons, $[e^-]$, which can exist in water is extremely minute and not possible to determine. However, $[e^-]$ must be the same for both of two half-reactions taking place in the same solution, so that it will always be possible to combine the constants for the half-reactions to obtain that of the over-all reactions, in this case

$$Ag\,(s) + Ce^{+4} \rightleftharpoons Ag^+ + Ce^{+3}$$

$$\frac{[Ag^+][e^-]}{\dfrac{[Ce^{+4}][e^-]}{[Ce^{+3}]}} = \frac{[Ag^+][Ce^{+3}]}{[Ce^{+4}]} = \frac{K_1}{K_2} = K_{eq}$$

Consequently, if it were possible to determine the constant for only one half-reaction, then equilibrium constants for over-all reactions in which this half-reaction takes part could be measured, and the constants for other half-reactions thus be determined. As mentioned above, however, to date it has not been possible to do this.

Because of the great utility that a series of constants for half-reactions would have, however, the half-reaction

$$\tfrac{1}{2}\,H_2\,(g) \rightleftharpoons H^+ + e^-$$

may be selected as a standard and its equilibrium constant defined arbitrarily as α

$$\frac{[H^+][e^-]}{p_{H_2}^{1/2}} = \alpha$$

(or in reality the standard oxidation *potential* has been defined as zero, $E° = 0.00$. See Chapter 13.). Now, if the equilibrium constant for any reaction involving the H_2–H^+ couple is determined, the value for the other couple (i.e., half-reaction) can be found in terms of α by comparison with the H_2–H^+ couple. For example, the reaction

$$H_2 \text{ (g)} + Br_2 \text{ (aq)} \rightleftharpoons 2\,H^+ + 2\,Br^-$$

is found to have the equilibrium constant

$$\frac{[H^+]^2[Br^-]^2}{p_{H_2}[Br_2]} = 10^{+35.8}$$

Since

$$\frac{[H^+]^2[e^-]^2}{p_{H_2}} = 10^{0.00}\alpha^2$$

then

$$\frac{[Br^-]^2}{[Br_2][e^-]^2} = \frac{10^{+35.8}}{\alpha^2}$$

for the half-reaction

$$Br_2 \text{ (aq)} + 2\,e^- \rightleftharpoons 2\,Br^-$$

Or, since by convention the reduced form of the couple (in this case Br^-) is always written on the left of a half-reaction

$$2\,Br^- \rightleftharpoons Br_2 \text{ (aq)} + 2\,e^-$$

then

$$\frac{[Br_2][e^-]^2}{[Br^-]^2} = 10^{-35.8}\alpha^2$$

Now, of course, it is possible to take *any* half-reaction whose equilibrium constant has been accurately determined in this way and use it in turn to determine the constant for some new half-reaction. For the reaction

$$2\,VO_2^+ + 2\,Br^- + 4\,H^+ \rightleftharpoons 2\,VO^{+2} + Br_2 \text{ (aq)} + 2\,H_2O$$

we have

$$\frac{[VO^{+2}]^2[Br_2]}{[VO_2^+]^2[Br^-]^2[H^+]^4} = 10^{-1.2}$$

Since

$$\frac{[Br_2][e^-]^2}{[Br^-]^2} = 10^{-35.8}\alpha^2$$

then

$$\frac{[VO^{+2}]^2}{[VO_2^+]^2[H^+]^4[e^-]^2} = \frac{10^{-1.2}}{10^{-35.8}} = \frac{10^{+34.6}}{\alpha^2}$$

or, in conformity to convention

$$\frac{[VO_2^+]^2[H^+]^4[e^-]^2}{[VO^{+2}]^2} = 10^{-34.6}\alpha^2$$

for the half-reaction

$$2\,VO^{+2} + 2\,H_2O \rightleftharpoons 2\,VO_2^+ + 4\,H^+ + 2\,e^-$$

Since this last equation can be simplified to

$$VO^{+2}+H_2O \rightleftharpoons VO_2{}^+ +2\,H^+ +e^-$$

we should take the square root of each side of the mathematical expression to give

$$\frac{[VO_2{}^+][H^+]^2[e^-]}{[VO^{+2}]} = 10^{-17.3}\alpha$$

When any two half-reactions are combined to give a complete reaction, both the $[e^-]$'s and the α's cancel out.

12–2.   The Effect of pH on Redox Equilibria

For a reaction such as

$$Cl_2\,(aq)+2\,Br^- \rightleftharpoons Br_2\,(aq)+2\,Cl^-$$

there is no *obvious* effect of pH, since H^+ does not enter into the reaction. For the reaction

$$I_2\,(aq)+H_2\,(g) \rightleftharpoons 2\,I^- +2\,H^+$$

or $$2\,NO_3{}^- +6\,I^- +8\,H^+ \rightleftharpoons 2\,NO\,(g)+3\,I_2\,(aq)+4\,H_2O$$

however, where H^+ is either directly or indirectly involved in the redox reaction, the fact that the position of the equilibrium will be changed by a change of pH is fairly obvious. Changing the pH will not, however, change the equilibrium *constant*.

If, on the other hand, a weak acid or base is involved in the equilibrium, the effect of change in pH may be felt not only through the change in hydrogen-ion concentration itself but also in the change of concentration of the anion of the weak acid or the cation of the weak base. For example, for the reaction

$$CN^- +S\,(s) \rightleftharpoons NCS^-$$

the lower the pH, the further the equilibrium will lie to the left, because as the hydrogen-ion concentration is increased, the concentration of CN^- is decreased by repression of ionization of the weak acid, HCN.

$$HCN \rightleftharpoons H^+ +CN^-$$

Although this is in fact merely another example of shifting one equilibrium through changing the concentrations of the substances involved, and in no way changes the *equilibrium constant* for the reaction

$$CN^- +S\,(s) \rightleftharpoons NCS^-$$

it is nevertheless more convenient to include the ionization equilibrium for HCN in the equilibrium expression, which will now automatically take into account the effect of changes of pH on the equilibrium between sulfur, cyanide ion, and thiocyanate ion

$$\frac{[NCS^-]}{[CN^-]} = 10^{+11.73}$$

$$\frac{[H^+][CN^-]}{[HCN]} = 4.8 \times 10^{-10} = 10^{-9.32}$$

and
$$\frac{[H^+][NCS^-]}{[HCN]} = 10^{+2.41}$$

for the reaction

$$HCN + S \text{ (s)} \rightleftharpoons H^+ + NCS^-$$

12–3. The Effect of Solubility on Redox Equilibria

The effect of changing pH on redox equilibria can be seen in another case. For the reaction

$$Fe^{+3} + Tl \text{ (s)} \rightleftharpoons Tl^+ + Fe^{+2}$$

the equilibrium is quite independent of pH so long as the pH is low.

(1)
$$\frac{[Tl^+][Fe^{+2}]}{[Fe^{+3}]} = 10^{18.8}$$

At higher pH, however, a pH-dependence sets in, and the equilibrium continues to shift regularly (with one modification) as the pH is raised, until very high pH is reached, whereupon the dependence of the equilibrium on pH once more disappears. It is found on examination of the system that the setting in of pH-dependence as the pH is raised takes place in the range in which the hydroxides of iron begin to precipitate out, and the removal of pH-dependence occurs at the pH at which TlOH begins to precipitate. Let us see why this is so. When the iron hydroxides precipitate, the concentrations of Fe^{+2} and Fe^{+3} will be affected by the pH through the solubility equilibria of the hydroxides. The equilibrium becomes first

$$Fe(OH)_3 \text{ (s)} + Tl \text{ (s)} \rightleftharpoons Fe^{+2} + Tl^+ + 3 \text{ OH}^-$$

(2) $$[Fe^{+2}][Tl^+][OH^-]^3 = 10^{-18.4}$$

as the very insoluble $Fe(OH)_3$ first precipitates. This comes from a combination of (1) with the K_{sp} expression for $Fe(OH)_3$.

$$[Fe^{+3}][OH^-]^3 = 10^{-37.2}$$

Then as $Fe(OH)_2$ begins to precipitate, the equilibrium becomes

$$Fe(OH)_3 \text{ (s)} + Tl \text{ (s)} \rightleftharpoons Fe(OH)_2 \text{ (s)} + Tl^+ + OH^-$$

(3) $$[Tl^+][OH^-] = 10^{-4.3}$$

This comes from a combination of (2) with the K_{sp} expression for $Fe(OH)_2$. Finally, when TlOH begins to precipitate, we have

$$Fe(OH)_3 \text{ (s)} + Tl \text{ (s)} \rightleftharpoons Fe(OH)_2 \text{ (s)} + Tl(OH) \text{ (s)}$$

and once more the equilibrium is pH-independent. (The expression obtained by combining (3) with the K_{sp} expression for TlOH, i.e.

(4) $$1 = \text{———————} = 10^{-4.1}$$

no longer makes sense. The constant obtained, however, does relate the relative concentrations of the metal ions remaining in solution.) Since the expression now is

$$\frac{[Fe^{+3}][OH^-]^3}{[Tl^+][Fe^{+2}][OH^-]^3} = 10^{-4.1}$$

and since the $[OH^-]$ appears to the same power in both numerator and denominator, the ratio of $[Fe^{+3}]$ to $[Tl^+][Fe^{+3}]$ must now remain fixed as $[OH^-]$ is increased, resulting in independence of the equilibrium on pH.

Other equilibria may also be affected by the precipitation of insoluble solids. For example, the equilibrium expression for the reaction

$$2\,MnO_4^- + 2\,I^- \rightleftharpoons 2MnO_4^{-2} + I_2 \text{ (s)}$$

is

$$\frac{[MnO_4^{-2}]^2}{[MnO_4^-]^2[I^-]^2} = 10^{0.9} \quad \text{or} \quad \frac{[MnO_4^{-2}]}{[MnO_4^-][I^-]} = 10^{0.45}$$

However, if the reaction takes place in the presence of Ba^{+2}, the slightly soluble $BaMnO_4$ precipitates

$$[Ba^{+2}][MnO_4^{-2}] = 10^{-9.61}$$

so that for the reaction

$$MnO_4^- + I^- + Ba^{+2} \rightleftharpoons BaMnO_4 \text{ (s)} + \tfrac{1}{2} I_2 \text{ (s)}$$

we have

(5) $$\frac{1}{[MnO_4^-][I^-][Ba^{+2}]} = \frac{10^{0.45}}{10^{-9.61}} = 10^{10.06}$$

12-4.   The Effect of Complex Formation on Redox Equilibria

In exactly the same way, equilibria are shifted by the formation of complex ions. For example, the equilibrium

$$Fe^{+3} + I^- \rightleftharpoons Fe^{+2} + \tfrac{1}{2} I_2 \text{ (s)}$$

has the constant

(6)
$$\frac{[Fe^{+2}]}{[Fe^{+3}][I^-]} = 10^{4.0}$$

In the presence of F^-, however, the concentration of Fe^{+3} is drastically reduced by the formation of fluoroferrate complex ions. In the presence of excess F^-, the FeF_6^{-3} will predominate, so we shall take the cumulative instability constant for

$$FeF_6^{-3} \rightleftharpoons Fe^{+3} + 6\,F^-$$

(7)
$$K_{inst} = \frac{[Fe^{+3}][F^-]^6}{[FeF_6^{-3}]} = 10^{-16.1}$$

Combining this with the equilibrium constant for the $Fe^{+3} + I^-$ reaction (6), we have for the new equilibrium

$$FeF_6^{-3} + I^- \rightleftharpoons Fe^{+2} + 6\,F^- + \tfrac{1}{2}\,I_2\,(s)$$

(8)
$$\frac{[Fe^{+2}][F^-]^6}{[FeF_6^{-3}][I^-]} = 10^{-12.1}$$

Consequently, the equilibrium which lay slightly to the right initially has been shifted way over to the left by addition of F^-.

12–5. General Redox Equilibria

It is by no means necessary that these effects which have been discussed be felt separately. On the contrary a given reaction may involve simultaneously insoluble solids, volatile gases, complex ions, and weak acids or bases along with the redox reaction. Let us consider, for example, the reaction

$$Hg_2HPO_4\,(s) + Cl_2\,(g) + 6\,Cl^- + 2\,H^+ \rightleftharpoons 2\,HgCl_4^{-2} + H_3PO_4\,(aq)$$

In order to obtain the equilibrium constant for this rather complicated reaction, let us first break it down into its component equilibria. First, we have the solubility equilibrium for Hg_2HPO_4

(9)
$$[Hg_2^{+2}][HPO_4^{-2}] = 10^{-12.40}$$

For the instability equilibrium of $HgCl_4^{-2}$, we have

(10)
$$\frac{[Hg^{+2}][Cl^-]^4}{[HgCl_4^{-2}]} = 10^{-15.08}$$

For the ionization equilibrium of H_3PO_4, we have

$$H_3PO_4 \rightleftharpoons H^+ + H_2PO_4^- \quad \text{and} \quad H_2PO_4^- \rightleftharpoons H^+ + HPO_4^{-2}$$

(11) $$\frac{[H^+][H_2PO_4^-]}{[H_3PO_4]} = 10^{-2.12}$$

(12) $$\frac{[H^+][HPO_4^{-2}]}{[H_2PO_4^-]} = 10^{-7.21}$$

Equations (11) and (12) combine to give

(13) $$\frac{[H^+]^2[HPO_4^{-2}]}{[H_3PO_4]} = 10^{-9.33}$$

for the reaction

$$H_3PO_4 \text{ (aq)} \rightleftharpoons 2\,H^+ + HPO_4^{-2}$$

The only reaction remaining to be considered now is the basic redox reaction

$$Hg_2^{+2} + Cl_2 \text{ (g)} \rightleftharpoons 2\,Hg^{+2} + 2\,Cl^-$$

which can be broken down into the half-reactions

$$Hg_2^{+2} \rightleftharpoons 2\,Hg^{+2} + 2\,e^-$$

and $$Cl^- \rightleftharpoons \tfrac{1}{2}\,Cl_2 \text{ (g)} + e^-$$

The equilibrium constants for these are

(14) $$\frac{[Hg^{+2}]^2[e^-]^2}{[Hg_2^{+2}]} = 10^{-31.18}\alpha^2$$

(15) $$\frac{p_{Cl_2}^{1/2}[e^-]}{[Cl^-]} = 10^{-23.04}\alpha$$

Squaring (15) and combining it with (14) gives us the equilibrium constant for the basic redox reaction

(16) $$\frac{\dfrac{[Hg^{+2}]^2[e^-]^2}{[Hg_2^{+2}]}}{\dfrac{p_{Cl_2}[e^-]^2}{[Cl^-]^2}} = \frac{[Hg^{+2}]^2[Cl^-]^2}{[Hg_2^{+2}]p_{Cl_2}} = \frac{10^{-31.18}}{(10^{-23.04})^2} = 10^{14.90}$$

Combining (16) and the square of (10) gives

(17) $$\frac{\dfrac{[Hg^{+2}]^2[Cl^-]^2}{[Hg_2^{+2}]^2 p_{Cl_2}}}{\dfrac{[Hg^{+2}]^2[Cl^-]^8}{[HgCl_4^{-2}]^2}} = \frac{[HgCl_4^{-2}]^2}{[Hg_2^{+2}]p_{Cl_2}[Cl^-]^6} = \frac{10^{14.90}}{(10^{-15.08})^2} = 10^{45.06}$$

for the reaction

$$Hg_2^{+2} + Cl_2 \text{ (g)} + 6\,Cl^- \rightleftharpoons 2\,HgCl_4^{-2}$$

Now combining (17) and (9) we have

$$(18) \quad [Hg_2{}^{+2}][HPO_4{}^{-2}]\frac{[HgCl_4{}^{-2}]^{-2}}{[Hg_2{}^{+2}]p_{Cl_2}[Cl^-]^6} = \frac{[HPO_4{}^{-2}][HgCl_4{}^{-2}]^{-2}}{p_{Cl_2}[Cl^-]^6}$$

$$= 10^{-12.40} \times 10^{45.06} = 10^{32.66}$$

for the reaction

$$Hg_2HPO_4 \,(s) + Cl_2 \,(g) + 6\,Cl^- \rightleftharpoons 2\,HgCl_4{}^{-2} + HPO_4{}^{-2}$$

Finally, combining (18) and (13) we have

$$(19) \quad \frac{\dfrac{[HPO_4{}^{-2}][HgCl_4{}^{-2}]^2}{p_{Cl_2}[Cl^-]^6}}{\dfrac{[H^+]^2[HPO_4{}^{-2}]}{[H_3PO_4]}} = \frac{[HgCl_4{}^{-2}]^2[H_3PO_4]}{p_{Cl_2}[Cl^-]^6[H^+]^2} = \frac{10^{32.66}}{10^{-9.33}} = 10^{41.99}$$

for the complete reaction

$$Hg_2HPO_4 \,(s) + Cl_2 \,(g) + 6\,Cl^- + 2\,H^+ \rightleftharpoons 2\,HgCl_4{}^{-2} + H_3PO_4 \,(aq)$$

12–6. Equilibrium Constants for Half-Reactions

Appendix 9 contains a list of basic half-reactions and their equilibrium constants in terms of α. The constants are given for the reactions *as written*, with the powers of α omitted. Half-reactions involving solid phases for which K_{sp}'s are available, those involving weak acids and bases, and those involving complex ions for which equilibrium constants are available are not included, since these can easily be obtained by the appropriate combination of the equilibrium expression for the basic half-reaction and the equilibrium constant for the insoluble salt, the acid or base, or the complex ion.

For example, to obtain the equilibrium constant for the half-reaction

$$Pb \,(s) + SO_4{}^{-2} \rightleftharpoons PbSO_4 \,(s) + 2\,e^-$$

we combine the expression for the basic half-reaction

$$Pb \,(s) \rightleftharpoons Pb^{+2} + 2\,e^-$$

which is

$$(20) \qquad\qquad [Pb^{+2}][e^-]^2 = 10^{4.2}\alpha^2$$

with the K_{sp} of $PbSO_4$, which is

$$(21) \qquad\qquad [Pb^{+2}][SO_4{}^{-2}] = 10^{-7.8}$$

Dividing (20) by (21) we have

$$(22) \qquad \frac{[Pb^{+2}][e^-]^2}{[Pb^{+2}][SO_4{}^{-2}]} = \frac{[e^-]^2}{[SO_4{}^{-2}]} = \frac{10^{4.2}\alpha^2}{10^{-7.8}} = 10^{12.0}\alpha^2$$

for the reaction

$$Pb \,(s) + SO_4{}^{-2} \rightleftharpoons PbSO_4 \,(s) + 2\,e^-$$

Likewise, for the reaction

$$Mn(OH)_2 \text{ (s)} + OH^- \rightleftharpoons Mn(OH)_3 \text{ (s)} + e^-$$

we combine the expression for the basic half-reaction

$$Mn^{+2} \rightleftharpoons Mn^{+3} + e^-$$

which is

(23) $$\frac{[Mn^{+2}][e^-]}{[Mn^{+2}]} = 10^{-25.6}\alpha$$

with the K_{sp}'s of $Mn(OH)_2$ and $Mn(OH)_3$

(24) $$[Mn^{+2}][OH^-]^2 = 10^{-13.3}$$

(25) $$[Mn^{+3}][OH^-]^3 = 10^{-36.0}$$

Thus, for the half-reaction

$$Mn(OH)_2 \text{ (s)} + OH^- \rightleftharpoons Mn(OH)_3 \text{ (s)} + e^-$$

we have

(26) $$\frac{[Mn^{+3}][e^-][Mn^{+2}][OH^-]^2}{[Mn^{+2}][Mn^{+3}][OH^-]^3} = \frac{[e^-]}{[OH^-]} = \frac{10^{-25.6} \times 10^{-13.3}}{10^{-36.0}}\alpha = 10^{-2.9}\alpha$$

Consequently Mn(II) is far more easily oxidized to Mn(III) in alkaline than in acidic solution.

In the case of half-reactions which are otherwise hydrogen ion-dependent, such as

$$ClO_3^- + H_2O \rightleftharpoons ClO_4^- + 2\,H^+ + 2\,e^-$$

(27) $$\frac{[ClO_4^-][H^+]^2[e^-]^2}{[ClO_3^-]} = 10^{-42.0}\alpha^2$$

the constant for the reaction in basic medium

$$ClO_3^- + 2\,OH^- \rightleftharpoons ClO_4^- + H_2O + 2\,e^-$$

can be obtained by observing that the two equations are related to each other through the water equilibrium. Consequently it is necessary merely to divide (27) by the square of the expression for the water equilibrium in order to obtain the equilibrium expression for the half-reaction in basic solution.

(28) $$\frac{[ClO_4^-][[H^+]^2[e^-]^2}{[ClO_3^-][H^+]^2[OH^-]^2} = \frac{[ClO_4^-][e^-]^2}{[ClO_3^-]^2[OH^-]^2} = \frac{10^{-42.0}}{(10^{-14.0})^2}\alpha^2$$

$$= 10^{-14.0}\alpha^2$$

In the case of insoluble solids or other substances for which equilibrium constants are not readily obtainable, however, explicit values are given in Appendix 9. Such cases would be

$$Mn^{+2} + 2\,H_2O \rightleftharpoons MnO_2 \text{ (s)} + 4\,H^+ + 2\,e^-$$

$$Co(CN)_6^{-4} \rightleftharpoons Co(CN)_6^{-3} + e^-$$

Also a few of the most important cases which are not basic equilibria, such as

$$Fe(CN)_6^{-4} \rightleftharpoons Fe(CN)_6^{-3} + e^-$$

are given.

(*It should be noted that although* [e^-] *has been given in all the expressions for half-reactions in order to facilitate use of them, it would not ordinarily be expressed in the mathematical equation for the equilibrium.*)

One further point should be considered, namely, that two or more half-reactions may be combined to obtain a new half-reaction. For example, if we want the equilibrium constant for the half-reaction

$$S^{-2} + 4\,H_2O \rightleftharpoons SO_4^{-2} + 8\,H^+ + 8\,e^-$$

for which no constant is given in Appendix 9, it can be obtained by combining the expressions for

$$S^{-2} \rightleftharpoons S + 2\,e^- \qquad (19)$$

$$S + 3\,H_2O \rightleftharpoons SO_3^{-2} + 6\,H^+ + 4\,e^- \quad (66)$$

$$SO_3^{-2} + H_2O \rightleftharpoons SO_4^{-2} + 2\,H^+ + 2\,e^- \quad (31)$$

$$\overline{S^{-2} + 4\,H_2O \rightleftharpoons SO_4^{-2} + 8\,H^+ + 8\,e^-}$$

where the numbers at the right are the numbers of the equations as they appear in Appendix 9. Omitting the [e^-]'s, we have

$$\frac{1}{[S^{-2}]} = 10^{15.8}\alpha^2 \qquad (19)$$

$$[SO_3^{-2}][H^+]^6 = 10^{-39.6}\alpha^4 \qquad (66)$$

$$\frac{[SO_4^{-2}][H^+]^2}{[SO_3^{-2}]} = 10^{3.4}\alpha^2 \qquad (31)$$

When these are all multiplied together we have

$$\frac{1}{[S^{-2}]} \times [SO_3^{-2}][H^+]^6 \times \frac{[SO_4^{-2}][H^+]^2}{[SO_3^{-2}]}$$

$$= \frac{[SO_4^{-2}][H^+]^8}{[S^{-2}]} = 10^{15.8} \times 10^{-39.6} \times 10^{3.4}\alpha^8 = 10^{-20.4}\alpha^8$$

12-7.   The Significance of the Equilibrium Constant

It will certainly have become apparent by now that the equilibrium constant is a measure of how far a reaction must go to reach equilibrium. The larger the constant is (i.e., the larger the positive exponent), the farther to the right the equilibrium lies; and the smaller the constant is (i.e., the larger the negative exponent), the farther to the left it lies. However, it should by now be obvious that the *magnitude* of the constant has no significance in itself, but must be related to the equation accepted for the reaction. For example, let us take the reaction

$$3 \, ZnS \, (s) + 2 \, NO_3^- + 8 \, H^+ \rightleftharpoons 3 \, Zn^{+2} + 3 \, S \, (s) + 2 \, NO \, (g) + 4 \, H_2O$$

for which we have the expression

$$\frac{[Zn^{+2}]^3 p_{NO}^2}{[NO_3^-]^2 [H^+]^8} = 10^{105.6}$$

Let us note, however, that the correct formula for sulfur is not S, but is rather S_8, and therefore the reaction should have the equation

$$24 \, ZnS \, (s) + 16 \, NO_3^- + 64 \, H^+ \rightleftharpoons 24 \, Zn^{+2} + 3 \, S_8 \, (s) + 16 \, NO \, (g) + 32 \, H_2O$$

The equilibrium expression for this is

$$\frac{[Zn^{+2}]^{24} p_{NO}^{16}}{[NO_3^-]^{16} [H^+]^{64}} = 10^{844.8}$$

The mere fact that we have written an equilibrium constant of $10^{844.8}$ instead of $10^{105.6}$ does not indicate that the equilibrium now lies farther to the right, for when we raised $10^{105.6}$ to the eighth power, we simultaneously raised everything on the left-hand side of the equation to the eighth power, so that in actual fact nothing has changed. It should now be apparent that in order to judge the position of an equilibrium one must do more than just look at the equilibrium constant. It is necessary also to look at the form of the equilibrium expression. For example, the expression for the reaction

$$Sn \, (s) + Pb^{+2} \rightleftharpoons Sn^{+2} + Pb \, (s)$$

is

$$\frac{[Sn^{+2}]}{[Pb^{+2}]} = 10^{0.4}$$

It is apparent from this that at equilibrium the reaction cannot be said to have proceeded to completion in either direction, the tin(II)-ion concentration being only $10^{0.4}$ (or 2.5) times the lead-ion concentration.

Likewise, for the reaction

$$V^{+3} + Fe(CN)_6^{-3} + H_2O \rightleftharpoons VO^{+2} + Fe(CN)_6^{-4} + 2 \, H^+$$

$$\frac{[VO^{+2}][Fe(CN)_6^{-4}][H^+]^2}{[V^{+3}][Fe(CN)_6^{-3}]} = 10^{0.0}$$

it can be seen that when $[H^+] = 1$ molar, $[VO^{+2}][Fe(CN)_6^{-4}] = [V^{+3}][Fe(CN)_6^{-3}]$, and the reaction proceeds exactly 50 percent when $[V^{+3}] = [Fe(CN)_6^{-3}]$.

On the other hand, for the reaction

$$In\ (s) + 3\ Tl^+ \rightleftharpoons In^{+3} + 3\ Tl\ (s)$$

$$\frac{[In^{+2}]}{[Tl^+]^3} = 10^{0.3}$$

This would seem to indicate that at equilibrium all concentrations would be roughly the same. However, a closer look will show us that because of the different powers to which the concentrations must be raised, this is definitely not so. For example, in a system in which the equilibrium concentration of Tl^+ is $10^{-3}\ M$

$$[In^{+3}] = 2.0\ [Tl^{+3}]^3 = 2.0 \times 10^{-9}\ M$$

so that $[In^{+3}]$ is only one five-hundred thousandth of the $[Tl^+]$, despite the fact that the constant is so close to unity.

Likewise, for the reaction

$$6\ Au^+ + 2\ Cr^{+3} + 7\ H_2O \rightleftharpoons 6\ Au\ (s) + Cr_2O_7^{-2} + 14\ H^+$$

$$\frac{[Cr_2O_7^{-2}][H^+]^{14}}{[Au^+]^6[Cr^{+3}]^2} = 10^{35.4}$$

it would be said that, under ordinary circumstances, the equilibrium would lie way over on the right. However, if $[H^+] = 1$ molar and the final equilibrium $[Au^+] = 10^{-7}\ M$, then

$$\frac{[Cr_2O_7^{-2}]}{[Cr^{+3}]^2} = 10^{-6.6}$$

and the equilibrium lies over on the left instead.

Consequently, it can be seen that whether an equilibrium can be said to lie in one direction or the other depends not only on the magnitude of the equilibrium constant, but also upon the powers to which the concentrations must be raised and, in addition, upon the actual concentrations existing at equilibrium.

When an equilibrium constant is very large and the equilibrium lies far over in one direction, the reaction is sometimes said to go to completion. In the strictest sense, of course, this cannot be, for in order for any of the concentrations of the reactants actually to reach zero, the equilibrium constant for the reaction would have to be infinity. However, in practice, an equilibrium constant may be so large that the concentrations of the reactants at equilibrium are quite negligible. In this sense, we are justified in speaking of a reaction's going to completion.

12-8.   The Prediction of Reactions

In using tables of equilibrium constants, it must be remembered that, just because a reaction is found to be favored to go, it does not follow that it must go in the way stated or that it need, in fact, go at all. For example, if the reaction cited at the end of Section 12-3 is carried out in acidic solution, the reaction

$$2 \, MnO_4^- + 10 \, I^- + 16 \, H^+ \rightleftharpoons 2 \, Mn^{+2} + 5 \, I_2 \, (s) + 8 \, H_2O$$

will be so much more favorable than

$$2 \, MnO_4^- + 2 \, I^- + 2 \, Ba^{+2} \rightleftharpoons BaMnO_4 \, (s) + I_2 \, (s)$$

that no $BaMnO_4$ will form, all the MnO_4^- being reduced to Mn^{+2} instead.

A second factor is the rate at which the reaction takes place. For example, although H_2 (g) and O_2 (g) are favored to react, because of the extreme slowness of the reaction at room temperature, a mixture of the two gases may stand for many years without forming a detectable amount of water.

The rate of reaction may affect the situation in yet a different way. If there are several different possible reactions, all thermodynamically favorable and with comparable rates, then all may occur in competition. For example, when HNO_3 is reduced by zinc, all three of the products NO_2, NO, and NH_4^+ appear. This subject will be taken up in more detail in Chapter 15.

12-9. The General Unknown

The general analysis of an unknown substance which is in solution or which is completely soluble in water is merely a combination of the procedures discussed in the foregoing chapters. Since it is standard practice to remove all cations which may interfere with anion analysis (by carbonate precipitation), and it is necessary to know whether phosphate or oxalate is present in order to determine how to proceed with the cation analysis, it is advisable to perform the analysis for anions first, proceeding as discussed in Chapter 11. After the anion analysis, the cation analysis is carried out as in Chapter 9.

If the sample is a water-soluble solid, dissolve about 150 mg (i.e., that amount of solid having about the same volume as two drops of water) in 10 ml of distilled water. (Beware of making too concentrated a solution, for this will result in precipitates too bulky to manage. On the other hand, too little may result in failure to detect those elements whose tests are not very sensitive.)

If the sample is insoluble or only partially soluble in water, grind it fine with mortar and pestle and treat it with Na_2CO_3 for anion analysis as described in Chapter 11 (Section 11–14). For cation analysis, it may be necessary to remove organic matter (12–A), as well as the interfering anions described in Chapter 9 (procedure 9–D).

12–A. *Removal of Organic Matter.* To test for the presence of organic matter, put a few milligrams of the solid sample into a small test tube and heat the dry solid in an open Bunsen flame. The presence of organic matter is revealed by the solid turning black or brown, or by a film of oil distilling onto the sides of the tube.

If organic matter is present, put about 200 mg of the sample (or more if much organic matter is present) into a small casserole and cover with concentrated H_2SO_4 (about 1 ml). Heat (hood!) until dense white fumes of SO_3 begin to be evolved. If organic material is present, the sample should now be black. Cool and *carefully* add 10 drops of concentrated HNO_3. Continue to heat, with additions of H_2SO_4 and HNO_3 as required, until the sample is light-colored, showing that the organic material has been oxidized away. Evaporate the solution *not quite to dryness*, cautiously add 2 ml of water and 2 drops of 6 M H_2SO_4. Transfer the mixture to a centrifuge tube, wash the casserole with water, and add the washings to the mixture. Centrifuge. Retain the supernate for cation analysis. Treat any residue as described in procedure (12–C).

12–B. *Treatment of Substances Not Soluble in Water.* If the substance to be analyzed is not soluble in water, the solubility of small portions of it in various reagents should be tested. The following reagents, both hot and cold, should be tried: 6 M HCl, 12 M HCl, 6 M HNO_3, 15 M HNO_3, hot 18 M H_2SO_4, aqua regia (1 part 15 M HNO_3 to 3 parts 12 M HCl; HOOD!), 12 M HCl plus a few drops of liquid Br_2 (CONSULT INSTRUCTOR), equal parts of 5 M KF and 6 M HNO_3 (CAUTION: avoid contact with the skin!), 15 M NH_4OH, and 6 M KOH. In the case of certain metals or alloys, although reaction with HNO_3 may be complete, insoluble oxides or hydroxides may be formed. This is particularly so in the case of tungsten, antimony, and tin. If this happens, the washed solids should be suspended in 0.3 M HCl and treated with hot CH_3CSNH_2. Metathesis to the corresponding sulfides will take place (as evidenced by a change of color); these sulfides may then be dissolved in aqua regia (tungsten may appear as white, insoluble H_2WO_4), and the solution added to that from which the insoluble chlorides are to be precipitated. (If Mo and W are known to be absent, HNO_3 is sufficient to dissolve these sulfides.) If none of these reagents completely dissolves the sample, the residue should be treated with Na_2CO_3 solution as described in procedure (12–C).

12–C. *Treatment of the Residue from the Removal of Organic Matter.* Transfer any residue obtained from the treatment described in 12–A, or 12–B, to a casserole and boil it with 2 ml of 1.5 M Na_2CO_3 for 10 minutes, from time to time replacing the water lost by evaporation. Centrifuge, discard the supernate, wash the residue with water, and then add a few drops of 6 M HNO_3. Add the solution obtained to that from procedure (12–A) or (12–B). If any residue still remains, repeat the Na_2CO_3 treatment. The only substances which resist this treatment are sulfur, carbon, silicates, the halides of silver, and certain extremely insoluble phosphates, such as $Zr_3(PO_4)_4$.

If the residue is a silver halide it will be soluble in excess 0.1 M $Hg(NO_3)_2$ in nitric acid.

$$AgX(s) + Hg^{+2} \rightleftharpoons Ag^+ + HgX^+$$

This, however, although a good diagnostic device, is not a convenient way to put the silver halides into solution. Either of two other methods is preferable.

(a) The insoluble residue is suspended in slightly acidic water, thioacetamide added and the mixture heated in the hot-water bath. The halides are metathesized to Ag_2S (see procedure 11–B), which is washed and then dissolved in hot nitric acid, the silver being detected in the usual way.

(b) Alternatively, the halides may be suspended in a little 1 M H_2SO_4 and reduced to free silver by adding a few small pieces of zinc metal. Wash the metallic silver with water to remove H_2SO_4, dissolve it in a minimum amount of 6 M HNO_3, and observe whether HCl gives a white precipitate which is soluble in NH_4OH.

Samples which contain silicates, certain oxides, and certain ignited salts may resist dissolution by all the foregoing procedures. If after the treatments described above dissolution is still not complete, the residue should be subjected to carbonate fusion (12–D).

12–D. *Carbonate Fusion.* Transfer any residue from the foregoing treatments to a small nickel (or iron, if nickel is not available) crucible. Support the crucible on a clay triangle and cover with a little solid Na_2CO_3 and K_2CO_3 mixed. Cover the crucible and heat it strongly in a blast lamp or Meeker burner, when the alkali carbonate mixture with the sample should go into solution. If there are any particles which still refuse to dissolve, add a little solid $NaNO_3$, and heat again for several minutes. Cool the crucible and place it in a casserole. Cover it with water and boil until the solid mass has disintegrated. Remove the crucible and wash it, combining the washings with the contents of the casserole. Transfer the contents of the casserole to a test tube, centrifuge, and separate the precipitate (A) and supernate (B), retaining both. To the precipitate (A) add 10 drops of 6 M HNO_3 and 1 ml of H_2O. When reaction has ceased, centrifuge and separate the precipitate (C) and supernate (D), retaining both. Any precipitate (C) may be silicic acid or metastannic acid. It should be suspended in 0.3 M HCl, with CH_3CSNH_2 added, and heated. Metastannic acid will form yellow SnS_2 which is treated in the usual way. Any white residue remaining unreacted is silicic acid and should be discarded. The solution (D) may contain cations dissolved from their oxides or carbonates, or in the case of Ag^+ from silver metal which may have arisen from the action of the fused carbonates on silver halides.

$$4\ AgCl\ (s) + 2\ CO_3^{-2} \to 4\ Ag\ (s) + 4\ Cl^- + 2\ CO_2\ (g) + O_2\ (g)$$

This solution should be analyzed separately for cations. Solution (B) should be acidified with 6 M HNO_3 and also analyzed separately for cations.

12–10. Questions and Problems

1. What is the function of the factor α in the equilibrium constant for the reaction
$$\tfrac{1}{2} H_2\ (g) \rightleftharpoons H^+ + e^-\,?$$

2. If sodium metal is dissolved in cold, very pure water, no hydrogen is evolved, but a deep-blue solution results which is thought to contain sodium ions and hydrated electrons. Discuss whether this reaction could be used to establish an absolute scale of redox equilibrium constants.

3. Why are we justified in combining the equilibrium constants for half-reactions to get the constant for an over-all reaction?

4. (a) If the equilibrium
$$CN^- + S\ (s) \rightleftharpoons NCS^-$$
were found not to change with change of pH, what could be said about the relative K_A's of HCN and HNCS?

(b) In actual fact, the equilibrium is found to obey very closely the expression derived in Section 12–2

$$\frac{[H^+][NCS^-]}{[HCN]} = 10^{2.33}$$

What, therefore, can be said about the ionization constant of HNCS?

5. Is the equilibrium constant for the reaction

$$2\ Cr(OH)_4^- + 3\ IO^- + 2\ OH^- \rightleftharpoons 2\ CrO_4^{-2} + 3\ I^- + 5\ H_2O$$

changed in the presence of Ba^{+2}? Explain.

6. Calculate the equilibrium constant for each of the following reactions

(a) $3\ HgS\ (s) + 2\ NO_3^- + 8\ H^+ \rightleftharpoons 3\ Hg^{+2} + 3\ S\ (s) + 2\ NO\ (g) + 4\ H_2O$

(b) $3\ HgS\ (s) + 2\ NO_3^- + 12\ Cl^- + 8\ H^+ \rightleftharpoons 3\ HgCl_4^{-2} + 3\ S\ (s) + 2\ NO\ (g) + 4\ H_2O$

(c) $H_3AsO_4 + 2\ I^- + 2\ H^+ \rightleftharpoons HAsO_2 + 2\ H_2O + I_2\ (s)$

(d) $H_3AsO_4 + HgI_4^{-2} + 2\ H^+ \rightleftharpoons HAsO_2 + 2\ H_2O + HgI_2\ (s) + I_2\ (s)$

(e) $2\ Fe^{+2} + MnO_4^{-2} + 4\ H^+ \rightleftharpoons 2\ Fe^{+3} + MnO_2\ (s) + 2\ H_2O$

(f) $2\ Fe^{+2} + BaMnO_4\ (s) + 4\ H^+ \rightleftharpoons 2\ Fe^{+3} + MnO_2\ (s) + 2\ H_2O$

(g) $2\ Cr^{+3} + 3\ H_2O_2 + H_2O \rightleftharpoons Cr_2O_7^{-2} + 8\ H^+$

(h) $2\ Cr(OH)_4^- + 3\ H_2O_2 + 2\ OH^- \rightleftharpoons 2\ CrO_4^{-2} + 8\ H_2O$

(i) $2\ Cr^{+3} + 3\ O_2 + 7\ H_2O \rightleftharpoons Cr_2O_7^{-2} + 3\ H_2O_2 + 8\ H^+$

(j) $H_2SeO_3 + Br_2\ (aq) + H_2O \rightleftharpoons SeO_4^{-2} + 2\ Br^- + 4\ H^+$

(k) $Ag_2SeO_3 + Br_2\ (aq) + H_2O \rightleftharpoons SeO_4^{-2} + 2\ AgBr\ (s) + 2\ H^+$

(l) $I_2 + 2\ S_2O_3^{-2} \rightleftharpoons S_4O_6^{-2} + 2\ I^-$

(m) $I_2 + Ag(S_2O_3)_2^{-3} \rightleftharpoons 2\ S_4O_6^{-2} + AgI\ (s) + I^-$

(n) $2\ FeO_4^{-2} + 3\ Cl^- + 5\ H_2O \rightleftharpoons 2\ Fe(OH)_3\ (s) + 3\ ClO^- + 4\ OH^-$

(o) $8\ FeO_4^{-2} + 3\ Cl^- + 40\ H^+ \rightleftharpoons 8\ Fe^{+3} + 3\ ClO_4^- + 20\ H_2O$

(p) $2\ Bi(OH)_3\ (s) + 3\ Sn(OH)_3^- + 3\ OH^- \rightleftharpoons 2\ Bi\ (s) + 3\ Sn(OH)_6^{-2}$

(q) $7\ Fe(OH)_2\ (s) + SO_3^{-2} + 3\ H_2O \rightleftharpoons FeS\ (s) + 6\ Fe(OH)_3\ (s) + 2\ OH^-$

(r) $4\ Mn^{+2} + MnO_4^- + 8\ H^+ \rightleftharpoons 5\ Mn^{+3} + 4\ H_2O$

(s) $FeO_4^{-2} + 3\ Fe^{+2} + 24\ F^- + 8\ H^+ \rightleftharpoons 4\ FeF_6^{-3} + 4\ H_2O$

(t) $3\ Tl^+ \rightleftharpoons 2\ Tl + Tl^{+3}$

(u) $2\ Sn(OH)_3^- \rightleftharpoons Sn\ (s) + Sn(OH)_6^{-2}$

(v) $2\ SnS\ (s) + S^{-2} \rightleftharpoons Sn\ (s) + SnS_3^{-2}$

(w) $Hg_2I_2\ (s) + 2\ I^- \rightleftharpoons Hg\ (l) + HgI_4^{-2}$

(x) $Cu\ (s) + Cu^{+2} + 2\ Cl^- \rightleftharpoons 2\ CuCl$

(y) $2\ Al\ (s) + 3\ Zn(OH)_4^{-2} \rightleftharpoons 2\ Al(OH)_4^- + 3\ Zn\ (s) + 4\ OH^-$

(z) $2\ VO^{+2} \rightleftharpoons V^{+3} + VO_2^+$

Chapter 13

Oxidation Potentials

13–1. The Meaning of the Oxidation Potential

We have so far considered abundant examples illustrating the equilibrium principle, in which we have seen that, when a system has reached equilibrium, the concentrations (or, better, the activities) of the substances taking part in the equilibrium reaction are related to each other through the equilibrium constant, whose value remains invariable provided the temperature of the system is not changed. So far, however, we have said very little about systems which are not at equilibrium, and what has been said has been rather cursory.

For example, in Section 2–6 it was pointed out from a qualitative point of view that, if a system is caused to go out of equilibrium by application of a stress, a certain driving force tending to relieve that stress and return the system to equilibrium would come into effect. This principle was first enunciated by Le Châtelier and is known by his name. Nothing quantitative was said, however, about the magnitude of the restoring force.

Again in Sections 2–1 and 3–1, the rates at which reactions run (and therefore at which they approach equilibrium) were discussed—this time from the quantitative point of view—relating the rates, through the rate constants, to the concentrations (or activities) of the substances involved. Again, however, nothing was said about the *driving force* of the reactions.

For example, we talked in Section 12–7 about the reaction

$$Sn\,(s) + Pb^{+2} \rightleftharpoons Sn^{+2} + Pb\,(s)$$

in terms of what conditions would exist when equilibrium is attained. It would be useful to know, however, how much tendency there would be for the reaction to go if strips of pure tin and lead were immersed in a solution containing Sn^{+2} and Pb^{+2} ions at concentrations different from those which would exist at equilibrium. It perhaps can be seen intuitively that the more the ratio of the concentrations of Sn^{+2} and Pb^{+2} ions differs from that at equilibrium, the greater will be the driving force toward equilibrium. If the chemical reaction is set up in such a way that the electrons involved must pass through an external circuit, their tendency to flow can be measured. This tendency is termed the electromotive force (emf). In describing the tendency for a reaction to go at an electrode, we speak of the electrode potential. For both of these terms, we may use the more general term *oxidation potential*. The unit of emf is the volt and the force or potential itself is frequently called the voltage.

13–2. The Galvanic Cell

If we immerse two platinum electrodes, one in a solution containing a mixture of Fe^{+2} and Fe^{+3} ions and the other in a solution containing I_3^- and I^- ions, and if the latter has a higher electron activity than the former (i.e., if the reaction

$$3\,I^- \rightarrow I_3^- + 2\,e^-$$

has a greater tendency to go to the right than has

$$Fe^{+2} \rightarrow Fe^{+3} + e^-$$

then if the two electrodes are connected by a wire, electrons will tend to flow from the $I^- - I_3^-$ solution through the wire to the $Fe^{+3} - Fe^{+2}$ solution. The iodide ions will tend to continue to furnish electrons according to the reaction above. This flow of electrons can take place only to an infinitesimal degree, however, for just as soon as any electrons flow out of the iodide solution, it will be left with a net positive charge from the cations which must also be present, and this will tend to prevent the loss of more of the electrons. In similar fashion, as soon as any electrons flow into the iron solution, there will be an excess of negative charge which will tend to repel any more electrons. Thus after the first infinitesimal movement of electrons when the wire is connected, the reaction must come to a halt. If now the two solutions are connected by a tube containing a salt solution (a "salt bridge"), negative ions can migrate from the iron solution to the iodide solution and positive ions in the reverse direction, to compensate for the electrons which are being transferred from the iodide ion to the iron(III) ion. If a voltmeter is now placed in the external circuit, the emf or potential (i.e., the driving force) of the reaction can be measured. The passage of electrons through the external circuit can be made to do work.

(It should be noted that, if the iron and iodide solutions were mixed together, electrons could pass directly from I^- to Fe^{+3} and the reaction would have exactly the same tendency to go as before. Consequently, even though we cannot now measure this tendency, we can still speak of the potential of the reaction.)

If an external voltage is applied to the cell in such a way that it opposes the natural flow of electrons, that flow will be exactly canceled when the external voltage is exactly equal to that of the cell. The applied external potential which results in no flow of current, then, measures the voltage of the cell. If the external voltage is increased beyond that of the cell, the flow of electrons is reversed and electrolysis takes place. In this case, I_3^- is reduced to I^- in one compartment and Fe^{+2} is oxidized to Fe^{+3} in the other.

The cell just described may be represented as

$$(Pt) \mid I^- \text{ (aq)}, I_3^- \text{ (aq)} \mid\mid Fe^{+2} \text{ (aq)}, Fe^{+3} \text{ (aq)} \mid (Pt)$$

where the inert platinum electrodes are shown as (Pt). The electrodes may themselves take part in the cell reaction, as when a lead electrode is dipped in a Pb^{+2} solution and is connected to a strip of tin dipping into a Sn^{+2} solution, and the two solutions are connected by a salt bridge. This cell would be represented as

$$Pb \mid Pb^{+2} \text{ (aq)} \mid\mid Sn^{+2} \text{ (aq)} \mid Sn$$

The junction between two phases is indicated by a single vertical line. A liquid junction (such as a salt bridge) is indicated by two vertical lines.

13–3. Half-Cells

Just as we did in the case of redox equilibria, we can break these reactions down into half-reactions—each being characteristic of what is taking place at one electrode of the galvanic cell. This we term the *half-reaction* and its part of the system is termed the *half-cell*.

In the case of the reaction

$$2 \, Fe^{+3} + 3 \, I^- \rightarrow 2 \, Fe^{+2} + I_3^-$$

the over-all potential may be considered to be the sum of the tendency of I^- to lose electrons

$$3 \, I^- \rightarrow I_3^- + 2 \, e^-$$

and of the resistance of Fe^{+3} to gaining them

$$Fe^{+3} + e^- \rightarrow Fe^{+2}$$

Another way of putting it is that the potential of the over-all reaction is the difference between the tendencies of the two reducing agents (I^- and Fe^{+2}) to lose their electrons

$$3 \, I^- \rightarrow I_3^- + 2 \, e^-$$

$$Fe^{+2} \rightarrow Fe^{+3} + e^-$$

Algebraically, these two statements amount to the same thing. Just as was argued for the case of redox equilibria (Section 12–6), therefore, if it were possible to establish the absolute potential of just one half-reaction it would then be possible to determine the potentials of all other half-reactions by measuring the emf of galvanic cells in which one of the half-reactions is the reference half-reaction. Again, however, it is not possible to measure the potential of a half-reaction by itself. Consequently, the oxidation potential of the half-reaction

$$\tfrac{1}{2} H_2 \, (g) \rightarrow H^+ + e^-$$

where the pressure of H_2 is 1 atm and the activity of H^+ is 1 *molal*, has been arbitrarily defined as $E^\circ = 0.00$ volts. All other potentials are compared to this standard.

13–4.   The Effect of Concentration on Potential

As has already been pointed out (Section 13–1), the more the ratio of concentrations (or activities) differs from that which would exist at equilibrium, the greater will be the driving force to attain equilibrium. The same concept can be applied to the half-reaction as well as to the over-all reaction. For example, in the half-reaction

$$Pb \, (s) \rightarrow Pb^{+2} \, (aq) + 2 \, e^-$$

the greater the concentration of Pb^{+2}, the greater will be the driving force to deposit it as metal from solution. Or, for the reaction

$$Fe^{+2} \rightarrow Fe^{+3} + e^-$$

the smaller is the ratio $\dfrac{[Fe^{+3}]}{[Fe^{+2}]}$ the greater will be the drive for Fe^{+2} ions to give up electrons to become Fe^{+3} ions. In other words, the potential of a reaction or a half-reaction is a function of the concentrations (or activities) of the substances taking part in it. The actual relationship for 25°C is the Nernst equation

$$E = E^\circ - \frac{0.05914}{n} \log Q$$

where E is the potential of the reaction or half-reaction under consideration, E° is the standard oxidation potential for the same reaction, n is the number of electrons exchanged, and Q is the product or ratio of the concentrations raised to the appropriate powers, and has exactly the same form as the expression for the equilibrium constant for the oxidation reaction.

13–5.   Standard Oxidation Potentials

The potential of a system when all activities are 1 molal is known as the *standard oxidation potential*. A knowledge of the standard oxidation potentials for the different half-reactions in conjunction with the Nernst equation will give the potential for any system under any conditions of concentration. From this we can determine whether it is possible for a given reaction to go. (It cannot predict, however, whether it *will* go.) The values of the standard oxidation potentials for half-reactions (Appendix 10) carry either positive or negative signs, depending on whether they have more tendency $(+)$ or less tendency $(-)$ to go as written than the corresponding half-reaction for hydrogen. By convention, the half-reactions are written with the free electrons on the right

$$Cu \rightarrow Cu^{+2} + 2\,e^- \qquad E° = -0.345$$

If the equations were turned around (i.e., if the reaction were reversed), the sign of the potential would be changed

$$Cu^{+2} + 2\,e^- \rightarrow Cu \qquad E° = +0.345$$

The standard oxidation potentials are extremely useful in determining whether a reaction is energetically favored to go. For example, let us ascertain whether the reaction

$$3\,Ag^+ + Sb\,(s) + H_2O \rightarrow 3\,Ag\,(s) + SbO^+ + 2\,H^+$$

may go as written when all activities are unity. The standard potential for the half-reaction

$$Sb\,(s) + H_2O \rightarrow SbO^+ + 2\,H^+ + 3\,e^-$$

is -0.212, while that for

$$Ag \rightarrow Ag^+ + e^-$$

is -0.799. Observing, however, that this latter half-reaction is reversed in the over-all equation, we have

$$Ag^+ + e^- \rightarrow Ag \qquad E° = +0.799$$

Now adding the two half-reactions (after multiplying the latter by three) to obtain the over-all reaction, we add the potentials to obtain the over-all potential

$$Sb\,(s) + H_2O \rightarrow SbO^+ + 2\,H^+ + 3\,e^- \qquad\qquad E° = -0.212$$

$$3\,Ag^+ + 3\,e^- \rightarrow 3\,Ag\,(s) \qquad\qquad E° = +0.799$$

$$\cancel{3\,e^-} + 3\,Ag^+ + Sb\,(s) + H_2O \rightarrow 3\,Ag\,(s) + SbO^+ + 2\,H^+ + \cancel{3\,e^-} \quad E° = +0.587$$

(The potential for the Ag–Ag$^+$ couple is not multiplied by three since the potential or driving force is independent of the total amount involved.) The potential difference is observed to be fairly large, and the fact that it is positive shows that the reaction is favored to go.

Let us now ask whether elemental chlorine can oxidize Mn^{+2} to MnO_4^- in 1 molal acid.

$$5\,Cl_2 + 2\,Mn^{+2} + 8\,H_2O \rightarrow 10\,Cl^- + 2\,MnO_4^- + 16\,H^+$$

The half-reactions are

$$Mn^{+2} + 4\,H_2O \rightarrow MnO_4^- + 8\,H^+ + 5\,e^- \qquad E° = -1.51$$

and $\qquad\qquad\qquad Cl^- \rightarrow \tfrac{1}{2}\,Cl_2 + e^- \qquad\qquad\qquad E° = -1.36$

Multiplying by the appropriate factors and subtracting the second from the first (or reversing the second and adding it to the first), we have

$$E° = -1.51 + 1.36 = -0.15$$

showing that chlorine *cannot* oxidize Mn^{+2} to MnO_4^- in 1 molal acid.

Let us ask whether VO^{+2} is stable with respect to disproportionation in 1 molal acid. That is, can the reaction

$$2\ VO^{+2} \rightarrow V^{+3} + VO_2^+$$

take place as written?

$$V^{+3} + H_2O \rightarrow VO^{+2} + 2\ H^+ + e^- \qquad E° = -0.36$$

$$VO^{+2} + H_2O \rightarrow VO_2^+ + 2\ H^+ + e^- \qquad E° = -1.00$$

Consequently, $E° = -1.00 + 0.36 = -0.64$, and the reaction can not run as written. In other words, VO^{+2} is *stable* with respect to disproportionation in 1 molal acid.

On the other hand, if we examine the system

$$2\ Cu^+ \rightarrow Cu\ (s) + Cu^{+2}$$

$$Cu\ (s) \rightarrow Cu^+ + e^- \qquad E° = -0.521$$

$$Cu^+ \rightarrow Cu^{+2} + e^- \qquad E° = -0.153$$

so that $E° = -0.153 + 0.521 = +0.368$, we see that Cu^+ is *unstable* with respect to disproportionation into Cu^{+2} and copper metal. It will be observed that, since the potential for the $Cu–Cu^+$ couple is more negative than that for the $Cu^+–Cu^{+2}$ couple, then Cu^+ must be a better oxidizing agent than Cu^{+2}. Likewise, since the potential for the $Cu^+–Cu^{+2}$ couple is more positive (i.e., less negative) than that for the $Cu–Cu^+$ couple, then Cu^+ must be a better reducing agent than Cu^0. *It is characteristic of intermediate oxidation states which are unstable with respect to disproportionation, that they are simultaneously better oxidizing agents than the higher states, and better reducing agents than the lower states to which they disproportionate.*

Since Appendix 10 has been organized in order of algebraically decreasing potential, the best reducing agents are at the top and the best oxidizing agents at the bottom. Thus any substance in the left-hand column may reduce any substance below it in the right-hand column and any substance in the right-hand column may oxidize any substance above it in the left-hand column.

13-6. The Standard Oxidation Potentials for Complete Reactions

It was stated in the preceding section that, in order to obtain the standard oxidation potential for any reaction, it was necessary only to take the difference between the standard oxidation potentials for its two component half-reactions, without consideration of the number of electrons involved. Examination of the Nernst relationships will show why this is so.

Let us use the form of the Nernst equation for the cell at equilibrium, where $E = 0$. Now

$$E^\circ = \frac{0.05914}{n} \log Q_{eq}$$

where Q_{eq} represents the activities of the substances involved in the redox reaction *at equilibrium* (Section 13–9). Using the reaction

$$2 \, \text{Tl (s)} + \text{Tl}^{+3} \rightarrow 3 \, \text{Tl}^+$$

as an example

$$E^\circ = \frac{0.05914}{2} \log \frac{[\text{Tl}^+]_{eq}^3}{[\text{Tl}^{+3}]_{eq}}$$

This is made up of the two half-reactions

$$\text{Tl (s)} \rightarrow \text{Tl}^+ + e^- \quad \text{and} \quad \text{Tl}^+ \rightarrow \text{Tl}^{+3} + 2 \, e^-$$

for which

$$E_1^\circ = 0.05914 \log [\text{Tl}^+]_{eq}$$

and

$$E_2^\circ = \frac{0.05914}{2} \log \frac{[\text{Tl}^{+3}]_{eq}}{[\text{Tl}^+]_{eq}}$$

In order to combine the two to give the same right-hand side as for the expression for the over-all reaction, the coefficient of the logarithm for the first must be divided by two and the concentration squared

$$E_1^\circ = \frac{0.05914}{2} \log [\text{Tl}^+]_{eq}^2$$

(which can be done without changing the value of the expression), and the second subtracted from it

$$E_1^\circ - E_2^\circ = \frac{0.05914}{2} \left(\log [\text{Tl}^+]_{eq}^2 - \log \frac{[\text{Tl}^{+3}]_{eq}}{[\text{Tl}^+]_{eq}} \right) = \frac{0.05914}{2} \log \frac{[\text{Tl}^+]_{eq}^3}{[\text{Tl}^{+3}]_{eq}}$$

It can now be seen that

$$E^\circ = E_1^\circ - E_2^\circ$$

in justification of the statement in Section 13–5.

13–7. Potentials for New Half-Reactions

It is frequently desirable to be able to calculate standard oxidation potentials for a new half-reaction from the known potentials of other half-reactions. For example, taking again the case of the thallium couples, what would be the standard oxidation potential for the half reaction

$$\text{Tl (s)} \rightarrow \text{Tl}^{+3} + 3 \, e^- \, ?$$

The Nernst expression for this would be

$$E_3{}^\circ = \frac{0.05914}{3} \log [\text{Tl}^{+3}]_{eq}$$

In order to obtain the same right-hand side from the expressions for the Tl (s)–Tl$^+$ and Tl$^+$–Tl^{+3} couples, we must rewrite the second as

$$2\,E_2{}^\circ = 0.05914 \log \frac{[\text{Tl}^{+3}]_{eq}}{[\text{Tl}^+]_{eq}}$$

and add them

$$E_1{}^\circ + 2\,E_2{}^\circ = 0.05914 \left(\log [\text{Tl}^+]_{eq} + \log \frac{[\text{Tl}^{+3}]_{eq}}{[\text{Tl}^+]_{eq}} \right)$$

$$= 0.05914 \log [\text{Tl}^{+3}]_{eq}$$

and divide each side by three

$$\frac{E_1 + 2\,E_2{}^\circ}{3} = \frac{0.05914}{3} \log [\text{Tl}^{+3}]_{eq}$$

Now it can be seen that

$$E_3{}^\circ = \frac{E_1 + 2\,E_2{}^\circ}{3}$$

or, to generalize,

$$E_3{}^\circ = \frac{n_1 E_1{}^\circ + n_2 E_2{}^\circ}{n_3}$$

where

$$n_3 = n_1 + n_2$$

Here the number of electrons *must* be taken into consideration. Taking the actual potentials

(1) $\qquad\qquad\qquad\qquad$ $\text{Tl} \rightarrow \text{Tl}^+ + e^-$ $\qquad\qquad\qquad$ $E_1{}^\circ = \quad 0.34$

(2) $\qquad\qquad\qquad\qquad$ $\text{Tl}^+ \rightarrow \text{Tl}^{+3} + 2\,e^-$ $\qquad\qquad$ $E_2{}^\circ = -1.25$

then, for the reaction

(3) $\qquad$ $\text{Tl} \rightarrow \text{Tl}^{+3} + 3\,e^-$ $\qquad$ $E_3{}^\circ = \dfrac{0.34 + 2(-1.25)}{3} = -0.72$

In the case of the copper couples

(1) $\qquad$ $\text{Cu} \rightarrow \text{Cu}^+ + e^-$ $\qquad$ $E_1 = -0.521$

(2) $\qquad$ $\text{Cu}^+ \rightarrow \text{Cu}^{+2} + e^-$ $\qquad$ $E_2 = -0.153$

(3) $\qquad$ $\text{Cu} \rightarrow \text{Cu}^{+2} + 2\,e^-$ $\qquad$ $E_3 = \dfrac{-0.521 - 0.153}{2} = -0.337$

Again, as in Section 13–5, it can be seen that Cu^+ in the reaction $\text{Cu}^+ \rightarrow \text{Cu}^{+2} + e^-$ is a better reducing agent than is Cu in the reaction

$Cu \rightarrow Cu^{+2} + 2\,e^-$, and simultaneously Cu^+ in the reaction $Cu^+ + e^- \rightarrow Cu$ is a better oxidizing agent than is Cu^{+2} in the reaction $Cu^{+2} + 2\,e^- \rightarrow Cu$.

Let us consider as a last example the calculation of the standard oxidation potential for the half-reaction

(1) $$MnO_2\,(s) + 2\,H_2O \rightarrow MnO_4^{-2} + 4\,H^+ + 2\,e^-$$

from the known potentials for the half-reactions

(2) $$MnO_4^{-2} \rightarrow MnO_4^- + e^- \qquad\qquad E_2^\circ = -0.564$$

and

(3) $$MnO_2\,(s) + 2\,H_2O \rightarrow MnO_4^- + 4\,H^+ + 3\,e^- \quad E_3^\circ = -1.695$$

From the relationship $n_1 E_1^\circ + n_2 E_2^\circ = n_3 E_3^\circ$, we have $2\,E_1^\circ + (-0.564) = 3(-1.695)$, so that

$$E_1^\circ = \frac{3(-1.695) - (-0.564)}{2} = -2.260$$

13-8.   Potential Diagrams

A very useful device for obtaining an over-all picture of the oxidation potential relationships for an element is the potential diagram. The usefulness of this device was made evident by the late Wendell M. Latimer in his classic text popularly known as *Oxidation Potentials* (Englewood Cliffs, N.J.: Prentice-Hall, Inc., 1952, 2nd ed.). The potential diagram brings together in an easily assimilated form all of the information on the oxidation potentials for an element. A single example will suffice to demonstrate its use.

POTENTIAL DIAGRAM FOR NITROGEN
(Normal Oxidation Potentials, 1 M H+)

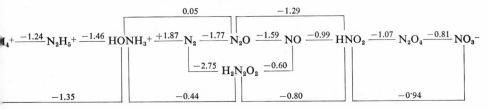

From this diagram potentials for the following reactions can be read

$2\,NH_4^+ \rightarrow N_2H_5^+ + 3\,H^+ + 2\,e^-$	$E^\circ = -1.24$
$N_2H_5^+ + 2\,H_2O \rightarrow 2\,HONH_3^+ + H^+ + 2\,e^-$	$E^\circ = -1.46$
$NH_4^+ + H_2O \rightarrow HONH_3^+ + 2\,H^+ + 2\,e^-$	$E^\circ = -1.35$
$2\,HONH_3^+ \rightarrow N_2 + 2\,H_2O + 4\,H^+ + 2\,e^-$	$E^\circ = +1.87$
$N_2 + H_2O \rightarrow N_2O + 2\,H^+ + 2\,e^-$	$E^\circ = -1.77$
$2\,HONH_3^+ \rightarrow N_2O + H_2O + 6\,H^+ + 4\,e^-$	$E^\circ = +0.05$
$2\,HONH_3^+ \rightarrow H_2N_2O_2 + 6\,H^+ + 4\,e^-$	$E^\circ = -0.44$
$N_2 + 2\,H_2O \rightarrow H_2N_2O_2 + 2\,H^+ + 2\,e^-$	$E^\circ = -2.75$

$$N_2O + H_2O \rightarrow 2\,NO + 2\,H^+ + 2\,e^- \qquad\qquad E° = -1.59$$
$$N_2O + 3\,H_2O \rightarrow 2\,HNO_2 + 4\,H^+ + 4\,e^- \qquad E° = -1.29$$
$$H_2N_2O_2 \rightarrow 2\,NO + 2\,H^+ + 2\,e^- \qquad\qquad E° = -0.60$$
$$H_2N_2O_2 + 2\,H_2O \rightarrow 2\,HNO_2 + 4\,H^+ + 4\,e^- \qquad E° = -0.80$$
$$2\,HNO_2 \rightarrow N_2O_4 + 2\,H^+ + 2\,e^- \qquad\qquad E° = -1.07$$
$$HNO_2 + H_2O \rightarrow NO_3^- + 3\,H^+ + 2\,e^- \qquad E° = -0.94$$
$$N_2O_4 + 2\,H_2O \rightarrow 2\,NO_3^- + 4\,H^+ + 2\,e^- \qquad E° = -0.81$$

and the potentials of many other half-reactions can be obtained by combination of those shown.

It can be seen by inspection of the diagram that substances which are unstable with respect to disproportionation are

$HONH_3^+$ into $N_2H_5^+$ and N_2

$HONH_3^+$ into $N_2H_5^+$ and N_2O (less strongly)

$HONH_3^+$ into $N_2H_5^+$ and $H_2N_2O_2$

$HONH_3^+$ into NH_4^+ and N_2, N_2O or $H_2N_2O_2$

$H_2N_2O_2$ into N_2 and NO or HNO_2

but *not* $H_2N_2O_2$ into $HONH_3^+$ and NO or HNO_2

NO into N_2O and HNO_2

but *not*   NO into $H_2N_2O_2$ and HNO_2

HNO_2 into N_2O and N_2O_4 or NO_3^-

and HNO_2 into NO and NO_3^-

but *not* HNO_2 into NO or $H_2N_2O_2$ and N_2O_4

or HNO_2 into $H_2N_2O_2$ and NO_3^-

Many other relationships can also be drawn from the diagram.

13–9. The Relationship of the Standard Oxidation Potential to the Equilibrium Constant

When a redox reaction is at equilibrium, the potential is zero, since there is no longer any driving force. Therefore the expression

$$E = E° - \frac{0.05914}{n} \log Q$$

becomes

$$E° = \frac{0.05914}{n} \log Q_{eq}$$

(as indicated in Section 13–7).

or

$$\log Q_{eq} = \frac{nE°}{0.05914}$$

where Q_{eq} is now the product of the concentrations raised to the appropriate powers *at equilibrium*. Since this product is equal to the equilibrium constant, $Q_{eq} = K_{eq}$, we can write

$$\log K_{eq} = \frac{nE^\circ}{0.05914}$$

13–10.   The Calculation of Oxidation Potentials

We are now ready to make some actual calculations of oxidation potentials. Let us first find the potential of the half-reaction $Pb \rightarrow Pb^{+2} + 2e^-$, where $[Pb^{+2}]$ is not 1 molal as required for the standard oxidation potential, but is 0.001 molal instead.

$$E = E^\circ - \frac{0.05914}{n} \log [Pb^{+2}]$$

$$E = 0.126 - \frac{0.05914}{2} \log 10^{-3} = 0.126 - \frac{0.05914(-3)}{2}$$

$$E = 0.215 \text{ v}$$

That is, the tendency of lead to dissolve to form Pb^{+2} is greater when the concentration of Pb^{+2} is lower.

Let us consider the reaction

$$3 \, PbO_2 + 2 \, MnO_2 + 4 \, H^+ \rightarrow 2 \, MnO_4^- + 3 \, Pb^{+2} + 2 \, H_2O$$

whose standard oxidation potential is

$$E^\circ = -1.695 + 1.455 = -0.240.$$

What would be the potential in a solution containing $0.1 \, M \, H^+$, $10^{-5} \, M$ Pb^{+2}, and $10^{-4} \, M \, MnO_4^-$?

$$E = -0.240 - \frac{0.05914}{6} \log \frac{[MnO_4^-]^2 [Pb^{+2}]^3}{[H^+]^4}$$

$$E = -0.240 - \frac{0.05914}{6} \log \frac{(10^{-4})^2 (10^{-5})^3}{(10^{-1})^4}$$

$$E = -0.240 - \frac{0.05914(-19)}{6} = -0.053 \text{ v}$$

13–11.   The Effect of pH on the Oxidation Potential

For such a reaction as

$$Cl_2 \, (aq) + 2 \, Br^- \rightarrow 2 \, Cl^- + Br_2 \, (aq)$$

there will be no *obvious* effect of pH on the oxidation potential, since neither $[H^+]$ nor $[OH^-]$ enters into the logarithmic term of the Nernst equation.

$$E = E° - \frac{0.05914}{2} \log \frac{[Cl^-]^2[Br_2]}{[Cl_2][Br^-]^2}$$

In the case of the last example in Section 13–10, however, it is easy to see that the potential will be strongly affected by change of pH. For example, at 0.01 M H^+ concentration, the potential will be

$$E = -0.240 - \frac{0.05914}{6} \log \frac{(10^{-4})^2(10^{-5})^3}{(10^{-2})^4} = -0.092 \text{ v}$$

On the other hand, if a weak acid or base is involved in the equilibrium, the effect may be felt not only through the change in hydrogen-ion concentration itself, but also in the change of concentration of the anion of the weak acid or the cation of the weak base. Taking the reaction cited in Section 12–2.

$$CN^- + S(s) \rightarrow NCS^-, \quad E° = 0.695$$

changing the pH will change the oxidation potential because of the effect of the equilibrium

$$HCN \rightleftharpoons H^+ + CN^-, \quad K_A = 10^{-9.32}$$

For the simple redox reaction, the potential in a solution containing 1 M CN^- and 1 M NCS^-—and having pH = 10, so that the CN^- will be essentially unhydrolyzed—is

$$E = 0.695 - \frac{0.05914}{2} \log \frac{[NCS^-]}{[CN^-]} = 0.695 \text{ v}$$

But if the same solution now has its pH changed to 8, then $[CN^-]$ becomes a function of $[H^+]$

$$[CN^-] = \frac{[HCN]}{[H^+]} 10^{-9.32}$$

and

$$E = 0.695 - \frac{0.05914}{2} \log \frac{[NCS^-]}{\dfrac{[HCN]}{[H^+]} 10^{-9.32}}$$

$$E = 0.695 - \frac{0.05914}{2} \log \frac{[H^+][NCS^-]}{[HCN]10^{-9.32}}$$

Since the total $[HCN] + [CN^-] = 1 \ M$,

then

$$[HCN] + \frac{[HCN]}{[H^+]} 10^{-9.32} = 1 \ M$$

and
$$E = 0.695 - \frac{0.05914}{2} \log \frac{[H^+][NCS^-]}{\frac{[H^+]}{[H^+]+10^{-9.32}} 10^{-9.32}}$$

$$E = 0.695 - \frac{0.05914}{2} \log \frac{([H^+]+10^{-9.32})[NCS^-]}{10^{-9.32}}$$

So that

$$E = 0.695 - \frac{0.05914}{2} \log \frac{(10^{-8}+10^{-9.32})(1)}{10^{-9.32}} = 0.683 \text{ v}$$

Let us also examine the effect of pH on the potential of the NH_4^+–N_2 couple. The standard oxidation potential of the NH_4^+–N_2 couple (1 M H^+) can be derived from the potential diagram for nitrogen

$$E° = \frac{-1.24-1.46+1.87}{3} = -0.28$$

for the half-reaction

$$2\ NH_4^+ \rightarrow N_2 + 8\ H^+ + 6\ e^-$$

Thus

$$E = -0.28 - \frac{0.05914}{6} \log \frac{[H^+]^8 p_{N_2}}{[NH_4^+]^2}$$

Change of pH, however, will affect not only $[H^+]$ but also $[NH_4^+]$. As an illustration, let us calculate $E_B°$ for the reaction

$$2\ NH_3 + 6\ OH^- \rightarrow N_2 + 6\ H_2O + 6\ e^-$$

for which all activities are one. In this solution

$$[NH_4^+] = \frac{[NH_3]K_B}{[OH^-]} = \frac{1 \times 1.8 \times 10^{-5}}{1} = 1.8 \times 10^{-5} \text{ M}$$

Therefore

$$E_B° = -0.28 - \frac{0.05914}{6} \log \frac{(10^{-14})^8}{(10^{-4.74})^2} = -0.73 \text{ v}$$

Whenever H^+ or OH^- enters into a reaction, the potential will be a function of the pH. For example, the potential for $4\ OH^- \rightarrow O_2 + 2\ H_2O + 4\ e^-$ is -0.40 volts, differing from that given in Appendix 10 for $2\ H_2O \rightarrow O_2 + 4\ H^+ + 4\ e^-$ by 0.83 volts. The potential for the half-reaction in 1 molar base ($E_B°$) can be derived from the normal oxidation potential by observing that in 1 molar base $[H^+] = 10^{-14}\ M$.

Therefore

$$E° = -1.23 - \frac{0.05914}{4} \log [H^+]^4 p_{O_2}$$

so that when $p_{O_2} = 1$ atm

$$E_B° = -1.23 - \frac{0.05914}{4} \log (10^{-14})^4(1) = -0.40$$

13–12.   The Effect of Solubility on the Oxidation Potential

Let us now calculate the potential of the half-reaction

$$Ag + I^- \rightarrow AgI + e^-$$

when the $[I^-] = 0.1$ molar.

This can be done in either of two ways. From the K_{sp} for AgI, $[Ag^+]$ can be calculated

$$[Ag^+][I^-] = 10^{-16.1}$$

$$[Ag^+] = \frac{10^{-16.1}}{10^{-1}} = 10^{-15.1} \; M$$

Then the Ag–Ag$^+$ potential can be calculated using the $[Ag^+]$ so obtained

$$E = -0.799 - \frac{0.05914}{1} \log 10^{-15.1} = 0.094 \text{ v}$$

Alternatively, it is better calculated simply by substituting for $[Ag^+]$ in the Nernst equation for the Ag–Ag$^+$ couple its equivalent $[Ag^+] = \dfrac{K_{sp}}{[I^-]}$.

Let us now find out whether excess solid I_2 in water is capable of oxidizing Ag. The half-reactions are

$$Ag \rightarrow Ag^+ + e^- \qquad\qquad E° = -0.7991$$

$$2\,I^- \rightarrow I_2 + 2\,e^- \qquad\qquad E° = -0.5355$$

giving

$$2\,Ag + I_2 \rightarrow 2\,Ag^+ + 2\,I^- \qquad\qquad E° = -0.2636$$

so that at first sight the reaction would appear not to be able to go. Let us observe, however, that the products will not be $1\ M$ Ag$^+$ and $1\ M$ I$^-$ as these $E°$'s call for, but rather the highly insoluble AgI, whose $K_{sp} = 10^{-16.08}$. For the basic redox reaction, we have

$$E = -0.2636 - \frac{0.05914}{2} \log [Ag^+]^2[I^-]^2$$

From the K_{sp} of AgI we have

$$[Ag^+]^2[I^-]^2 = (10^{-16.08})^2 = 10^{-32.16}$$

Therefore

$$E = -0.2636 - \frac{0.05914}{2} \log 10^{-32.16} = +0.6864$$

Consequently, because of the great insolubility of AgI, free iodine will easily react with silver metal, even though at first sight the normal oxidation potentials would seem to indicate that it would not.

The effect of solubility can be seen in the change of the potential of the reaction

$$Fe^{+3} + Tl\ (s) \rightarrow Tl^+ + Fe^{+2}$$

The potential remains constant at low pH's, but pH-dependence sets in when the pH is high enough for $Fe(OH)_3$ first to precipitate. When $Fe(OH)_2$ begins to precipitate, the rate of change of the potential with pH alters, and finally when TlOH begins to precipitate at very high pH, the potential once more becomes invariant with pH change. The discussion of this system in Section 12–3 will suffice to explain the changing dependences.

Let us now calculate the potential for the half-reaction

$$Fe(OH)_2 + OH^- \rightarrow Fe(OH)_3 + e^-$$

in 0.01 molar NaOH. The oxidation potential for the Fe^{+2}–Fe^{+3} couple is

$$E = -0.771 - 0.05914 \log \frac{[Fe^{+3}]}{[Fe^{+2}]}$$

From the K_{sp}'s of the hydroxides

$$[Fe^{+3}] = \frac{10^{-37.2}}{[OH^-]^3} = 10^{-31.2}$$

$$[Fe^{+2}] = \frac{10^{-14.7}}{[OH^-]^2} = 10^{-10.7}$$

Therefore

$$E = -0.771 - 0.05914 \log \frac{10^{-31.2}}{10^{-10.7}}$$

$$E = -0.771 + 0.05914 \, (20.5) = 0.441 \text{ v}$$

13–13. The Effect of Complex Formation on the Oxidation Potential

The effect of complex-ion formation can be seen from the following example. Under ordinary circumstances, oxygen at 1 atm pressure is not capable of oxidizing gold.

$$Au + 3 H_2O \rightarrow Au(OH)_3 \text{ (s)} + 3 H^+ + 3 e^- \qquad E^\circ = -1.45$$

$$2 H_2O \rightarrow O_2 + 4 H^+ + 4 e^- \qquad E^\circ = -1.25$$

and $\quad 4 Au + 3 O_2 + 6 H_2O \rightarrow 4 Au(OH)_3 \qquad E^\circ = -0.22$

Oxidation to Au^+ is even less favorable

$$Au \rightarrow Au^+ + e^- \qquad E^\circ = -1.68$$

$$4 OH^- \rightarrow O_2 + 2 H_2O + 4 e^- \qquad E^\circ = -0.40$$

so that

$$4 Au + O_2 + 2 H_2O \rightarrow 4 Au^+ + 4 OH^- \qquad E^\circ = -1.28$$

Even if AuOH were to precipitate, we should have (assuming $K_{sp} = 10^{-11}$)

$$E = -1.28 - \frac{0.05914}{4} \log \frac{[Au^+]^4[OH^-]^4}{p_{O_2}}$$

$$E = -1.28 - \frac{0.05914}{4} \log \frac{10^{-44}}{10^0} = -0.63$$

On the other hand, if gold is exposed to oxygen in a 1-molar cyanide solution in which the very stable $Au(CN)_2^-$ complex ($K_{inst} = 10^{-38.3}$) may form, we have the reaction

$$4\,Au + O_2 + 8\,CN^- + 2\,H_2O \rightarrow 4\,Au(CN)_2^- + 4\,OH^-$$

The concentration of Au^+ in this solution will be

$$[Au^+] = \frac{[Au(CN)_2^-]10^{-38.3}}{[CN^-]^2}$$

If we take $[Au(CN)_2^-] = 0.01\ M$ as a reasonable degree of reaction, then

$$[Au^+] = \frac{(10^{-2})(10^{-38.3})}{(1)^2} = 10^{-40.3}$$

Now noting that $[OH^-] = [Au(CN)_2^-]$

$$E = -1.28 - \frac{0.05914}{4} \log \frac{(10^{-40.3})^4(10^{-2})^4}{10^0} = +1.22$$

Consequently, in the presence of cyanide ion, gold is easily oxidized by oxygen.

13–14.   Illustrative Experiments

13–A Trends in Oxidation Potential. The Nitrogen Family. (1). Add 10 drops of KNO_3 to 10 drops of $MnCl_2$ and 10 drops of 3 M HCl.

(2) Repeat (1) with 2 drops of 0.5 M NaH_2PO_4 and 8 drops of water in place of KNO_3.

(3) Repeat (1) with 10 drops of H_3AsO_4 in place of the KNO_3 in the first experiment.

(4) Repeat (1) with a pinch of $NaBiO_3$ and 10 drops of water in place of KNO_3. Centrifuge the solution and observe the color, if any.

(5) Add 20 drops of concentrated HNO_3 to 10 drops of 0.1 M H_3AsO_3 and heat the mixture almost to boiling over an open flame for 5 minutes. (*Be careful not to splatter your neighbor!*) Then add 10 drops of $AgNO_3$ and 6 M NaOH, dropwise with shaking, until a brown-red (or brown) precipitate is obtained. Add 6 M HNO_3, dropwise with shaking, until the precipitate barely dissolves, and then add 3 M NH_4OH, dropwise with shaking, until a permanent precipitate is formed.

(6) Add 2 drops of 3 M NH_4OH to 10 drops of H_3AsO_3 and 10 drops of $AgNO_3$.

(7) Add 10 drops of KNO_3 to 10 drops of $FeSO_4$ and 10 drops of 3 M HCl.

(8) Repeat (7) with 2 drops of 0.5 M NaH_2PO_4 and 8 drops of water in place of KNO_3.

(9) Repeat (7) with 10 drops of H_3AsO_4 in place of KNO_3.

(10) Repeat (7) with a pinch of $NaBiO_3$ and 10 drops of water instead of KNO_3. Centrifuge the solution and observe the color, if any.

(a) From the results of experiments (1–4) which of the elements in the fifth family in the $+5$ oxidation state is the strongest oxidizing agent?

(b) What were the precipitates formed in (5) and in (6)?

(c) From the results of experiments (7–10) which of the elements in the fifth family in $+5$ oxidation state is the poorest oxidizing agent?

(d) List the order of the elements in the fifth period from the strongest to the poorest oxidizing agent.

13–B *Trends in Oxidation Potential. The Chalcogens.* (1). Add a few crystals of Na_2SO_3 to 10 drops of a saturated solution of bromine in water and 1 drop of 3 M HCl. (Solid Na_2SO_3 is used rather than Na_2SO_3 solution because Na_2SO_3 solution is easily oxidized by the air.)

$$2 SO_3^{-2} + O_2 \rightarrow 2 SO_4^{-2}$$

(2) Add 10 drops of 0.1 M H_2SeO_3 to 10 drops of a saturated solution of bromine in water and 1 drop of 3 M HCl.

(a) Which is the stronger reducing agent, S(IV) or Se(IV)?

(b) Is the relative reducing power of S(IV) and Se(IV) analogous to that of P(III) and As(III) in the adjoining family?

(c) By analogy with the nitrogen family, which would you expect to be the strongest oxidizing agent, SO_4^{-2}, SeO_4^{-2}, H_6TeO_6, or PoO_3?

(d) Could you predict the relative oxidizing power from simple electronegativity concepts?

13–C *Trends in Oxidation Potential. The Halogens.* (1). Add 10 drops of 0.1 M KI to 10 drops of 0.1 M $Fe(NO_3)_3$. Add 8 drops of CCl_4 and shake the solution thoroughly. (CCl_4 dissolves any I_2 which might be formed in the solution.) Add 10 ml of water, pour off the supernate, and repeat before recording the color of the CCl_4 solution.

(2) Repeat (1) with 0.1 M KBr in place of KI.

(3) Add 10 drops of 0.1 M KBr to 10 drops of 0.1 M $KBrO_3$ and 5 drops of 6 M H_2SO_4. Repeat the CCl_4 treatment as in (1).

(4) Add 10 drops of 0.1 M KCl to 10 drops of 0.1 M $KBrO_3$ and 5 drops of 6 M H_2SO_4. Heat the solution to boiling and note the odor, if any, of any gaseous product.

(5) Add 10 drops of 0.1 M KCl to 10 drops of 0.01 M $KMnO_4$ and 5 drops of 6 M H_2SO_4. Heat the solution to boiling and note the odor.

(6) Prepare 0.1 M KF solution by adding 1 drop of 5 M KF to 2.5 ml of water. Repeat (5) with 10 drops of this 0.1 M KF solution in place of the KCl solution.

(a) List the halide ions in order of increasing reducing power, from the poorest to the best reducing agent.

(b) List the halides in order of decreasing electronegativity.

(c) Does the trend in reducing power follow the trend in electronegativity?

(d) The elements in groups V and VI are analogous to those in VII. List the following elements in order of increasing oxidizing power: Se, Po, Te, O_2, and

S. List the following compounds in order of increasing reducing power: AsH_3, SbH_3, PH_3, BiH_3, and NH_3.

13–D *Trends in Oxidation Potential. The Transition Elements.* (1). Add 2 drops of 0.3 M Na_3VO_4 to 5 drops of 3 M HCl. Now add 10 drops of 0.1 M KI and boil the solution until all the I_2 is removed (a few minutes).

(2) Add 10 drops of 0.1 M $SnCl_2$ to 5 drops of 3 M HCl and 2 drops of 0.3 M Na_3VO_4 and heat the solution.

(3) Finally add a small amount of Zn metal to solution (2) and heat the solution.

(4). Add 5 drops of 0.1 M $Cr(NO_3)_3$ to 10 drops of 0.01 M $KMnO_4$ and 6 drops of 3 M HCl. Neutralize the solution with 3 M NH_4OH, add 6 M HAc until barely acidic, and then 5 drops of 0.2 M $PbAc_2$.

(5) Add 10 drops of 0.1 M KBr to 5 drops of 1 M K_2CrO_4 and 20 drops of 6 M H_2SO_4 in a 6-inch test tube. Add several drops of CCl_4 to this solution and shake thoroughly. Fill the test tube with water and decant this from the CCl_4. Repeat. Notice the color of the CCl_4.

(6) Repeat (5) with 16 drops of 0.3 M Na_3VO_4 in place of K_2CrO_4.

In answering the questions, remember that VO_2^+ is yellow, VO^{+2} is blue, V^{+3} is green, and V^{+2} is purple. Also Zn is a better reducing agent than Sn^{+2}, which is better than I^-.

(a) List the vanadium ions in order of increasing oxidizing power.

(b) Does the electronegativity increase or decrease as the oxidizing power increases for the different oxidation states of this element?

(c) Which would you expect to be the strongest oxidizing agent: Cr^{+3} or CrO_4^{-2}? Cu^{+2} or Cu^{+3}? Mn^{+2} or Mn^{+3}?

(d) List the states V(V), Cr(VI), and Mn(VII) in order of increasing oxidizing power in acidic solution.

(e) List them in order of increasing electronegativity.

(f) Predict the relative oxidizing power of SiO_2, $HClO_4$, H_3PO_4, and H_2SO_4.

13–E. *Shifting Redox Equilibria.* (1) *By Precipitation of an Insoluble Salt.* (a) To another 10-drop portion of H_2SeO_3, add $AgNO_3$ solution until no further precipitation of Ag_2SeO_3 takes place. Now add a little saturated bromine water. Why does the color of the Br_2 disappear? Assuming that one of the products of reaction is AgBr, write a balanced chemical equation for this reaction. Show by means of the equilibrium involved why the reaction proceeded "to completion" in this case but not in (13–*B*, 2). (The equilibrium constant for the reaction

$$H_2SeO_3 + Br_2 + H_2O \rightleftharpoons HSeO_4^- + 3\,H^+ + 2\,Br^-$$

is 0.88 at 25°C.)

Now add more bromine water a little at a time until the Br_2 color persists. Place the tube in a hot-water bath IN THE HOOD until the excess Br_2 is driven off. Digest the AgBr until the supernate is clear. Centrifuge and decant some of the clear liquid and add to it some $Ba(NO_3)_2$ solution. Heat the solution in a boiling-water bath and then centrifuge. What is the precipitate?

(b) Prepare some freshly precipitated copper metal by reducing 5 drops of 0.1 M Cu^{+2} solution with $Na_2S_2O_4$ as in the Cu–Cd separation (procedure 5–*H*). Centrifuge. Remove the supernate and wash the precipitate with water. Add 1 drop of 6 M H_2SO_4 and then 10 drops of 0.1 M Cu^{+2} solution. Shake and examine for any signs of reaction. Now add 15 drops of 0.1 M KI solution. By means of the equilibria involved, explain what happened, remembering that under normal circumstances the equilibrium

$$2\ Cu^+ \rightleftharpoons Cu + Cu^{+2}$$

lies far to the right.

(2) *By Formation of Complexes.* (a) Review Illustrative Experiment 6 for "The Insoluble Chloride Group."

(b) Prepare some freshly precipitated copper as above. After washing, cover it with distilled water and shake, allowing access of air. Examine for any signs of reaction. Now add 1 ml of 15 M NH_4OH and shake for 2 minutes, or until an obvious change has occurred. Centrifuge. Explain what has happened, remembering that atmospheric O_2 is an oxidizing agent.

(3) *By Change of pH.* Add 10 drops of 0.1 M H_3AsO_4 solution to 10 drops of 0.1 M KI. Observe. Now add 10 drops of 3 M HCl to the solution. What has happened? Now make the solution alkaline with NaOH. Explain the result, making use of the equilibria involved.

13–15. Questions and Problems

1. Explain why the oxidation potential of a system at equilibrium is zero.

2. What is the function of the platinum electrodes in the first illustration given in Section 13–2?

3. Explain the function of the salt bridge in a galvanic cell.

4. (a) A lead storage battery, which functions on the reaction

$$Pb\ (s) + PbO_2\ (s) + 2\ H_2SO_4 \rightarrow 2\ PbSO_4\ (s) + 2\ H_2O$$

provides current at a potential of 2.05 volts when fully charged (H_2SO_4 density, 1.20). What is the minimum voltage that must be applied externally in order to recharge a spent battery?

(b) When a lead storage battery is discharged, it has a voltage of only 1.91 volts, and the H_2SO_4 density is 1.05. Explain why the density changes as current is drawn from the battery and explain why the change in density affects the voltage.

5. Is the disproportionation of Cu^+ consistent with the positions of the Cu–Cu^+ and Cu^+–Cu^{+2} couples in Appendix 10?

6. (a) Predict from the following potential diagram which oxidation states of ruthenium are stable with respect to disproportionation in 1 M HCl and which are not.

$$Ru \xrightarrow{-0.45} Ru^{+2} \xrightarrow{-0.3} RuCl_5^{-2} \xrightarrow{-1.3} RuCl_5OH^{-2} \xrightarrow{-1.7} HRuO_4^- \xrightarrow{-1.6}$$
$$RuO_4^- \xrightarrow{-1.0} RuO_4$$

(b) Complete the diagram showing potentials for all other possible couples (e.g., Ru^{+2}–$HRuO_4^-$).

7. Using information given in Appendix 10, calculate the standard oxidation potentials for the following reactions

(a) $HPH_2O_2 + H_2O + Ni^{+2} \rightarrow H_2PHO_3 + Ni\ (s) + 2\ H^+$

(b) $Sn^{+2} + 2\ Cr^{+3} \rightarrow Sn^{+4} + 2\ Cr^{+2}$

(c) $H_2PHO_3 + H_2O + Cd^{+2} \rightarrow H_3PO_4 + Cd\,(s) + 2\,H^+$

(d) $3\,V^{+2} + P\,(s) + 3\,H^+ \rightarrow 3\,V^{+3} + PH_3\,(g)$

(e) $2\,H_2S + H_2SO_3 \rightarrow 3\,S\,(s) + 3\,H_2O$

(f) $PH_3\,(g) + 3\,HPH_2O_2 \rightarrow 4\,P\,(s) + 6\,H_2O$

(g) $I_2 + H_2O_2 \rightarrow 2\,HIO$

(h) $2\,HIO + H_2O_2 \rightarrow I_2 + O_2\,(g) + 2\,H_2O$

(i) $H_2O_2 + O_2 \rightarrow H_2O + O_3$

(j) $S_2O_8^{-2} + 2\,Ag^+ \rightarrow 2\,SO_4^{-2} + 2\,Ag^{+2}$

(k) $4\,FeO_4^{-2} + 20\,H^+ \rightarrow 4\,Fe^{+3} + 3\,O_2 + 10\,H_2O$

(l) $Cl_2 + PdCl_4^{-2} \rightarrow PdCl_6^{-2}$

(m) $MnO_2\,(s) + H_2O_2 + 2\,H^+ \rightarrow Mn^{+2} + 2\,H_2O + O_2\,(g)$

8. Using information given in Appendix 10, calculate the standard oxidation potentials for the following half-reactions

(a) $Ni\,(s) + 2\,H_2O \rightarrow NiO_2\,(s) + 4\,H^+ + 4\,e^-$

(b) $V^{+2} + H_2O \rightarrow VO^{+2} + 2\,H^+ + 2\,e^-$

(c) $Cl^- + H_2O \rightarrow HClO + H^+ + 2\,e^-$

(d) $I^- + 3\,H_2O \rightarrow IO_3^- + 6\,H^+ + 6\,e^-$

(e) $I^- + 6\,H_2O \rightarrow H_5IO_6 + 7\,H^+ + 8\,e^-$

(f) $AsH_3 + 4\,H_2O \rightarrow H_3AsO_4 + 8\,H^+ + 8\,e^-$

(g) $Mn^{+2} + 4\,H_2O \rightarrow MnO_4^{-2} + 8\,H^+ + 4\,e^-$

(h) $2\,H_2S + 8\,H_2O \rightarrow S_2O_8^{-2} + 20\,H^+ + 18\,e^-$

(i) $HO_2 \rightarrow O_2\,(g) + H^+ + e^-$

(j) $Au^+ + 3\,H_2O \rightarrow Au(OH)_3\,(s) + 3\,H^+ + 2\,e^-$

(k) $Re\,(s) + 2\,H_2O \rightarrow ReO_2\,(s) + 4\,H^+ + 4\,e^-$

(l) $H_2O + HO_2 \rightarrow O_3\,(g) + 3\,H^+ + 3\,e^-$

(m) $U + 2\,H_2O \rightarrow UO_2^{+2} + 4\,H^+ + 6\,e^-$

9. Calculate potentials for the following half-reactions assuming unit activities

(a) $H_2SO_3 + Ba^{+2} + H_2O \rightarrow BaSO_4\,(s) + 4\,H^+ + 2\,e^-$

(b) $Cu\,(s) + I^- \rightarrow CuI\,(s) + e^-$

(c) $Pb\,(s) + SO_4^{-2} \rightarrow PbSO_4\,(s) + 2\,e^-$

(d) $Bi\,(s) + H_2O + Cl^- \rightarrow BiOCl\,(s) + 2\,H^+ + 3\,e^-$

(e) $Hg\,(l) + 4\,I^- \rightarrow HgI_4^{-2} + 2\,e^-$

(f) $Au\,(s) + 4\,NSC^- \rightarrow Au(NCS)_4^- + 3\,e^-$

(g) $Fe\,(s) + 6\,CN^- \rightarrow Fe(CN)_6^{-4} + 2\,e^-$

(h) $Mn\,(s) + 2\,OH^- \rightarrow Mn(OH)_2\,(s) + 2\,e^-$

(i) $Fe\,(s) + 3\,OH^- \rightarrow Fe(OH)_3\,(s) + 3\,e^-$

(j) $Zn\,(s) + 4\,OH^- \rightarrow Zn(OH)_4^{-2} + 2\,e^-$

(k) $Zn\,(s) + 4\,NH_3 \rightarrow Zn(NH_3)_4^{+2} + 2\,e^-$

(l) $Sn\,(s) + 3\,OH^- \rightarrow Sn(OH)_3^- + 2\,e^-$

(m) $Sn\,(s) + 6\,OH^- \rightarrow Sn(OH)_6^{-2} + 4\,e^-$

10. Calculate potentials for the following half-reactions assuming unit activities

(a) $PbS\,(s) + 4\,H_2O \rightarrow PbSO_4\,(s) + 8\,H^+ + 8\,e^-$

(b) $CN^- + H_2O \rightarrow HNCO + H^+ + 2\,e^-$

(c) $NiS\,(s) + 6\,NH_3 \rightarrow Ni(NH_3)_6^{+2} + S\,(s) + 2\,e^-$

(d) $Cr(NH_3)_6^{+3} + Ba^{+2} + 8\,OH^- \rightarrow BaCrO_4\,(s) + 6\,NH_3 + 4\,H_2O + 3\,e^-$

(e) $2\,Ag + CO_3^{-2} \rightarrow Ag_2CO_3\,(s) + 2\,e^-$

(f) $Hg\,(l) + S^{-2} \rightarrow HgS\,(s) + 2\,e^-$

(g) $HgS\,(s) \rightarrow Hg^{+2} + S\,(s) + 2\,e^-$

(h) $2 IO_3^- + 2 CrO_4^{-2} + 5 H_2O \rightarrow 2 H_5IO_6 + Cr_2O_7^{-2} + 4 e^-$

(i) $Al (s) + 6 HF \rightarrow AlF_6^{-3} + 6 H^+ + 3 e^-$

(j) $Hg_2I_2 (s) + 2 S^{-2} \rightarrow 2 HgS (s) + 2 I^- + 2 e^-$

(k) $AgNO_2 (s) + H_2O \rightarrow Ag^+ + NO_3^- + 2 H^+ + 2 e^-$

11. From the potentials given for the following half-reactions, calculate the quantity asked for

(a) $U(OH)_4 (s) + 2 Na^+ + 4 OH^- \rightarrow Na_2UO_4 (s) + 4 H_2O + 2 e^-$
$$E_B^° = 1.61 \quad K_{sp} \text{ of } Na_2UO_4$$

(b) $Pd + 4 Br^- \rightarrow PdBr_4^{-2} + 2 e^- \qquad E^° = -0.6 \quad K_{inst} \text{ of } PdBr_4^{-2}$

(c) $Pt + 4 Br^- \rightarrow PtBr_4^{-2} + 2 e^- \qquad E^° = -0.58 \quad K_{inst} \text{ of } PtBr_4^{-2}$

(d) $Co(OH)_2 (s) + OH^- \rightarrow Co(OH)_3 (s) + e^- \quad E_B^° = -0.17 \quad K_{sp} \text{ of } Co(OH)_3$

(e) $Ag_2O (s) + 2 OH^- \rightarrow 2 AgO (s) + H_2O + 2 e^- \quad E_B^° = -0.57 \quad K_{sp} \text{ of } AgO$

(f) $Os (s) + 9 OH^- \rightarrow HOsO_5^- + 4 H_2O + 8 e^-$
$$E_B^° = -0.02 \quad K_A \text{ of } H_2OsO_5 (= OsO_4 + H_2O)$$

(g) $O_2^- \rightarrow O_2 (g) + e^- \qquad\qquad E_B^° = 0.56. \quad K_A \text{ of } HO_2.$

(h) $Mo (s) + 8 OH^- \rightarrow MoO_4^{-2} + 4 H_2O + 6 e^-$
$$E_B^° = 1.05 \quad K_1K_2 \text{ of } H_2MoO_4 (= MoO_3 + H_2O)$$

(i) $Fe(OH)_4^- + 4 OH^- \rightarrow FeO_4^{-2} + 4 H_2O + 3 e^-$
$$E_B^° = -0.9 \quad K_A \text{ of } Fe(OH)_3 (s)$$

(j) $Sn (s) + 6 F^- \rightarrow SnF_6^{-2} + 4 e^- \qquad E^° = 0.25 \quad K_{inst} \text{ of } SnF_6^{-2}$

12. Calculate standard oxidation potentials for the following reactions and indicate whether they should go as written

(a) $(CN)_2 (g) + 2 OH^- \rightarrow CN^- + NCO^- + H_2O$

(b) $2 Cl_2 (g) + 4 OH^- \rightarrow 3 Cl^- + ClO_2^- + 2 H_2O$

(c) $P_4 (s) + 3 OH^- + 3 H_2O \rightarrow PH_3 (g) + 3 PH_2O_2^-$

(d) $2 As (s) + OH^- + 3 H_2O \rightarrow AsH_3 (g) + As(OH)_4^-$

(e) $2 Sn(OH)_3^- \rightarrow Sn (s) + Sn(OH)_6^{-2}$

(f) $Cu_2O (s) + H_2O \rightarrow Cu (s) + Cu(OH)_2 (s)$

(g) $2 CrPO_4 (s) + 2 MnO_4^- + 3 H_2O \rightarrow Cr_2O_7^{-2} + 2 H_3PO_4 + 2 MnO_2$

(h) $4 Co(NH_3)_4^{+2} + 8 NH_3 + O_2 (g) + 2 H_2O \rightarrow 4 Co(NH_3)_6^{+3} + 4 OH^-$

(i) $Ag_2SeO_3 (s) + H_2O + Br_2 (aq) \rightarrow 2 AgBr (s) + SeO_4^{-2} + 2 H^+$

(j) $2 FeS (s) + S (s) \rightarrow Fe_2S_3 (s)$

(k) $Ag(NCS)_2^- + Br_2 (aq) \rightarrow AgBr (s) + (NCS)_2 + Br^-$

(l) $Hg_2Br_2 (s) + 2 Br^- \rightarrow Hg (l) + HgBr_4^{-2}$

(m) $2 Cu^{+2} + 4 NCS^- \rightarrow 2 CuNCS (s) + (NCS)_2$

(n) $2 Cu(NH_3)_2^+ \rightarrow Cu (s) + Cu(NH_3)_4^{+2}$

(o) $2 ZnI^+ + Fe(CN)_6^{-3} \rightarrow Zn_2Fe(CN)_6 (s) + \frac{1}{2} I_2 + I^-$

(p) $2 Co(NH_3)_6^{+3} + 3 MnS (s) + 6 H_2O \rightarrow$
$$2 CoS (s) + S (s) + 3 Mn(OH)_2 (s) + 6 NH_4^+ + 6 NH_3 (aq)$$

(q) $Cu(NH_3)_4^{+2} + 3 CrO_4^{-2} + 2 H_2O \rightarrow$
$$CuCrO_4 (s) + N_2 (g) + Cr(OH)_3 (s) + 2 NH_3 (aq) + 4 OH^-$$

(r) $2 Co(NH_3)_6^{+3} + Ag(S_2O_3)_2^{-3} \rightarrow$
$$2 Co(NH_3)_4^{+2} + Ag(NH_3)_2^+ + S_4O_6^{-2} + 2 NH_3 (aq)$$

(s) $Hg_2I_2 (s) + 2 S (s) \rightarrow 2 HgS (s) + I_2$

(t) $2 AgNO_2 (s) \rightarrow Ag^+ + NO_3^- + Ag (s) + NO (g)$

(u) $HgO (s) + 2 Cl_2 (aq) + H_2O \rightarrow 2 HClO + HgCl_2 (aq)$

(v) $4 AgClO_3 + 3 Cl_2 (aq) \rightarrow 4 AgCl + 6 ClO_2 (g)$

(w) $2 ClO_3^- + H_2C_2O_4 + 2 H^+ \rightarrow 2 ClO_2 (g) + 2 CO_2 (g) + 2 H_2O$

13. Calculate potentials for the following systems and tell whether the reactions will go as written

(a) MnO_4^- (0.001 M)+Fe^{+2} (10^{-4} M)+H^+ (0.1 M) →

$$Mn^{+2} (0.1\ M) + Fe^{+3} (10^{-5}\ M) + 4\ H_2O$$

(b) Pt (s)+Cl_2 (5 atm)+Cl^- (0.1 M) → $PtCl_6^{-2}$ (0.01 M)

(c) Os (s)+O_2 (0.5 atm) → OsO_4 (0.01 M)

(d) V^{+3} (0.1 M)+Br_2 (10^{-4} M)+H_2O →

$$VO^{+2} (0.01\ M) + Br^- (0.01\ M) + H^+ (10^{-7}\ M)$$

(e) $Fe(OH)_2$ (s)+OH^- (0.001 M)+I_2 (s) → $Fe(OH)_3$ (s)+I^- (0.001 M)

(f) $U(OH)_4$ (s)+Na^+ (0.1 M)+OH^- (0.1 M) →

$$Na_2UO_4 (s) + U(OH)_3 (s) + H_2O \quad \text{(See problem 11–a.}$$

14. If AuS has a K_{sp} of 10^{-78} and the Au^+–Au^{+2} has a normal oxidation potential of -1.90 volts, calculate whether AuS is stable with respect to decomposition into its elements.

$$\text{AuS (s)} \rightarrow \text{Au (s)} + \text{S (s)}$$

15. A solution of 0.1 M HCl and one of 10^{-4} M HCl are connected by a salt bridge and a platinum electrode is placed in each, with H_2 gas bubbling over it at 1 atm. When the electrodes are connected to a voltmeter, the meter is found to have a reading different from zero. What is the reading?

16. What is the potential difference between a 0.1 M $AgNO_3$, solution and a 0.005 M $AgNO_3$ solution measured with silver electrodes?

17. What is the potential difference between a solution containing 0.1 M Sn^{+2} and 0.05 M Sn^{+4} and one containing 10^{-4} M Sn^{+2} and 6×10^{-3} M Sn^{+4} measured with platinum electrodes?

18. What is the potential difference between a 0.001 molar solution of $SnCl_2$ in 0.1 M NaOH and a suspension of solid SnS in 0.1 M NaOH measured with tin electrodes?

13–16.   References

Latimer, W. M., Hildebrand, J. H., *Reference Book of Inorganic Chemistry*, 3d ed. New York: The Macmillan Company, 1951, Appendices I, II, III.

Latimer, W. M., *The Oxidation States of the Elements and Their Potentials in Aqueous Solutions* ("Oxidation Potentials"), 2d ed. Englewood Cliffs, N.J.: Prentice-Hall, Inc., 1952.

Charlot, G., *Selected Constants—Oxidation-Reduction Potentials*. London: Pergamon Press, 1958.

Chapter 14

The Rules of Oxidation State. Devising an

Analytical Scheme. The Platinum Metals

14–1. Oxidation State and Electronic Structure

Many of the relationships of the oxidation states of the elements can be predicted from a knowledge of their electronic structures. For example, you are already familiar with the idea that, because the alkali metals have one valence electron each, they exhibit a uniform oxidation state of $+1$. Likewise, the alkaline-earth metals, having two valence electrons, have a uniform oxidation state of $+2$. In other words, an element, in general, can lose or share electrons up to the maximum number in its valence level. Since the number of valence electrons is generally the same as the number of the column of the periodic table in which the element occurs, the rule may be stated that

> The maximum positive oxidation state of an element is equal to N, where N is the column number.

The exceptions to this rule are O, F, Br, and the elements in the group

Fe	Co	Ni	Cu
Rh	Pd	Ag	
Ir	Pt	Au	

Since a high positive oxidation state results only when an element combines with another much more electronegative than itself, and since oxygen and fluorine are the most electronegative of all the reactive elements, it is obvious why these elements do not exhibit the $+N$ state. The case of the transition elements is the result of the gradually lessening availability of the d electrons as the d level becomes filled, so that there is a more or less smooth transition from the high-column numbers on the left to the low-column numbers on the right. Although ten elements are shown as exceptions, there are regularities among the exceptions which make remembering the actual maximum oxidation states much easier than it would seem otherwise. Thus, the maximum states between Mn $(+7)$ and Zn $(+2)$ are

$$Mn\ (+7),\quad Fe\ (+6),\quad Co\ (+5),\quad Ni\ (+4),\quad Cu\ (+3),\quad Zn\ (+2)$$

If, now, it be also noted that all members of the copper family (Cu, Ag, Au) have maximum states of $+3$, and that the four members of the platinum group have maximum states of $+6$ (e.g., RhO_4^{-2}, PdO_3, IrO_4^{-2}, IrF_6, PtO_4^{-2}, PtF_6), the relationship becomes very easy to remember. (The evidence for Co(V) and Pd(VI) is somewhat doubtful, and the maximum states of these elements may be $+4$.) The maximum oxidation states of these elements now show the following systematics

VI	VII	VIII			I	II
Cr $(+6)$	Mn $(+7)$	Fe $(+6)$	Co $(+5)*$	Ni $(+4)$	Cu $(+3)$	Zn $(+2)$
Mo $(+6)$	Tc $(+7)$	Ru $(+8)$	Rh $(+6)$	Pd $(+6)*$	Ag $(+3)$	Cd $(+2)$
W $(+6)$	Re $(+7)$	Os $(+8)$	Ir $(+6)$	Pt $(+6)$	Au $(+3)$	Hg $(+2)$

* Or $(+4)$.

The reason that bromine does not conform to the rule of maximum oxidation state is too complex to be discussed here. It will be considered in Chapter 16.

Oxidation State $= N-2$. As we have seen in Chapter 10, the elements in the columns of the periodic table to the right of the copper family are characterized by having a pair of s electrons and at a higher level a number (zero to six) of p electrons all of very similar energy. It is possible for these elements to use their p electrons (either for covalent bonding or by loss to form an ion) without using the s pair. Since the column number (N) and maximum oxidation state are equal to the sum of the s and p electrons for these elements, this results in there being an important oxidation state equal to $N-2$.

Compounds or ions exemplifying these states are shown in Table 14–1. It can be seen from the examples given that the low oxidation states at the lower left of the table are characteristically ionic, and the high states at the upper right characteristically covalent, while the intermediate states may be either ionic or covalent depending upon the circumstances. Thus In^+, Tl^+, and Pb^{+2} are well defined cations, whereas N(III), S(IV), Cl(V), and Br(V) *never* exist as simple cations—all their compounds involve covalent bonding. On the other hand, Ge(II), Sb(III), and Bi(III) may occur either as the simple cations, Ge^{+2}, Sb^{+3}, and Bi^{+3}, or with covalent bonding, as in GeI_2, $Sb(OH)_2^+$, and $Bi(CH_3)_3$. Regardless of the kind of bonding, however, the

$N-2$ state is more important for all of these elements than any other, except the $+N$ and the $N-8$. (In the case of the heavier elements, as we shall see (Section 14–2), it is the most important of all.)

TABLE 14–1. REPRESENTATIVE EXAMPLES OF THE $N-2$ OXIDATION STATE

II	III	IV	V	VI	VII
0	+1	+2	+3	+4	+5
——	——	CO (g) carbon monoxide	NO_2^- nitrite ion	$\left(\begin{array}{c}O_3\\ozone\end{array}\right)$	——
——	——	CCl_2	NF_3	——	——
——	——	SiO (g) silicon monoxide	P_4O_6 phosphorus sesquioxide	SO_3^{-2} sulfite ion	ClO_3^- chlorate ion
——	AlCl (g)	——	PCl_3	SF_4	ClO_2F
(Zn^0)	Ga^+	Ge^{+2}	AsO_3^{-3} arsenite ion	SeO_3^{-2} selenite ion	BrO_3^- bromate ion
——	GaI	GeI_2	AsI_3	$SeCl_4$	BrF_5
(Cd^0)	In^+	Sn^{+2}	Sb^{+3}	TeO_3^{-2} tellurite ion	IO_3^- iodate ion
——	InI	SnI_2	SbI_3	$TeCl_4$	IF_5
(Hg^0)	Tl^+	Pb^{+2}	Bi^{+3}	PoO_3^{-2} polonite ion	AtO_3^- astatate ion
$Hg(IF_5)_2$	TlI	PbI_2	BiI_3	$PoCl_4$	$AtF_5(?)$

Oxidation State $= N-8$. An important characteristic of the more electronegative elements on the right side of the periodic table is the tendency to add electrons (either by forming negative ions or by forming covalent bonds) up to the number of the next noble gas. Since the number of valence electrons one of these elements has is N (the column number) and the next noble gas has 8, a total of $8-N$ electrons must be added in order to build the number up to that of the next noble gas. Since electrons are negative, the element must now have a charge or oxidation state of $-(8-N)$ or $N-8$. Thus the halogens in column VII add one electron for $N-8 = -1$, the hydrogen halides and the halide ions resulting

$$HF, \quad F^-, \quad HCl, \quad Cl^-, \quad HBr, \quad Br^-, \quad HI, \quad I^-, \quad HAt, \quad At^-$$

The chalcogens in column VI add two electrons for $N-8$

$$O^{-2}, \quad OH^-, \quad H_2O, \quad S^{-2}, \quad H_2S, \quad Se^{-2}, \quad H_2Se, \quad Te^{-2}, \quad H_2Te, \quad Po^{-2}, \quad H_2Po$$

In the nitrogen family, the simple ions are difficult to obtain because of the high charge which would have to be placed on a single atom, so for $N-8 = -3$, the neutral compounds are more characteristic: NH_3, PH_3, AsH_3, SbH_3, and BiH_3—ammonia, phosphine, arsine, stibine, and bismuthine, respectively. The simple anions can be produced, however, in certain crystalline solids: e.g., Cs_3N, Cs_3P, Na_3As, $LaSb$, and $LaBi$. In the carbon family ($N-8 = -4$) the simple anions are essentially nonexistent, but again the $N-8$ state is represented by neutral compounds: CH_4, SiH_4, GeH_4, SnH_4, and PbH_4—methane, silane, germane, stannane, and plumbane, respectively.

When we pass to the left of the carbon family, an ambiguity arises, for just as GeH_4 may be looked upon equally well as consisting of Ge^{-4} and H^+, or as consisting of Ge^{+4} and H^-, so ions such as $BH_4{}^-$, which are usually considered to consist of B^{+3} and H^-, might just as well be considered to consist of B^{-5} and H^+. Generally, oxidation states are not considered to go lower (algebraically) than -4. However, in view of the fact that the boron atom in $BH_4{}^-$,

$$
\begin{array}{c}
\text{H} \\
\overset{\cdot\cdot}{\underset{\cdot\cdot}{\text{H}:\text{B}:\text{H}}} \quad {}^{(-)} \\
\text{H}
\end{array}
$$

has five more electrons than an isolated neutral boron atom, there is some justification for calling this a representative of the -5 oxidation state ($N-8 = -5$). Similarly, we have $AlH_4{}^-$, $GaH_4{}^-$ and $InH_4{}^-$. In the same way, the tetramethylzincate ion, $Zn(CH_3)_4{}^{-2}$,

$$
\begin{array}{c}
\text{H} \\
\overset{\cdot\cdot}{\text{H}:\text{C}:\text{H}} \quad {}^{(-2)} \\
\overset{\text{H}}{\underset{\text{H}}{\overset{\cdot\cdot}{\underset{\cdot\cdot}{\text{H}:\text{C}}}}} : \overset{\cdot\cdot}{\underset{\cdot\cdot}{\text{Zn}}} : \overset{\text{H}}{\underset{\text{H}}{\overset{\cdot\cdot}{\underset{\cdot\cdot}{\text{C}:\text{H}}}}} \\
\overset{\cdot\cdot}{\text{H}:\text{C}:\text{H}} \\
\text{H}
\end{array}
$$

may be considered to have zinc in the -6 oxidation state.

14–2. Relative Stability of Oxidation States

For the elements on the right-hand side of the periodic table (i.e., to the right of the copper family) fairly regular trends in the relative stabilities of the oxidation states, N, $N-2$, and $N-8$ exist, which may be simply summarized in the following diagram, where the lines indicate the most stable states.

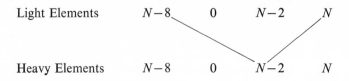

That is, for the lightest element in any column, the extreme states ($N-8$ and N) are the most stable, whereas for the heaviest element the mean ($N-2$) state is most stable. Thus for carbon, the compound CO, representing C(II), is unstable by 0.63 volts with respect to disproportionation into carbon and carbon dioxide in 1 molar acid

$$2\,CO \rightarrow C + CO_2$$

and unstable by 0.38 volts with respect to disproportionation into CH_4 and CO_2

$$4\,CO + 2\,H_2O \rightarrow CH_4 + 3\,CO_2$$

On the other hand, Pb^{+2} does not disproportionate either into Pb and PbO_2 or into PbH_4 and PbO_2. It is stable with respect to the reaction

$$2\,Pb^{+2} + 2\,H_2O \rightarrow Pb + PbO_2 + 4\,H^+$$

by -1.58 volts, and with respect to the reaction

$$4\,Pb^{+2} + 6\,H_2O \rightarrow PbH_4 + 3\,PbO_2 + 8\,H^+$$

by -2.03 volts. Table 14–2 shows the degree of stability of each element in its $N-2$ oxidation state with respect to disproportionation into the $+N$ state and either the zero or the $N-8$ state in terms of oxidation potentials.

TABLE 14–2. STABILITY OF $N - 2$ OXIDATION STATE IN 1 M H^+ IN TERMS OF OXIDATION POTENTIALS FOR THE DISPROPORTIONATION REACTIONS*

B	C	N	O	F	
very unstable	0.63	0.51			
unstable	**0.38**	**0.40**			
Al	Si	P	S	Cl	
	ca. 0.25	−0.22	0.28	0.28	
	ca. 0.8	**0.0**	**0.18**	**0.26**	
					unstable
					stable
Ga	Ge	As	Se	Br	
0.64	ca. 0.0	−0.31	−0.41	ca. −0.6	
	ca. 0.2	**−0.74**	**−0.61**	**ca. −0.7**	
In	Sn	Sb	Te	I	
0.32	−0.29	−0.37	−0.40	−0.5	
	−0.53	**−0.73**	**−0.83**	**−0.5**	
unstable					
stable					
Tl	Pb	Bi	Po	At	
−1.59	−1.58	−1.3(?)	−0.8(?)	−0.3(??)	
	−2.03	**−1.9(?)**	**−1.3(?)**	**−0.5(??)**	

* Disproportionation to $+N$ and free elements in roman type. Disproportionation to $+N$ and ($N - 8$) in bold-face. (?) doubtful.

It can be seen that with the exception of phosphorus the pattern is fairly regular. The $N-2$ states are unstable in the light elements, but become generally increasingly stable lower in the periodic table. The borderline between stability and instability occurs farther down in the table, the farther to the left we go. Phosphorus is anomalous in several respects. These anomalies will be discussed in Chapter 16.

Unfortunately, the degree of stability of any given oxidation state does not change perfectly smoothly in going down any given column, nor does the oxidizing power of any given state. Consequently, the trends must be taken only as a generality. However, there are a number of regular trends in oxidizing and reducing power which can be pointed out.

The $N-8$ state becomes a better reducing agent, the lower in the column of the periodic table the element is situated. The potentials for the reactions $(N-8) \rightarrow 0$ (e.g., $H_2S \rightarrow S + 2H^+ + 2e^-$) are given in Table 14–3 for $1 M H^+$.

TABLE 14–3. OXIDATION POTENTIALS FOR $M^{(N-8)} \rightarrow M^0$ COUPLES*

BH_4^-	CH_4	NH_4^+	H_2O	HF
0.25	-0.13	-0.28	-1.23	-3.06
	SiH_4	PH_3	H_2S	Cl^-
	-0.10	$+0.065$	-0.14	-1.36
	GeH_4	AsH_3	H_2Se	Br^-
	$> +0.3$	$+0.60$	$+0.40$	-1.07
	SnH_4	SbH_3	H_2Te	I^-
	$> +0.5$	$+0.51$	$+0.72$	-0.535
	PbH_4	BiH_3	H_2Po	At^-
	>0.8	>0.8	>1.0	-0.2

* The values designated $>$ are highly uncertain.

The trends for the positive oxidation states of these elements are complicated by a number of factors too complex to be discussed here, so that there appear to be many irregularities in going down the columns. On the other hand, as one passes from left to right in any given period, the oxidizing power becomes regularly greater (as shown by the increasing negativity of the potential given in Table 14–4).

TABLE 14–4. POTENTIALS FOR THE REACTIONS $M^0 \rightarrow M^{+(N-2)}$ IN $1 M H^+$

B^+	CO	HNO_2	O_3	FO_3^-*
$< +0.87$	-0.51	-1.45	-1.65	< -2.0
Al^+	SiO	H_3PO_3	H_2SO_3	ClO_3^-
$< +1.66$	$\approx +0.75$	$+0.50$	-0.45	-1.47
Ga^+	Ge^{+2}	$HAsO_2$	H_2SeO_3	BrO_3^-
$\approx +0.14$	0.0	-0.248	-0.74	-1.52
In^+	Sn^{+2}	SbO^+	TeO_2H^+	IO_3^-
$+0.13$	$+0.136$	-0.212	-0.559	-1.20
Tl^+	Pb^{+2}	BiO^+	PoO_2	AtO_3^-
$+0.3363$	$+0.126$	-0.32	-0.74	-1.2

* Doesn't exist.

The same is true for the $+N$ states as shown in Table 14–5.

TABLE 14–5. POTENTIALS FOR THE REACTION $M^{+(N-2)} \to M^{+N}$ IN 1 M H^+

	H_3BO_3	CO_2	NO_3^-	O_4^*	FO_4^{-*}
	$> +0.87$	$+0.116$	-0.94	< -1.65	?
	Al^{+3}	SiO_2	H_3PO_4	SO_4^{-2}	ClO_4^-
	$> +1.66$	$\approx +1.0$	$+0.276$	-0.17	-1.19
Zn^{+2}	Ga^{+3}	GeO_2	H_3AsO_4	SeO_4^{-2}	BrO_4^-
$+0.763$	$+0.78$	$+0.3$	-0.559	-1.15	≈ -2.1
Cd^{+2}	In^{+3}	Sn^{+4}	Sb_2O_5	H_6TeO_6	H_5IO_6
$+0.403$	$+0.45$	-0.15	-0.581	-0.96	-1.7
Hg^{+2}	Tl^{+3}	Pb^{+4}	Bi_2O_5	PoO_3	H_5AtO_6
-0.854	-1.25	-1.7	≈ -1.67	≈ -1.57	$\approx 1.5?$

* Doesn't exist.

14–3. The Unstable Oxidation States of the Nonmetals

The fact that the most important (i.e., the most stable) oxidation states of the elements on the right-hand side of the periodic table conform to the three rules cited above does not imply that other oxidation states do not exist. On the contrary, many other states are found; they are, however, almost always less stable than the states which do conform.

In solution, in solids, and in gaseous compounds other than oxides, the oxidation states found are usually odd for elements of odd atomic number (which have an odd number of electrons) and even for even-numbered elements. In a very small number of cases involving oxides, primarily in the gas phase, certain of the elements of odd atomic number exist in even states. These latter cases are almost entirely confined to the elements nitrogen, chlorine, and bromine in their higher oxidation states. The important examples of this are NO, NO_2, ClO_2, ClO_3, BrO_2, and BrO_3. Even these in the liquid and solid phases show a strong tendency to dimerize with resulting pairing of electrons, giving N_2O_4, Cl_2O_6, and Br_2O_6. For example

$$2 \quad \overset{O}{\underset{-O}{\diagdown}} N^+ \cdot \; \rightleftharpoons \; \overset{O}{\underset{-O}{\diagdown}} \overset{+}{N} - \overset{+}{N} \overset{O}{\underset{O-}{\diagup}}$$

Examples of compounds of the various oxidation states of the halogens are shown in Table 14–6.

The relative instability of the compounds of all oxidation states besides -1, $+5$, and $+7$ is clearly brought out in the potential diagrams given in Table 14–7.

In the case of the chalcogens, there are no *important* oxides or simple oxy compounds which correspond to states other than the $+N$, $N-2$, and $N-8$. (However, see Section 14–4). (Sulfur forms SO (g), stable only at high temperature; tellurium forms the unusual oxide TeO; and polonium

TABLE 14–6. REPRESENTATIVE COMPOUNDS OF THE HALOGENS

Oxidation State	Chlorine	Bromine	Iodine
−1	HCl, KCl, CH_3Cl	HBr, KBr, CH_3Br	HI, KI, CH_3I
0	Cl_2	Br_2	I_2
+1	$HClO$, $KClO$, Cl_2O, ClF, $ClNH_2$	$HBrO$, Br_2O, BrF, $BrCl$, $BrNH_2$	HIO, ICl, IBr, $IClO_4$
+3	$HClO_2$, $KClO_2$, ClF_3	BrF_3, $KBrF_4$, $[BrF_2][SO_3F]$	ICl_3, $KICl_4$, $(C_6H_5)_3I$, $[(C_6H_5)_2I]OH$, C_6H_5IO, $[IO][IO_3]$, $I(IO_3)_3$, $I(NO_3)_3$, $I(ClO_4)_3$
+4	ClO_2	BrO_2	
+5	$HClO_3$, $KClO_3$, ClO_2F, $[ClO_2][BF_4]$	$HBrO_3$, $KBrO_3$, BrO_2F, $[BrO_2][BF_4]$, BrF_5	HIO_3, KIO_3, I_2O_5, IO_2F, $[IO_2][IF_6]$, $[IO_2][BF_4]$, IF_5, KIF_6, $C_6H_5IO_2$
+6	ClO_3	BrO_3	
+7	$HClO_4$, $KClO_4$, CH_3ClO_4, Cl_2O_7, ClO_3F, $[ClO_3][BF_4]$, ClO_3NH_2, $KClO_3NH$, K_2ClO_3N		H_5IO_6, Ag_5IO_6, KIO_4, IO_3F, $[IO_3][BF_4]$, IF_7

probably forms PoO.) Important halides of the $+2$ state are formed, however, such as SCl_2, $SeCl_2$, $SeBr_2$, $SeBr_2$, SeI_2, $TeCl_2$, $TeBr_2$, and TeI_2. Polonium probably forms all the dihalides as well as PoS and Po^{+2} in solution. No exact potentials can be given for any of these except for Po^{+2}, which apparently is fairly stable in acidic solution.

$$H_2Po \xrightarrow{\geq 1.0} Po \xrightarrow{ca.-0.65} Po^{+2} \xrightarrow{ca.-0.8} PoO_2 \text{ (s)} \xrightarrow{-1.3} PoO_3 \text{ (s)}$$

In the case of the nitrogen-family elements, the only *important* examples of *simple* compounds not corresponding to the $+N$, $N-2$, and $N-8$ states are NO and NO_2. The relationship of these to other compounds of nitrogen can be seen in the potential diagram for nitrogen given in Section 13–8.

The carbon family elements have no compounds which fall outside the three important oxidation states (except, again, see Section 14–4). Likewise, with the boron family, there are no exceptions to the rules except for the peculiar, but important, boron hydrides, such as B_2H_6, B_4H_{10}, and so on, which are beyond the scope of this text. For more information on these, the reader is referred to such advanced inorganic texts as Moeller, *Inorganic Chemistry*, or Eméleus and Anderson, *Modern Aspects of Inorganic Chemistry*.

One additional point should be noted. For compounds involving only single bonds, the compounds of the $+1$ state of the halogens have the same electronic configuration as the *covalent* -1 state. (Compare $H \colon \ddot{I} \colon$ and

TABLE 14–7. STANDARD OXIDATION POTENTIAL DIAGRAMS FOR THE HALOGENS

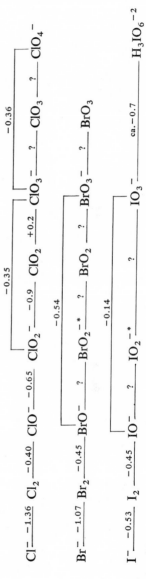

Acidic Solutions

Basic Solutions

* Not known to exist.

: Cl : I :, in which iodine is considered to be -1 and $+1$, respectively.)
This imparts a certain additional stability to the $+1$ state, even though in
a formal sense it does not conform to the rules. Likewise the $+2$ state of the
chalcogens corresponds in electronic structure to the -2 state (compare
H : S : H and : Cl : S : Cl :), and therefore there are certain compounds (particularly halides) of the formal $+2$ state which have unexpected stability. In
the nitrogen family, the electronic structure corresponding to the -3 state
is the same as that of the $+3$ state

$$
\begin{array}{ccc}
\text{H} & & \text{: Cl :} \\
\text{: N : H} & \text{and} & \text{: N : Cl :} \\
\text{H} & & \text{: Cl :}
\end{array}
$$

and except for NO and NO_2, *all* stable compounds of this family correspond
to the -3, $+3$ case, with one unshared pair of electrons, or to the $+5$ case,
in which there are *no* unshared electrons, as in

$$
\begin{array}{ccc}
\text{.O.} & & \text{H} \\
\text{H : O : N} \overset{+}{} & \text{or} & \text{H : N : H}^{(+)} \\
\text{.O.}^{-} & & \text{H}
\end{array}
$$

In the carbon family, the electronic structure of the -4 state corresponds to
that of the $+4$ state and (besides the compounds belonging to the $+2$—or
($N-2$)—state) *no* simple ones are known.

14–4. Apparent Violations of the Oxidation State Rules

Examination of the rules of oxidation state given in Section 14–1 reveals
that they may be rephrased in terms of electronic structure, as follows:

(1) There is an important oxidation state corresponding to complete use
of the valence electrons (with the exceptions noted in Section 14–1).
(2) There is an important oxidation state for the non-metallic elements
corresponding to the existence of one unshared pair of electrons.
(3) There is an important oxidation state for the nonmetallic elements
corresponding to the existence of four pairs of electrons, shared or unshared.

In some families it will happen that two of the three rules apply to the
same electronic structure.

The relationships can be seen in Table 14–8, which shows the oxidation
states in each family of nonmetals which corresponds to each of the above
rules.

TABLE 14-8. CORRESPONDENCE OF OXIDATION STATES TO
ELECTRONIC STRUCTURE RULES

	Rule		
Family	1	2	3
Zinc	+2	0	+2, −6
Boron	+3	+1	+3, −5
Carbon	+4	+2	+4, −4
Nitrogen	+5	+3	+3, −3
Chalcogen	+6	+4	+2, −2
Halogen	+7	+5	+1, −1

There are many cases of covalent compounds in which elements actually have an electronic structure specified by the rules of oxidation state, and yet, because they are attached simultaneously to two different elements, one of which is, by convention, usually considered to be positive and the other negative, they *appear* to violate the rules. As an example, let us consider the series of compounds CH_4, CH_3Cl, CH_2Cl_2, $CHCl_3$, and CCl_4. In each of these, carbon is attached by one pair of electrons each to four other atoms, and conforms in electronic structure to rules 1 and 3.

$$
\begin{array}{ccccc}
\text{H} & \text{H} & \text{H} & :\!\overset{..}{\text{Cl}}\!: & :\!\overset{..}{\text{Cl}}\!: \\
\text{H}:\overset{..}{\text{C}}:\text{H} & \text{H}:\overset{..}{\text{C}}:\overset{..}{\text{Cl}}: & \text{H}:\overset{..}{\text{C}}:\overset{..}{\text{Cl}}: & \text{H}:\overset{..}{\text{C}}:\overset{..}{\text{Cl}}: & :\overset{..}{\text{Cl}}:\overset{..}{\text{C}}:\overset{..}{\text{Cl}}: \\
\text{H} & \text{H} & :\!\overset{..}{\text{Cl}}\!: & :\!\overset{..}{\text{Cl}}\!: & :\!\overset{..}{\text{Cl}}\!:
\end{array}
$$

Nevertheless, because of the conventional oxidation states of +1 for H and −1 for Cl, only CH_4, $CHCl_3$, and CCl_4 correspond to the states specified by the rules (−4, +2, and +4), and of these, $CHCl_3$ does not *really* correspond to rule 2, because the $N-2$ state should have one *unshared* pair of electrons. Consequently, it is best, in the case of *covalent* compounds, to distinguish only between those oxidation states in which there is no unshared pair of electrons (in this case $+N$ and $N-8$) and those in which there is an unshared pair of electrons (the $N-2$ state). By this approach, all of the compounds in the above series—despite the fact that the carbon has formal oxidation states of −4, −2, 0, +2, and +4, respectively—actually have carbon with a *valence* of *four* (without attempting to specify whether it is + or −).

The series CH_4, CH_3OH, CH_2O, HCO_2H, and CO_2 and the series CH_4, CNH_3, CN_6H_6, HCN, and CN_2H_2 are cases of the same sort in which, if H = +1 and O = −2 and N = −3, then the carbon appears to have oxidation states of −4, −2, 0, +2, +4; and −4, −2, 0, +2, +4, respectively. Examination of the structures of the compounds, however, reveals that in every case the carbon atom is associated with *four* pairs of electrons

$$
\begin{array}{cccc}
\text{H} & \text{H} & \text{H} & :\!\overset{..}{\text{O}}\!:\text{H} \\
\text{H}:\overset{..}{\text{C}}:\text{H} & \text{H}:\overset{..}{\text{C}}:\overset{..}{\text{O}}:\text{H} & \text{H}:\overset{..}{\text{C}}::\overset{..}{\text{O}}: & \text{H}:\overset{..}{\text{C}}::\overset{..}{\text{O}}: \\
\text{H} & \text{H} & &
\end{array}
$$

$$:\overset{..}{O}::C::\overset{..}{O}:\qquad H:\overset{\overset{\displaystyle H}{..}}{\underset{\underset{\displaystyle H}{..}}{C}}:H\qquad H:\overset{\overset{\displaystyle H}{..}}{\underset{\underset{\displaystyle H}{..}}{C}}:\overset{..}{\underset{..}{N}}:H\qquad H:\overset{\overset{\displaystyle H}{..}}{\underset{\underset{\displaystyle H}{..}}{C}}:\overset{\overset{\displaystyle H}{..}}{\underset{..}{N}}:\overset{..}{\underset{..}{N}}:H$$

$$H:C:::N:\qquad H:\overset{..}{\underset{\underset{\displaystyle H}{..}}{N}}:C:::N:$$

Consequently, carbon in every one of these compounds must be considered to have a valence of four.

In compounds such as CO and RNC (where R may be any organic group) with structures $:O:::C:$ and $R:N:::C:$, the carbon must be considered to be in the $N-2$ state—with one unshared pair of electrons.

Other elements fall into the same general pattern. For example, in the series NH_3, NH_2Cl, $NHCl_2$, NCl_3, nitrogen has formal oxidation states of -3, -1, $+1$, and $+3$. However, in each case the nitrogen atom shares three pairs of electrons and has *one* unshared pair. This corresponds to the $N-2$ and $N-8$ states.

$$H:\overset{\overset{..}{}}{\underset{\underset{\displaystyle H}{}}{N}}:H\qquad H:\overset{\overset{..}{}}{\underset{\underset{\displaystyle H}{}}{N}}:\overset{..}{\underset{..}{Cl}}:\qquad H:\overset{\overset{..}{}}{\underset{\underset{\displaystyle :\overset{..}{\underset{..}{Cl}}:}{}}{N}}:\overset{..}{\underset{..}{Cl}}:\quad\text{and}\quad :\overset{..}{\underset{..}{Cl}}:\overset{\overset{..}{}}{\underset{\underset{\displaystyle :\overset{..}{\underset{..}{Cl}}:}{}}{N}}:\overset{..}{\underset{..}{Cl}}:$$

In the case of the chalcogens, we have H_2O, CF_3OF, and OF_2, in which, if $H = +1$, $C = +4$, and $F = -1$, then the oxygen atoms must have oxidation states of -2, 0, and $+2$. The structures, however, are

$$H:\overset{..}{\underset{..}{O}}:H\qquad :\overset{..}{\underset{..}{F}}:\overset{\overset{\displaystyle :\overset{..}{\underset{..}{F}}:}{}}{\underset{\underset{\displaystyle :\overset{..}{\underset{..}{F}}:}{}}{C}}:\overset{..}{\underset{..}{O}}:\overset{..}{\underset{..}{F}}:\quad\text{and}\quad :\overset{..}{\underset{..}{F}}:\overset{..}{\underset{..}{O}}:\overset{..}{\underset{..}{F}}:$$

in which the oxygen atoms *share* two pairs of electrons and have two unshared pairs of electrons. Since there are four pairs of electrons around the oxygen atoms, this corresponds to the $N-8$ or -2 state in all three cases. In ozone, O_3, however, the structure is

so that the *central* oxygen atom, having only *one* unshared pair of electrons, must be considered to be in the $N-2$ ($+4$) oxidation state.

Likewise, for sulfur we have H_2S, CCl_3SCl, SCl_2, SCl_4, and SF_6. These have formal oxidation states (for sulfur) of -2, 0, $+2$, $+4$, and $+6$ (if

C = +4). The first two, however, have sulfur with two unshared pairs of electrons

$$H : \overset{\cdot\cdot}{\underset{\cdot\cdot}{S}} : H, \qquad : \overset{\cdot\cdot}{\underset{\cdot\cdot}{Cl}} : \overset{\cdot\cdot}{\underset{\cdot\cdot}{C}} : \overset{\cdot\cdot}{\underset{\cdot\cdot}{S}} : \overset{\cdot\cdot}{\underset{\cdot\cdot}{Cl}} :$$

and therefore correspond to the covalent $N-8$ state. The third has one unshared pair of electrons

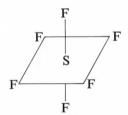

corresponding to the $N-2$ state. The last has *no* unshared pairs of electrons

which corresponds to the $+N$ state.

The same story may be repeated with the halogens, for example, in the series HI, CH_3I (C = −4), RIO (R = +1), RIO_2, IF_5, and IF_7.

In the same way, in the BH_4O^- ion, in which the boron atom apparently has an oxidation state of −3, the structure is

$$\overset{\displaystyle H}{\underset{\displaystyle H}{H : B : \overset{\cdot\cdot}{\underset{\cdot\cdot}{O}} : H}} {}^{(-1)}$$

so that the boron atom has four pairs of electrons required by its $N-8$ state.

14–5. Catenation Compounds

There are many compounds in addition to those discussed above which *appear* to violate the rules of oxidation state. Some of them even seem to involve fractional oxidation states. These latter are invariably *catenation* compounds, i.e., compounds in which two or more atoms of the same element are bonded directly together. The element for which this behavior is most common is carbon—the vast multiplicity of organic compounds being the result of the unrivaled ability of carbon atoms to form stable bonds with other carbon atoms. This gives rise to a myriad of compounds in which carbon apparently has an infinite array of fractional oxidation states. For example, although carbon in methane, CH_4, may be said fairly unambiguously to have an oxidation state of -4, and in CCl_4 and CO_2 to have an oxidation state of $+4$, in the compound $C_{36}H_{10}O_3$ (stearic anhydride), if $H = +1$ and $O = -2$, carbon appears to have an oxidation state of 1.778. Upon examination of the structure of the compound, however, the carbon atoms are found to have their usual valence of four. A simpler example will illustrate this point. The compound ethane, C_2H_6, appears to have carbon in the -3 oxidation state. The structure of the compound, however, is

$$
\begin{array}{cc}
H & H \\
\cdot\cdot & \cdot\cdot \\
H : C : C : H \\
\cdot\cdot & \cdot\cdot \\
H & H
\end{array}
$$

in which it is seen that each carbon atom shares four pairs of electrons with other atoms, so that it has its usual valence of *four*.

In the same way, the compounds of nitrogen in the *formal* $+2$ and -2 states (e.g., N_2F_4 and N_2H_4) *actually* have electronic structures corresponding to the $N-2$ or $N-8$ states

$$
\begin{array}{cc}
\cdot\cdot & \\
: F : & H \\
\cdot\cdot\ \ \cdot\cdot\ \ \cdot\cdot\ \ \cdot\cdot & \cdot\cdot\ \ \cdot\cdot \\
: F : N : N : F : & \quad H : N : N : H \\
\cdot\cdot\ \ \cdot\cdot\ \ \cdot\cdot\ \ \cdot\cdot & \cdot\cdot\ \ \cdot\cdot \\
: F : & H \\
\cdot\cdot &
\end{array}
$$

Likewise, the nitrogen compounds which apparently exhibit a $+1$ state, such as $H_2N_2O_2$ and N_2F_2, actually correspond to the $N-2$ or $N-8$ state with one unshared pair of electrons, e.g.

$$
\begin{array}{ccc}
\cdot\cdot\ \ \cdot\cdot\ \ \cdot\cdot\ \ \cdot\cdot & & \cdot\cdot\ \ \cdot\cdot\ \ \cdot\cdot\ \ \cdot\cdot \\
H : O : N : : N : O : H & \text{and} & : F : N : : N : F : \\
\cdot\cdot\ \ \cdot\cdot & & \cdot\cdot\ \ \cdot\cdot
\end{array}
$$

Many more compounds in this class might be cited, such as Si_2H_6, Ge_2H_6, $(CH_3)_6Sn_2$, $(CH_3)_6Pb_2$, P_2H_4, P_4S_3, H_2O_2, H_2S_2, $H_2S_2O_3$, $H_2S_2O_4$, $H_2S_2O_6$, $H_2S_6O_6$, $(CH_3)_2S_2$, $(CH_3)_2Te_2$, Cl_2O_6, B_2Cl_4, B_4Cl_4, and so forth. The point is that when there is covalent bonding between atoms of the same element there must be *apparent* unusual oxidation states. Nevertheless, the *electronic structures* of the elements involved must generally still conform to one of those required by one of the rules cited in Section 14–4.

It is not necessary that all the atoms of the same element have the same electronic environment. Several examples of nitrogen and sulfur compounds will illustrate this point. In nitramide

$$
\begin{array}{cc}
 & \ddot{\text{O}} \\
\text{H} : \overset{..}{\underset{..}{\text{N}}} : \overset{+}{\text{N}} \cdot \overset{..}{\cdot} \\
\text{H} & \overset{..}{\underset{..}{\text{O}}} \overset{.}{\underset{-}{}}
\end{array}
$$

one nitrogen atom has an unshared pair of electrons, while the other does not. In the thiosulfate ion

$$
\begin{array}{c}
: \ddot{\text{O}} : \quad {}^{(-2)} \\
\\
: \overset{..}{\underset{..}{\text{S}}} : \overset{..}{\underset{..}{\text{S}}} : \overset{..}{\underset{..}{\text{O}}} : \\
\\
: \ddot{\text{O}} :
\end{array}
$$

one of the sulfur atoms is in the $+6$ oxidation state and the other in the -2. The same is true of the various polythionate ions, e.g., tetrathionate and hexathionate

$$
\begin{array}{cc}
: \ddot{\text{O}} : \quad : \ddot{\text{O}} : \quad {}^{(-2)} & : \ddot{\text{O}} : \quad : \ddot{\text{O}} : \quad {}^{(-2)} \\
: \ddot{\text{O}} : \overset{..}{\underset{..}{\text{S}}} : \overset{..}{\underset{..}{\text{S}}} : \overset{..}{\underset{..}{\text{S}}} : \overset{..}{\underset{..}{\text{S}}} : \ddot{\text{O}} : \; \text{and} \; : \ddot{\text{O}} : \overset{..}{\underset{..}{\text{S}}} : \overset{..}{\underset{..}{\text{S}}} : \overset{..}{\underset{..}{\text{S}}} : \overset{..}{\underset{..}{\text{S}}} : \overset{..}{\underset{..}{\text{S}}} : \overset{..}{\underset{..}{\text{S}}} : \ddot{\text{O}} : \\
: \ddot{\text{O}} : \quad : \ddot{\text{O}} : & : \ddot{\text{O}} : \quad : \ddot{\text{O}} :
\end{array}
$$

On the other hand, the so-called pyrosulfite ion has the structure

$$
\begin{array}{c}
: \ddot{\text{O}} : \\
: \ddot{\text{O}} : \overset{..}{\underset{..}{\text{S}}} : \overset{..}{\underset{..}{\text{S}}} : \ddot{\text{O}} : \quad {}^{(-2)} \\
: \ddot{\text{O}} \; \ddot{\text{O}} :
\end{array}
$$

in which there is one $+6$ and one $+4$ sulfur.

It can thus be seen that because of catenation many cases of apparently anomalous oxidation states arise which are not real, the elements actually conforming to the electronic rules. However, despite the fact that the formal oxidation states are artificial, they are still very useful for balancing oxidation-reduction equations, because the oxidation or reduction equivalence of a substance corresponds to its formal oxidation state rather than to its real valence. For example, sulfur in the trithionate ion, $S_3O_6^{-2}$, has a formal oxidation state of $3\frac{1}{3}$. Therefore, in the permanganate oxidation of $S_3O_6^{-2}$ to SO_4^{-2}, there is a loss of $6 - 3\frac{1}{3} = 2\frac{2}{3}$ electrons per sulfur atom or a total of 8 electrons per $S_3O_6^{-2}$ ion. If MnO_4^- is reduced to Mn^{+2}, we have

$$
\underset{\underset{\longrightarrow}{\mid -8\,e^-}}{S_3O_6^{-2}} + \underset{\underset{\longrightarrow}{\mid +5\,e^-}}{MnO_4^-} \rightarrow SO_4^{-2} + Mn^{+2}
$$

giving as the balanced equation

$$5\ S_3O_6^{-2} + 8\ MnO_4^- + 4\ H^+ \rightarrow 15\ SO_4^{-2} + 8\ Mn^{+2}$$

14-6. The Oxidation Potentials of the Transition Elements

Trends in oxidation potential are also quite evident among the transition elements. Just as we have seen for the nonmetals, the maximum $(+N)$ oxidation states become better oxidizing agents as N increases. The normal oxidation potentials in 1 M H^+ for the formation of the maximum $(+N)$ oxidation state is shown in Table 14–9 for all the transition elements exhibiting the $+N$ state.

TABLE 14–9. OXIDATION POTENTIALS OF THE M°–M^{+N} COUPLES IN 1 M H+

$+N=$	3	4	5	6	7	8
	Sc	Ti	V	Cr	Mn	Fe
	2.08	0.86*	0.253	−0.325	−0.74	$< -1.08\dagger$
	Y	Zr	Nb	Mo	Tc	Ru
	2.37	1.43*	0.62	−0.1	−0.5	−1.05
	La	Hf	Ta	W	Re	Os
	2.52	1.57*	0.71	0.03	−0.365	−0.7
	Ac	Th	Pa	U		
	≈2.6	2.06	≈1.5	0.915		

* To MO_2.
† That is, more negative than FeO_4^{-2} (probably about −1.5).

It can be seen from the data in Table 14–9 that this trend is very regular. In addition, it can be seen that the lower an element is in any column the poorer oxidizing agent its $+N$ state is. This trend is also perfectly regular.

Another generality is that the oxidizing power of any particular oxidation state increases from left to right in the periodic table. Data for the second and third transition series are fragmentary, but the potentials are known for most of the possible oxidation states of the first transition series. These are presented in Table 14–10. Again it will be observed that there is a great deal of regularity in the trends to higher oxidizing power as we move to the right at any given level of oxidation state. Thus Cr(VI), Mn(VI), and Fe(VI) are increasingly powerful oxidizing agents. The same is true for the M^0–M^{+3} couples. In the case of the M^0–M^{+2} couples, however, certain irregularities appear which can be attributed to the electronic structures of the elements. Likewise, some of the stepwise potentials show the same irregularities. For example, for the M^{+2}–M^{+3} couples, we have the following potentials

Sc	Ti	V	Cr	Mn	Fe	Co	Ni	Cu
≈2.0	0.37	0.25	0.41	−1.51	−0.771	−1.82	?	< -1.8

The reason for these irregularities will be discussed in Chapter 16.

TABLE 14–10. OXIDATION POTENTIALS OF THE M^0–M^{+N} COUPLES IN 1 M H^+

Ox'n State \ Column	III	IV	V	VI	VII	VIII			I	II
7					MnO_4^- -0.74					
6				$Cr_2O_7^{-2}$ -0.325	MnO_4^{-2} -0.77	FeO_4^{-2} -1.08				
5			VO_2^+ 0.253	$Cr(V)$	MnO_4^{-3}	$Fe(V)$	$Co(V)$			
4		TiO^{+2} 0.89	VO^{+2} 0.56	$Cr(IV)$	MnO_2* -0.03	$Fe(IV)$	CoO_2 -0.53	NiO_2 -0.75		
3	Sc^{+3} 2.08	Ti^{+3} 1.21	V^{+3} 0.87	Cr^{+3} 0.74	Mn^{+3} 0.28	Fe^{+3} 0.036	Co^{+3} -0.42	Ni^{+3}	Cu^{+3} < -0.5	
2		Ti^{+2} 1.63	V^{+2} 1.18	Cr^{+2} 0.74	Mn^{+2} 1.18	Fe^{+2} 0.440	Co^{+2} 0.277	Ni^{+2} 0.250	Cu^{+2} -0.337	Zn^{+2} 0.763
1									Cu^+ -0.521	

*Estimated for Mn^{+4} ion.

14–7. The Intermediate Oxidation States of the Transition Elements

It can be seen from Table 14–10 that the $+4$, $+5$, and $+6$ states of Mn are more powerful oxidizing agents than MnO_4^- in 1 molar acid and are therefore unstable with respect to disproportionation. From the fact that Cr(IV), Cr(V), Fe(IV), and Fe(V) cannot be obtained in 1 molar acid because of disproportionation, it follows that these states are also better oxidizing agents than Cr(VI) and Fe(VI), respectively. It is found, then, that in general the oxidation potentials of the transition elements follow the pattern shown in Fig. 14–1. Whenever an intermediate oxidation state is a better oxidizing agent than a higher oxidation state (or a better reducing agent than a lower one), it must be unstable with respect to disproportionation into the higher and lower state. It follows that when the $+6$ state exists, the $+4$ and $+5$ states (or when the $+7$ state exists, the $+6$ state also)—as shown in the diagram—must be unstable with respect to disproportionation. This is in fact found to be the case for Cr, Mn, and Fe, which have higher states than $+5$, but not for vanadium, which does not. (This picture changes in alkaline solution.)

The case of the elements of the second and third transition series is not nearly so clean-cut. These elements are generally more electronegative than their congeners in the first transition series and therefore tend to form much

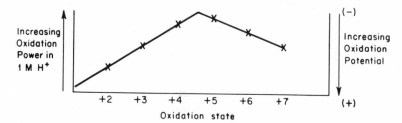

Fig. 14–1. Variation of Oxidizing Power with Oxidation State for the Transition Elements.

more stable complex ions. It therefore becomes very difficult to observe simple (or merely hydrated) ions of these elements in solution, since they are usually complexed by the anions present. This, of course, affects the observed oxidation potentials and, since it is frequently impossible to tell the stability of the complex in question (or often even what it is), potentials for the simple ions in most cases have not been determined. If they were known, however, it may reasonably be expected that they would follow the pattern of Fig. 14–1.

14–8. Limitations on the Oxidation States Obtainable in Aqueous Solution

In considering the oxidation states of an element, it is necessary to consider the environment of the element. For example, the mere physical state of the substance may decide whether a particular oxidation state is stable. This is shown in the fact that at elevated temperature, where the product is gaseous, $CrCl_4$ is stable

$$CrCl_3 \text{ (s)} + \tfrac{1}{2} Cl_2 \text{ (g)} \rightarrow CrCl_4 \text{ (g)}$$

At room temperature, however, where $CrCl_4$ is solid, the reverse reaction takes place

$$CrCl_4 \text{ (s)} \rightarrow CrCl_3 \text{ (s)} + \tfrac{1}{2} Cl_2 \text{ (g)}$$

so that Cr(IV) is stable as the chloride in the gas phase, but not in the solid phase.

More important examples from our point of view involve the stability of oxidation states in and out of water. We are accustomed to thinking of zirconium as having only a +4 state. However, by such reactions as

$$ZrCl_4 \text{ (s)} + \tfrac{1}{2} H_2 \text{ (g)} \rightarrow ZrCl_3 \text{ (s)} + HCl \text{ (g)}$$

and

$$Zr \text{ (s)} + ZrI_4 \text{ (s)} \rightarrow 2 \, ZrI_2 \text{ (s)}$$

at high temperature, it is possible to obtain the whole series $ZrCl_4$, $ZrCl_3$, $ZrCl_2$, and $ZrCl$. When the lower halides are brought into contact with water, however, reaction immediately takes place

$$ZrCl_2 \text{ (s)} + H_2O \rightarrow ZrO^{+2} + 2 \, Cl^- + H_2 \text{ (g)}$$

with the zirconium being oxidized to the familiar +4 state.

Another example is the substance Ga_2O, produced by the high temperature reaction

$$2 \, Ga \text{ (l)} + CO_2 \text{ (g)} \rightarrow Ga_2O \text{ (s)} + CO \text{ (g)}$$

which on contact with water disproportionates

$$3 \, Ga_2O \text{ (s)} + 3 \, H_2O \rightarrow 4 \, Ga \text{ (s)} + 2 \, Ga(OH)_3 \text{ (s)}$$

Likewise, the salt K_3CrO_4, produced by the high-temperature reaction

$$2 \, K_2CrO_4 \text{ (s)} + 2 \, KOH \text{ (l)} \rightarrow 2 \, K_3CrO_4 \text{ (s)} + \tfrac{1}{2} O_2 \text{ (g)} + H_2O \text{ (g)}$$

reacts with water in part, according to the equation

$$3 \, K_3CrO_4 \text{ (s)} + 4 \, H_2O \rightarrow 9 \, K^+ + 2 \, CrO_4^{-2} + Cr(OH)_4^- + 4 \, OH^-$$

but also in part according to

$$K_3CrO_4 \text{ (s)} + 3 \, H_2O \rightarrow 3 \, K^+ + Cr(OH)_4^- + 2 \, OH^- + \tfrac{1}{2} O_2 \text{ (g)}$$

in which molecular oxygen is released from the water.

A more clear-cut case is that of Cu_2O_3, which is made in very concentrated alkali by the reaction

$$2 \, Cu(OH)_2 \text{ (s)} + ClO^- \rightarrow Cu_2O_3 \text{ (s)} + Cl^- + H_2O$$

This reacts with water with liberation of oxygen

$$Cu_2O_3 \text{ (s)} + 2\,H_2O \rightarrow 2\,Cu(OH)_2 \text{ (s)} + \tfrac{1}{2}\,O_2 \text{ (g)}$$

In exactly the same way, although we normally consider platinum to have a maximum oxidation state of +4, it is possible to produce the substance PtF_6 by the reaction

$$PtF_4 \text{ (s)} + F_2 \text{ (g)} \rightarrow PtF_6 \text{ (g)}$$

When this is brought into contact with water, a vigorous reaction ensues in which the platinum is reduced and oxygen is liberated

$$PtF_6 \text{ (s)} + H_2O \rightarrow PtF_6^{-2} + 2\,H^+ + \tfrac{1}{2}\,O_2 \text{ (g)}$$

It is apparent from these examples that water, by its very nature, imposes limitations upon the oxidation states which can exist in it. There are at least two factors which are involved in this problem besides the mere effect of physical state. The first of these is the ability of water itself to be oxidized and reduced. We have seen that the potentials for the hydrogen couples are as follows

$$\tfrac{1}{2}\,H_2 \text{ (g)} \rightarrow H^+ \,(1\ M) + e^- \qquad\qquad E = 0.000 \text{ v}$$

$$\tfrac{1}{2}\,H_2 \text{ (g)} \rightarrow H^+ \,(10^{-7}\ M) + e^- \qquad\qquad E = 0.414 \text{ v}$$

$$\tfrac{1}{2}\,H_2 \text{ (g)} + OH^- \,(1\ M) \rightarrow H_2O + e^- \qquad\qquad E = 0.828 \text{ v}$$

According to the discussions in Chapter 13, then, the reduced form of any couple having a more positive potential than the hydrogen couple under the pertinent conditions of pH, *should* reduce H^+ out of water. Therefore, the reduced form *should* be incapable of existence in aqueous solution. However, the rate of reaction is frequently very slow, so that many reducing agents with potentials sufficiently positive to reduce water do so either very slowly or not at all. For example, we find that Cr^{+2} liberates hydrogen from acidic solutions

$$Cr^{+2} \rightarrow Cr^{+3} + e^- \qquad\qquad E° = +0.41$$

$$Cr^{+2} + H^+ \rightarrow Cr^{+3} + \tfrac{1}{2}\,H_2 \text{ (g)}$$

whereas HPH_2O_2, with a potential of +0.49

$$HPH_2O_2 + H_2O \rightarrow H_2PHO_3 + 2\,H^+ + 2\,e^-$$

does not.

$$HPH_2O_2 + H_2O \nrightarrow H_2PHO_3 + H_2 \text{ (g)}$$

Likewise, the reaction

$$B \text{ (s)} + 3\,H_2O \nrightarrow H_3BO_3 + \tfrac{3}{2}\,H_2 \text{ (g)}$$

does not go despite a potential of 0.87 volts for the half-reaction

$$B \text{ (s)} + 3\,H_2O \rightarrow H_3BO_3 + 3\,H^+ + 3\,e^-$$

There are several reasons for the slowness of such reactions, varying from "passivation" of surfaces to complexity of the molecules or of the reaction mechanisms. In general, if radical changes are to be made in the molecules (as in HPH_2O_2), the reaction will be slow. Likewise, if more than one electron is involved, the reaction *may* be slow. Even in the case of the Cr^{+2}–H^+ reaction, however, the liberation of hydrogen is nowhere nearly as rapid as one would expect, since a certain "overvoltage" is required in the liberation of hydrogen. That is, a potential above that predicted by the normal oxidation potential is required to drive the reaction

$$H^+ + e^- \rightarrow \tfrac{1}{2} H_2 \text{ (g)}$$

to the right. These factors will be more fully discussed in Chapter 15. Suffice it to say here, however, that all of these factors which tend to slow down or eliminate the reaction of reducing agents with water tend to increase the range of reducing agents which can exist in water for short, or even indefinite, periods.

In like manner, the potentials for the oxidation of water are

$$H_2O \rightleftharpoons \tfrac{1}{2}O_2 \text{ (g)} + 2\,H^+ \text{ (1 }M\text{)} + 2\,e^- \qquad E = -1.229$$

$$H_2O \rightleftharpoons \tfrac{1}{2}O_2 \text{ (g)} + 2\,H^+ \text{ (10}^{-7}\,M\text{)} + 2\,e^- \qquad E = -0.815$$

and $\qquad 2\,OH^- \text{ (1 }M\text{)} \rightleftharpoons \tfrac{1}{2}O_2 \text{ (g)} + H_2O + 2\,e^- \qquad E = -0.401$

Consequently, the oxidized form of any couple having a potential more negative than the appropriate H_2O–O_2 couple should liberate O_2 from water and therefore be incapable of existing in aqueous solution. In this case, even more than in the case of reducing agents, however, the reaction may be extremely slow because of the overvoltage for the production of O_2 (corresponding to that mentioned above for H_2), which may be especially large when highly oxygenated species (e.g., ClO_4^-, $H_4IO_6^-$) are involved. Thus the following species liberate oxygen fairly rapidly from water

$$Ce^{+4}: \quad Ce^{+3} \rightleftharpoons Ce^{+4} + e^- \qquad E° = -1.61$$

$$Pb^{+4}: \quad Pb^{+2} \rightleftharpoons Pb^{+4} + 2\,e^- \qquad E° = -1.69$$

$$Co^{+3}: \quad Co^{+2} \rightleftharpoons Co^{+3} + e^- \qquad E° = -1.84$$

$$Ag^{+2}: \quad Ag^+ \rightleftharpoons Ag^{+2} + e^- \qquad E° = -1.98$$

On the other hand, the following oxidants oxidize water only slowly, if at all

$$MnO_4^-: \quad Mn^{+2} + 4\,H_2O \rightleftharpoons MnO_4^- + 8\,H^+ + 5\,e^- \qquad E° = -1.52$$

$$H_5IO_6: \quad IO_3^- + 3\,H_2O \rightleftharpoons H_5IO_6 + H^+ + 2\,e^- \qquad E° = -1.7$$

$$HN_3: \quad N_2 \text{ (g)} + NH_4^+ \rightleftharpoons HN_3 + 3\,H^+ + 2\,e^- \qquad E° = -1.82$$

and even $S_2O_8^{-2}$ decomposes water only slowly

$$2\,SO_4^{-2} \rightleftharpoons S_2O_8^{-2} + 2\,e^- \qquad E° = -2.05$$

Nevertheless, for many elements the potentials for liberation of H_2 and O_2 from water set real limits on what oxidation states can be obtained in aqueous solution. Thus, we find that Mn^{+3} cannot be obtained in aqueous solution in the absence of complexing agents, not because it is unstable with respect to disproportionation, but rather because it oxidizes the water

$$Mn^{+2} \rightleftharpoons Mn^{+3} + e^- \qquad E° = -1.51$$

In the same way, one would expect to find Cd_2^{+2} corresponding to Hg_2^{+2}; however, the potential which has been reported for the Cd_2^{+2}–Cd^{+2} couple ($> +0.6$) makes it impossible to exist for any appreciable length of time in aqueous solution, even if it did not disproportionate.

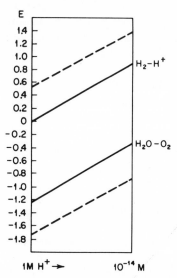

Fig. 14–2. Region of Stability of Oxidizing and Reducing Agents in Aqueous Solutions.

All things being taken into consideration, then, both members of couples whose oxidation potentials fall within the limits of the dotted lines of Fig. 14–2 should be stable in water solution. If the potential lies below this region, the oxidized form should be unstable in water with respect to the liberation of oxygen. If the potential lies above this region, the reduced form should be unstable in water with respect to the liberation of hydrogen. The solid lines show the region of stability that would exist if overvoltage could be eliminated.

14–9. Devising an Analytical Scheme

As was pointed out in the Preface, qualitative analytical schemes for the sake of analysis are of very little worth in this day of spot tests and instrumentation. They are, however, of unrivaled value in teaching some of the systematics of inorganic chemistry, familiarizing the student with the reactions of the elements, and in providing clues to separation procedures which are a necessary preamble to analyses, even by the most modern methods. To this end it is a most useful exercise for the student to study the properties of a group of unfamiliar elements and to devise a system of analytical separations from those properties. Let us first consider the various trends or particular characteristics of which advantage can be taken in devising the scheme.

Perhaps the first trend in properties to come to mind is that of solubilities. We have seen, for example, how the solubilities of the chlorides, sulfides, hydroxides, carbonates, and sulfates, as well as other salts of the metals, vary as a function of ionic size, of ionic charge, and of electronegativity as we cross the periodic table. Again, we have seen the change in solubility of the salts of a particular cation as we change the anion, e.g., as with LiF, LiCl, LiBr, LiI or AgF, AgCl, AgBr, AgI.

Trends in acidity and basicity can be taken advantage of, for example, in the precipitation of metal hydroxides or carbonates, and also in the separation of the salts of acids of differing strength, such as, for example, sulfate and phosphate which can be separated as the barium salts precipitated under different conditions of pH. Differences in amphoterism (or hydroxy complex formation) allow the separation of Be, Al, Cr, and many elements on the right side of the periodic table from the non-amphoteric elements.

Trends in formation of other complex ions, such as with NH_3, allow separation of a group of certain of the transition elements. We have seen how the differences in ability of Ag(I), Pb(II), and Tl(I) to form thiosulfate complexes allows identification of the thallium in the presence of the other two. This is an example of a trend, since the pK_{inst}'s of the thiosulfate complexes, as for the thio complexes and many others, is a function of the difference in electronegativity. This makes the thallium complex the least stable, so that TlI does not dissolve appreciably in thiosulfate solutions, whereas AgI and PbI_2 do. The general ability of the elements of high oxidation state on the left of the periodic table to form colored peroxy complexes (even when the simple ion is colorless) is useful in separating and identifying them, e.g., as with Ti, V, Cr, Nb, Mo, Ta, W, U, Pu. The ability of many of these elements to form complexes (heteropoly anions) with a group of elements on the right side of the table is useful in many separation and identification reactions. Thus we have tungsto-, molybdo-, and vanado-silicates, -germanates, -stannates (possibly), -phosphates, -arsenates, possibly -tellurates, -borates and -iodates.

Trends in oxidation and reduction potential may be used for separation. You have used these in many cases: separation of Cu and Cd, isolation of As, identification of Bi, separation and identification of Cr, and the like. The ability of certain elements to exist in several different oxidation states of different characteristics is very useful. Thus Mn can be made insoluble as MnO_2 or soluble as Mn^{+2} or MnO_4^-. Likewise, U and Pu may be separated because, although both UF_4 and PuF_4 are insoluble in aqueous HF, and both UO_2F_2 and PuO_2F_2 are soluble, U^{+4} is much more easily oxidized to UO_2^{+2} ($E° = -0.334$) than Pu^{+4} is to PuO_2^{+2} ($E° = -1.02$); hence, mild reducing agents (such as H_2O_2 ($E° = -0.682$)) will reduce PuO_2^{+2} to Pu^{+4} while leaving uranium as UO_2^{+2}, making it possible to precipitate PuF_4 away from the UO_2^{+2}, which is left in solution. It is distinctly possible to have as one group in an analytical scheme all those elements which can be reduced to the elementary state by a particular reducing agent. For example a hydrazine-in-acid-reducible group would contain the elements Se, Hg, Au, Ag, Pt, and Pd.

Another characteristic of which advantage can be taken is volatility. Thus OsO_4 and RuO_4 are distinguished from all other metal oxides by their high volatility and can easily be distilled away from others by treatment with strong oxidizing agents. Likewise, $AsCl_3$ and $GeCl_4$ can be distilled out of dilute HCl solutions and separated from all other metals. (Small amounts of $SbCl_3$, $SnCl_4$, and $HgCl_2$ may also distil from concentrated HCl.) Certain oxyhalides of the transition elements (e.g., CrO_2Cl_2) can also be distilled from *concentrated* HCl. Certain volatile fluorides can be distilled from $HF-H_2SO_4$ mixtures. The commonest of these is SiF_4, but others which also distil are BF_3 and AsF_3. This latter affords a distinction between As(III) and As(V), since arsenates do not give AsF_5 under the same conditions. Similarly, a number of the elements on the right of the table may be reduced and volatilized as hydrides. These include H_2S, H_2Se, H_2Te, PH_3, AsH_3, and SbH_3 from acidic solution.

Another property of which advantage can be taken is extractability into organic solvents. This is, indeed, so versatile a tool that a whole qualitative-analysis scheme might be built around it. The only example you have met so far is the extraction of blue peroxychromic acid away from orange peroxy-vanadic acid in the separation and identification of the two elements. In having an extractable peroxy complex, chromium is unique. There are, on the other hand, many complexing agents which could be used as group reagents for extraction. For example, from 10 M HNO_3 the nitrato complexes of U(VI), Pu(VI), Pu(IV), Th(IV), Ce(IV) (but not Ce(III)), and Sn(IV) are extracted into solvents such as tributyl phosphate, methyl iso-butyl ketone, triglycoldichloride, ethyl acetate, and the like. A much larger group of elements including all of the above and also Fe(III), Hg(II), As(III), Sb(III), and many others are extracted into a variety of solvents as their chloro and thiocyanato complexes. In addition to inorganic complexing agents, there are many organic ones which form extractable complexes. These include acetylacetone, diphenylthiocarbazone ("dithizone"), glycine, thiosalicylic acid, and dimethylglyoxime, just to name a few. The complexes of some of these (e.g., acetylacetone and dithizone) are frequently extract-able into nonpolar solvents like CCl_4 and chloroform.

In a scheme of qualitative analysis, any or all of these properties may be used in succession to remove small groups of elements from the others and then to separate and identify the individual elements in the groups.

The scheme of qualitative analysis presented in this book is based on the hydrogen sulfide procedure developed by Fresenius, and first appearing in his *Qualitative Analysis*, published in 1840.

The group separations in this scheme are (1) insoluble chlorides (Ag^+, Hg_2^{+2}, Pb^{+2}); (2) acid-insoluble sulfides (Hg^{+2}, Pb^{+2}, Bi^{+3}, Cu^{+2}, Cd^{+2}, Sn^{+2}, Sn^{+4}, As^{+3}, Sb^{+3}); (3) NH_4OH-insoluble hydroxides and sulfides (Al^{+3}, Cr^{+3}, Mn^{+2}, Fe^{+3}, Co^{+2}, Ni^{+2}, Zn^{+2}) or (3a) NH_4OH-insoluble hydroxides (Al^{+3}, Cr^{+3}, Mn^{+2}, Fe^{+3}) and (3b) alkali-insoluble sulfides (Co^{+2}, Ni^{+2}, Zn^{+2}); (4) insoluble carbonates (Ba^{+2}, Sr^{+2}, Ca^{+2}); and (5) Mg^{+2}, Na^+, and K^+. A scheme developed by Cornog again precipitates (1) insoluble chlorides (Ag^+, Hg_2^{+2}, Pb^{+2}); but then precipitates (2) sulfides from buffered acetic acid (Hg^{+2}, Bi^{+3}, Fe^{+3}, Cu^{+2}, Ni^{+2}, Cd^{+2}, Pb^{+2},

Zn^{+2}, As^{+3}, Sb^{+3}, Sn^{+4})—a very large group which must then be broken down into smaller ones; (3) insoluble oxalates (Ba^{+2}, Ca^{+2}); (4) alkali-insoluble phosphates (Mn^{+2}, Mg^{+2}, Al^{+3}, Cr^{+3}); and (5) a soluble group. A scheme developed by Brockman, after the initial chloride precipitation (1), provided for precipitation of (2) sulfates insoluble in aqueous alcohol (Ca^{+2}, Sr^{+2}, Ba^{+2}, Pb^{+2}); (3) hydroxides insoluble in $KOH-Na_2O_2$ (Mn^{+2}, Fe^{+3}, Bi^{+3}, Mg^{+2}, Cu^{+2}, Hg^{+2}, Co^{+2}, Ni^{+2}, Cd^{+2}); and (4) Sn^{+4}, Al^{+3}, Sb^{+3}, Zn^{+2}, Cr^{+3}, As^{+3}. The scheme of West, Vick, and Le Rosen precipitates from hot HCl (1) insoluble chlorides (Ag^+, Hg_2^{+2}); (2) basic salts insoluble in a benzoate buffer (Sn^{+4}, Bi^{+3}, Sb^{+3}, Fe^{+3}, Al^{+3}, Cr^{+3}); (3) insoluble fluorides (Mg^{+2}, Ca^{+2}, Sr^{+2}, Ba^{+2}, Pb^{+2}); (4) NaOH-insoluble hydroxides (Mn^{+2}, Fe^{+3}, Hg^{+2}, Cu^{+2}, Ni^{+2}, Cd^{+2}, Co^{+2}); and (5) amphoteric elements (Sn^{+4}, As^{+3}, Zn^{+2}).

In any system of qualitative analysis, it is necessary that the separations be clean; i.e., the elements in the group being separated must be separated quantitatively (an exception to this is $PbCl_2$ in the insoluble-chloride group) and that no elements from subsequent groups precipitate partially as contaminants. Secondly, precipitates must be of a nature easy to work with—crystalline if possible. (In this respect, precipitates such as $Fe(OH)_3$ are poor because they are flocculant and tend to form colloidal suspensions.) A third requirement is that the group-precipitating reagent not introduce substances which make subsequent analysis of the group itself difficult, or interfere with the analysis of subsequent groups.

With these factors in mind, then, we shall proceed with the devising of some illustrative schemes of qualitative analysis for the platinum metals (Ru, Rh, Pd, Os, Ir, Pt). But first, we must know something about their chemical behavior.

14–10. The Platinum-Group Elements

The platinum-group elements make a good subject for study because their chemistries are closely related to each other, and also to those of iron, cobalt, and nickel. The six platinum metals, and silver, and gold all have high electronegativities and are all easily reduced from their compounds to free metal. Because of this, they ordinarily occur free (native) in nature, very frequently as alloys of one another (also frequently containing small amounts of iron, nickel, copper, and other metals). Crude native platinum usually falls within the following ranges of percentage compositions: Pt, 60–80; Fe, 5–10; Pd, 1–2; Rh, 0.5–2; Ru, 0.5–2; Os, 1–10; Ir, 1–10. The natural alloy platiniridium has the percentage composition: Pt, 19–55; Ir, 76–27; Rh, up to 7; Fe, up to 4; Cu, up to 3; Pd, trace; As, trace. The natural alloy osmiridium consists largely of osmium and iridium (50–75 percent) with small amounts of the other metals. Compounds of the platinum metals are found in nature, but are always rare. These include sperrylite, $PtAs_2$ (which may be formed by passing AsH_3 into a platinum salt solution); laurite,

RuS_2; cooperite, $Pt(AsS)_2$, which actually assays 64.2 percent Pt and 9.4 percent Pd; and stibiopalladinite, Pd_3Sb.

TABLE 14–11. PHYSICAL PROPERTIES OF THE PLATINUM METALS

	Ru	Rh	Pd	Os	Ir	Pt
Atomic Number	44	45	46	76	77	78
Atomic Weight	101.7	102.91	106.7	190.8	193.1	195.23
Density	12.10	12.40	12.1	22.50	22.42	21.40
Hardness (Moh)	6.5	5.7	4.8	7.0	6.0	4.3
Melting Point (°C)	2310	1960	1555	2700	2443	1770
Boiling Point (°C)	4111	3960	3560	4400	4350	4010
Abundance in earth's crust (%)	10^{-11}	0^{-11}	10^{-9}	10^{-10}	10^{-10}	10^{-9}
Electronegativity	2.0*	2.1	2.1	2.0	2.1	2.1

* Ru(III).

Ruthenium and osmium metals are gray, like iron. The others are silvery-white, rhodium being one of the whitest metals known. Osmium has the greatest density of any naturally occurring element and is hard enough to scratch glass.

A second consequence of the high electronegativities of these elements, as suggested in Sections 14–6 and 14–7, is that they have a great tendency to form complex ions. Indeed, it is doubtful in some cases whether simple (i.e., hydrated) ions have been obtained. This fact perhaps more than any other causes these elements to be different from iron, cobalt, and nickel. However, in the cases in which iron, cobalt, and nickel form stable covalent complexes, the platinum metals very closely resembled them, as can be seen by reference to Fig. 10–17.

Like iron, ruthenium and osmium both form the halides MX_2 and MX_3. The dihalides, however, are difficult to obtain and are much more easily oxidized than the corresponding iron dihalides. Unlike FeI_3, which does not exist because of the reaction $FeI_3 \rightarrow FeI_2 + \frac{1}{2} I_2$, the iodides RuI_3 and OsI_3 are stable. Like iron, ruthenium and osmium form sulfides MS_2, which are disulfides (S_2^{-2}) of the $+2$ oxidation state, and have pyrites structure. The oxide FeO is well established (although it never has exactly this formula, always having excess oxygen), but RuO and OsO probably do not exist. The oxides Ru_2O_3 and Os_2O_3 also probably do not exist. The hydroxides $Ru(OH)_2$ and $Ru(OH)_3$ have been prepared, but are very easily oxidized. The complex ions of the $+2$ and $+3$ states are similar to those of iron, though more abundant.

The dioxide of iron is known only in the form of its solid compounds, the "perferrites," such as $SrFeO_3$. The dioxides RuO_2 and OsO_2 are quite stable, however, as are some other compounds of the $+4$ oxidation state, including $Ru(OH)_4$, $Ru(OH)Cl_3$, $RuCl_4 \cdot 5 H_2O$, $Ru(SO_4)_2$, $Os(OH)_4$, OsF_4, $OsCl_4$, $Os(OH)Cl_3$, and OsI_4. The complex ions of the $+4$ state are similar to those of platinum. Compounds of iron in the $+5$ oxidation state seem to be entirely lacking. Indeed, the only known $+5$ compounds of any of

TABLE 14-12. OXIDATION POTENTIALS OF THE PLATINUM METALS IN 1 M H$^+$

$$Ru \xrightarrow{-0.45} Ru^{+2} \xrightarrow{-0.3} RuCl_5^{-2} \xrightarrow{-1.3} RuCl_5OH^{-2} \xrightarrow{-1.7} RuO_4^{-2} \xrightarrow{-1.6} RuO_4^{-} \xrightarrow{-1.0} RuO_4$$

$$Rh \xrightarrow{-0.6} Rh^{+2} \xrightarrow{-0.9} Rh^{+3} \xrightarrow{-1.40} RhO^{+2} \xrightarrow{-1.46} RhO_4^{-2} \quad\quad RhO_4^{-2}$$

$$Pd \xrightarrow{-0.98} Pd^{+2} \xrightarrow{<-1.6} Pd^{+4} \xrightarrow{ca.-2.} PdO_3$$
$$Pd^{+2} \xrightarrow{-0.64} PdCl_4^{-2} \xrightarrow{-1.29} PdCl_6^{-2}$$

$$Os \xrightarrow{-0.7} Os^{+2} \xrightarrow{-0.3} OsCl_6^{-3} \xrightarrow{-0.85} OsCl_6^{-2} \xrightarrow{-1.0} OsO_4$$

$$Ir \xrightarrow{<-1.0} Ir^{+2} \xrightarrow{>-1.0} Ir^{+3} \xrightarrow{-1.2} IrO_2 \xrightarrow{>-1.4} IrO_4^{-2}$$

$$Pt \xrightarrow{-1.2} Pt^{+2} \xrightarrow{-1.1} PtO_2 \xrightarrow{<-2.0} PtO_3$$
$$Pt \xrightarrow{-0.73} PtCl_4^{-2} \xrightarrow{-0.72} PtCl_6^{-2}$$

TABLE 14-13. OXIDATION POTENTIALS OF THE PLATINUM METALS IN 1 M OH$^-$

$$Ru \xrightarrow{0.35} Ru_2O_3 \xrightarrow{0.2} Ru(OH)_6^{-2} \xrightarrow{-0.4} RuO_4^{-2} \xrightarrow{-0.6} RuO_4^{-} \xrightarrow{-1.0} RuO_4$$

$$Rh \xrightarrow{-0.04} Rh_2O_3 \xrightarrow{>-0.9} RhO_2 \xrightarrow{>-0.9} RuO_4^{-2}$$

$$Pd \xrightarrow{-0.1} Pd(OH)_2 \xrightarrow{ca.-0.8} Pd(OH)_4^{-2} \xrightarrow{ca.-1.2} PdO_3$$

$$Os \xrightarrow{?} Os_2O_3 \xrightarrow{?} OsO_2 \xrightarrow{-0.1} OsO_4^{-2} \xrightarrow{-0.3} OsO_4$$
$$0.15$$

$$Ir \xrightarrow{-0.1} Ir_2O_3 \xrightarrow{-0.1} IrO_2 \xrightarrow{>-0.4} IrO_4^{-2}$$

$$Pt \xrightarrow{-0.16} Pt(OH)_2 \xrightarrow{ca.-0.2} Pt(OH)_6^{-2} \xrightarrow{<-0.4} PtO_4^{-2}$$

these elements are RuF_5 and OsF_5. These compounds are immediately destroyed by moisture yielding, for example, RuO_2, RuO_4 and HF.

In the $+6$ state, ruthenium and osmium form salts of the ion MO_4^{-2}, very similar to CrO_4^{-2}, MnO_4^{-2}, FeO_4^{-2}, MoO_4^{-2}, WO_4^{-2}, and ReO_4^{-2}. In common with MnO_4^{-2}, FeO_4^{-2}, and ReO_4^{-2}, RuO_4^{-2} (ruthenate) and OsO_4^{-2} (osmate) are unstable in acidic solution. The solubilities of the salts of all of these anions are very similar. In addition to salts of these ions, however, $+6$ ruthenium and osmium form many other compounds which are more nearly like those formed by molybdenum and tungsten. Examples of these are the dark-purple $Rb_2[RuO_2Cl_4]$; and the compounds $[RuO_2(NH_3)_2(OH)_2]$; $[RuO_2(NH_3)_2(H_2O)_2]Cl_2$; $M_2[OsO_2X_4]$ (where $X = Cl$, Br, CN, NO_2, $\frac{1}{2} C_2O_4$, SO_3Na); $M_2[OsO_3X_2]$ (where $X = Cl$, Br, NO_2, $\frac{1}{2} C_2O_4$); and $M_2[OsNX_5]$ (where $X = Cl$, Br). The trioxides are not known. The hexafluorides of the second transition metal series are not known after MoF_6, but the complete series, WF_6, ReF_6, OsF_6, IrF_6, and PtF_6, is known. They are extremely reactive compounds, hydrolyzing instantaneously in water, the last four with liberation of oxygen or higher oxides or oxyfluorides (such as $ReOF_4$ and OsO_4).

The $+7$ oxidation state is known only for ruthenium, and only in the perruthenates, such as the black $KRuO_4$, which is *not* isomorphous with $KMnO_4$.·

Ruthenium and osmium are unique in forming compounds of the $+8$ oxidation state. The only known $+8$ compound of ruthenium is the brown or yellow, volatile RuO_4 (melting point (brown) 27°C, (yellow) 25.5°C; boiling point about 100°C, with decomposition). It begins to sublime as low as 7°C. It is an unstable compound, being decomposed by organic matter, reducing agents, alkalies (with formation of oxygen and ruthenate or perruthenate), and slowly by water, in which it is soluble to the extent of 2.21 grams at 25°C and 2.28 grams at 75°C per hundred milliliters. The yellow solution is quite stable, however, in the presence of a little free chlorine.

Osmium tetroxide, OsO_4, on the other hand, although still a good oxidizing agent, is much more easily produced than RuO_4, and is probably the most characteristic of all osmium compounds. It is produced by oxidation of finely divided metallic osmium by air. It is a colorless or yellow solid, melting about 40° and boiling about 130°C. It dissolves in water to the extent of 5.8 grams per hundred milliliters at 15°C. It is appreciably volatile at room temperature. Osmium tetroxide is very poisonous, and has the specific property of attacking the eyes. (There is some disagreement as to whether RuO_4 is poisonous.) Other compounds of $+8$ osmium are the fluoride, OsO_3F_2, and the related salts, $M[OsO_3F_3]$; and the interesting osmiamates, $M[OsO_3N]$, which are like the corresponding perrhenates, $M[ReO_4]$, permanganates, $M[MnO_4]$, and perchlorates, $M[ClO_4]$. The supposed existence of OsF_8 has recently been disproved.

Rhodium and iridium are related to cobalt in much the same way as ruthenium and osmium are related to iron—that is, the higher oxidation states become more stable in the order Co, Rh, Ir. Thus, as with ruthenium and osmium, the $+2$ oxidation state is very easily oxidized, although somewhat more stable. Rhodium *may* form RhO and RhS. The chloride $RhCl_2$ has been claimed. For iridium, IrS, $IrCl_2$, $IrBr_2$, and IrI_2 are known, but are very easily oxidized.

The $+3$ state is much more important for rhodium and iridium than for ruthenium and osmium, being their most important. Rhodium and iridium in the $+3$ state very closely resemble trivalent cobalt, which is also almost entirely a covalent state. The $+3$ oxides and hydroxides of both elements are known, as are Rh_2S_3 and Ir_2S_3. All the trihalides, with the possible exception of IrF_3, are known. Rhodium iodide, RhI_3, is remarkable for its extreme insolubility, which is sometimes used to separate rhodium and iridium. If a mixture of the chlorides is boiled for some time with hydriodic acid, RhI_3 precipitates, leaving iridium in solution. The sulfates, $Rh_2(SO_4)_3$ and $Ir_2(SO_4)_3$, with various amounts of water of crystallization, can be made by dissolving the hydroxides in sulfuric acid. Both sulfates—like $Co_2(SO_4)_3$ —form alums, such as $CsRh(SO_4)_2 \cdot 12\,H_2O$ and $MIr(SO_4)_2 \cdot 12\,H_2O$ (where M = K, Rb, Cs, NH_4, Tl). Both are yellow. If $Rh_2(SO_4)_3$ solutions are boiled, or if $Rh(OH)_3$ is dissolved in hot H_2SO_4, a red solution is obtained which contains a complex sulfatorhodate ion, such as $[Rh(H_2O)_4(SO_4)_2]^-$. This last is reminiscent of the sulfates of Cr(III). It would be impossible to give a complete discussion of all the complexes of Rh(III) and Ir(III), which (like those of Co(III)) are extremely numerous. However, it may be noted that complexes such as $M(NH_3)_6{}^{+3}$, $M(NH_3)_5 X^{+2}$, $M(NH_3)_4 X_2{}^+$, $M(NH_3)_3 X_3$, $M(CN)_6{}^{-3}$, $M(NO_2)_6{}^{-3}$, $M(C_2O_4)_3{}^{-3}$, $MF_6{}^{-3}$, and so on, are common to all three elements. Although not known for cobalt, the complexes $M(NH_3)_2 X_4{}^-$, $M(NH_3) X_5{}^{-2}$ and $MX_6{}^{-3}$, where X = Cl, Br, I, are known for rhodium and iridium.

The $+4$ oxidation state of rhodium is not easily attained, although a hydrate of the dioxide, $RhO_2 \cdot 1-2\,H_2O$, is known as the sole representative of Rh(IV), unless the reported RhF_4 actually exists. Iridium in the $+4$ state is considerably more stable. (For example, solutions of the ionic $Ir_2(SO_4)_3$ must be protected from the air to avoid oxidation.) The potential for the $IrCl_6{}^{-3}$–$IrCl_6{}^{-2}$ couple is -1.02 volts, so that, although not oxidized by air, $IrCl_6{}^{-3}$ is oxidized to $IrCl_6{}^{-2}$ by most good oxidizing agents, including free chlorine. Iridium forms a well-defined dioxide and disulfide, IrO_2 and IrS_2. The latter does not have pyrites structure and is therefore probably a true sulfide of Ir(IV). The fluoride, IrF_4, is a slightly volatile, viscous yellow oil which is instantaneously hydrolyzed by water. The chloride, $IrCl_4$, a brown, hygroscopic solid, is known in impure form, but $IrBr_4$ and IrI_4 probably do not exist. The complex fluorides, chlorides, and bromides, M_2IrX_6, are well-defined salts. Other complexes include ammines, such as $[Ir(NH_3)_4Cl_2]^{+2}$, and an oxalato complex, $Ir(C_2O_4)_3{}^{-2}$, as well as complexes of organic amines.

Compounds of rhodium(V) and iridium(V) apparently do not exist.

Very little is known about +6 rhodium, which is apparently produced by electrolytic or chemical oxidation of the lower states. In the blue alkaline solutions, the rhodate ion, RhO_4^{-2}, is probably present. The blue acidic solutions may contain a rhodyl ion, RhO_2^{+2}, or some complex of it. Iridium(VI) is only slightly easier to obtain. The oxide, IrO_3, is said to be formed by reaction of powerful oxidants, like Na_2O_2, with IrO_2 in concentrated or fused alkali. It is unstable in acidic media, liberating oxygen or oxidizing the medium. The compounds IrS_3, $IrSe_3$, and $IrTe_3$ are known, but seem unlikely to be really compounds of Ir(VI). The best characterized compound of Ir(VI) is IrF_6, yellow, with a melting point of $+44°C$ and a boiling point of $+53°C$. It reacts violently with small amounts of water, giving $IrOF_4$ and lower fluorides.

The chemistry of palladium and platinum is almost solely that of their complexes. Even in the hydrated palladium(II) ion, $Pd(H_2O)_4^{+2}$, the water appears to be held unusually strongly, and $Pd(H_2O)_4^{+2}$ (in contrast to hydrated Ni^{+2}) is diamagnetic. The electronic configuration of $Ni(H_2O)_6^{+2}$ is

	3d					4s	4p		
Argon Core	↓↑	↓↑	↓↑	↓	↓				

whereas that of $Pd(H_2O)_4^{+2}$ is

	4d					5s	5p		
Krypton Core	↓↑	↓↑	↓↑	↓↑					

showing that one of the 4d orbitals is being used to bond the water molecules, the hybridization being planar dsp^2.

The +2 oxidation state is the most important for palladium, as for nickel. The +4 state is well-defined, however. With platinum, both states are important, the +4 perhaps having a slight edge. The compounds MO, $M(OH)_2$, MS, MF_2, MCl_2, MBr_2, and MI_2 are all known for both elements, but are *not* ionic. Palladium forms $Pd(NO_3)_2$, $PdSO_4·2H_2O$, and $PdSeO_4$, all very easily hydrolyzed. As with Ni^{+2}, Pd^{+2} gives a yellow precipitate with ammoniacal dimethylglyoxime. The red-brown precipitate with α-nitroso-β-naphthol is unique in the platinum group. Platinum forms the similar compounds $PtSO_4$ and $Pt(NO_3)_2$, which are also easily hydrolyzed. The complexes of both elements are extremely numerous. The only ones which will be specifically mentioned here are $M(NH_3)_4^{+2}$ and MX_4^{-2} (where X = Cl, Br, I, CN, NO_2, $\frac{1}{2}C_2O_4$, and so on). These are all of the square coplanar type. As with cobalt(III) mixed complexes such as $Pt(NH_3)_3Cl^+$, $Pd(NH_3)_2Cl_2$, and $Pt(NH_3)(NO_2)_3^-$ can be obtained.

The +3 states of these elements are unimportant in water solution, but are represented by such compounds as Pd_2O_3, PdF_3, PtI_3, $K[Pt(SO_4)_2]_2$, and so forth.

Palladium(IV) is known in simple compounds only in PdO_2 (hydrated), PdS_2, $PdSe_2$, and $PdTe_2$. For platinum, the simple compounds include PtO_2 (hydrated and anhydrous), PtS_2, $PtSe_2$, $PtTe_2$, PtF_4, $PtCl_4$, $PtBr_4$, and PtI_4. These are all covalent substances. The easily hydrolyzed $Pt(NO_3)_4$ and $Pt(SO_4)_2$ are also known. Known complexes of Pd(IV) are limited in number, the most important being PdS_3^{-2}, PdF_6^{-2}, $PdCl_6^{-2}$, and $PdBr_6^{-2}$. The more accessible platinum(IV), on the other hand, forms a tremendous variety of complexes, of which may be mentioned $Pt(NH_3)_6^{+4}$ and PtX_6^{-2} with all the possible mixed complexes (e.g., $Pt(NH_3)_2X_4$, $Pt(NH_3)_5X^{+3}$, and so on, where X may be F, Cl, Br, I, NCS, OH, NO_2, NO_3, $\frac{1}{2} C_2O_4$, $\frac{1}{2} S$, and so on). Mixed complexes with H_2O, organic amines in place of NH_3, and combinations of the X groups are also common. No complex $Pt(CN)_6^{-2}$ is known, but the ion $PtCl_2(CN)_4^{-2}$ is easily obtained by oxidizing $Pt(CN)_4^{-2}$ with Cl_2.

The evidence for palladium(VI) is very scanty. The compound PdO_3 may possibly be produced under very strongly oxidizing conditions in alkaline solution. If it exists, it is an oxidizing agent second only to ozone in potency in alkali. The oxide PtO_3 is somewhat more easily obtained. It is uncertain whether the anion PtO_4^{-2} actually exists. The fluoride PtF_6 is known and is an extremely powerful oxidizing (or fluorinating) agent. The +6 state for these elements is only of minor importance.

Some of the reactions of the platinum metals in massive form are very slow and cannot be predicted from a knowledge of the oxidation potentials and of the compounds of the elements alone. Consequently, the action of several common reagents on the massive free metals is given in Table 14–14. Since the platinum metals are most frequently handled in HCl solution (either having been obtained as chlorides or having been present in the supernate from the precipitation of the insoluble-chloride group), a listing of the reactions of the commonest chlorides of these elements with various reagents is also useful, and is given in Table 14–15.

14–11. Devising Analytical Schemes for the Platinum Group

Let us first consider as an illustration the separation of the platinum elements as it is carried out commercially on bullion containing all six elements plus silver and gold, but containing no base metals or osmiridium alloy as such. The bullion is first digested with aqua regia, which dissolves platinum, palladium, and gold, leaving the other platinum elements unreacted (Os does not react in the presence of the other metals) and the silver precipitating as AgCl. The solution containing $PtCl_6^{-2}$, $PdCl_6^{-2}$, and $AuCl_4^-$ is reduced with $FeCl_2$ or with boiling oxalic acid solution, the most easily reduced gold separating as metal, the others remaining in solution as $PtCl_6^{-2}$ and $PdCl_4^{-2}$. Addition of NH_4Cl precipitates $(NH_4)_2PtCl_6$, which, upon ignition, gives Pt^0. Ammonium hydroxide is added to the $PdCl_4^{-2}$ solution in just sufficient amount to precipitate $Pd(NH_3)_2Cl_2$

TABLE 14–14. REACTIONS OF PLATINUM METALS IN COMPACT FORM*

Reagent	Ruthenium	Rhodium	Palladium	Osmium	Iridium	Platinum
Aqua regia (boiling)	Dissolves slowly $\rightarrow RuCl_5^{-2}$	Dissolves very slowly (except faster in some alloys) $\rightarrow RhCl_6^{-3}$	Soluble $\rightarrow PdCl_6^{-2}$	Soluble $\rightarrow OsO_4$	Dissolves very slowly $\rightarrow IrCl_6^{-2}$	Soluble $\rightarrow PtCl_6^{-2}$
HNO_3 (boiling)	Insoluble	Insoluble	Dissolves slowly $\rightarrow Pd(NO_3)_2$	Insoluble	Insoluble	Insoluble
H_2SO_4 (boiling)	Insoluble	Insoluble	Dissolves slowly $\rightarrow PdSO_4$	Insoluble	Insoluble	Attacked slightly
$KHSO_4$ (molten)	Insoluble	Yields soluble $KRh(SO_4)_2$	Dissolves $\rightarrow PdSO_4$	Partially oxidized to OsO_4	Oxidized but not dissolved	Slightly attacked $\rightarrow$ basic sulfate slowly at 250°C
$KOH + KNO_3$ (molten)	Yields K_2RuO_4, green, soluble in water, giving orange solution	Oxidized $\rightarrow RhO_2$	Oxidized $\rightarrow PdO$	Dissolves $\rightarrow K_2OsO_4$	Oxidized to Ir_2O_3 and soluble and insoluble iridates	Attacked $\rightarrow Pt(OH)_6^{-2}$
Iodine solution	—	—	Black stain	—	—	No action
Spongy metal heated in oxygen	RuO_2 at 700–1200°C	Rh_2O_3 slowly below 1150°C	PdO slowly at 700°C	OsO_4 slowly at 200°C	IrO_2 slowly at 1050°C	PtO slowly at 450°C
Spongy metal heated in chlorine	K_2RuCl_6 when KCl is present	$RhCl_3$	$PdCl_2$	$OsCl_4$ at 700°C	K_2IrCl_6 when KCl is present	$PtCl_2$ at 360°C

* Adapted from J. N. Friend, *Textbook of Inorganic Chemistry*, **Vol. IV**, p. 331.

TABLE 14-15. REACTIONS OF PLATINUM-GROUP CHLORIDES

Reagent	$RuCl_3$	$RhCl_3$	$PdCl_2$	$OsCl_4$	$IrCl_4$	$PtCl_4$
Color (dilute solution)	Dark brown	Red	Brownish-yellow	Yellow	Dark brown	Yellow
H_2S at 80°C	Azure-blue color (Ru^{+2}) on prolonged treatment	Brownish-black ppt., Rh_2S_3	Brownish-black ppt., PdS	Brownish-black ppt., OsS_2	Brownish-black ppt., Ir_2S_3	Brownish-black ppt., PtS_2
$(NH_4)_2S$	Dark-brown ppt., difficultly soluble in excess	Dark-brown ppt., Rh_2S_3, insoluble in excess	Black ppt., PdS, insoluble in excess	Dark ppt., insoluble in excess	Brown ppt., Ir_2S_3, soluble in excess	Brown ppt., PtS_2, soluble in excess $\rightarrow PtS_3{}^{-2}$
Alkali hydroxides	Black ppt., insoluble in excess	Yellow-brown ppt., $Rh(OH)_3$, somewhat soluble in excess	Yellowish-brown ppt., soluble in excess	Brownish-red ppt., insoluble in excess	Green solution + brownish-black, M_2IrCl_6	Dark ppt., soluble in excess
Warm NH_4OH	Greenish color	Slow decolorization	Decolorization	Yellowish-brown ppt.	Colored complexes	Slow decolorization
Saturated NH_4Cl	Brown ppt.	No ppt.	No ppt.	Red ppt.	Black ppt.	Yellow ppt.
Saturated KCl	Violet cryst. ppt., K_2RuCl_5	Red cryst. ppt., K_2RhCl_5	Red ppt., K_2PdCl_4	Brown cryst. ppt., K_2OsCl_6	Brownish-red ppt., K_2IrCl_6	Yellow ppt., K_2PtCl_6
KI (0.1%)	No change	No change	Black ppt., PdI_2	No change	Yellow color	Slow red-brown color
$Hg(CN)_2$ solution	No change	No change	White ppt. $Pd(CN)_2$	No change	No change	No change
KNCS (1%)	Dark-violet color	Yellow color	No change	No change	Decolorization	Increased yellow color
N_2H_4 in HCl solution	Yellow color	Yellow color	Black ppt., Pd^0	No change	Yellow color	Black ppt., Pt^0
Dimethylglyoxime	Yellow ppt.	No change	No change	No change	No change	No change
Metallic zinc	Ppt., Ru^0	Ppt., Rh^0	Ppt., Pd^0	Ppt., Os^0	Ppt., Ir^0	Ppt., Pt^0
Rubeanic acid	Blue color	—	Red cryst. ppt.	No change	—	Red cryst. ppt.

* Adapted from J. N. Friend, *Textbook of Inorganic Chemistry*, Vol. IX, Part I, p. 332.

which upon ignition gives Pd^0. The mixture of Ir, Ru, Rh, Os, and AgCl is smelted with lead, giving a lead alloy.

$$2 \, AgCl + Pb \rightarrow PbCl_2 + 2 \, Ag$$

The lead alloy is extracted with nitric acid, which dissolves the lead and silver. The residue is fused with $KHSO_4$, which dissolves the rhodium. The residue from this is fused with KOH and KNO_3, which dissolves ruthenium and osmium as K_2RuO_4 and K_2OsO_4. The oxidized iridium residue is dissolved in aqua regia, precipitated as $(NH_4)_2IrCl_6$ with NH_4Cl, and ignited to give iridium metal. The solution containing K_2RuO_4 and K_2OsO_4 is treated with chlorine and distilled, removing both RuO_4 and OsO_4. The distillate is reduced with methanol and HCl, giving $RuOCl_2$. The OsO_4 is now distilled out and reduced to osmium metal with ethanol and hydrogen. Various other modifications may be made, such as removing the silver from the original bullion by boiling with sulfuric acid.

Osmiridium is usually fused with zinc, which gives an alloy soluble in aqua regia. The aqua regia solution is heated to distil out OsO_4. The iridium is precipitated as $(NH_4)_2IrCl_6$ along with any platinum present. The mother liquor (supernate) may contain some ruthenium and rhodium.

From the information given, let us now devise some separations schemes for the six platinum elements in HCl solution. It can be seen from Table 14–15, that there are at least four reagents which will separate just one of these elements from the other five. Acidic H_2S precipitates all but ruthenium; NH_4OH precipitates only osmium; cold, dilute KI and $Hg(CN)_2$ precipitate only palladium. The first of these has the disadvantage of precipitating all but one element. The element which is supposed to remain in solution may be entrained by the others (especially since it does have an insoluble sulfide, RuS_2). The last of these has the disadvantage of adding to the solution an undesirable substance, $Hg(CN)_2$, which may cause trouble later. In the case of KI, however, neither of these objections can be raised. Furthermore, the subsequent heating of the iodide solution will allow separation of RhI_3. As the first step of our procedure, then, let us add 0.1 percent KI in the cold, precipitating black PdI_2. Heating the solution for an extended time now precipitates RhI_3. Since hydrazine in acidic solution reduces only palladium and platinum to the free metals, addition of hydrazine will now precipitate platinum by itself. If the solution now be treated with aqua regia and distilled, the volatile oxides OsO_4 and RuO_4 will distil out, leaving only iridium in the solution. If the acidic distillate containing ruthenium and osmium be treated at 80°C with H_2S, osmium will be precipitated as OsS_2, while Ru^{+2} remains in solution. The complete separation of the six elements has thus been accomplished.

An alternative procedure would be to treat the sample with successive portions of $(NH_4)_2S$ to precipitate Rh_2S_3, PdS, and OsS_2, and dissolve Ir, Pt, and Ru as thio complexes. (Several treatments are necessary to obtain complete solution of ruthenium.) The precipitated sulfides may be dissolved in aqua regia, and OsO_4 distilled out. From the remaining solution, palladium metal may be precipitated out with hydrazine, leaving rhodium in solution. The supernate from the sulfide precipitation may now be boiled with aqua regia to remove volatile RuO_4. If the remaining liquid is reduced with hydrazine, platinum precipitates, leaving iridium in solution, and again the separation of the six elements has been accomplished.

Finally, for purposes of comparison, the method of Gilchrist and Wickers will be given:

To a solution of the chlorides in a distilling apparatus is added HNO_3, and the solution is distilled in a current of air into 6 N HCl saturated with SO_2 (which traps the OsO_4 and reduces it to $OsCl_6^{-2}$). Sodium bicarbonate is added to the distillate solution, which is boiled to precipitate OsO_2.

The HNO_3 solution is evaporated to dryness and the residue taken up in water; H_2SO_4 and $NaBrO_3$ are added. Distillation in a current of air into HCl saturated with SO_2 gives RuO_2. These first two separations take advantage both of the volatility of OsO_4 and RuO_4 and of the differing ease with which osmium and ruthenium are oxidized to the tetroxides. The $NaBrO_3$ mother liquor is treated cautiously with HCl to decompose the bromate and then evaporated.

$$BrO_3^- + 5\,Cl^- + 6\,H^+ \rightarrow \tfrac{5}{2}\,Cl_2 + \tfrac{1}{2}\,Br_2 + 3\,H_2O$$

The solution is diluted, heated to boiling, and $NaBrO_3$ and $NaHCO_3$ added. The hydrated dioxides RhO_2, PdO_2, and IrO_2 precipitate, while the more acidic oxide of platinum (the most electronegative of these elements) remains in solution as $Pt(OH)_6^{-2}$. The supernate containing $Pt(OH)_6^{-2}$ is evaporated, dissolved in HCl, and treated with H_2S to precipitate PtS_2, which is ignited to give platinum metal. The precipitate of RhO_2, PdO_2, and IrO_2 is dissolved in HCl with dimethylglyoxime added to precipitate palladium. The supernate containing complex chlorides of rhodium and iridium is treated with H_2SO_4 and HNO_3 and boiled to drive off HCl. After cooling, diluting, and reheating, a solution of $TiCl_3$ (a good reducing agent) is added. The solution is boiled. A precipitate of rhodium separates, leaving iridium in solution.

From the information given in the description of these elements, many other separations schemes can be devised. It will be a very useful exercise for the student to compose some alternate schemes.

14–12. Questions and Problems

1. Explain the rules of oxidation state from considerations of atomic structure.

2. Explain why ClO^- is more stable than ClO_2^-, although neither one corresponds to the oxidation state rules. Does this explain the stability of such compounds as OF_2, SCl_2, and S_2Cl_2?

3. Explain why such substances as $SiHCl_3$, PH_2Br, H_2CO, CF_3SF_5, BH_3OH^-, HPH_2O_2, and so forth, are stable even though they appear to violate the oxidation state rules.

4. Explain the apparent anomaly of such compounds as N_2H_4, $H_2N_2O_2$, N_3F (compare HN_3), $S_2O_4^{-2}$, S_2O, Cl_2O_6, B_2Cl_4, and so forth.

5. Explain (a) why the oxidation potential of the V^{+3}–VO^{+2} couple should be more negative than that of the V^{+2}–V^{+3} couple, (b) why the potential of the VO^{+2}–VO_2^+ couple should be more negative than that of the Ti^{+3}–TiO^{+2} couple, and (c) why that of the V^{+3}–VO^{+2} couple should be more negative than that of the Ti^{+3}–TiO^{+2} couple.

6. Elemental bromine, Br_2, can be dissolved in water to form stable solutions; elemental fluorine, F_2, cannot. Explain.

7. Samarium forms a stable chloride, $SmCl_2$, although $SmCl_3$ is the usual chloride. The dichloride, however, cannot be obtained in water. Explain.

8. Discuss the quantitative requirements of any qualitative analytical scheme.

9. Discuss the necessary qualifications of any reagent used in a qualitative analytical scheme.

10. Devise two new analytical schemes for the platinum elements, including iron, nickel, silver, gold, and molybdenum.

11. Devise an analytical scheme for the elements zinc, gallium, indium, thallium, germanium, and arsenic.

14–13. References

Cornog, J., *Semimicro Qualitative Analysis.* Boston: Houghton Mifflin Company, 1948.

Brockman, C. J., "Qualitative Analysis without Hydrogen Sulfide," *Journal of Chemical Education*, Vol. 16 (1939), p. 133.

West, P. W., Vick, M. M., and Le Rosen, A. L., *Qualitative Analysis and Analytical Chemical Separations.* New York: The Macmillan Company, 1953.

Hampel, C. A., ed., *Rare Metals Handbook.* New York: Reinhold Publishing Corporation, 1954.

Kleinberg, J., *Unfamiliar Oxidation States and Their Stabilization.* Lawrence, Kans.: University of Kansas Press, 1950.

Vines, R. F., *The Platinum Metals and Their Alloys.* New York: The International Nickel Company, 1941.

Druce, J. G. F., *Rhenium.* Cambridge: Cambridge University Press, 1948.

Tribilat, S., *Rhénium et Technétium.* Paris: Gauthiers-Villars, 1957 (in French).

Einecke, Erich, *Das Gallium.* Leipzig: Verlag von Leopold Voss, 1937 (in German).

Ludwick, M. T., *Indium.* New York: Indium Corporation of America, 1950.

Skinner, G., Johnston, H. L., and Beckett, C., *Titanium and Its Compounds.* Columbus, Ohio: Herrick L. Johnston Enterprises, 1954.

Barksdale, J., *Titanium, Its Occurrence, Chemistry, and Technology.* New York: The Ronald Press Company, 1949.

Bimbach, R., and Michel, A. J., *Beryllium: Its Production and Applications.* New York: Chemical Catalogue Company, Inc., 1932.

Kemp, P. H., *The Chemistry of the Borates.* London: Borax Consolidated, 1956.

Schoeller, W. R., *The Analytical Chemistry of Tantalum and Niobium.* London: Chapman and Hall, Ltd., 1937.

Gonser, B. W., and Sherwood, E. M., eds., *Symposium on Columbium (Niobium).* New York: John Wiley and Sons, Inc., 1958.

Audley, J. A., *Silica and the Silicates.* New York: D. Van Nostrand Company, Inc., 1921.

Blumenthal, W. B., *The Chemical Behavior of Zirconium.* New York: D. Van Nostrand Company, Inc., 1958.

Miller, G. L., *Zirconium,* 2d ed. London: Butterworths Scientific Publications, 1957.

Yost, D. M., Russell, Jr., H., and Garner, C. S., *The Rare Earth Elements.* New York: John Wiley and Sons, Inc., 1947.

Vickery, R. C., *Chemistry of the Lanthanons.* London: Butterworths Scientific Publications, 1953.

Bagnall, K. W., *Chemistry of the Rare Radioelements, Polonium—Actinium.* New York: Academic Press, Inc., 1957.

Seaborg, G. T., and Katz, J. J., eds., *The Actinide Elements.* New York: McGraw-Hill Book Company, Inc., 1954.

Seaborg, G. T., and Katz, J. J., eds., *The Transuranium Elements.* New York: McGraw-Hill Book Company, Inc., 1956.

Rodden, C. J., ed., *Analytical Chemistry of the Manhattan Project: Uranium and Thorium.* New York: McGraw-Hill Book Company, Inc., 1956.

DeMent, J., and Drake, H. C., *Uranium and Atomic Power.* Brooklyn, N.Y.: Chemical Publishing Company, Inc., 1945.

Katz, J. J., and Rabinowitch, E., *The Chemistry of Uranium.* New York: McGraw-Hill Book Company, Inc., 1951.

Noyes, A. A., and Bray, W. C., *A System of Qualitative Analysis for the Rare Elements.* New York: The Macmillan Company, 1927.

Chapter 15

The Mechanisms of Chemical Reactions

15–1. Slow Reactions

We have had occasion many times to observe that reactions that should be expected to go either do not go at all or go very slowly. For example, according to the oxidation potentials Cr^{+2} should instantaneously reduce aqueous H^+, but actually does so only slowly. Likewise, peroxydisulfate ion, $S_2O_8^{-2}$, should instantaneously release oxygen from water or oxidize organic substances, but actually does so only slowly. Again, although mercury amides form immediately in NH_4OH, silver imide, Ag_2NH, or silver nitride, Ag_3N, which should precipitate rapidly from an ammoniacal solution of a silver salt, does so only over a long period of time, separating slowly as shining black, excessively explosive crystals (Section 4–2). The greatly differing rates of oxidation of $Cr(OH)_3$ and $Mn(OH)_2$ by air (Section 7–8) may also be recalled. Perhaps the classic case is that of a mixture of hydrogen and oxygen gases which is strongly favored to react, but at room temperature produces no detectable water even after many years. In the terms of Section 2–2, these reactions have high activation energy.

In order to understand why certain reactions are fast and certain others are slow it is necessary to know something about the mechanisms of the reactions, that is, about the paths the reactions take, what steps they go through, or what activated complexes are formed, in order to get from starting materials to final products. It is frequently found that what appears to be a very simple reaction is in fact very complicated. Take, for example, the precipitation of CuS by H_2S from a solution of a $Cu(II)$ salt. It will be realized immediately that this must involve an ionization of the H_2S, either before

$$H_2S \rightleftharpoons H^+ + HS^-$$

$$Cu^{+2} + HS^- \rightleftharpoons CuHS^+, \quad \text{etc.}$$

or after

$$Cu^{+2} + H_2S \rightleftharpoons Cu(H_2S)^{+2}$$

$$Cu(H_2S)^{+2} \rightleftharpoons CuHS^+ + H^+, \quad etc.$$

reaction of the H_2S with the Cu^{+2}. (This includes, of course, elimination of water by H_2S from the coordination sphere of the Cu^{+2}.) As discussed in Section 6–4, it also involves loss of H_2S by the neutral hydrosulfide

$$Cu(SH)_2 \rightleftharpoons H_2S + CuS$$

In addition, as discussed in Section 3–3, it also requires either the prior presence or the formation of nuclei for crystallization. All of this makes it a pretty complicated process, and it would not be surprising if the precipitation reaction were a little slow. Upon examination of the CuS formed, however, it becomes apparent that the precipitation process must be far more complicated even than indicated above, for the precipitate turns out to be not just a simple array of Cu(II) and S($-$II) ions or atoms, but rather to have a very complex structure involving, in addition, Cu(I) and $S_2(-II)$ (polysulfide) groups. Thus, in addition to all the usual steps of a precipitation reaction, there has also been an oxidation-reduction reaction, formation of S—S bonds, and finally the component Cu(II), Cu(I), S($-$II), and $S_2(-II)$ units have been arranged into the crystal structure of covellite (CuS).

Again, in a reaction such as the disproportionation of $KClO_3$, just above its melting point

$$4\ KClO_3 \xrightarrow{\ 370°\ } 3\ KClO_4 + KCl$$

it is necessary for one ClO_3^- ion to transfer an oxygen atom to each of three other ClO_3^- ions, presumably in three individual steps. Because of the number of steps, as well as the necessity of making and breaking strong Cl—O bonds, this is a complicated process. It is not surprising, therefore, to find that the reaction proceeds slowly even at 370°C.

The generation of AsH_3 from AsO_4^{-3} by Al metal in alkaline solution is too slow to be detected, presumably because it is necessary first to break the strong As—O multiple bonds. With $As(OH)_4^-$ there is no such strong bond to be broken and reduction to arsine proceeds rapidly. The same argument may be used to explain why SO_2 in dilute aqueous acid can reduce H_2SeO_3 to red selenium, but does not affect H_2SeO_4, even though H_2SeO_4 is a much stronger oxidant than H_2SeO_3.

Qualitative considerations such as these, however, or a mere examination of the over-all equation for a chemical reaction, can give us very little information about the actual mechanism of a reaction. It must be emphasized that *the reaction equation represents only the initial and final states* and tells nothing about what goes on in between.

15-2.   Simple Kinetic Studies—Reaction Orders

Much information about mechanisms can be obtained by studying the rates of reaction under varying conditions. The study of chemical reaction rates is known as chemical *kinetics*. It might be thought that when carbon dioxide is dissolved in aqueous alkali it combines with water to form carbonic acid, which then ionizes

(1) $$CO_2 + H_2O \rightleftharpoons H_2CO_3$$

(2) $$H_2CO_3 + H_2O \rightleftharpoons OH_3^+ + HCO_3^-$$

The oxonium ion formed would then react with the hydroxide ion of the alkaline solution

(3) $$OH_3^+ + OH^- \rightleftharpoons 2\,H_2O$$

Addition of equations (1), (2), and (3) gives

(4) $$CO_2 + OH^- \rightleftharpoons HCO_3^-$$

which is the over-all reaction. This reaction, of course, might go directly, according to equation (4), instead of through the three steps represented by equations (1), (2), and (3). It is found that the actual rate of reaction is slow enough to be measured and that it is proportional to $[CO_2]$ and $[OH^-]$. Let us now observe that in any reaction involving several steps, the rate of the over-all reaction can be no greater than the rate of the slowest step. This slowest step is known as the "rate-controlling step." In this case, since we know that step (3) is practically instantaneous, it cannot be the slow step in the reaction. Since the three-step process depends upon $[OH^-]$ only in step (3), the three-step process therefore cannot be correct, steps (1) and (2) being independent of $[OH^-]$. Therefore, the direct process (4), for which the rate must depend on $[CO_2] \times [OH^-]$, i.e.

$$\text{rate} = k[CO_2][OH^-]$$

must be correct.

The reaction of H_2 (g) and I_2 (g) is an example in which the expected relationship is actually observed. From the chemical equation

$$H_2\,(g) + I_2\,(g) \rightarrow 2\,HI$$

we should predict, and we find

$$\text{rate} = kp_{H_2}p_{I_2}.$$

We may therefore visualize molecules of H_2 and I_2 colliding to form an activated complex, which then splits apart with the atoms having transferred partners

$$
\begin{array}{ccccc}
H & I & H\cdots I & H{-}I & \\
| + | & \rightarrow & |\quad\quad| & \vdots\quad\vdots & \rightarrow 2\,H{-}I \\
H & I & H\cdots I & H{-}I &
\end{array}
$$

The success of our prediction of this rate law from the chemical equation must not be taken as evidence that this can generally be done, however. We shall examine below a number of examples to the contrary. In particular, the case of the reaction between H_2 and Br_2, which might be expected to have a mechanism identical to that of the reaction between H_2 and I_2, will be seen (Section 15–3) in fact to be quite different.

Another simple case is that of the thermal decomposition of gaseous NO_2

$$2 NO_2 (g) \rightarrow 2 NO (g) + O_2 (g)$$

The rate of this reaction is found to be proportional to the square of the partial pressure of NO_2

$$\text{rate} = k p_{NO_2}{}^2$$

This is in accord with the expectation that the initial (and rate-determining) step is the reaction of two colliding NO_2 molecules.

On the other hand, at room temperature, the rate of decomposition of N_2O_5, according to the equation

$$2 N_2O_5 (g) \rightarrow 4 NO_2 (g) + O_2 (g)$$

is found *not* to be proportional to the square of the partial pressure of N_2O_5, but rather to the *first* power of the partial pressure of N_2O_5

$$\text{rate} = k p_{N_2O_5}$$

One reaction mechanism which has been proposed to account for this is

$$N_2O_5 (g) \rightarrow N_2O_3 (g) + O_2 (g)$$

$$N_2O_3 (g) \rightarrow NO (g) + NO_2 (g)$$

$$N_2O_5 (g) + NO (g) \rightarrow 3 NO_2 (g)$$

Since the second and third reactions are known to be rapid, the fact that the first is slow (which agrees with the fact that the number of unpaired electrons changes) would account for the decomposition rates being proportional to the *first* power of the partial pressure of N_2O_5. The decomposition of N_2O_5 is said to be a *first-order* reaction (i.e., the rate depends upon the *first* power of the concentration), while that of NO_2 is a *second-order* reaction. The reaction of CO_2 with aqueous alkali is also a *second-order* reaction (i.e., second-order in *all* the concentrations), but is first-order in CO_2 and first-order in OH^-.

True third-order (or higher-order) reactions are very rare. The reason for this is the very low mathematical probability that three molecules will collide simultaneously, or that such a collision will be effective if it does occur. Third-order reactions proceed only when the three-body collision is much more effective than any possible two-body collision. Such reactions will always be slow. Two of the small number of third-order homogeneous gas reactions known are

$$2\,NO + Cl_2 \rightarrow 2\,NOCl$$

and

$$2\,NO + Br_2 \rightarrow 2\,NOBr$$

for which

$$\text{rate} = k[NO]^2[X_2]$$

where

$$X = Cl\ \text{or}\ Br$$

The kinetics of the oxidation of H_2O_2 by aqueous Ce^{+4}

$$H_2O_2 + 2\,Ce^{+4} \rightarrow O_2\,(g) + 2\,Ce^{+3} + 2\,H^+$$

has been studied. It is not a third-order reaction, but rather is found to be second-order (i.e., first-order in H_2O_2 and first-order in Ce^{+4}). This indicates a mechanism involving two one-electron steps, the first of which is slow

$$Ce^{+4} + H_2O_2 \rightarrow Ce^{+3} + H^+ + HO_2 \quad \text{(slow)}$$

$$Ce^{+4} + HO_2 \rightarrow Ce^{+3} + H^+ + O_2 \quad \text{(fast)}$$

In the case of the reaction between peroxydisulfate ion, $S_2O_8^{-2}$, and I^-

$$S_2O_8^{-2} + 2\,I^- \rightarrow 2\,SO_4^{-2} + I_2$$

it is found that the reaction is not third-order, as the over-all equation indicates, but only second-order (i.e., first-order in both $[S_2O_8^{-2}]$ and $[I^-]$). This agrees with a first slow step

$$S_2O_8^{-2} + I^- \rightarrow SO_4^{-2} + SO_4I^-$$

followed by a fast step

$$SO_4I^- + I^- \rightarrow SO_4^{-2} + I_2$$

A simple case in which the pH-dependence of the reaction gives a clue to the reacting species is that of the decomposition of dithionates. Dilute solutions of dithionic acid do not decompose at room temperature at an appreciable rate. However, if *acidified* dithionates are warmed to about 50°, the rate of decomposition under these conditions is found to be directly proportional to the dithionate-ion concentration and the hydrogen-ion concentration.

$$\text{rate} = k[H^+][S_2O_6^{-2}]$$

It thus is apparent that the species primarily responsible for the decomposition in dilute solution is $HS_2O_6^-$, which is produced by the reverse of the second ionization of dithionic acid. This, like all neutralizations of oxy anions in water solution, is a rapid reversible reaction

$$HS_2O_6^- \rightleftharpoons H^+ + S_2O_6^{-2} \qquad K_{A2} = 10^{-3.4}$$

The actual decomposition reaction, which is slow, is

$$HS_2O_6^- + H_2O \rightarrow H_2SO_3 + HSO_4^-$$

This, of course, is proportional to $[HS_2O_6^-]$

$$\text{rate} = k'[HS_2O_6^-]$$

But since

$$\frac{[H^+][S_2O_6^{-2}]}{[HS_2O_6^-]} = 10^{-3.4}$$

or

$$[HS_2O_6] = 10^{+3.4}[H^+][S_2O_6^{-2}]$$

then

$$\text{rate} = k' \cdot 10^{+3.4} \cdot [H^+][S_2O_6^{-2}] = k[H^+][S_2O_6^{-2}]$$

Another case of pH-dependence is that of the decomposition of nitramide, H_2NNO_2, in aqueous solution. The decomposition equation is

$$H_2NNO_2 \rightarrow N_2O + H_2O$$

The rate of decomposition in both basic and acidic solutions is greater than in neutral solution, but the rate is accelerated much more by base than by acid. Since nitramide is known to be weakly acidic

$$\frac{[H^+][HNNO_2^-]}{[H_2NNO_2]} = 2.55 \times 10^{-7} \quad \text{(at 15°C)}$$

the dependence of the decomposition on $[OH^-]$ indicates that the anion, $HNNO_2^-$, decomposes more rapidly than the neutral molecule

$$HNNO_2^- \rightarrow N_2O + OH^-$$

The much lower dependence of the rate of decomposition on $[H^+]$ indicates that although the species $H_3NNO_2^+$ decomposes more rapidly than does neutral H_2NNO_2, nitramide is a weaker base than it is an acid, and therefore the concentration of $H_3NNO_2^+$ is never very high.

$$H_3NNO_2^+ \rightarrow N_2O + H_3O^+$$

(The basic ionization constant for nitramide

$$\frac{[H_3NNO_2^+][OH^-]}{[H_2NNO_2]} = K_B$$

is not known.)

15–3. More Complex Kinetic Studies

In the reduction of Tl^{+3} by Fe^{+2}

$$Tl^{+3} + 2\,Fe^{+2} \rightarrow Tl^+ + 2\,Fe^{+3}$$

it is found that the reaction is first-order in Tl^{+3} and second-order in Fe^{+2}, but that Fe^{+3} exerts an inhibiting effect, i.e., the more Fe^{+3} is present, the more slowly it goes. It thus appears that the first step is the rapid *and* reversible production of the unstable Tl^{+2}

$$Tl^{+3} + Fe^{+2} \rightleftharpoons Tl^{+2} + Fe^{+3}$$

$$\frac{[Tl^{+2}][Fe^{+3}]}{[Tl^{+3}][Fe^{+2}]} = K$$

The second, slow step is

$$Tl^{+2} + Fe^{+2} \rightarrow Tl^{+} + Fe^{+3}$$

$$\text{rate} = k'[Tl^{+2}][Fe^{+2}]$$

But since

$$[Tl^{+2}] = K\frac{[Tl^{+3}][Fe^{+2}]}{[Fe^{+3}]}$$

then $$\text{rate} = k'K\frac{[Tl^{+3}][Fe^{+2}]^2}{[Fe^{+3}]} = k\frac{[Tl^{+3}][Fe^{+2}]^2}{[Fe^{+3}]}$$

This reaction is said to be of the "minus-one-order" in Fe^{+3}.

A similar case is that of the decomposition of HNO_2

$$3\ HNO_2 \rightarrow H^+ + NO_3^- + 2\ NO\ (g) + H_2O$$

whose rate is decreased by the presence of NO. The rate expression for the decomposition is

$$\text{rate} = k\frac{[HNO_2]^4}{p_{NO}^2}$$

This is the result of the fact that the first step of the reaction

$$4\ HNO_2 \rightleftharpoons N_2O_4 + 2\ NO + 2\ H_2O$$

$$\frac{[N_2O_4]p_{NO}^2}{[HNO_2]^4} = K$$

is rapid and reversible, while the second and rate-determining step is

$$N_2O_4 + H_2O \rightarrow HNO_2 + H^+ + NO_3^-$$

$$\text{rate} = k'[N_2O_4]$$

Therefore, since

$$[N_2O_4] = K\frac{[HNO_2]^4}{p_{NO}^2}$$

$$\text{rate} = k'K\frac{[HNO_2]^4}{p_{NO}^2} = k\frac{[HNO_2]^4}{p_{NO}^2}$$

The complications of the mechanisms sometimes lead to nonintegral orders of reaction. For example, in the oxidation of NO_2 to N_2O_5 by ozone, according to the equation

$$2\ NO_2 + O_3 \rightarrow N_2O_5 + O_2$$

it is found that the rate of disappearance of the ozone is a function of the N_2O_5 concentration

$$\text{rate} = k[N_2O_5]^{2/3}[O_3]^{2/3}$$

This is probably a result of the fact that the lower oxides of nitrogen all react with ozone, and that the product, N_2O_5, decomposes at a known rate (Section 15–2) to give NO_2. Complete details of the mechanism of this reaction have not been worked out.

Another case of this sort is that of the reaction of H_2 (g) and Br_2 (g). (Recall the reaction of H_2 and I_2 discussed in Section 15–2.) The reaction equation is

$$H_2 \text{ (g)} + Br_2 \text{ (g)} \rightarrow 2\,HBr$$

However, the reaction rate is found to be proportional not to the product of the first powers of the partial pressures of the reactants, but rather to the square roots of the partial pressures. The reaction is not the result of collision of H_2 and Br_2 molecules (as in the case of $H_2 + I_2$), but takes the course

(1) $$Br_2 \rightleftharpoons 2\,Br$$

(2) $$Br + H_2 \rightarrow HBr + H$$

(3) $$H + Br_2 \rightarrow HBr + Br$$

(4) $$H + HBr \rightarrow H_2 + Br$$

The reaction rate consequently depends on [Br] and [H]. Since, from step (1), however

$$\frac{[Br]^2}{[Br_2]} = K$$

and

$$[Br] = \sqrt{K[Br_2]}$$

the rate depends upon the square root of the concentration of the Br_2. This reaction is an example of a *chain reaction*. In a chain reaction, each step produces a substance needed in the next step, and the reaction is *self-propagating*. In this case, steps (2) and (3), one producing H atoms, the other Br atoms, are the chain-propagating steps. Step (2), however, is *endothermic* by 16 kcal per mole. Therefore the probability that a bromine atom will react with a hydrogen molecule on collision is $e^{-16,000/RT}$, which at 177°C is 1.75×10^{-8}. This means that on the average a bromine atom will react only after 10^8 collisions or 0.01 second after it has been produced. This lifetime gives it more than one chance to combine with another bromine atom

$$Br + Br \rightarrow Br_2$$

thus breaking the chain (a chain-terminating step). Consequently, the reaction chains in this case must be very short, and many bromine atoms must disappear without starting a chain at all. Consequently, the reaction does not proceed at a measurable rate below 200°C.

In the case of hydrogen and iodine, the step

$$I + H_2 \rightarrow HI + H$$

is so endothermic (32 kcal per mole) as to preclude this reaction mechanism altogether, the reaction proceeding via the $(HI)_2$ = activated complex, as described in Section 15–2.

In the case of hydrogen and chlorine, however, the step

$$Cl + H_2 \rightarrow HCl + H$$

is only *slightly* endothermic (0.7 kcal per mole), so that the reaction proceeds readily at slightly elevated temperatures and is characterized by long chain lengths.

An example of a fairly complicated rate expression is that for the decomposition of the salts of hyponitrous acid in alkaline solution. The overall reaction equation is

$$N_2O_2^{-2} + H_2O \rightarrow N_2O \text{ (g)} + 2\,OH^-$$

The expression for the rate of production of N_2O is found to be

$$\text{rate} = \frac{k[N_2O_2^{-2}]_{\text{total}}}{[OH^-](1 + \beta[OH^-])}$$

where $[N_2O_2^{-2}]_{\text{total}}$ stands for the total concentration of hyponitrite in all forms, and k and β are constants. Since both ionization constants of $H_2N_2O_2$ are small ($K_{A1} = 9 \times 10^{-8}$, $K_{A2} = 1.0 \times 10^{-11}$), hydrolysis will be extensive, and $N_2O_2^{-2}$ and $HN_2O_2^-$ will both be present in solution

$$K_{H_1} = \frac{[HN_2O_2^-][OH^-]}{[N_2O_2^{-2}]}$$

$$K_{H_2} = \frac{[H_2N_2O_2][OH^-]}{[HN_2O_2^-]}$$

Since decomposition is more rapid in acidic solution, the rate-controlling step may be assumed to be

$$H_2N_2O_2 \rightarrow N_2O \text{ (g)} + H_2O$$

for which

$$\text{rate} = k'[H_2N_2O_2]$$

But since

$$[N_2O_2^{-2}]_{\text{total}} = [N_2O_2^{-2}] + [HN_2O_2^-]$$

$$= [H_2N_2O_2]\left(\frac{[OH^-]^2}{K_{H_1}K_{H_2}} + \frac{[OH^-]}{K_{H_2}}\right)$$

the rate equation takes the form

$$\text{rate} = \frac{k'[N_2O_2^{-2}]_{\text{total}}}{[OH^-]\left(\dfrac{1}{K_{H_2}} + \dfrac{[OH^-]}{K_{H_1}K_{H_2}}\right)} = \frac{k'K_{H_2}[N_2O_2^{-2}]_{\text{total}}}{[OH^-]\left(1 + \dfrac{[OH^-]}{K_{H_1}}\right)}$$

Now if

$$k'K_{H_2} = k \quad \text{and} \quad \frac{1}{K_{H_1}} = \beta$$

then

$$\text{rate} = \frac{k[N_2O_2^{-2}]_{\text{total}}}{[OH^-](1+\beta[OH^-])}$$

15-4. Catalysis

The specific role of catalysts in catalyzed reactions can frequently be explained by kinetic studies. For example, at room temperature, peroxydisulfate ion, $S_2O_8^{-2}$, does not oxidize Mn^{+2}, Cr^{+3}, VO^{+2}, $H_2C_2O_4$, N_2H_4, NH_3, and so on. However, in the presence of silver salts, it oxidizes all of these, the reaction rate being found to be proportional to $[Ag^+]$ and $[S_2O_8^{-2}]$, but independent of the concentration of the reducing agent

$$\text{rate} = k[Ag^+][S_2O_8^{-2}]$$

The mechanism of the reaction has been found to have two important steps, first, a slow oxidation of Ag^+ by $S_2O_8^{-2}$

$$S_2O_8^{-2} + Ag^+ \rightarrow 2\,SO_4^{-2} + Ag^{+3}$$

and second, the rapid oxidation of the reducing agent by Ag^{+3}

$$Ag^{+3} + \text{reductant} \rightarrow Ag^+ + \text{oxidized product}$$

Since the slow step in the reaction is the first step, whose rate is proportional to the silver-ion and peroxydisulfate-ion concentrations, the lack of dependence of the reaction rate on the concentration of reducing agent is explained. (Confirmation of this mechanism is provided by the fact that, in the absence of a reducing agent, black Ag_2O_3 is slowly formed. The Ag_2O_3 slowly decomposes to black AgO and O_2, and eventually to Ag_2O and O_2 (or Ag^+ if the solution is acidic).

Again, the decomposition of H_2O_2 is catalyzed by I^- in alkaline solution. The reaction steps are presumed to be

$$H_2O_2 + I^- \rightarrow H_2O + IO^-$$

$$H_2O_2 + IO^- \rightarrow H_2O + O_2 + I^-$$

The over-all reaction is

$$2\,H_2O_2 \rightarrow 2\,H_2O + O_2$$

In similar fashion, transition-metal ions (of variable oxidation states) catalyze the decomposition of H_2O_2. The steps involved in the decomposition are

(1) $$Fe^{+2} + H_2O_2 \rightleftharpoons FeOH^{+2} + OH$$

(2) $$OH + H_2O_2 \rightarrow H_2O + HO_2$$

(3) $HO_2 + H_2O_2 \rightarrow H_2O + O_2 + OH$

(4) $Fe^{+3} + H_2O_2 \rightleftharpoons Fe^{+2} + HO_2 + H^+$

(5) $Fe^{+3} + HO_2 \rightarrow Fe^{+2} + O_2 + H^+$

(6) $Fe^{+2} + OH \rightarrow FeOH^{+2}$

It can be seen that this is a chain reaction, steps (1) and (4) being chain-initiators, (2) and (3) chain-propagators, and (5) and (6) chain-terminators. It can also be seen that, because the species HO, HO_2, H_2O_2 are weak acids

$$HO \rightleftharpoons H^+ + O^- \qquad\qquad K > 10^{-14}$$

$$HO_2 \rightleftharpoons H^+ + O_2^- \qquad\qquad K \cong 6 \times 10^{-3}$$

$$H_2O_2 \rightleftharpoons H^+ + HO_2^- \qquad\qquad K = 2.4 \times 10^{-12}$$

the reaction will be pH-dependent.

Transition-metal ions are frequently good redox catalysts. Another example is the catalysis by Mn^{+2} of the reaction between Cl_2 and $C_2O_4^{-2}$. The steps of the reaction are

$$MnC_2O_4^+ \rightarrow Mn^{+2} + CO_2 + CO_2^-$$

$$CO_2^- + Cl_2 \rightarrow CO_2 + Cl + Cl^-$$

$$Cl + Mn^{+2} \rightarrow Mn^{+3} + Cl^-$$

$$Mn^{+3} + C_2O_4^{-2} \rightleftharpoons MnC_2O_4^+$$

This gives

$$Cl_2 + C_2O_4^{-2} \rightarrow 2\,Cl^- + 2\,CO_2$$

for the over-all reaction.

Likewise, Cu^{+2} catalyzes the reaction

$$2\,Fe^{+3} + 2\,S_2O_3^{-2} \rightarrow 2\,Fe^{+2} + S_4O_6^{-2}$$

This probably proceeds through steps such as

$$Cu^{+2} + S_2O_3^{-2} \rightleftharpoons CuS_2O_3\ (aq)$$

$$2\,CuS_2O_3\ (aq) \rightarrow 2\,Cu^+ + S_4O_6^{-2}$$

$$Cu^+ + Fe^{+3} \rightarrow Cu^{+2} + Fe^{+2}$$

The catalyses discussed in Section 2–2 are also cases of this sort.

The action of palladium and platinum as hydrogenation catalysts is probably similar. Thus, for the reaction

$$2\,H_2 + O_2 \rightarrow 2\,H_2O$$

a key step in the reaction is probably the dissociation of the H_2 molecules,

$$H_2 \rightarrow 2\,H$$

a very endothermic reaction. It is known that H_2 reacts with palladium, for example, to form an unstable hydride, Pd_2H, the equilibrium constant for the reaction

$$4 \text{ Pd (s)} + H_2 \text{ (g)} \rightleftharpoons 2 \text{ Pd}_2H \text{ (s)}$$

being close to one. This reaction has brought about the breaking of the H—H bonds, so that now the hydrogen atoms can react readily with O_2 (or other oxidant).

$$4 \text{ Pd}_2H \text{ (s)} + O_2 \text{ (g)} \rightarrow 8 \text{ Pd (s)} + 2 \text{ H}_2O \text{ (g)}$$

15-5. Alternate Courses of Reaction

A set of reactants may react simultaneously by two (or more) different reaction paths. For example, when hydrazine, N_2H_4, is oxidized with I_2, IO_3^- or Tl^{+3}, the sole oxidation product is N_2, e.g.

$$2 \text{ Tl}^{+3} + N_2H_4 \rightarrow N_2 + 2 \text{ Tl}^+ + 4 \text{ H}^+$$

The reaction path is thought to be

$$N_2H_4 + Tl^{+3} \rightleftharpoons TlN_2H_4^{+3}$$

$$TlN_2H_4^{+3} \rightarrow Tl^+ + N_2H_2 + 2 \text{ H}^+$$

$$N_2H_2 + Tl^{+3} \rightleftharpoons TlN_2H_2^{+3}$$

$$TlN_2H_2^{+3} \rightarrow Tl^+ + N_2 + 2 \text{ H}^+$$

The Tl^{+3} is a "two-electron" oxidizing agent (see Section 15-6). On the other hand, if N_2H_4 is oxidized with "one-electron" oxidants, such as Ce^{+4}, Fe^{+3}, or Mn^{+3}, a mixture of N_2 and NH_3 results, the proportions depending on the ratio of oxidant to hydrazine in the original solution. The indefinite stoichiometry is thought to be the result of alternate paths being available. The proposed mechanism is

$$N_2H_4 + Ce^{+4} \rightarrow N_2H_3 + H^+ + Ce^{+3}$$

and then either

$$N_2H_3 + Ce^{+4} \rightarrow N_2H_2 + H^+ + Ce^{+3}$$

$$N_2H_2 + 2 \text{ Ce}^{+4} \rightarrow N_2 + 2 \text{ H}^+ + 2 \text{ Ce}^{+3}$$

or

$$2 \text{ N}_2H_3 \rightarrow N_4H_6$$

$$N_4H_6 \rightarrow N_2 + 2 \text{ NH}_3$$

A similar situation is found in the oxidation of sulfites by various reagents. The halogens oxidize sulfites rapidly and quantitatively to sulfate, e.g.

$$Cl_2 + SO_3^{-2} + H_2O \rightarrow 2 \text{ Cl}^- + SO_4^{-2} + 2 \text{ H}^+$$

On the other hand, oxidizing agents like Fe^{+3}, RuO_4, MnO_2, $KMnO_4$,

H_2O_2, and so on, produce varying amounts of SO_4^{-2} and $S_2O_6^{-2}$ (dithionate), depending on conditions and the particular oxidant. Manganese dioxide produces mainly dithionate

$$2 \, MnO_2 \, (s) + 2 \, SO_3^{-2} + 2 \, H^+ \rightarrow Mn_2O_3 \, (s) + S_2O_6^{-2} + H_2O$$

but some sulfate is always produced by the slightly slower competing reaction

$$MnO_2 \, (s) + SO_3^{-2} + 2 \, H^+ \rightarrow Mn^{+2} + SO_4^{-2} + H_2O$$

A classic example of competitive reactions is the so-called "clock reaction." In acidic solution, iodate ion reacts at a moderate rate with sulfurous acid to give iodide and sulfate

$$IO_3^- + 3 \, H_2SO_3 \rightarrow I^- + 3 \, SO_4^{-2} + 6 \, H^+$$

In a competing, but somewhat slower reaction, iodate ion reacts with iodide ion to give iodine

$$IO_3^- + 5 \, I^- + 6 \, H^+ \rightarrow 3 \, I_2 + 3 \, H_2O$$

but the liberated iodine reacts rapidly with H_2SO_3

$$I_2 + H_2SO_3 + H_2O \rightarrow 2 \, I^- + SO_4^{-2} + 4 \, H^+$$

The last reaction is so rapid that no color of iodine is observed until all the sulfurous acid has been oxidized. At that point, if a little starch indicator has been added, the solution suddenly becomes blue, as the iodine released by the second reaction is no longer used up. Since the time required for the blue color to appear is a function of temperature and concentrations, the reaction may be used as a clock. The time in seconds from the time of mixing until the time of appearance of the color is given by the formula

$$t_{sec} = \frac{906.05 - 23.01 \, T + 0.1888 \, T^2}{C_S^{0.904} \, C_I^{1.642}}$$

where C_S and C_I are the concentrations of H_2SO_3 and HIO_3 expressed in moles per cubic meter of solution, and T is the temperature in degrees centigrade.

The course of a reaction can thus be seen to be a function of many different conditions. The presence or absence of a catalyst may frequently cause one reaction course to be favored over another. This has already been discussed in Section 2–2 with respect to the effect of catalysts on the atmospheric oxidation of ammonia.

Several rather dramatic examples of the effect of catalysts on oxidation reactions can be drawn from the field of electrochemistry. If acidic solutions of chromic salts are electrolyzed with shiny platinum electrodes, the principal anode product is oxygen. The same is true if iodic acid is electrolyzed. However, if a little lead salt is added, or if a lead anode is used, almost quantitative production of dichromate or periodic acid results

$$2 \, Cr^{+3} + 7 \, H_2O \rightarrow Cr_2O_7^{-2} + 14 \, H^+ + 6 \, e^-$$

$$HIO_3 + 3 \, H_2O \rightarrow H_5IO_6 + 2 \, H^+ + 2 \, e^-$$

The reaction mechanism obviously involves the oxidation of the lead to PbO_2 (which can accomplish the oxidations). The PbO_2 and reducing agent then react to give the final products.

Negative catalysis is also possible. If an aqueous mixture of sodium acetate and acetic acid is electrolyzed, using a shiny platinum anode, the "Kolbe synthesis" takes place with about 90 percent efficiency

$$2 CH_3CO_2^- \rightarrow C_2H_6 (g) + 2 CO_2 (g) + 2 e^-$$

However, if a little manganese salt is added, oxygen becomes the only anode product

$$2 H_2O \rightarrow O_2 (g) + 4 H^+ + 4 e^-$$

An interesting case of positive and negative catalysis is the dehydration of $Cu(OH)_2$ (blue) to CuO (black)

$$Cu(OH)_2 (s) \rightarrow CuO (s) + H_2O$$

This reaction, which is very slow at room temperature, is greatly speeded up by H_2O_2 (which is incidentally catalytically decomposed at the same time). The mechanism presumably involves the oxidation of the $Cu(OH)_2$ to $Cu(OH)_3$ which spontaneously dehydrates and is then reduced to CuO

$$2 Cu(OH)_2 (s) + H_2O_2 \rightarrow 2 Cu(OH)_3 (s)$$
$$2 Cu(OH)_3 (s) \rightarrow Cu_2O_3 (s) + 3 H_2O$$
$$Cu_2O_3 (s) + H_2O_2 \rightarrow 2 CuO (s) + O_2 (g) + H_2O$$

This reaction is completely prevented in the presence of magnesium salts. The reason for this is unknown, but we may speculate that the divalent $Mg(OH)_2$, which cannot be oxidized, mixed with the divalent $Cu(OH)_2$, prevents the latter from being oxidized and thereby dehydrated. (See the case of MnO in the presence of Al_2O_3 and TiO_2 in Section 15–9.)

15–6. One- and Two-Electron Reactions

Oxidizing and reducing agents can be classified as one-electron or two-electron agents. The one-electron agents are those which have two important oxidation states, differing from each other by only one electron. A number of these are shown in Table 15–1.

TABLE 15–1. ONE-ELECTRON REDUCTANTS AND OXIDANTS

Reductant	Oxidant
Fe^{+2}	Fe^{+3}
Ti^{+3}	Ti^{+4}
Ag	Ag^+
Cr^{+2}	Cr^{+3}
Eu^{+2}	Eu^{+3}
Ce^{+3}	Ce^{+4}
Co^{+2}	Co^{+3}
$Fe(CN)_6^{-4}$	$Fe(CN)_6^{-3}$
MnO_4^{-2}*	MnO_4^-*

* In alkaline solution.

An electrode of inert material (e.g., graphite or Pt) acts also as a one-electron agent. Two-electron agents are those which have two important oxidation states separated by *two* electrons, *with no stable state in between.* Examples of these are given in Table 15–2.

TABLE 15–2. TWO-ELECTRON REDUCTANTS AND OXIDANTS

Reductant	Oxidant
Pb^{+2}	PbO_2
Sn^{+2}	Sn^{+4}
Tl^+	Tl^{+3}
Bi^{+3}	Bi_2O_5
Sb^{+3}	Sb_2O_5
AsO^+	H_3AsO_4
H_2TeO_3	H_6TeO_6
H_2SeO_3	H_2SeO_4
H_2S	S
HIO_3	H_5IO_6
Ni	Ni^{+2}

Many reagents can act either as one- or two-electron agents, depending on the nature of the other reactant in the system and on the conditions of reaction. For example, Cu^{+2} may be a two-electron oxidant ($Cu^{+2}+2\,e^- \rightarrow Cu$) or a one-electron oxidant ($Cu^{+2}+e^- \rightarrow Cu^+$). Sulfite ion may be a two-electron reductant ($SO_3^{-2}+H_2O \rightarrow SO_4^{-2}+2\,H^+ +2\,e^-$) or a one-electron reductant ($SO_3^{-2} \rightarrow SO_3^- +e^-$; $2\,SO_3^- \rightarrow S_2O_6^{-2}$). Halide ions in acidic solution may be one-electron reducing agents ($I^- \rightarrow I+e^-$; $2\,I \rightarrow I_2$), but in alkaline solution are more likely to be two-electron reducing agents ($I^- +2\,OH^- \rightarrow IO^- +H_2O+2\,e^-$). Several other examples of this are cited in Sections 15–4 and 15–5.

Whether a reagent is preferentially a one- or two-electron agent can now be seen to have a decided effect on the course of reaction. In addition to the examples which have already been given, one more will be cited.

When HNO_2 is reduced with Fe^{+2} (a weak reducing agent) or with Ti^{+3} (a powerful reducing agent), gaseous NO (which immediately escapes from solution) is the sole product

$$HNO_2 + Fe^{+2} + H^+ \rightarrow NO\ (g) + Fe^{+3} + H_2O$$

$$HNO_2 + Ti^{+3} \rightarrow NO\ (g) + TiO^{+2} + H^+$$

On the other hand, if Sn^{+2} (a reducing agent of intermediate strength) is used, the main product is N_2O (which escapes from solution), but further reduction to hydroxylamine—or even all the way to ammonia—also takes place.

$$HNO_2 + Sn^{+2} + 2\,H^+ \rightarrow HNO + Sn^{+4} + H_2O$$

$$2\,HNO \rightarrow H_2O + N_2O\ (g)$$

$$2\,HNO \rightarrow H_2N_2O_2$$

$$HNO + Sn^{+2} + 3\,H^+ \rightarrow HONH_3^+ + Sn^{+4}$$

$$HONH_2 + Sn^{+2} + 3\,H^+ \rightarrow NH_4^+ + Sn^{+4} + H_2O$$

15-7. Hydrogen Overvoltage

The fact has already been discussed (Section 14–8) that a certain excess of voltage over that predicted by the normal oxidation potentials is required to liberate hydrogen from aqueous solution, and that reducing agents (such as Cr^{+2}) which, according to their oxidation potentials, should instantaneously produce hydrogen from water do so only slowly if at all.

All the details of the mechanism of reduction of hydrogen ion to hydrogen gas are by no means thoroughly understood. It is generally accepted, however, that the first step in the process is the transfer of an electron from reducing agent or cathode to the hydrogen ion

(1) $$OH_3^+ + e^- \rightarrow H + H_2O$$

producing some form of hydrogen atom. In some manner or other, two hydrogen atoms combine to give a hydrogen molecule

(2) $$2\,H \rightarrow H_2$$

If the reaction is completely homogeneous, then the potential of the hydrogen-ion discharge step (1) will be considerably higher than the equilibrium or standard oxidation potential ($E^\circ = 0.00$ volts) for the over-all reaction

$$2\,OH_3^+ + 2\,e^- \rightleftharpoons H_2\,(g) + 2\,H_2O$$

since monatomic hydrogen is much less stable than molecular hydrogen. The overvoltage for the homogeneous reduction of aqueous hydrogen ion is in fact much smaller (about 0.5 volts) than would be expected if actual hydrogen atoms were produced (2.10 volts), consequently the hydrogen atoms are undoubtedly present in hydrated form. The homogeneous reduction process (as, for example $H^+ + Cr^{+2}$) might therefore be represented as

$$OH_3^+ + e^- \rightarrow OH_3$$

$$2\,OH_3 \rightarrow H_2\,(g) + 2\,H_2O$$

Various metallic catalysts, which are capable of forming weak metal-hydrogen bonds (as discussed for Pd in Section 15–4), can lower the overvoltage because the monatomic hydrogen forms a more stable association with the metal than with water molecules

$$OH_3^+ + e^- + Pd \rightarrow H_2O + Pd—H$$

The hydrogen so held on a cathode surface is probably negatively charged (essentially an adsorbed hydride ion, H^-)

$$Pd—H + e^- \rightarrow Pd—H^-$$

and then further reacts with hydrogen ions from solution

$$Pd-H^- + H_3O^+ \rightarrow Pd + H_2 \text{ (g)} + H_2O$$

The ability of different metals to do this will depend upon their affinity for hydrogen. It is found that hydrogen overvoltage varies correspondingly from one metal to another, as is shown in Table 15-3.

TABLE 15-3. MINIMUM HYDROGEN OVERVOLTAGES IN 2 N H$_2$SO$_4$

Metal	Overvoltage	Metal	Overvoltage
Platinized Pt	0.005	Graphite	0.31*
Au	0.02	Cd	0.48
Fe (1 N NaOH)	0.08	Al	0.50*
Shiny Pt	0.09	Sn	0.53
Ag	0.15	Pb	0.64
Ni	0.21	Zn	0.70
Cu	0.23	Hg	0.78

* In 1 N H$_2$SO$_4$ at 0.001 amp/cm^2.

Overvoltage on metal surfaces is also influenced by other factors, such as the physical condition of the surface (note the difference between platinized and shiny platinum) and the presence of oxide films (which increase the electrical resistance and therefore raise the overvoltage). The presence of impurities in the metals also has a great influence. For example, a trace of platinum in a mercury cathode will drastically reduce the hydrogen overvoltage. On the other hand, a trace of arsenic (a potent catalyst poison) in or on a platinum cathode greatly increases the overvoltage.

One additional factor in producing overvoltage, that of making and breaking bonds, e.g., in a reducing agent like hypophosphorous acid, has already been discussed in Section 14-8.

15-8.   Oxygen Overvoltage

The production of oxygen from aqueous solution is a far more complicated process than the production of hydrogen, because of the fact that there are many more steps possible between H$_2$O and O$_2$ than between H$^+$ and H$_2$. Without implying that the various species shown are necessarily involved in the oxidation of water to oxygen, reference may be made to the potential diagram for oxygen, which shows the stability relationships of the various

In 1 M H$^+$

$$2 H_2O \xrightarrow{-2.82} \underset{H_2O}{OH} \xrightarrow{-0.72} H_2O_2 \xrightarrow{-1.5} HO_2 \xrightarrow{0.1} O_2$$

$$\underset{-1.77}{\underline{\hspace{3cm}}} \quad \underset{-0.68}{\underline{\hspace{3cm}}}$$

In 1 M OH$^-$

$$2 OH^- \xrightarrow{-2.0} \underset{OH^-}{OH} \xrightarrow{0.26} HO_2^- \xrightarrow{-0.4} O_2^- \xrightarrow{0.6} O_2$$

$$\underset{-0.87}{\underline{\hspace{3cm}}} \quad \underset{0.08}{\underline{\hspace{3cm}}}$$

intermediate states. It can be seen that all of the intermediate states are unstable with respect to decomposition into H_2O (or OH^-) and O_2, and, consequently, to make them from H_2O would require much more energy than to make oxygen itself. *If, therefore, the oxidation of water were to proceed through the steps*

$$H_2O \rightarrow OH + H^+ + e^-$$

$$H_2O + OH \rightarrow H_2O_2 + H^+ + e^-$$

$$H_2O_2 \rightarrow HO_2 + H^+ + e^-$$

$$HO_2 \rightarrow O_2 + H^+ + e^-$$

(an assumption which is by no means proven), then a total voltage comparable to the most negative in the potential diagram (-2.82 volts) should be expected. This in comparison to the normal oxidation potential of -1.23 volts for

$$2\,H_2O \rightleftharpoons O_2 + 4\,H^+ + 4\,e^-$$

would give an overvoltage of $-2.82 + 1.23 = -1.59$ volts, which is much larger than observed for homogeneous reactions such as

$$4\,Co^{+3} + 2\,H_2O \rightarrow 4\,Co^{+2} + O_2 + 4\,H^+$$

which proceeds fairly rapidly, despite the fact that the net potential for the reaction is only $+0.59$ volts. As in the case of the reduction of hydrogen ion, there is probably some sort of association complex which makes the intermediate states easier to attain, e.g.

$$Co^{+3} + H_2O \rightarrow CoOH^{+2} + H^+$$

$$2\,CoOH^{+2} \rightarrow 2\,Co^{+2} + H_2O_2$$

and so forth. If this were the case, only the potential for the H_2O–H_2O_2 couple (-1.77 volts) would have to be considered. Thus for a reaction in which H_2O is oxidized essentially directly to H_2O_2 as the first step, the overvoltage should be only $-1.77 + 1.23 = -0.54$ v. Consequently, Co^{+3} should be able to accomplish this oxidation, as observed

$$2\,Co^{+3} + 2\,H_2O \rightarrow 2\,Co^{+2} + H_2O_2 + 2\,H^+ \qquad E° = +0.05\ \text{v}$$

The further reactions

$$Co^{+3} + H_2O_2 \rightarrow Co^{+2} + HO_2 + H^+ \qquad E° = +0.3\ \text{v}$$

$$Co^{+3} + HO_2 \rightarrow Co^{+2} + O_2 + H^+ \qquad E° = +1.9\ \text{v}$$

would then proceed without difficulty. On this basis, it would be predicted that an oxidant like Ce^{+4}

$$Ce^{+3} \rightarrow Ce^{+4} + e^- \qquad E° = -1.6\ \text{v}$$

should produce oxygen from 1 molar aqueous acids only at a very slow rate, since for

$$2 \text{ Ce}^{+4} + 2 \text{ H}_2\text{O} \rightarrow 2 \text{ Ce}^{+3} + \text{H}_2\text{O}_2 + 2 \text{ H}^+$$

$E°$ is -0.1 v. The prediction is consistent with the facts.

In the case of electrolytic production of oxygen, there is considerable evidence that at least in certain cases the metal of the anode is oxidized to a higher oxide, which then decomposes, liberating oxygen, e.g.

$$\text{Pt} + 3 \text{ H}_2\text{O} \rightarrow \text{PtO}_3 + 6 \text{ H}^+ + 6 \ e^-$$

$$2 \text{ PtO}_3 \rightarrow 2 \text{ PtO}_2 + \text{O}_2$$

The overvoltage is then the potential required to form the higher oxide.

15–9. Applications to the Reactions of Qualitative Analysis

The first case we meet in the analytical scheme where rates of reaction are important is the selective precipitation of HgNH_2Cl from ammonium hydroxide solution. Although no quantitative data are available, this can be qualitatively explained on the basis of the relative acidities of the ammines formed. The silver ion forms $\text{Ag(NH}_3)_2{}^+$ in ammoniacal solution. In ammoniacal solution containing high concentrations of $\text{NH}_4{}^+$, Hg^{+2} likewise forms $\text{Hg(NH}_3)_4{}^{+2}$. As the $\text{NH}_4{}^+$ concentration is reduced, however, this (in the presence of Cl^-) goes over to $\text{Hg(NH}_3)_2\text{Cl}_2$ and eventually to HgNH_2Cl. This would appear to be a function of the relative acidities of $\text{Ag(NH}_3)_2{}^+$ and $\text{Hg(NH}_3)_4{}^{+2}$. The K_A's (or hydrolysis constants) for $\text{Ag(H}_2\text{O})_2{}^+$ and $\text{Hg(H}_2\text{O})_4{}^{+2}$ are about 10^{-12} and 10^{-2}, respectively. The K_A's of $\text{Ag(NH}_3)_2{}^+$ and $\text{Hg(NH}_3)_4{}^{+2}$ are not known, but judging from the K_A of the $\text{Rh(NH}_3)_6{}^{+3}$ (10^{-11}) and $\text{Co(NH}_3)_6{}^{+3}$ (about 10^{-11}), the K_A's should be about 10^{-20} and 10^{-11} respectively for

$$\text{Ag(NH}_3)_2{}^+ \rightleftharpoons \text{Ag(NH}_3)\text{NH}_2 + \text{H}^+$$

and
$$\text{Hg(NH}_3)_4{}^{+2} \rightleftharpoons \text{Hg(NH}_3)_3\text{NH}_2{}^+ + \text{H}^+$$

Consequently, the amidomercuric complex should be present in solution to a much higher extent than the amidosilver complex. Furthermore, since it is known that *very* weak acids actually ionize much less rapidly than strong acids, it should be expected that the amidomercuric ion will be produced much more rapidly than the amidosilver complex. In addition, since under analytical conditions the mercury is already associated with chloride, it is not necessary for it to go through the $\text{Hg(NH}_3)_4{}^{+2}$ stage. The course of reaction is probably

$$\text{Hg}_2\text{Cl}_2 \text{ (s)} + 2 \text{ NH}_3 \rightarrow \text{Hg}_2\text{Cl}_2 \cdot 2 \text{ NH}_3 \text{ (s)}$$

$$\text{Hg}_2\text{Cl}_2 \cdot 2 \text{ NH}_3 \text{ (s)} \rightarrow \text{H}_2\text{NHg}_2\text{Cl} \text{ (s)} + \text{NH}_4{}^+ + \text{Cl}^-$$

$$\text{H}_2\text{NHg}_2\text{Cl} \text{ (s)} \rightarrow \text{Hg} \text{ (}l\text{)} + \text{HgNH}_2\text{Cl} \text{ (s)}$$

The next slow reaction encountered is the reduction of W(VI) in HCl solution to "tungsten blue", which requires heating. The reason for this probably lies in the insolubility and complexity of tungstic acid in acidic solution. Although we have represented the precipitate obtained when an alkali tungstate is acidified as H_2WO_4, it is in fact a highly polymeric substance, its complexity increasing as the acidity increases. Thus, just as CrO_4^{-2} undergoes reactions such as

$$2\ CrO_4^{-2} + 2\ H^+ \rightleftharpoons Cr_2O_7^{-2} + H_2O$$

$$Cr_2O_7^{-2} + CrO_4^{-2} + 2\ H^+ \rightleftharpoons Cr_3O_{10}^{-2} + H_2O$$

$$2\ Cr_2O_7^{-2} + 2\ H^+ \rightleftharpoons Cr_4O_{13}^{-2} + H_2O$$

and VO_4^{-3} undergoes reactions such as

$$2\ VO_4^{-3} + 2\ H^+ \rightleftharpoons V_2O_7^{-4} + H_2O$$

$$V_2O_7^{-4} + VO_4^{-3} + 4\ H^+ \rightleftharpoons V_3O_9^{-3} + 2\ H_2O$$

$$V_3O_9^{-3} + V_2O_7^{-4} + 4\ H^+ \rightleftharpoons V_5O_{14}^{-3} + 2\ H_2O$$

$$2\ V_3O_9^{-3} + 4\ H^+ \rightleftharpoons H_2V_6O_{17}^{-2} + H_2O$$

$$2\ V_5O_{14}^{-3} + 2\ H^+ \rightleftharpoons H_2V_{10}O_{28}^{-4}$$

so WO_4^{-2} gives

$$2\ WO_4^{-2} + 2\ H^+ \rightleftharpoons W_2O_7^{-2} + H_2O$$

$$W_2O_7^{-2} + WO_4^{-2} + 2\ H^+ \rightleftharpoons W_3O_{10}^{-2} + H_2O$$

$$2\ W_2O_7^{-2} + 2\ H^+ \rightleftharpoons W_4O_{13}^{-2} + H_2O$$

$$W_3O_{10}^{-2} + W_2O_7^{-2} + 2\ H^+ \rightleftharpoons W_5O_{16}^{-2} + H_2O$$

$$2\ W_3O_{10}^{-2} + 2\ H^+ \rightleftharpoons W_6O_{19}^{-2} + H_2O$$

$$6\ W_2O_7^{-2} + 2\ H^+ \rightleftharpoons W_{12}O_{41}^{-10} + H_2O$$

(The commercial "tungstate of soda" or "sodium paratungstate" is $Na_{10}W_{12}O_{41} \cdot 28\ H_2O$.)

Just as the polychromates and polyvanadates begin to depolymerize in very concentrated HCl to give simpler compounds

$$Cr_4O_{13}^{-2} + 2\ H^+ + 4\ Cl^- \rightleftharpoons 4\ CrO_3Cl^- + H_2O$$

$$CrO_3Cl^- + 2\ H^+ + Cl^- \rightleftharpoons CrO_2Cl_2 + H_2O$$

$$H_2V_{10}O_{28}^{-4} + 14\ H^+ + 20\ Cl^- \rightleftharpoons 10\ VO_2Cl_2^- + 8\ H_2O$$

$$VO_2Cl_2^- + 2\ H^+ + 2\ Cl^- \rightleftharpoons VOCl_4^- + H_2O$$

so the polytungstates tend to do the same thing. However, because of the lower solubility of the polymerized tungstic acid and its lesser tendency to give reactions like

$$W_{12}O_{41}^{-10} + 34\ H^+ + 36\ Cl^- \rightleftharpoons 12\ WO_2Cl_3^- + 17\ H_2O$$

it is necessary to heat the mixture in order to get the tungsten into solution sufficiently fast to give a practical test with Sn^{+2}.

The next case of a slow reaction is the slow and incomplete precipitation of As_2S_3 from H_3AsO_4 solution. This has been dealt with in Section 5–13, as has also the failure of AsH_3 to be formed from AsO_4^{-3} (Section 15–1). The general case of the precipitation of metal sulfides from CH_3CSNH_2 solutions, however, deserves additional attention.

When thioacetamide is used for precipitation of metal sulfides, either of at least two paths is possible for the reaction: (a) the thioacetamide may first hydrolyze

$$(1) \qquad CH_3CSNH_2 + H_2O \rightleftharpoons CH_3CONH_2 + H_2S$$

the H_2S so formed then reacting with the metal ion in one of the ways described earlier

$$(2) \qquad M^{+2} + H_2S \rightarrow MS\ (s) + 2\ H^+$$

or (b) the thioacetamide may form a compound or a complex with the metal ion which subsequently decomposes hydrolytically

$$(3) \qquad M^{+2} + CH_3CSNH_2 \rightarrow CH_3CSNHM^+ + H^+$$

$$(4) \qquad CH_3CSNHM^+ + H_2O \rightarrow CH_3CONH_2 + MS\ (s) + H^+$$

Swift and Butler have examined the rate of hydrolysis of thioacetamide and compared it at different pH's with the rate of precipitation of PbS from thioacetamide solutions under the same conditions. They found that at pH's less than 3, the rate of precipitation of PbS was identical with the rate of hydrolysis of CH_3CSNH_2. Consequently, under these conditions, hydrolysis of CH_3CSNH_2 must come first in a slow reaction, and subsequently the H_2S produced must react rapidly with Pb^{+2}. On the other hand, at pH's greater than 5, the rate of precipitation of PbS was found to be 1000 times the rate of hydrolysis of CH_3CSNH_2. Consequently, under these conditions, the principal reaction *cannot* be the hydrolysis of CH_3CSNH_2 prior to the precipitation of the PbS. Although this evidence in itself is not sufficient to prove that a complex is formed, there is ample evidence available to show that under similar conditions the heavy metals *do* form thioacetamide complexes. Thus CH_3CSNH_2 gives, with $HgCl_2$, a compound which precipitates as difficultly soluble needles. With CuCl, prisms are formed, while with $CuCl_2$, a *white* precipitate is obtained. With $PtCl_2$, bright yellow crystals, with H_2PtCl_6, a brown-yellow precipitate, and with a mixture of $PtCl_2$ and Na_2PtCl_6, an orange-yellow crystalline precipitate result.

With Bi^{+3}, thioacetamide gives a yellow-green complex. The elements gallium, indium, and thallium likewise form complexes. In the case of Ag^+, the complex which results is extremely unstable with respect to hydrolysis, for even at room temperature, black Ag_2S *immediately* precipitates. The fact that a complex is formed undoubtedly increases the rate of hydrolysis of the thioacetamide, since the metal atom attracts electrons toward itself, making it easier for a water molecule to attach itself to the carbon atom and displace the sulfur.

$$^{+}M : S : C \longleftarrow : O : H \rightleftharpoons\ ^{+}M : S : C : O : H \rightleftharpoons MS + C :: O + H^{+}$$

$$\overset{CH_3}{\underset{HN\quad H}{}} \qquad \overset{CH_3}{\underset{HN^-\quad H^+}{}} \qquad \overset{CH_3}{\underset{HNH}{}}$$

The effect of pH on the mechanism can be seen from equation (3), from which it can be seen that the formation of the complex will be more favored, the lower the H^{+} concentration. Consequently, at low pH's where very little complex is formed, the route through the hydrolysis of CH_3CSNH_2 is predominant. At higher pH's, the complexes become stable and the route through the complex is favored.*

A catalytic reaction which is not met in the ordinary qualitative scheme under ideal conditions, but which may occur when careful control over the separations reactions is not exercised, is the catalytic effect of bismuth on alkali stannite reductions. Ordinarily alkaline stannite will reduce $Pb(OH)_3^{-}$ only on long standing or when warmed, and will reduce $Cd(OH)_2$ not at all. In the presence of traces of $Bi(OH)_3$, however, $Pb(OH)_3^{-}$ is rapidly reduced at room temperature, and $Cd(OH)_2$, in hot solution. The probable action of the bismuth is illustrated in the following equations

$$Bi(OH)_3\ (s) + Sn(OH)_3^{-} \rightarrow Bi^{+} + Sn(OH)_6^{-2}$$

$$Bi^{+} + Pb(OH)_3^{-} \rightarrow Bi(OH)_3\ (s) + Pb\ (s)$$

The reduction of Sb(III), Tl(I), and Cu(II) is likewise accelerated. Consequently, only trace contamination by bismuth salts will produce a positive test for bismuth if, through incomplete separation, lead, cadmium, antimony, thallium, or copper salts are present at the time bismuth is tested for.

The reason for the necessity for heating the reaction mixture in the confirmatory test for antimony is the same as that for heating thioacetamide solutions during the precipitation of sulfides, i.e., to hasten the hydrolysis of the thiosulfatoantimonate complex formed.

$$2\ Sb(S_2O_3)_3^{-3} + 3\ H_2O \rightarrow Sb_2OS_2\ (s) + 2\ SO_4^{-2} + S_2O_3^{-2} + 6\ H^{+}$$

(Although there is no information on the thiosulfatoantimonate complex, comparable complexes are known for Cu, Ag, Zn, Cd, Hg, Tl, Pb, and Bi.)

In like manner, $Ag_2S_2O_3$, white, which precipitates in the anion analysis along with AgCl, AgBr, AgI, and AgSCN if thiosulfate is present, undergoes hydrolysis on standing

$$Ag_2S_2O_3\ (s) + H_2O \rightarrow Ag_2S\ (s) + H^{+} + HSO_4^{-}$$

* After this writing, "A Study of the Mechanism and Intermediates in the Precipitation of Cations with Thioacetamide," by D. Rosenthal and T. I. Taylor, was published in the *Journal of the American Chemical Society*, Vol. 82, (1960), p. 4169.

(The complex, $Ag(S_2O_3)_2^{-3}$, of importance in photography, is much more stable.)

In the precipitation of the insoluble-hydroxide group, advantage is taken of the fact that although $Mn(OH)_2$ is fairly rapidly oxidized by air, $Cr(OH)_3$ is not, although the potentials for the two oxidations are very similar

$$Mn(OH)_2 \text{ (s)} + OH^- \rightarrow Mn(OH)_3 \text{ (s)} + e^- \qquad\qquad E_B^\circ = -0.1 \text{ v}$$

$$Mn(OH)_2 \text{ (s)} + 2 \, OH^- \rightarrow MnO(OH)_2 \text{ (s)} + H_2O + 2 \, e^- \qquad E_B^\circ = 0.05 \text{ v}$$

$$Cr(OH)_3 \text{ (s)} + 5 \, OH^- \rightarrow CrO_4^{-2} + 4 \, H_2O + 3 \, e^- \qquad\qquad E_B^\circ = 0.13 \text{ v}$$

$$(4 \, OH^- \rightarrow O_2 \text{ (g)} + 4 \, H^+ + 4 \, e^- \qquad\qquad E_B^\circ = -0.401 \text{ v})$$

The explanation of the different rates of oxidation lies in the fact that chromium has no oxidation states between $+3$ and $+6$ which are stable in dilute alkali, whereas manganese does have $(Mn(OH)_3, Mn_3O_4, MnO_2)$. Consequently, the simple oxidation steps which manganese undergoes

$$Mn(OH)_2 \text{ (s)} + O_2 \text{ (g)} + OH^- \rightarrow Mn(OH)_3 \text{ (s)} + O_2^-$$

or $\qquad Mn(OH)_2 \text{ (s)} + O_2 \text{ (g)} + OH^- \rightarrow MnO(OH)_2 \text{ (s)} + HO_2^-$

are not available to chromium.

An interesting sidelight on manganese oxidations is the following, which shows one of the effects of other substances which may be present. If MnO, intimately mixed with Al_2O_3, is subjected to atmospheric oxidation, Mn_2O_3 results. If, however, the MnO is mixed with TiO_2, the product is MnO_2. Since Al_2O_3 has the same crystal structure as one form of Mn_2O_3, and TiO_2 has the same structure as MnO_2, it is obvious that the degree of oxidation of the MnO has been dictated by the structure of the substance with which it is mixed.

One of the reactions which is to be avoided in the analysis for chromium is the reduction of Cr(VI) to Cr(III), either when the alkaline solution in which the H_2O_2-oxidation was carried out is acidified, or during the confirmation of chromium (and vanadium) as the peroxy complex. The reduction of chromate by hydrogen peroxide in acidic solution is a slow reaction. Although this reaction itself has not been studied in detail, its probable course can be given by analogy with the reaction of chromic acid and alcohols. The first step of this latter reaction is the addition of the alcohol to the acid to form a chromate ester

$$
\begin{array}{ccc}
\text{H} & \overset{..}{:}\text{O}\overset{..}{:} & \text{H} \quad \overset{..}{:}\text{O}\overset{..}{:} \\
\overset{..}{\text{R}:\text{C}:\text{O}:\text{H}} \!\!\!\!\! & + \;\; \text{H}:\text{O}:\text{Cr}:\text{O}:\text{H} & \rightarrow \;\; \text{R}:\text{C}:\text{O}:\text{Cr}:\text{O}:\text{H} \;\; + \;\; \text{H}_2\text{O} \\
\text{H} & \overset{..}{:}\text{O}\overset{..}{:} & \text{H} \qquad \overset{..}{:}\text{O}\overset{..}{:}
\end{array}
$$

(R is any organic group.) The ester now undergoes a relatively slow decomposition by "heterolytic cleavage" of the bond between the chromium and the oxygen of the alcohol—i.e., both electrons of the bond go to the chromium, which now becomes Cr(IV)

$$R:\overset{\displaystyle H}{\underset{\displaystyle H}{C}}:\ddot{O} \Big\} :\overset{\displaystyle :\ddot{O}:}{\underset{\displaystyle :\ddot{O}:}{Cr}}:\ddot{O}:H \quad\to\quad R:\overset{\displaystyle H}{\underset{\displaystyle H}{C}}:\ddot{O}^+ \ +\ CrO_3H^-$$

The electron-deficiency of the oxygen in the organic fragment causes rearrangement of the electrons with production of an aldehyde or ketone and loss of a hydrogen ion to the solvent.

$$R:\overset{\displaystyle H}{\underset{\displaystyle H}{C}}:\ddot{O}^+ \to R:\overset{\displaystyle H}{C}::\ddot{O} \ +\ H^+$$

The unstable chromium(IV) undergoes disproportionation or oxidizes the water

$$3\ CrO_3H^- + 9\ H^+ \to 2\ Cr^{+3} + H_2CrO_4 + 5\ H_2O$$

$$4\ CrO_3H^- + 16\ H^+ \to 4\ Cr^{+3} + O_2\ (g) + 10\ H_2O$$

The slowness of the reaction is probably due both to the drastic rearrangement of bonds required, and also to the fact that the chromium must go first to the unstable +4 state. (That chromium(IV) is formed in this reaction has been definitely established by F. W. Westheimer and co-workers.)

The reaction between chromate and H_2O_2 in acidic solution can be viewed in the same light. The first step is the relatively rapid addition of H_2O_2 to the chromate (which is again shown as H_2CrO_4, although under the conditions usually prevailing it is more likely $Cr_2O_7^{-2}$ or $HCrO_4^-$).

$$H:\ddot{O}:\ddot{O}:H \ +\ H:\ddot{O}:\overset{\displaystyle :\ddot{O}:}{\underset{\displaystyle :\ddot{O}:}{Cr}}:\ddot{O}:H \quad\to\quad H:\ddot{O}:\ddot{O}:\overset{\displaystyle :\ddot{O}:}{\underset{\displaystyle :\ddot{O}:}{Cr}}:\ddot{O}:H \ +\ H_2O$$

That this happens is demonstrated by the appearance of the blue peroxychromic acid under appropriate conditions. By analogy with the ester decomposition, the peroxychromic acid now undergoes slow heterolytic cleavage at the chromium–peroxide bond.

$$H:\ddot{O}:\ddot{O} \Big\} :\overset{\displaystyle :\ddot{O}:}{\underset{\displaystyle :\ddot{O}:}{Cr}}:\ddot{O}:H \quad\to\quad H:\ddot{O}:\ddot{O}^+ \ +\ CrO_3H^-$$

The HOO^+ ion now undergoes rearrangement to satisfy the electron-deficient oxygen

$$HOO^+ \rightarrow O_2 \, (g) + H^+$$

The slowness of precipitation of $MgNH_4PO_4$, CaC_2O_4, and $NaZn$-$(UO_2)_3(C_2H_3O_2)_9 \cdot 6 \, H_2O$ observed in the analysis of the alkali and alkaline-earth groups is primarily a matter of slowness of nucleation, which has been discussed in Section 3–3.

In the analysis for anions, a number of slow reactions are met. The first of these, while not of great importance in *qualitative* analysis, is important in quantitative analysis and biology. That is the slow decomposition of carbonic acid

$$H_2CO_3 \rightleftharpoons H_2O + CO_2$$

When an acid is added to a carbonate or when a bottle of a carbonated beverage is opened, there is an immediate release of much of the CO_2 which is dissolved as such. This is followed by the slow evolution of more bubbles of CO_2 as the H_2CO_3 undergoes its slow decomposition reaction. In quantitative analysis, the slowness of liberation of CO_2 when carbonates are titrated with acid gives a false endpoint to the titrations. Heating the solutions, however, hastens the reaction and drives the CO_2 out of solution. In living organisms, slowness of release of CO_2 from the bloodstream would be a serious difficulty. In the lungs, however, the reaction is catalyzed by an enzyme (organic catalyst), carbonic anhydrase. The activation energy for the decomposition is about 19 kcal per mole. The reaction probably requires first the allocation of two hydrogen ions to the same oxygen atom, followed by splitting of the carbon–oxygen bond before one of the hydrogens has a chance to leave

$$O=C=OH^+ + H_2O \rightarrow CO_2 + OH_3^+$$

Another slow reaction is that between MnO_4^- and $H_2C_2O_4$. The reaction of MnO_4^- with most reducing agents in acidic solution is characterized by an initial slowness. The reaction is strongly hastened as the Mn^{+2} increases during the reaction, or by addition of manganese(II) salts on purpose at the beginning. Manganese(II) is found to react with MnO_4^- fairly rapidly to produce low concentrations of Mn^{+3} and MnO^{+2}. These latter then rapidly oxidize the reducing agent. A possible course of reaction is

$$Mn^{+2} + MnO_4^- \rightleftharpoons MnO^{+2} + MnO_3^-$$

$$Mn^{+2} + MnO_3^- \rightleftharpoons MnO^{+2} + MnO_2^-$$

$$MnO_2^- + 4 H^+ \rightleftharpoons Mn^{+3} + 2 H_2O$$

Using SO_3^{-2} as a representative reducing agent, then

$$MnO^{+2} + SO_3^{-2} \rightleftharpoons Mn^{+2} + SO_4^{-2}$$

$$Mn^{+3} + SO_3^{-2} \rightleftharpoons Mn^{+2} + SO_3^-$$

$$2 SO_3^- \rightleftharpoons S_2O_6^{-2}$$

In the reaction between MnO_4^- and $H_2C_2O_4$, the situation is further complicated by the formation of oxalato complexes, which then must undergo slow internal oxidation and reduction

$$MnO_3^- + H_2C_2O_4 \rightleftharpoons MnO_2C_2O_4^- + H_2O$$

$$MnO_2C_2O_4^- \rightarrow MnO_2^- + 2 CO_2$$

$$Mn^{+3} + C_2O_4^{-2} \rightleftharpoons MnC_2O_4^+$$

$$MnC_2O_4^+ \rightarrow Mn^{+2} + CO_2 + CO_2^-$$

$$Mn^{+3} + CO_2^- \rightarrow Mn^{+2} + CO_2$$

(see Section 15–4). Several of these steps are slow, and it is necessary to raise the temperature in order to get the reaction to go at a reasonable rate.

Another reaction which may require heating is the precipitation of ammonium molybdophosphate in the confirmatory test for phosphate. It must be remembered that in acidic solution molybdate exists in a complicated polymeric form (see tungstate, above). For example, the following species are known: pH 14–6.5, MoO_4^{-2}; pH 6.3–4.5, $Mo_3O_{11}^{-4}$; pH 4.5–1.5, $Mo_6O_{21}^{-6}$; pH 1.25, $Mo_{12}O_{41}^{-10}$; pH 1.0, $Mo_{24}O_{78}^{-12}$. It is necessary to unscramble the complicated isopolymolybdic acid and rearrange the units appropriately in an orderly fashion around a core of a phosphate ion in order to obtain the complicated but symmetrical heteropolymolybdophosphoric acid.

$$Mo_{24}O_{78}^{-12} + 2 PO_4^{-3} + 12 H^+ \rightarrow 2 PMo_{12}O_{40}^{-3} + 6 H_2O$$

Such a complicated rearrangement must necessarily be slow.

In the brown-ring test for nitrite and nitrate, these two ions are distinguished by their different rates of reaction with iron(II) salts, the reaction of nitrite

$$NO_2^- + 2 Fe^{+2} + 2 H^+ \rightleftharpoons FeNO^{+2} + Fe^{+3} + H_2O$$

proceeding much faster than the reaction of nitrate

$$NO_3^- + 4 Fe^{+3} + 4 H^+ \rightleftharpoons FeNO^{+2} + 3 Fe^{+3} + 2 H_2O$$

That the rate of the reaction of nitrate is dependent upon pH is shown by the fact that, whereas both reactions run fairly rapidly in concentrated H_2SO_4, in glacial acetic acid in which the pH is not nearly so low, only the reaction of nitrite takes place, the nitrate reaction being so slow as no longer to compete. Since in concentrated H_2SO_4 the species present are probably $H_2Fe(SO_4)_2$ and NO_2^+, it is probable that a salt such as $NO_2HFe(SO_4)_2$ is formed, which then undergoes internal oxidation and reduction

$$NO_2HFe(SO_4)_2 \rightarrow NO_2 + HFe(SO_4)_2$$

$$2 NO_2 + 3 H_2SO_4 \rightarrow NO^+ + NO_2^+ + OH_3^+ + 3 HSO_4^-$$

The NO_2^+ so produced goes through the process again, while the NO^+ (either from this reaction or from HNO_2) undergoes the reaction

$$NOHFe(SO_4)_2 \rightarrow NO + HFe(SO_4)_2$$

$$NO + H_2Fe(SO_4)_2 \rightarrow FeNO^{+2} + 2 HSO_4^-$$

The difference between nitrous and nitric acids probably lies in the difference in their strengths as bases. Nitrous acid is a much stronger base than nitric with respect to the reactions

$$HNO_2 + H^+ \rightleftharpoons NO^+ + H_2O$$

$$HNO_3 + H^+ \rightleftharpoons NO_2^+ + H_2O$$

Consequently, the weak acetic acid can produce an appreciable concentration of NO^+, but not of NO_2^+.

One more example which will be considered is the rate of hydrolysis of cyano complexes. It has been noted (Section 11–15) that the hexacyano-ferrate(II) ion, $Fe(CN)_6^{-4}$, (K_6 inst = 5×10^{-9}) is very resistant to hydrolysis. On the other hand, the dicyanoaurate(I) ion, which is thermodynamically much more stable against dissociation (K_2 inst $\approx 10^{-16}$) is rapidly hydrolyzed. (A calculation for stability would be one to determine the concentration of free cyanide ion present in a 1-molar solution of the complex.) Making the crude assumptions,

    (1) $[CN^-]$ = $[Fe(CN)_5^{-3}]$ and (2) $[CN^-]$ = $[AuCN]$ ag

        (1) $[CN^-]^2$ = 5×10^{-9}

           $[CN^-]$ = $7 \times 10^{-5} M$

        (2) $[CN^-]^2$ = 10^{-16}

           $[CN^-]$ = $10^{-8} M$

The reason for the much greater rapidity of hydrolysis of $Au(CN)_2^-$

$$Au(CN)_2^- + OH^- \rightarrow Au(OH)CN^- + CN^-$$

lies in the difference in electronic structure. The gold atom has unused valence orbitals

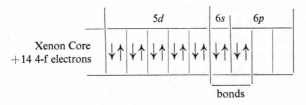

so that a hydroxide ion can easily add

$$Au(CN)_2{}^- + OH^- \rightarrow Au(CN)_2OH^{-2}$$

giving electronic structure

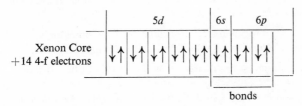

and then a cyanide ion dissociate

$$Au(CN)_2OH^{-2} \rightarrow Au(OH)CN^- + CN^-$$

to give the hydrolyzed product. The iron atom, on the other hand, has no unused valence orbitals, the electronic structure being

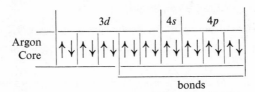

Consequently hydrolysis must await prior dissociation of the complex to make an orbital available.

$$Fe(CN)_6{}^{-4} \rightleftharpoons Fe(CN)_5{}^{-3} + CN^-$$

$$Fe(CN)_5{}^{-3} + OH^- \rightarrow Fe(CN)_5OH^{-4}$$

Since K_{inst} for this dissociation is small (5×10^{-9}), this will be a very slow process in comparison to the hydrolysis of $Au(CN)_2{}^-$.

The cases considered in this chapter are in no way complete, and certainly many of the mechanisms suggested are speculative. It is hoped, however, that the student will hereby have gained some appreciation of the complexities of chemical reactions and some insight into their mechanisms.

15–10.   References

Electrode Processes, A General Discussion of the Faraday Society, No. 1. London: Gurney and Jackson, 1947.

The Kinetics and Mechanism of Inorganic Reactions in Solution ("Special Publication No. 1"). London: The Chemical Society, 1954.

Glasstone, S., and Hickling, A., *Electrolytic Oxidation and Reduction*. New York: D. Van Nostrand Company, Inc., 1936.

Allen, M. J., *Organic Electrode Processes*. New York: Reinhold Publishing Corporation, 1958.

Yost, D. M., and Russell, H., *Systematic Inorganic Chemistry*. Englewood Cliffs, N.J.: Prentice-Hall, Inc., 1946.

Basolo, F., and Pearson, R. G., *Mechanisms of Inorganic Reactions*. New York: John Wiley and Sons, Inc., 1958.

Waters, W. A., "Mechanisms of Oxidation by Compounds of Chromium and Manganese," *Quarterly Reviews*, Vol. XII (1958), p. 277.

Westheimer, F. H., and others, "The Kinetics of the Oxidation of Isopropyl Alcohol by Chromic Acid," *Journal of Chemical Physics*, Vol. 11 (1943), p. 506. "The Mechanisms of Chromic Acid Oxidations," *Chemical Reviews*, Vol. 45 (1949), p. 419. "The Kinetics of the Oxidation of 2-Deuteropropanol-2 by Chromic Acid," *Journal of the American Chemical Society*, Vol. 71 (1949), p. 25. "The Chemistry of Diisopropyl Chromate," *Ibid*, Vol. 74 (1952), p. 4383. "The Chromic Acid Oxidation of Isopropyl Alcohol in 86.5 % Acetic Acid Solution. The Chemistry of the Chlorochromate Ion," *Ibid*, Vol. 74 (1952), p. 4387. "The Mechanism of the Cleavage of Phenyl-*t*-butylcarbinol by Chromic Acid," *Ibid*, Vol. 78 (1956), p. 306. "The Kinetics of the Chromic Acid Oxidation of Benzaldehyde," *Ibid*, Vol. 80 (1958), p. 3030.

Swift, E. H., and Butler, E. A., *Analytical Chemistry*, Vol. 28 (1956), p. 146.

Dainton, F. S., *Chain Reactions, An Introduction*. New York: John Wiley and Sons, Inc., 1956.

Stott, R. H., *Electronic Theory and Chain Reactions*. New York: Longmans, Green and Company, 1943.

Chapter *16*

Apparent Anomalies in the Periodic Table

16–1. Irregularities in Atomic Radii

Before it is possible to understand irregularities in chemical behavior, it is necessary to understand the irregularities in atomic structure which underlie them. One of the simplest periodic functions of the elements is the radius, and yet it is found upon examination that it varies in a fashion which is by no means regular. There are several different radii which may be considered—covalent radii of different sorts, van der Waals' radii, and ionic radii of ions of different charges. All of these vary in much the same way and for the same reasons. Unfortunately it is not possible to find a single consistent set of radii in terms of which the whole periodic table can be discussed, so it will be necessary to use different types of radii from time to time during the discussion. Altogether, however, the subject will be seen to give a consistent picture. The principal consideration is that as the atomic number is increased the radius decreases, *so long as the electrons are added to the same quantum level.* As electrons are added to each new quantum level, the radius increases. Let us consider some examples, first, however, defining the different types of radius. The radius of an atom is the closest distance to which it will approach another atom under the circumstances specified. The three different types of radius mentioned above can be illustrated with chlorine as an example. The ionic radius of the chloride ion is the radius it exhibits in a crystal like NaCl in which the Na^+ and Cl^- ions are packed together with their outermost shells of electrons in contact with each other (see Fig. 1–8). If the radius of the Na^+ ion is taken to be 0.98 Å (i.e., 0.98×10^{-8} cm), then the radius of the Cl^- ion must be 1.81 Å, since the distance between the centers of adjacent Na^+ and Cl^- ions is 2.79 Å. Again in the LiCl crystal, in which the Li^+ ions are so small that the neighboring Cl^- ions actually touch each other, the distance between the centers of neighboring Cl^- ions is 3.62 Å, so that the radius of each Cl^- ion must be 1.81 Å.

The covalent radius is the apparent radius of an atom toward another to which it is covalently bonded. For example, the distance between the centers of the two chlorine atoms in the Cl_2 molecule is 1.98 Å, so that the covalent radius of chlorine is 0.99 Å. In the same way, the distance between atoms in Br_2 is 2.28 Å. Consequently it should be expected that the distance between the two atoms in the BrCl molecule will be 2.13 Å (the sum of the covalent radii of Br and Cl).

The van der Waals' radius is the radius of closest approach of an atom to another with which it forms no bond. For nonmetals, the van der Waals' radius is close to the anion radius. Thus, in crystalline chlorine, the atoms within the molecules are 1.98 Å apart, but the atoms in neighboring molecules are 3.62 Å apart, so that the individual radii of the two nonbonded atoms in contact (the van der Waals' radii) are 1.81 Å.

One other kind of radius which may be informative is the radius of metal atoms in metal crystals. This cannot be described in terms of such simple electronic structures as the other types of radius.

The effect of increasing atomic number (i.e., nuclear charge) can be seen on both the covalent and the van der Waals' radii of the second period elements.

	Li	Be	B	C	N	O	F	Ne
Covalent Radius (Å)	1.33	1.07	0.89	0.77	0.75	0.74	0.72	
Van der Waals' Radius (Å)			2.08	1.85	1.54	1.40	1.33	1.60

The increase in radius exhibited by neon is characteristic of the last member of the series where the electron shell is finally closed.

As the electronic structure is compressed more toward the end of the period, it will resist further compression more firmly. This results in a decrease in the rate at which the size changes. For example, although there is a difference of 0.26 Å between the covalent radii of lithium and beryllium, there is a difference of only 0.02 Å between oxygen and fluorine. This trend is carried over into the next period. Since the L electrons are already somewhat crowded, the L shell will resist further compression as the M electrons are added. This can be seen in the comparison of the second and the third periods, the over-all decrease being more in the second period (0.61 Å from Li to F) than in the third period (0.58 Å from Na to Cl).

	Na	Mg	Al	Si	P	S	Cl
Covalent Radii (Å)	1.57	1.36	1.25	1.17	1.10	1.04	0.99

Again, in the fifth period, the inner electrons resist further compression so strongly that the rate of decrease in the fifth period (0.83 Å from Rb to I) is less than that in the fourth (0.88 Å from K to Br). The rate of decrease in size continues to diminish throughout the rest of the periodic table.

The effect of increasing nuclear charge on *ionic* size can be seen in the radii of the M^{+3} ions of the lanthanide (rare-earth) elements.

	La^{+3}	Ce^{+3}	Pr^{+3}	Nd^{+3}	Pm^{+3}	Sm^{+3}	Eu^{+3}	Gd^{+3}	Tb^{+3}	Dy^{+3}
Ionic Radius	1.04	1.02	1.00	0.99	0.98	0.97	0.97	0.95	0.93	0.91
Number of f electrons	0	1	2	3	4	5	6	7	8	9

	Ho^{+3}	Er^{+3}	Tu^{+3}	Yb^{+3}	Lu^{+3}
Ionic Radius	0.89	0.87	0.85	0.84	0.83
Number of f electrons	10	11	12	13	14

The electronic changes which are taking place are occurring so deep within the atom (in the $4f$ orbitals) that there is almost no effect on the ionic radii. This kind of diminution in atomic size within a period as the nuclear charge increases is known as the "lanthanide contraction." Although first recognized for the lanthanide elements, it is by no means confined to them.

The modifications of the normal contraction brought about by location of *valence* electrons in different energy levels are exemplified by the atomic radii of the lanthanide elements in the crystalline metals.

	La	Ce	Pr	Nd	Pm	Sm	Eu	Gd
Radius (Å)	1.690	1.646	1.648	1.642		1.66	1.850	1.614
No. of electrons								
$6s$	2	2	2	2	2	2	2	2
$5d$	1	1	0	0	0	0	0	1
$4f$	0	1	3	4	5	6	7	7

	Tb	Dy	Ho	Er	Tu	Yb	Lu
Radius (Å)	1.592	1.589	1.580	1.567	1.562	1.699	1.557
No. of electrons							
$6s$	2	2	2	2	2	2	2
$5d$	0	0	0	0	0	0	1
$4f$	9	10	11	12	13	14	14

Note the distinct increase in size at europium and ytterbium, where the $4f$ level is exactly half or completely filled.

In the case of the ions of the first transition series, the $3d$ level, into which the electrons are being put, is essentially a valence level. Again, the changes in structure are reflected in changes in size superimposed upon the general contraction.

	Ca^{+2}	(Sc^{+2})	Ti^{+2}	V^{+2}	Cr^{+2}	Mn^{+2}	Fe^{+2}	Co^{+2}	Ni^{+2}	Cu^{+2}
Radius (Å)	1.06	———	0.76(?)	0.82	0.80	0.83	0.80	0.78	0.74	0.72
No. of electrons										
$4s$										
$3d$	0	1	2	3	4	5	6	7	8	9

	Zn^{+2}	(Ga^{+2})	Ge^{+2}
Radius (Å)	0.75	———	0.65
No. of electrons			
$4s$		1	2
$3d$	10	10	10

Again note the marked increase in radius at Mn^{+2} and Zn^{+2}, when the $3d$ level is half or completely filled.

On the other hand, going down the periodic table, as electrons are added to new shells, the radius usually increases. This is illustrated in the cases of the alkali-metal and the halogen covalent radii.

Covalent Radii (Å)

Li	1.225	F	0.72
Na	1.572	Cl	0.994
K	2.025	Br	1.142
Rb	2.16	I	1.334
Cs	2.35		

These data also illustrate the increase in size from the end of one period to the beginning of the next.

On the other hand, the covalent radii of the titanium-family elements show a reversal between zirconium and hafnium.

Covalent Radii (Å)

Sc	1.44	Ti	1.32	V	1.22	Cr	1.17	Mn	1.17	Fe	1.17
Y	1.62	Zr	1.45	Nb	1.34	Mo	1.29	Tc		Ru	1.24
La	1.69	Hf	1.44	Ta	1.34	W	1.30	Re	1.28	Os	1.26

The reason for this is that, although there are no elements between yttrium and zirconium, there are the fourteen rare-earth elements between lanthanum and hafnium, whose radii steadily decrease from La to Lu, so that although La is larger than Y, Lu (1.56 Å) is distinctly smaller than Y. Correspondingly, Hf is slightly smaller than Zr. Passing to the right, however, the lower rate of decrease in size of the sixth-period elements compared with the fifth-period elements results in the former slowly becoming larger again than the corresponding ones of the fifth period.

Because of the size relationships, the chemistries of zirconium and hafnium are almost identical—they can be separated from each other only with the greatest difficulty. Niobium and tantalum are also very much alike, and even molybdenum and tungsten are very similar. The size relationships also account for the fact that, although electronegativity decreases down the columns on the extreme right and extreme left of the periodic table, in the center it increases (see Section 1–9).

16–2. Irregularities in Electronic Structure

In Section 10–1 (cf. Appendix 8) there appear several irregularities in electronic structure which were not explained. The usual "explanation" given for why chromium (for example) has the structure $3d^5\,4s^1$, instead of $3d^4\,4s^2$, is that the "half-filled sublevel is especially stable." A more fundamental reason can be found in the energy relationships involved.

It must first be realized that the picture of the energy levels in the atom given in Chapter 10 was oversimplified. The impression was probably gained that the energy levels described have the same relationship in all atoms. This however is not true. It is fairly easy to see that as the nuclear charge is increased the electrons in the $1s$ level (for example) will be more and more strongly held. It will require more energy to remove them from the atom, and therefore from our point of view their energy (or the energy of the $1s$ quantum level) has decreased. The same will be true of the $2s$ and $2p$ levels. However, *the effect of increasing nuclear charge on levels of different l values is not the same.* The rate at which the energy of the quantum levels decreases with increasing nuclear charge increases with increasing values of *l*. Consequently the rate of decrease of energy becomes greater in the order $s < p < d < f$, and so on, for which $l = 0, 1, 2, 3$, and so on. The result is that

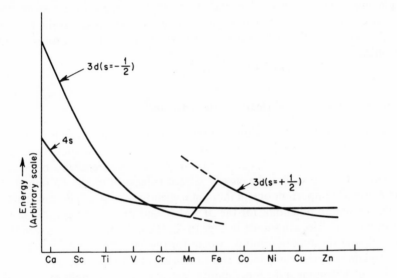

Fig. 16–1. Idealized Relationship between 3d and 4s Levels.

although the $4s$ level is lower than the $3d$ for scandium ($Z = 21$), by the time chromium ($Z = 24$) is reached, the reverse is so. So far we have been dealing only with d electrons of spin $-\frac{1}{2}$. Beginning with iron ($Z = 26$), however, d electrons of spin $+\frac{1}{2}$ must be added, i.e., the d electrons must be paired. Since the pairs have higher energy, the $3d$ level once more climbs above the $4s$. However, by the time copper ($Z = 29$) is reached, the $3d$ level has once more subsided below the $4s$. An idealized graph of these relationships is shown in Fig. 16–1. It is the result of the $3d$ level falling below the $4s$, then, which causes chromium to have structure $3d^5 4s^1$ and copper to have $3d^{10} 4s^1$. That it is not due to any innate "desire" on the part of the d level to be exactly half-filled is shown by the fact that in the second transition series, due to the energy levels' crossing earlier, the shift comes before there are enough electrons to give a half-filled $4d$ level. Thus we have Zr, $4d^2 5s^2$, and Nb, $4d^4 5s^1$. As a matter of fact, in this period the $5s$ level is never again far enough below the $4d$ to be able to hold two electrons. Therefore, after Mo, $4d^5 5s^1$, we have Tc, $4d^6 5s^1$, Ru, $4d^7 5s^1$, and Rh, $4d^8 5s^1$, and by this time the $4d$ level has fallen so far below the $5s$ that all of the electrons fall into the $4d$ in Pd, $4d^{10} 5s^0$. Nevertheless, there is usually a sufficient energy gap between a half-filled or completely filled sublevel and the next sublevel (or spin difference) to give the former the appearance of especial stability by comparison. Consequently, the notion is still a very useful one. The other irregularities of electronic structure are explainable by arguments of the same sort.

The question now arises: If the $3d$ electrons have higher energy than the $4s$ (in cobalt, for example), why is the structure of Co^{+2} $3d^7 4s^0$? Ignoring effects such as solvation, a simple answer can be seen in the effect expected of placing a positive charge on the atom. This amounts to increasing the nuclear charge. All the electrons remaining are drawn closer to the nucleus and the cobalt is effectively moved to the right in Fig. 16–1. Consequently the ionization gives

$$Co\ (4s^2\, 3d^7) \rightarrow Co^{+2}\ (3d^7\, 4s^0) + 2\ e^-$$

16–3. Irregularities in Oxidation State (Metals)

The irregularities in electronic structure discussed above result in irregularities of other properties as well, such as ionization energies, oxidation potentials, and so forth. A consideration of ionization energies is outside the scope of this text, but the closely related subject of oxidation potentials is an extremely important one in inorganic chemistry, and will be considered.

The oxidation potentials for the M^0–M^{+2} and M^{+2}–M^{+3} couples of the first transition series are shown in Fig. 16–2. It can immediately be seen that although a fairly smooth trend is evident for the M^0–M^{+2} couples, there are four deviant couples, manganese and zinc being much more positive than the trend, and chromium and copper more negative (chromium only very slightly so). The high positive values for the manganese and zinc couples reflect the fact that the $4s$ electrons for these elements lie clearly higher in energy than the half-filled and completely filled d levels, which results in especially easy removal of these electrons. The low potentials (algebraically speaking) for the chromium and copper couples reflect the fact that in each case one electron must be taken from the half-filled or completely filled d level. The fact that the $3d$ level has fallen farther below the $4s$ level in copper than in chromium is shown by its greater deviation from the trend.

The same effect can be seen in the M^{+2}–M^{+3} couples. The potential for the Fe^{+2}–Fe^{+3} couple is much more positive than the trend, because the sixth $3d$ electron of iron ($s = +\frac{1}{2}$), being paired, lies energetically distinctly above the five $3d$ electrons ($s = -\frac{1}{2}$) which constitute the half-filled level. Presumably the Sc^{+2}–Sc^{+3} couple also lies higher than the trend, possibly even more positive than the Sc^0–Sc^{+2} couple, so that Sc^{+2} is unstable with respect to disproportionation into Sc^0 and Sc^{+3}. (Scandium is not known to form any $+2$ compounds.)

On the other hand, the Mn^{+2}–Mn^{+3} and Zn^{+2}–Zn^{+3} couples are more negative than the trend because, to obtain the $+3$ ion, an electron must be removed from the half-filled or completely filled $3d$ level. This, in fact, makes the Zn^{+2}–Zn^{+3} couple so negative that no zinc(III) compounds are known at all. (The Cr^{+2}–Cr^{+3} couple is also found to be more positive than expected, presumably because of the complexity of Cr(III) salts.)

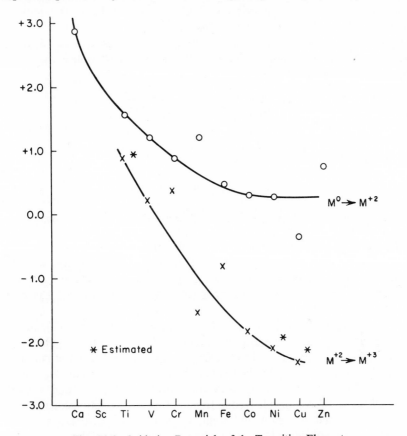

Fig. 16–2. Oxidation Potentials of the Transition Elements.

The electronic structure of complexes also has considerable to do with their oxidation potentials and stability. For example, although Fe^{+2} is more easily oxidized to Fe^{+3} than Co^{+2} is to Co^{+3}, the opposite is true of the cyanide complexes.

$$Fe^{+2} \rightarrow Fe^{+3} \qquad\qquad E° = +0.77 \text{ v}$$

$$Co^{+2} \rightarrow Co^{+3} \qquad\qquad E° = -1.84 \text{ v}$$

$$Fe(CN)_6{}^{-4} \rightarrow Fe(CN)_6{}^{-3} \qquad\qquad E° = -0.36 \text{ v}$$

$$Co(CN)_5{}^{-3} \rightarrow Co(CN)_6{}^{-3} \qquad\qquad E° = +0.83 \text{ v}$$

The reason for this is that $Fe(CN)_6^{-4}$ and $Co(CN)_6^{-3}$ have krypton electronic structure, which is particularly stable. It is because the inner complexes of Co(III) have krypton structure that they are so very stable, even though Co^{+3} itself is not (i.e., $Co(H_2O)_6^{+3}$ is not an inner complex and does not have krypton structure). Thus we find stable complexes such as $Co(CN)_6^{-3}$, $Co(NH_3)_6^{+3}$, $Co(NO_2)_6^{-3}$, $Co(C_2O_4)_3^{-3}$, $Co(SO_3)_3^{-3}$, and many others. A complete description of all the known cobalt(III) complexes would fill several volumes the size of this one.

Nickel(IV), which in inner six-coordinate complexes also has krypton structure, is also much more stable than Ni^{+4} ion. An example is the ortho-phenylenediarsine complex, shown in Fig. 16–3.

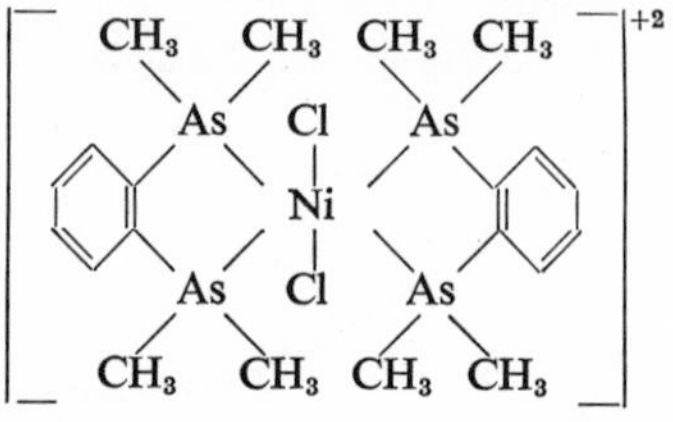

Fig. 16–3. Bis[orthophenylenebis(dimethylarsine)]dichloronickel(IV) Ion.

In the same manner, simple Mn^+ is not stable in aqueous solution, but Mn(I) can be obtained in the complex $Mn(CN)_6^{-5}$, which has krypton structure. Again the compound $Cr(CO)_6$, a compound of chromium(0) has krypton-like structure. Even a complex of V(−I) with dipyridyl has been claimed.

One case of great irregularity is that of the common oxidation states of Cu, Ag, and Au. To the beginning student, if he sees any regularity of oxidation states at all, it is always perplexing to be told that the common states of the three very closely related elements Cu, Ag, and Au are all different—and not only that, but they are respectively +2, +1, and +3, not even following a recognizable trend. In actual fact, the relationships are not nearly so confused as they would seem. If the trend of each state from Cu to Ag to Au is considered, it is found to be regular. It is the interplay of the three trends that brings about the apparent irregularities. Going in each case from Cu to Ag to Au, we find that the +1 state becomes a progressively better oxidant—i.e., the standard oxidation potential for the M^0–M^+ couple becomes more negative. The +2 state likewise becomes a better oxidant (considering the M^+–M^{+2} couple), but much more rapidly than the +1 state. Furthermore, the +2 state (in Cu^{+2}) starts out more stable than the +1. The +3 state, on the other hand, becomes progressively more stable (i.e., a poorer oxidant). The explanation usually given is that as the electronegativity increases the lower ionic states (+1 and +2) become less stable, while the higher covalent state (+3) becomes more stable. The result is shown in Figure 16–4, where the numbers represent the higher oxidation state of the one-electron couple (i.e., (2) represents the M^+-M^{+2} couple). If a low oxidation state occurs higher in the diagram than a higher state then it is unstable with respect to disproportionation into the higher and the zero states, or any lower state below it in the diagram. Thus, Cu^+ is unstable ($2\ Cu^+ \rightarrow Cu^0 + Cu^{+2}$), while Cu^{+3} is stable to disproportionation but oxidizes water. All states of silver are stable to disproportionation, but both Ag^{+2} and Ag^{+3} oxidize water. With gold, Au^+ is unstable ($3\ Au^+ \rightarrow 2\ Au^0 + Au^{+3}$, but *not* $2\ Au^+ \rightarrow Au^0 + Au^{+2}$), while Au^{+2} is very unstable

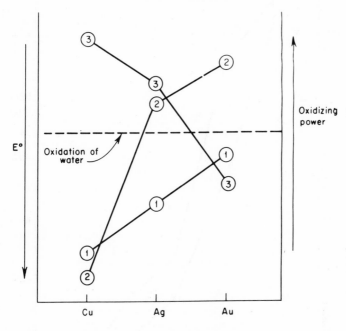

Fig. 16-4. Relationship of Oxidation States of Cu, Ag and Au.

($2\ Au^{+2} \rightarrow Au^+ + Au^{+3}$, and especially $3\ Au^{+2} \rightarrow Au^0 + 2\ Au^{+3}$) and in addition oxidizes water. The result, therefore, is that Cu^{+2}, Ag^+, and Au^{+3} are the usual oxidation states for these elements in aqueous solution.

Another irregularity in oxidation potentials occurs in the alkali metals, where we find

	Li	Na	K	Rb	Cs
E°	3.045	2.714	2.925	2.925	3.02

for the M^0-M^+ couples in water. In order to explain this trend, it is necessary to realize that, to a first approximation, the oxidation potential arises from a combination of the ionization energy (which opposes the process) and the hydration energy of the ion (which favors the process). As in the case of the solubilities of the alkali salts (see Section 3-6), *both* of these energies decrease from Li to Cs. Consequently, the important thing is which decreases more rapidly. The very high oxidation potential of lithium is a result of the high hydration energy of the very small lithium ion. At

	Li	Na	K	Rb	Cs
Ionization Potential (ev)	5.390	5.138	4.339	4.176	3.893
Hydration Energy (kcal)	123	97	77	70	63

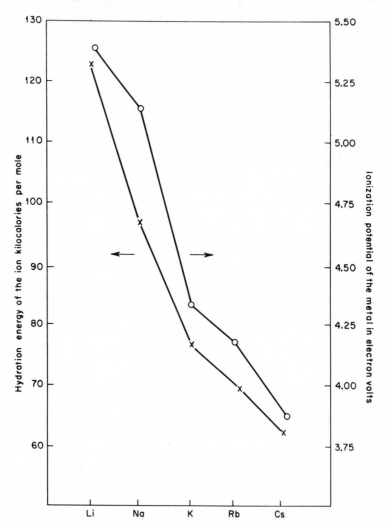

Fig. 16–5. Comparison of Ionization Potentials and Hydration Energies of the Alkali Metals.

first, the hydration energy falls off faster than the ionization potential, so that the oxidation potential decreases, but eventually the hydration energy falls off less rapidly than the ionization potential, so that the oxidation potential again rises, and for cesium is almost as high as for lithium.

16–4. Irregularities in Oxidation State (Nonmetals)

In Section 14–2 (Table 14–3) it was pointed out that the stability of the covalent binary hydrides decreases as one moves away from fluorine in the periodic table (i.e., the hydrides become progressively stronger reducing agents) until the hydrides of the carbon-family elements are reached, whereupon the stability suddenly increases. The reason for this apparently lies in the nature of the bonds formed. In the compounds HF, H_2O, and NH_3 the bonds are pure or nearly pure p bonds (i.e., the central atom uses a pure p orbital to form the bond). These decrease in strength as expected as the difference in electronegativity between the central element and hydrogen decreases, and also as the principal quantum number of the p orbital is increased (e.g., from F to I). The hydrides of the carbon-family elements, on the other hand, in order to form four bonds use sp^3 hybrid orbitals. It will be recalled from the discussion in Section 10–12 (Table 10–2) that, whereas the relative strength of a p bond is 1.732, that of an sp^3 hybrid bond (*other things being equal*) is 2.000. The change in bond type therefore explains the increase in stability. The proof of this should be to see what happens to the stability of one of these compounds on changing its bond type. It is found that, whereas the normal oxidation potential for $CH_4 \rightarrow C + 4\,H^+ + 4\,e^-$ is -0.13 volts and that for $NH_3 \rightarrow \frac{1}{2} N_2 + 3\,H^+ + 3\,e^-$ is -0.09 volts, when the hybridization of the nitrogen is changed to sp^3 by making it an ammonium ion, then for $NH_4^+ \rightarrow \frac{1}{2} N_2 + 4\,H^+ + 3\,e^-$, the potential is -0.27 volts, making NH_4^+ more stable than CH_4 as predicted above. The third member of the sp^3 hybrid sequence, BH_4^-, has a potential of $+0.25$ volts for the reaction $BH_4^- \rightarrow B + 4\,H^+ + 5\,e^-$, making BH_4^- less stable than CH_4, which is less stable than NH_4^+, as expected. Furthermore, if the carbon be made to use p-bonding by taking a proton away from CH_4 to form CH_3^-, methide ion, then the estimated potential for the reaction $CH_3^- \rightarrow C + 3\,H^+ + 4\,e^-$ (using $CH_4 \rightleftharpoons H^+ + CH_3^-$ (aq), $K_A = 10^{-50}$) is $+0.61$ volt; this makes CH_3^- much less stable than NH_3, as predicted, whereas the potential for $OH_3^+ \rightarrow \frac{1}{2} O_2 + 3\,H^+ + 2\,e^-$ is -1.23 volts, making OH_3^+ more stable than NH_3.

A second irregularity in this part of the periodic table is the stability of the N–2 oxidation state of phosphorus in its oxygen compounds (the only stable N–2 state in the third period). In order to understand this anomaly, it is necessary to keep in mind the definition of the N–2 state—namely, that it is that positive state having one unshared pair of electrons. It is found that all the compounds of the third-period elements which contain oxygen and an unshared pair of electrons are thermodynamically unstable in water solution. The thermodynamic stability of the apparent N–2 state of phosphorus arises from the fact that it is not a true N–2 state. Phosphorous acid is not

$$\overset{\displaystyle ..}{\text{HO—P—OH}}$$
$$|$$
$$\text{OH}$$

but rather

$$
\begin{array}{c}
\text{H} \\
| \\
\text{HO—P—OH} \\
\| \\
\text{O}
\end{array}
$$

True *N*–2 compounds can be obtained—for example, triethyl phosphite

$$
\begin{array}{c}
\cdot\cdot \\
\text{C}_2\text{H}_5\text{O—P—OC}_2\text{H}_5 \\
| \\
\text{OC}_2\text{H}_5
\end{array}
$$

This is less stable, however, than diethyl ethylphosphonate

$$
\begin{array}{c}
\text{C}_2\text{H}_5 \\
| \\
\text{C}_2\text{H}_5\text{O— P—OC}_2\text{H}_5 \\
\| \\
\text{O}
\end{array}
$$

to which it can easily be rearranged. The question should be, then, not why is the *N*–2 state of phosphorus stable (it really isn't), but why do the +3 (and +1) compounds of phosphorus tend to have four things attached to the phosphorus rather than the expected three?

For the answer to this question, let us examine the properties we should expect of the ion

$$
\left[
\begin{array}{c}
\cdot\cdot \\
\text{HO—P—OH} \\
\| \\
\text{O}
\end{array}
\right]^{-}
$$

Since in phosphorus-oxygen compounds there is a considerable multiple bonding between the phosphorus and the oxygen, the negative charge will be distributed about equally between the phosphorus and the lone oxygen. If we now compare the relative basicities of the phosphorus and oxygen atoms in order to decide on which a hydrogen ion would choose to alight, we must compare similar molecules in which phosphorus and oxygen have the same charge. Comparing PH_2^- and OH^-, the PH_2^- is a much stronger base than OH^- (i.e., PH_3 is a weaker acid than H_2O). Comparing PH_3 and H_2O, best estimates for the K_B of PH_3 are about 10^{-14} whereas K_B for water is 1.8×10^{-16} (i.e., $\dfrac{10^{-14}}{55.5}$). Thus again, PH_3 is a (slightly) stronger base than H_2O and, in competition between phosphine and water for hydrogen ion, most of the hydrogen ion would go to the phosphine (assuming equal activities of PH_3 and H_2O). Consequently, it should be expected that unless the negative charge concentrated very heavily on the oxygen atom in the $PO(OH)_2^-$ ion, the proton would be attached to the phosphorus.

Some similar cases may be considered. Where is the hydrogen atom located in a formate ion, CHO_2^-? If the hydrogen ion were removed, the resulting ion, CO_2^{-2}, would be isoelectronic with a nitrite ion, NO_2^-, the structure being

$$^- \; :C \overset{\cdot\cdot}{\underset{\cdot\cdot}{\cdot}} \; \begin{matrix} :\overset{\cdot\cdot}{O}: \; ^- \\ \\ :\overset{\cdot\cdot}{O}: \end{matrix}$$

so that the carbon atom must carry a negative charge and the oxygen atoms must carry a negative charge (actually distributed between the two). We may thus compare the two ends of the molecule to the methide ion, CH_3^-, and the hydroxide ion, OH^-. Of the two, CH_3^- is by far the stronger base (i.e., CH_4 is a much weaker acid than H_2O). Consequently, the structure of formate ion is

$$H-C \overset{\displaystyle O^-}{\underset{\displaystyle O}{\Big<}}$$

In the similar case of nitrous acid HNO_2 the nitrite ion is

$$:N \; \begin{matrix} :\overset{\cdot\cdot}{O}: \; ^- \\ \\ :\overset{\cdot\cdot}{O}: \end{matrix}$$

We must now compare the basicities of NH_3 (i.e., a neutral nitrogen atom) and OH^-. Since the latter is a much stronger base than the former, the structure of HNO_2 is

$$:N \overset{\displaystyle OH}{\underset{\displaystyle O}{\Big<}}$$

We can now understand why sulfurous acid is not stabilized by having a hydrogen atom attached to the sulfur. If in the hydrogen sulfite ion,

$$\left[HO-\overset{\cdot\cdot}{\underset{\underset{\displaystyle O}{\|}}{S}}-O \right]^-$$

there is about the same amount of multiple bonding as in $H_2PO_3^-$, we may once again assume that the negative charge is distributed fairly equally between sulfur and oxygen. If we now compare the relative basicities of OH^-

and SH^- or of H_2O and H_2S, the oxygen molecules are overwhelmingly more basic in either case. Consequently, the structure of sulfurous acid is

$$HO—\overset{\displaystyle ..}{S}—OH$$
$$\underset{\displaystyle O}{\overset{\displaystyle \|}{}}$$

One further irregularity in stability will be examined. It was pointed out in Section 14–1 that no perbromates and no perfluorates (or for that matter any compounds of "positive" fluorine) are known. Likewise, in Section 14–2 it was pointed out that the oxidizing power of the nonmetals, rather than following a smooth trend from the top to the bottom of each column, instead undergoes an alternation, the elements in the second, fourth, and sixth periods being much better oxidants in their higher oxidation states than the elements in the third and fifth (and seventh?). In order to arrive at an explanation for this, let us consider the electronic structure which each perhalate ion, XO_4^-, would have to have if it existed. Because fluorine has only four possible bonding orbitals, $2s\,2p^3$, the structure of FO_4^- would be

$$:\!O\!:^-$$
$$^-:\!O:F^{+3}:O\!:^-$$
$$:\!O\!:\ _-$$

This places a unit negative charge on each oxygen atom, but much worse, a $+3$ charge on the fluorine, the most electronegative of the elements! This is surely a most unlikely situation. In ClO_4^-, on the other hand, the chlorine has the orbitals $3s\,3p^3\,3d^5$ which can all be used to some degree. For ClO_4^-, the electronic structure seems to be approximately

$$:\!O\!:^-$$
$$O::Cl^+::O$$
$$:\!O\!:\ _-$$

most of the adverse charge distribution being removed by multiple bonding, which is actually symmetrically distributed. Consequently, ClO_4^- is far more stable than FO_4^- (which does not even exist).

To understand the nonexistence of BrO_4^-, we must first consider what the multiple bonds in ClO_4^- are. In Section 10–7, the double bond in $COCl_2$ was described in terms of a *sigma* (σ) bond and a *pi* (π) bond. An sp^2 hybrid orbital of the carbon atom was said to overlap end-on with a p orbital of the oxygen atom to form the σ-bond (Fig. 16–6). Then, (showing the σ-bond as a straight line) the remaining p orbital of the carbon atom overlapped a

p orbital of the oxygen atom above and below the plane of the three σ-bonds, to form the π-bond (Fig. 16–7). In ClO_4^- the "π-bonding" involves not a p orbital of chlorine, but rather a d orbital, overlapping a p orbital of oxygen.

Fig. 16–6. Endwise Overlap of Orbitals Forming a Sigma Bond.

In contrast to the p orbital used in π-bonding, which is perpendicular to the *sigma* bond, the d orbitals used for π-bonding form an acute angle with the σ-bond. The angle is such and the extension of the d orbital is such that effective π-bonding can take place in ions such as ClO_4^-, SO_4^{-2}, PO_4^{-3},

Fig. 16–7. Sidewise Overlap of P Orbitals Forming a Pi Bond.

and so on (Fig. 16–8). (It should also be noted that the energy of the p orbitals is not unfavorable.) Now bromine also has available d orbitals whose energy is favorable and which extend farther out than those of chlorine. But because of the fact that the angle between the σ-bond and the d orbitals must remain the same, and that the Br—O bond must be longer

Fig. 16–8. Overlap of an Oxygen 2p Orbital and a Chlorine 3d Orbital in ClO_4^- to Form a Pi Bond.

(1.54 Å) than the Cl—O bond (1.48 Å) the overlap is less, and the π-bonding is less effective (Fig. 16–9). Consequently BrO_4^- is less stable than ClO_4^-. Likewise, SeO_4^{-2} is less stable than SO_4^{-2}, AsO_4^{-3} is less stable than PO_4^{-3}, and so forth.

Fig. 16–9. Effect of Increased Bond Length in BrO_4^- on Overlap of Oxygen 2p Orbital and Bromine 4d Orbital Forming Pi Bond.

With iodine, however, we find IO_4^- stable once more. This does not mean that the d orbitals have magically become available again, but rather that the f orbitals (4f) have now become available. The angle which the f orbitals, used in π-bonding, make with the σ-bond is more acute than that of the d orbitals, so that despite the even greater length of the I—O bond (1.79 Å), overlap can again be effective. The story is repeated with the longer bond in AtO_4^-, however, so that once again AtO_4^- is less stable than IO_4^-, PoO_4^{-2} is less stable than TeO_4^{-2}, and so forth.

16–5. Conclusion

These are but a few of the irregularities and seeming anomalies for which explanations are known or can be postulated. An attempt to treat any significant fraction of them is clearly beyond the scope of this book. It is hoped, however, that the cases which have been treated have served to instil a little rhyme and reason into the vast and often perplexing field of inorganic chemistry.

16–6. References

Seaborg, G. T., "Place in Periodic System and Electronic Structure of the Heaviest Elements," *Nucleonics*, Vol. 5, No. 5 (1949), p. 16.

Herzberg, G., *Atomic Spectra and Atomic Structure*, 2d rev. ed. New York: Dover Publications, 1944 (especially Chapter III).

Wyckoff, R. W. G., *The Structure of Crystals*. New York: Chemical Catalogue Company, 1924.

Atomic Radii: Zachariasen, W. H., Fried, S., and Hagemann, F., "The Preparation and Identification of Some Pure Actinium Compounds," *Journal of the American Chemical Society*, Vol. 72 (1950), p. 771.

Hugus, Z. Z., "The Possible Use of 4 f Orbitals in Bonding," *Journal of the American Chemical Society*, Vol. 74 (1952), p. 1076; Connick, R. E., and Hugus, Z. Z., *ibid*, p. 6012.

Craig, D. P., and Magnusson, E. A., "Pi-Bonding from d-Orbital Contraction in Chemical Bonding," *Journal of the Chemical Society* (London), 1956, p. 4908.

Allred, L., Rochow, E. G., and Stone, F. G. A., "The Nature of the Silicon-Oxygen Bond," *Journal of Inorganic and Nuclear Chemistry*, Vol. 2 (1956), p. 416.

Simultaneous Equilibria in a Mixture

of Weak Acids

For a solution 0.1 molar in HF and 0.1 molar in HN_3

(1) $$[H^+][F^-] = 5.6 \times 10^{-4} [HF]$$

(2) $$[H^+][N_3^-] = 1.9 \times 10^{-5} [HN_3]$$

from which

(3) $$[F^-][HN_3] = 29 [N_3^-][HF]$$

(4) $$[H^+] = [F^-]+[N_3^-]$$

(5) $$0.1 = [HF]+[F^-]$$

(6) $$0.1 = [HN_3]+[N_3^-]$$

from (1) and (4)

(7) $$[F^-]^2+[N_3^-][F^-] = 5.6 \times 10^{-4} [HF]$$

from (3) and (5)

(8) $$[F^-][HN_3] = 2.9 [N_3^-]-29 [N_3^-][F^-]$$

from (5) and (7)

(9) $$[F^-]^2+[N_3^-][F^-] = 5.6 \times 10^{-5}-5.6 \times 10^{-4} [F^-]$$

from (6) and (8)

(10) $$0.1 [F^-]+28 [N_3^-][F^-] = 2.9 [N_3^-]$$

from (9) and (10)

(11) $$[F^-]^3-0.164 [F^-]^2-1.14 \times 10^{-4} [F^-]+5.8 \times 10^{-6} = 0$$

from which
$$[F^-] = 5.6 \times 10^{-3} M$$

The Hydrolysis of the Salts of Weak Acids

and Weak Bases

In the hydrolysis of the salt of a weak acid and a weak base, $BA + H_2O \rightleftharpoons BOH + HA$, three basic equilibria are involved

(a) $$B^+ + H_2O \rightleftharpoons BOH + H^+$$

(b) $$A^- + H_2O \rightleftharpoons HA + OH^-$$

(c) $$H_2O \rightleftharpoons H^+ + OH^-$$

for which we have the equilibrium expressions

(1) $$\frac{[BOH][H^+]}{[B^+]} = \frac{K_w}{K_B}$$

(2) $$\frac{[HA][OH^-]}{[A^-]} = \frac{K_w}{K_A}$$

(3) $$[H^+][OH^-] = K_w$$

There are also certain conservation equations which can be set up. Thus, the total salt concentration (T) must be equal to the total cation concentration in both its hydrolyzed and its unhydrolyzed forms, i.e.

(4) $$T = [B^+] + [BOH]$$

Likewise, for the anion

(5) $$T = [A^-] + [HA]$$

In addition, there must be over-all neutrality of charge, i.e., the sum of the positive charges must be equal to the sum of the negative charges

(6) $$[B^+] + [H^+] = [A^-] + [OH^-]$$

438

Eliminating [BOH] between (1) and (4)

(7) $\qquad \dfrac{(T-[B^+])[H^+]}{[B^+]} = \dfrac{K_w}{K_B}; \ K_B T[H^+] = (K_w + K_B[H^+])[B^+]$

Eliminating [HA] between (2) and (5)

(8) $\qquad \dfrac{(T-[A^-])[OH^-]}{[A^-]} = \dfrac{K_w}{K_A}$

Eliminating [OH⁻] between (3) and (8)

(9) $\qquad \dfrac{(T-[A^-])K_w}{[H^+][A^-]} = \dfrac{K_w}{K_A}; \ TK_A = (K_A + [H^+])[A^-]$

Eliminating [OH⁻] between (3) and (6)

(10) $[H^+]+[B^+] = \dfrac{K_w}{[H^+]} + [A^-]; \ [H^+]^2 + [B^+][H^+] = K_w + [A^-][H^+]$

Eliminating [A⁻] between (9) and (10)

(11) $\qquad \dfrac{K_A T[H^+]}{K_A + [H^+]} + K_w = [H^+]^2 + [B^+][H^+]$

Eliminating [B⁺] between (7) and (11)

(12) $\qquad \dfrac{K_A T[H^+]}{K_A + [H^+]} + K_w = [H^+]^2 + \dfrac{K_B T[H^+]^2}{K_w + K_B[H^+]}$

which becomes

$$K_B[H^+]^4 + (K_B T + K_A K_B + K_w)[H^+]^3 + (K_A K_w - K_B K_w)[H^+]^2$$
$$- (K_A K_w T - K_A K_B K_w - K_w^2)[H^+] - K_A K_w^2 = 0$$

For fairly large values of T, and for values of K_A and K_B small compared to T, but large compared to K_w, this simplifies to

(12′) $\qquad [H^+]^3 + T[H^+]^2 + \dfrac{(K_A - K_B)K_w}{K_B}[H^+] - \dfrac{K_A K_w T}{K_B} = 0$

Again, if T is fairly large compared with K_A and K_B, the first and third terms of equation (12′) will be small compared to the second and fourth terms, and may be dropped. This gives

$$[H^+]^2 = \dfrac{K_A K_w}{K_B}$$

or $\qquad\qquad\qquad [H^+] = \sqrt{\dfrac{K_A K_w}{K_B}}$

as described in Section 7–7.

The Hydrolysis of Ampholytes

Let us take as an example of an ampholyte the monohydrogen anion of a dibasic acid, HA^-. The same argument applied below will be valid for any ampholyte, however.

In the hydrolysis of an ampholyte the over-all equation may be represented as

$$2\ HA^- \rightleftharpoons H_2A + A^{-2}$$

However, in actual fact, the individual reactions with water cannot be ignored and, unless the second ionization constant, K_2, and the hydrolysis constant, K_w/K_1, are of about the same order of magnitude, it cannot be said that $[H_2A]$ is identically equal to $[A^{-2}]$.

The individual equilibria involved are

(1)
$$\frac{[H_2A][OH^-]}{[HA^-]} = \frac{K_w}{K_1}$$

(2)
$$\frac{[H^+][A^{-2}]}{[HA^-]} = K_2$$

(3)
$$[H^+][OH^-] = K_w$$

In addition, the sum of the concentrations of all the species derived from HA^- must equal the total concentration of HA^- originally added (T).

(4)
$$T = [H_2A] + [HA^-] + [A^{-2}]$$

In addition, there must be over-all neutrality of charge, i.e., the sum of the positive charges must be equal to the sum of the negative charges. Taking the concentration of positive charges as equal to the original concentration of salt, say KHA, plus the $[H^+]$ produced by the hydrolysis

(5)
$$[HA^-] + 2\ [A^{-2}] + [OH^-] = T + [H^+]$$

Eliminating [HA$^-$] between (4) and (5)

(6) $$[A^{-2}]+[OH^-] = [H_2A]+[H^+]$$

Eliminating [HA$^-$] between (1) and (2)

(7) $$[H_2A][OH^-]K_2 = [H^+][A^{-2}]\frac{K_w}{K_1}$$

Eliminating [HA$^-$] between (2) and (4)

(8) $$[H^+][A^{-2}] = K_2(T-[H_2A]-[A^{-2}])$$

$$[A^{-2}] = \frac{K_2T-K_2[H_2A]}{[H^+]+K_2}$$

Eliminating [OH$^-$] between (3) and (6)

(9) $$[A^{-2}]+\frac{K_w}{[H^+]} = [H_2A]+[H^+]$$

$$[A^{-2}] = \frac{[H^+]^2+[H_2A][H^+]-K_w}{[H^+]}$$

Eliminating [OH$^-$] between (3) and (7)

(10) $$K_2K_w\frac{[H_2A]}{[H^+]} = [H^+][A^{-2}]\frac{K_w}{K_1}$$

$$[A^{-2}] = \frac{K_1K_2[H_2A]}{[H^+]^2}$$

Eliminating [A^{-2}] between (9) and (10)

(11) $$[H^+]^3+[H_2A][H^+]^2-K_w[H^+] = K_1K_2[H_2A]$$

$$[H_2A] = \frac{[H^+]^3-K_w[H^+]}{K_1K_2-[H^+]^2}$$

Eliminating [A^{-2}] between (8) and (9)

(12) $$\frac{K_2T-K_2[H_2A]}{[H^+]+K_2} = \frac{K_1K_2[H_2A]}{[H^+]^2}$$

$$[H_2A] = \frac{T[H^+]^2}{[H^+]^2+K_1[H^+]+K_1K_2}$$

Eliminating [H$_2$A] between (11) and (12)

(13) $$\frac{[H^+]^3-K_w[H^+]}{K_1K_2-[H^+]^2} = \frac{T[H^+]^2}{[H^+]^2+K_1[H^+]+K_1K_2}$$

and therefore

$$[H^+]^4+(K_1+T)[H^+]^3+(K_1K_2-K_w)[H^+]^2-(K_1K_w+K_1K_2T)[H^+]$$
$$-K_1K_2K_w = 0$$

If T is large in comparison to K_1 and $[H^+]$ is neither too large nor too small, equation (13) simplifies, with the first, third, and fifth terms dropping out, giving

$$T[H^+]^3 = K_1K_2T[H^+]$$

or

$$[H^+] = \sqrt{K_1K_2}$$

which is the same as the expression derived in Section 8–12. However, if T is not large in comparison to K_1, a rigorous solution is required.

As an illustration, let us take the hydrolysis of 0.001 M $KH_3P_2O_7$. For $H_4P_2O_7$, $K_1 = 1.4 \times 10^{-1}$, $K_2 = 1.1 \times 10^{-2}$. From equation (2), it can be seen that $[H^+] \approx 10^{-3}$ M, so that the terms in (13) are in order of magnitude $[H^+]^4 \approx 10^{-12}$, $(K_1+T)[H^+]^3 \approx 10^{-10}$, $(K_1K_2-K_w)[H^+]^2 \approx 10^{-9}$, $(K_1K_w +K_1K_2T)[H^+] \approx 10^{-9}$, $K_1K_2K_w = 1.54 \times 10^{-17}$. The first and last terms can therefore be neglected in comparison to the others, and the equation becomes

$$(K_1+T)[H^+]^2+(K_1K_2-K_w)[H^+]-(K_1K_w+K_1K_2T) = 0$$

or

$$[H^+]^2+(1.09 \times 10^{-2})[H^+]-1.09 \times 10^{-5} = 0$$

from which, by the quadratic formula

$$[H^+] = 9 \times 10^{-4} \ M$$

showing that the estimate of the sizes of the terms in equation (13) was correct, and that we were justified in dropping the first and last terms. The other concentrations follow from $[H^+]$.

(3)
$$[OH^-] = \frac{1 \times 10^{-14}}{9 \times 10^{-4}} = 1.1 \times 10^{-10} \ M$$

(6)
$$[H_2P_2O_7^{-2}]-[H_4P_2O_7] = 9 \times 10^{-4}$$

(7) $(1.10 \times 10^{-10})(1.1 \times 10^{-2})[H_4P_2O_7]$

$$= (9 \times 10^{-4})\left(\frac{1 \times 10^{-14}}{1.4 \times 10^{-1}}\right)[H_2P_2O_7^{-2}]$$

Therefore

$$[H_2P_2O_7^{-2}] = 1.88 \times 10^4[H_4P_2O_7]$$

and

$$[H_4P_2O_7] = 4.8 \times 10^{-8} \ M$$

$$[H_2P_2O_7^{-2}] = 9 \times 10^{-4} \ M$$

$$[H_3P_2O_7^-] = 7.4 \times 10^{-5} \ M$$

(If the simplification described in Section 6–5 had been used in this case, i.e., that

$$[H_4P_2O_7] = [H_2P_2O_7^{-2}] = X$$

$$\frac{X^2}{(10^{-3})^2} = \frac{1 \times 10^{-14}}{1.4 \times 10^{-1}} \times \frac{1.1 \times 10^{-2}}{1 \times 10^{-14}} = 7.9 \times 10^{-2}$$

$$X = [H_4P_2O_7] = [H_2P_2O_7^{-2}] = 2.8 \times 10^{-4} \ M$$

which is quite different from what was calculated above, and, moreover

$$[H^+] = \frac{(1.1 \times 10^{-2})(10^{-3} - 5.6 \times 10^{-4})}{2.8 \times 10^{-4}} = 1.7 \times 10^{-2} M$$

which is impossible.)

Thus, if K_2 and K_w/K_1 are very far apart, or the total molar concentration of ampholyte is considerably less (one order of magnitude or more) than K_2, the rigorous solution must be used. For most cases, however, the approximate solution described in Section 8–12 is adequate and will give a result approximately the same as the rigorous solution.

pK_A's of Acids

Substance	Formula	pK_{A1}	pK_{A2}	pK_{A3}	pK_{A4}
Arsenous acid	$As(OH)_3$	9.22			
Arsenic acid	H_3AsO_4	2.30	7.03	11.53	
Cacodylic acid	$(CH_3)_2AsO_2H$	6.12			
Boric acid	$B(OH)_3$	9.24			
n-Butylboric acid	$C_4H_9B(OH)_2$	9.74			
Phenylboric acid	$C_6H_6B(OH)_2$	7.86			
Hydrobromic acid	HBr	$-9.$			
Hypobromous acid	HBrO	8.60			
Carbonic acid	H_2CO_3	3.82	10.32		
	CO_2 (aq) $+ H_2O$	6.38	10.32		
Formic acid	HCO_2H	3.68			
Acetic acid	CH_3CO_2H	4.73			
Chloroacetic acid	$ClCH_2CO_2H$	2.85			
Dichloroacetic acid	Cl_2CHCO_2H	1.26			
Trichloroacetic acid	CCl_3CO_2H	0.20			
Trifluoroacetic acid	CF_3CO_2H	-0.26			
Propionic acid	$C_2H_5CO_2H$	4.85			
Phenol	C_6H_5OH	10.0			
Benzoic acid	$C_6H_5CO_2H$	4.18			
Salicylic acid	$HOC_6H_4CO_2H$	2.96			
Ortho-nitrobenzoic acid	$O_2NC_6H_4CO_2H$	2.22			
Benzenediazoic acid	$C_6H_5N_2OH$	4.92			
Oxalic acid	$H_2C_2O_4 = HO_2CCO_2H$	1.42	4.30		
Malonic acid	$HO_2CCH_2CO_2H$	2.80	5.85		
Succinic acid	$HO_2C(CH_2)_2CO_2H$	4.17	5.64		
Sebacic acid	$HO_2C(CH_2)_8CO_2H$	4.55	5.5		
Tartaric acid	$(HOCHCO_2H)_2$	2.93	4.23		
Citric acid	$HO_2CC(OH)(CH_2CO_2H)_2$	3.07	4.75	5.2	
Hydrocyanic acid	HCN	9.32			
Cyanic acid	HOCN	3.66			
Cyanamide	H_2NCN	8.68			
Hydrochloric acid	HCl	-7.4			
Hypochlorous acid	HClO	7.53			

Substance	Formula	pK_{A1}	pK_{A2}	pK_{A3}	pK_{A4}
Chlorous acid	$HClO_2$	1.96			
Chloric acid	$HClO_3$	−2.7			
Perchloric acid	$HClO_4$	−7.3			
Chromic acid	H_2CrO_4	0.745	6.49		
Dichromic acid	$H_2Cr_2O_7$	−1.4	1.64		
Hydrofluoric acid	HF	3.25			
Carbonylferric acid	$H_2Fe(CO)_4$	4.44	14.0		
Cyanoferric acid	$H_4Fe(CN)_6$	?	?	3.0	4.25
Germanic acid	H_4GeO_4	9.4			
Hydriodic acid	HI	−9.5			
Hypoiodous acid	HIO	10.4			
Iodic acid	HIO_3	0.785			
Periodic acid	H_5IO_6	1.64	8.36	14.98	>15
Molybdic acid	H_2MoO_4	1.8	4.1		
Dimolybdic acid	$H_2Mo_2O_7$	5.02			
Permanganic acid	$HMnO_4$	−2.25			
Hydrazoic acid	HN_3	4.72			
Hyponitrous acid	$H_2N_2O_2$	7.05	11.0		
Nitramide	H_2NNO_2	6.59			
Nitrous acid	HNO_2	3.29			
Nitric acid	HNO_3	−1.35			
Water	H_2O	15.74			
Hydrogen peroxide	H_2O_2	11.75			
Hydrogen superoxide	HO_2	2.2			
Oxonium ion	H_3O^+	−1.74			
Osmium tetroxide	OsO_4	12.10			
Hypophosphorus acid	HPH_2O_2	1.07			
Phosphorous acid	H_2PHO_3	2.00	6.70		
Hypophosphoric acid	$H_4P_2O_6$	2.2	2.81	7.27	10.03
Fluorophosphoric acid	H_2PO_3F	0.55	4.80		
Phosphoric acid	H_3PO_4	2.12	7.21	12.0	
Pyrophosphoric acid	$H_4P_2O_7$	0.85	1.96	6.54	8.46
Perrhenic acid	$HReO_4$	−1.25			
Hydrosulfuric acid	H_2S	7.00	12.92		
Dithionous acid	$H_2S_2O_4$	?	2.45		
Thiosulfuric acid	$H_2S_2O_3$	0.60	1.72		
Sulfurous acid	H_2SO_3	1.764	7.205		
Dithionic acid	$H_2S_2O_6$	0.2	3.4		
Sulfuric acid	H_2SO_4	−2.01	1.900		
Antimonic acid	$H[Sb(OH)_6]$	4.4			
Tristrifluoromethyl-antimonic acid	$H[Sb(CF_3)_3(OH)_3]$	1.85			
Hydroselenic acid	H_2Se	3.80	11.0		
Selenious acid	H_2SeO_3	2.57	8.32		
Selenic acid	H_2SeO_4	?	2.05		
Silicic acid	H_4SiO_4	9.8			
Dimethylstannic acid	$H_2[Sn(CH_3)_2(OH)_4]$	3.11			
Hydrotelluric acid	H_2Te	2.64	11.		
Tellurous acid	H_2TeO_3	2.57	7.74		
Telluric acid	H_6TeO_6	7.61	10.39	15.	
Vanadic acid	H_3VO_4	?	8.95	14.4	
Tungstic acid	H_2WO_4	?	4.2		

Appendix 5

Ionization Constants of Bases

Base	Equilibrium	K_B	pK_B	Molal Concentration of Saturated Solution
Silver hydroxide	$AgOH \rightleftharpoons Ag^+ + OH^-$	5.0×10^{-3}	2.30	4×10^{-6}
Arsenous acid	$AsOOH \rightleftharpoons AsO^+ + OH^-$	4.7×10^{-15}	14.33	0.19
Cacodylic acid	$(CH_3)_2AsOOH \rightleftharpoons (CH_3)_2AsO^+ + OH^-$	5.6×10^{-13}	12.25	6.0
Barium hydroxide	$Ba(OH)_2 \rightleftharpoons BaOH^+ + OH^-$	strong		0.28
	$BaOH^+ \rightleftharpoons Ba^{+2} + OH^-$	1.41×10^{-1}	0.85	
Calcium hydroxide	$Ca(OH)_2 \rightleftharpoons CaOH^+ + OH^-$	strong		0.021
	$CaOH^+ \rightleftharpoons Ca^{+2} + OH^-$	3.55×10^{-2}	1.45	
Mercury(II) hydroxide	$Hg(OH)_2 \rightleftharpoons HgOH^+ + OH^-$	1×10^{-14}	14.	2.4×10^{-4}
	$HgOH^+ \rightleftharpoons Hg^{+2} + OH^-$	1.2×10^{-8}	7.9	
Methylmercury(II) hydroxide	$CH_3HgOH \rightleftharpoons CH_3Hg^+ + OH^-$	3×10^{-10}	9.5	>0.73
Ethylmercury(II) hydroxide	$C_2H_5HgOH \rightleftharpoons C_2H_5Hg^+ + OH^-$	8×10^{-10}	9.1	≈ 0.5
Phenylmercury(II) hydroxide	$C_6H_5HgOH \rightleftharpoons C_6H_5Hg^+ + OH^-$	1.0×10^{-10}	10.0	0.018
Hypoiodous acid	$IOH \rightleftharpoons I^+ + OH^-$	3.2×10^{-10}	9.49	v. sol.
Lithium hydroxide	$LiOH \rightleftharpoons Li^+ + OH^-$	6.8×10^{-1}	0.17	5.5
Ammonia (ammonium hydroxide)	$NH_3 + H_2O \rightleftharpoons NH_4^+ + OH^-$	1.75×10^{-5}	4.758	*
Methylamine	$CH_3NH_2 + H_2O \rightleftharpoons CH_3NH_3^+ + OH^-$	5.2×10^{-4}	3.28	$0.5^{\,1\,atm}$

* Miscible in all proportions.

Base	Equilibrium	K_B	pK_B	Molal Concentration of Saturated Solution
Dimethylamine	$(CH_3)_2NH + H_2O \rightleftharpoons (CH_3)_2NH_2^+ + OH^-$	1.07×10^{-3}	2.97	v. sol.
Trimethylamine	$(CH_3)_3N + H_2O \rightleftharpoons (CH_3)_3NH^+ + OH^-$	8.1×10^{-5}	4.09	v. sol.
Ethylamine	$C_2H_5NH_2 + H_2O \rightleftharpoons C_2H_5NH_3^+ + OH^-$	4.7×10^{-4}	3.33	*
Aniline (phenylamine)	$C_6H_5NH_2 + H_2O \rightleftharpoons C_6H_5NH_3^+ + OH^-$	4.2×10^{-10}	9.38	0.37
Diphenylamine	$(C_6H_5)_2NH + H_2O \rightleftharpoons (C_6H_5)_2NH_2^+ + OH^-$	7.1×10^{-14}	13.15	1.8×10^{-3}
Guanidine	$(H_2N)_2CNH + H_2O \rightleftharpoons C(NH_2)_3^+ + OH^-$	3.0×10^{-1}	0.52	v. sol.
Pyridine	$C_5H_5N + H_2O \rightleftharpoons C_5H_5NH^+ + OH^-$	1.51×10^{-9}	8.82	*
Benzenediazonium hydroxide	$C_6H_5N_2OH \rightleftharpoons C_6H_5N_2^+ + OH^-$	1.20×10^{-3}	2.92	v. sol.
Hydrazine	$N_2H_4 + H_2O \rightleftharpoons N_2H_5^+ + OH^-$	9.1×10^{-7}	6.04	
	$N_2H_5^+ + H_2O \rightleftharpoons N_2H_6^{+2} + OH^-$	1.32×10^{-15}	14.88	
Hydroxylamine	$HONH_2 + H_2O \rightleftharpoons HONH_3^+ + OH^-$	9.6×10^{-10}	9.02	*
Hydrazoic acid	$HN_3 + H_2O \rightleftharpoons H_2N_3^+ + OH^-$	3.9×10^{-21}	20.41	*
Nitrous acid	$NOOH \rightleftharpoons NO^+ + OH^-$	7×10^{-19}	18.2	v. sol.
Sodium hydroxide	$NaOH \rightleftharpoons Na^+ + OH^-$	5.0	-0.70	12.9
Neptunyl(V) hydroxide	$NpO_2OH \rightleftharpoons NpO_2^+ + OH^-$	8×10^{-6}	5.1	8×10^{-5}
Water	$H_2O + H_2O \rightleftharpoons H_3O^+ + OH^-$	1.82×10^{-16}	15.74	55.5
Hydrogen peroxide	$H_2O_2 + H_2O \rightleftharpoons H_3O_2^+ + OH^-$	1×10^{-17}	17.	*
Lead hydroxide	$Pb(OH)_2 \rightleftharpoons PbOH^+ + OH^-$	1.0×10^{-3}	3.0	2.6×10^{-4}
	$PbOH^+ \rightleftharpoons Pb^{+2} + OH^-$	1.5×10^{-8}	7.8	
Plutonyl(V) hydroxide	$PuO_2OH \rightleftharpoons PuO_2^+ + OH^-$	5×10^{-5}	4.3	8×10^{-2}
Antimony hydroxide	$SbOOH \rightleftharpoons SbO^+ + OH^-$	8×10^{-14}	13.1	1×10^{-3}
Trimethyltin(IV) hydroxide	$(CH_3)_3SnOH \rightleftharpoons (CH_3)_3Sn^+ + OH^-$	1.6×10^{-5}	4.8	v. sol.
Tellurous acid	$TeO(OH)_2 \rightleftharpoons TeO_2OH^+ + OH^-$	3.2×10^{-11}	10.5	0.03
Thallium(I) hydroxide	$TlOH \rightleftharpoons Tl^+ + OH^-$	1.4×10^{-1}	0.85	1.6
Diethylthallium(III) hydroxide	$(C_2H_5)_2TlOH \rightleftharpoons (C_2H_5)_2Tl^+ + OH^-$	9.0×10^{-1}	0.05	v. sol.
Zinc hydroxide	$Zn(OH)_2 \rightleftharpoons ZnOH^+ + OH^-$	1.2×10^{-7}	6.9	1.0×10^{-5}
	$ZnOH^+ \rightleftharpoons Zn^{+2} + OH^-$	4.1×10^{-5}	4.4	

* Miscible in all proportions.

Cumulative pK_{inst}'s *of Complex Ions*

Simple Ion	pK_1	pK_{12}	pK_{123}	pK_{1234}	pK_{12345}	pK_{123456}
			Acetates ($C_2H_3O_2{}^-$)			
Ag^+	0.73*	0.64				
Cd^{+2}	1.7					
Cu^{+2}	2.16	3.20*				
In^{+3}	3.50	5.95	7.90*	9.08		
Ni^{+2}	0.67	1.25*				
Pb^{+2}	2.52	4.0*	6.4	8.5		
Tl^+	−0.11*					
Tl^{+3}	?	?	?	15.4		
$UO_2{}^{+2}$	2.38	4.36*	6.34			
Zn^{+2}	1.03					
			Ammines (NH_3)			
Ag^+	3.315	7.23				
Au^+	?	27.				
Au^{+3}	?	?	?	≈ 30.		
Cd^{+2}	2.51	4.47	5.77	6.56		
Co^{+2}	1.99	3.50	4.43	5.07	5.13	4.39
Co^{+3}	7.3	14.0	20.1	25.7	30.8	35.21
Cu^+	5.93	10.86				
Cu^{+2}	3.99	7.33	10.06	12.03	11.43	8.9
Fe^{+2}	?	?	?	3.7		
Hg^{+2}	8.8	17.5	18.5	19.3		
Ni^{+2}	2.68	4.80	6.40	7.47	7.99	7.91
Tl^+	−0.9					
Tl^{+3}	?	?	?	17.(?)		
Zn^{+2}	2.18	4.43	6.74	8.70		
			Azides ($N_3{}^-$)			
Ag^+	2.5*	4.2	3.9	3.7		
Cd^{+2}	1.6	2.8*	3.3	3.9		
Cu^{+2}	2.6					
Fe^{+3}	5.06					
Tl^+	0.39*					

* Neutral molecules in solution.

Simple Ion	pK_1	pK_{12}	pK_{123}	pK_{1234}	pK_{12345}	pK_{123456}

Bromides: See Table 4–2

Carbonates (CO_3^{-2})

| UO_2^{+2} | ? | 14.6 | 18.3 | | | |

Chlorides: See Table 4–2

Citrates ($C_6H_5O_7^{-3}$)

Ba^{+2}	2.84					
Ca^{+2}	4.85					
Cu^{+2}	14.21					
Fe^{+2}	3.08					
Fe^{+3}	11.85*					
Pb^{+2}	6.50					
Ra^{+2}	2.36					
Sr^{+2}	2.90					

Cyanates (NCO^-)

| Ag^+ | ? | 5.00 | | | | |

Cyanides (CN^-)

Ag^+	?	19.85	20.55	19.42		
Au^+	?	38.3				
Au^{+3}	?	?	?	56.		
Cd^{+2}	5.18	9.60*	13.92	17.11		
Co^{+2}	?	?	?	?	?	19.09
Co^{+3}	?	?	?	?	?	64.
Cu^+	?	24.0	28.6	29.3		
Cu^{+2}	?	?	?	25.(?)		
Fe^{+2}	?	?	?	?	15.7	24.
Fe^{+3}	?	?	?	?	?	31.
Hg^{+2}	18.00	34.70*	38.53	41.51		
Ni^{+2}	?	?	?	31.0	30.3	
Pb^{+2}	?	?	?	10.3(?)		
Tl^{+3}	?	?	?	35.		
Zn^{+2}	?	?	17.	19.		

Dithiooxamide (Rubeanic Acid) Complexes ($C_2H_3N_2S_2^-$)

| Ru^{+2} | 13.38 | ? | 38.14 | | | |

Fluorides (F^-)

Ag^+	0.36*					
Al^{+3}	7.10	11.98	15.83*	18.53	20.20	20.67
B^{+3}	?	8.3†	13.5‡	19.4§		
Be^{+2}	5.89	10.83*	14.39	16.38		
Cd^{+2}	0.46	0.53*				
Ce^{+3}	3.99					
Cr^{+3}	5.20	8.54	11.02*			
Cu^{+2}	1.23					
Fe^{+3}	6.04	10.74	13.74*	15.74	16.10	≈ 16.10

* Neutral molecules in solution.
† For $BF_2(OH)_2^- + H_2O \rightleftharpoons H_3BO_3 + H^+ + 2 F^-$.
‡ For $BF_3OH^- + 2H_2O \rightleftharpoons H_3BO_3 + 2 H^+ + 3 F^-$.
§ For $BF_4^- + 3 H_2O \rightleftharpoons H_3BO_3 + 3 H^+ + 4 F^-$.

Simple Ion	pK_1	pK_{12}	pK_{123}	pK_{1234}	pK_{12345}	pK_{123456}
Ga^{+3}	5.86	6.46	6.02*			
Gd^{+3}	4.26					
Hg^{+2}	1.56					
In^{+3}	4.63	7.41	10.23*			
La^{+3}	3.56					
Mg^{+2}	1.82					
Mn^{+3}	5.76					
Pu^{+4}	7.94					
Sc^{+3}	7.08	12.88	17.33*	20.81		
Si^{+4}	?	?	?	38.20†	?	44.39‡
Sn^{+2}	4.85	?	≈10.			
Sn^{+4}	?	?	?	?	?	≈25.
Th^{+4}	8.65					
Tl^+	0.10*					
TiO^{+2}	6.44					
UO_2^{+2}	4.4	7.7*	10.3	11.7		
VO^{+2}	3.30					
Zn^{+2}	1.26					
Zr^{+4}	9.80	17.37	23.45			

Formates (CHO_2^-)

Ba^{+2}	0.60					
Ca^{+2}	0.80					
Cu^{+2}	1.98					
In^{+3}	2.74	4.72	5.70*	6.70		
Sr^{+2}	0.66					

Hydrazine Complexes (N_2H_4)

Cd^{+2}	2.25	2.40	2.78	3.89		
Ni^{+2}	2.76	5.20	7.35	9.20	10.75	11.99
Zn^{+2}	3.40	3.70	3.78	3.88		

Hydroxides: See Table 9–12

Hydroxylamine Complexes ($HONH_2$)

Zn^{+2}	0.40	1.01

Hypophosphites ($PH_2O_2^-$)

Fe^{+3}	2.77

Iodates (IO_3^-)

Ag^+	0.82*	1.85
Ba^{+2}	1.1	
Ca^{+2}	0.89	
Cu^{+2}	0.82	
Sr^{+2}	0.98	
Th^{+4}	2.88	4.79	7.15

Iodides: See Table 4–2

* Neutral molecules in solution.
† For $SiF_4 + 4 H_2O \rightleftharpoons Si(OH)_4 + 4 H^+ + 4 F^-$.
‡ For $SiF_6^{-2} + 4 H_2O \rightleftharpoons Si(OH)_4 + 4 H^+ + 6 F^-$.

Simple Ion	pK_1	pK_{12}	pK_{123}	pK_{1234}	pK_{12345}	pK_{123456}
			Nitrates NO_3^-)			
Ag^+	−0.29*					
Ba^{+2}	0.92					
Bi^{+3}	1.26					
Ca^{+2}	0.28					
Cd^{+2}	0.40					
Ce^{+3}	0.4					
Fe^{+3}	1.0					
Hg_2^{+2}	0.08	−0.26*				
Hg^{+2}	0.35	≈0.*				
K^+	−0.24*					
La^{+3}	−0.26					
Li^+	−1.45*					
Pb^{+2}	1.18					
Pu^{+4}	0.54					
$RuNO^{+3}$	−0.3	−1.0	−0.7*			
Sr^{+2}	0.82					
Th^{+4}	0.78	1.11	1.00	0.74*		
Tl^+	0.33*					
Tl^{+3}	0.92					
UO_2^{+2}	−0.3					
Zr^{+4}	0.34	0.11	−0.26	−0.82*	≈ −1.5	≈ −1.7
			Nitrito or Nitro Complexes (NO_2^-)			
Ag^+	1.88*	2.83				
Cd^{+2}	1.80	3.01*	3.81	3.1		
Cu^{+2}	1.26	1.56*	1.16			
Hg^{+2}	?	?	?	13.54		
			Nitroso Complexes (NO) $[p_{NO} = atm]$			
$Co(NH_3)_5^{+2}$	1.32					
Fe^{+2}	−0.18					
			Oxalates $(C_2O_4^{-2})$			
Ag^+	0.					
Al^{+3}	?	13.	16.3			
Ba^{+2}	2.3*					
Be^{+2}	≈4.*	≈2.5				
Ca^{+2}	≈3.*					
Cd^{+2}	4.00*	5.77				
Ce^{+3}	6.52	10.48	11.30			
Co^{+2}	4.7*	6.7	9.7			
Cu^{+2}	6.7*	10.3				
Fe^{+2}	?	4.52	5.22			
Fe^{+3}	9.4	16.2	20.2			
Mg^{+2}	2.55*	4.38				
Mn^{+2}	3.82*	5.25				
Mn^{+3}	9.98	16.57	19.42			
Nd^{+3}	7.21	11.51	>13.5			
Ni^{+2}	>5.3*	6.51	≈14.			
Pb^{+2}	?	6.54				

* Neutral molecules in solution.

Simple Ion	pK_1	pK_{12}	pK_{123}	pK_{1234}	pK_{12345}	pK_{123456}
Sr^{+2}	2.54*					
Tl^+	2.03					
Yb^{+3}	7.30	11.89	>12.9			
Zn^{+2}	5.00*	7.36	8.15			

Phosphates (PO_4^{-3})

Ce^{+3}	18.53*					

Phosphates (HPO_4^{-2})

Ca^{+2}	2.70*					
Fe^{+3}	9.35					
K^+	0.49					
Li^+	0.72					
Mg^{+2}	2.50*					
Na^+	0.60					

Phosphates ($H_2PO_4^-$)

Al^{+3}	≈3.	≈5.3	≈7.6*			
Ca^{+2}	1.08					
Fe^{+3}	?	?	?	9.15		
UO_2^{+2}	3.00	5.43*	7.33			

Phosphates (H_3PO_4)

Pu^{+4}	2.3					
Th^{+4}	1.89	3.86				
UO_2^{+2}	<1.88	3.88	5.23			

Pyrophosphates ($P_2O_7^{-4}$)

Ba^{+2}	4.64					
Ca^{+2}	5.00					
Cd^{+2}	5.6	4.18				
Ce^{+3}	17.15					
Co^{+2}	4.					
Cu^+	?	26.72				
Cu^{+2}	5.20	10.30				
Fe^{+3}	?	5.55				
K^+	0.80					
Li^+	2.39					
Mg^{+2}	5.70					
Na^+	2.22					
Pb^{+2}	11.24					
Sn^{+2}	≈14.					
Sr^{+2}	4.66					
Tl^+	1.69	≈1.9				
Zn^{+2}	6.45	7.24				

Pyrophosphates ($HP_2O_7^{-3}$)

Cu^{+2}	6.4	10.0				
Li^+	1.03					
Na^+	1.52					

Pyrophosphates ($H_2P_2O_7^{-2}$)

Sn^{+2}	4.48*	6.08				
$SnOH^+$	5.48	7.30				

* Neutral molecules in solution.

Simple Ion	pK_1	pK_{12}	pK_{123}	pK_{1234}	pK_{12345}	pK_{123456}

Pyridine Complexes (C_5H_5N)

Ag^+	1.97	4.35				
Cd^{+2}	1.27	2.14	?	2.50		
Co^{+2}	1.14	1.54				
Cu^+	?	3.3				
Cu^{+2}	2.52	4.38	5.69	6.54		
Fe^{+2}	0.71	?	?	6.7		
Hg^{+2}	5.1	10.0	10.4			
Ni^{+2}	1.78	2.82	3.13			
Zn^{+2}	1.41	1.11	1.61	1.93		

Rubeanic Acid: See Dithiooxamide

Selenates (SeO_4^{-2})

Cd^{+2}	2.27*	
Zn^{+2}	2.19*	

Selenites (SeO_3^{-2})

Cd^{+2}	?	5.15
Hg^{+2}	?	12.48

Selenocyanates ($NCSe^-$)

Ag^+	?	10.7	13.90	
Cd^{+2}	?	?	?	3.6
Hg^{+2}	?	?	27.5	29.95

Selenosulfates ($SeSO_3^{-2}$)

Hg^{+2}	?	36.8

Sulfates (SO_4^{-2})

Ag^+	1.3	2.		
Ca^{+2}	2.31*			
Cd^{+2}	2.31*			
Ce^{+3}	3.37			
Ce^{+4}	3.3			
Co^{+2}	2.47*			
Co^{+3}	1.34			
Cu^{+2}	2.34*			
Fe^{+3}	4.18	7.4		
Hg_2^{+2}	1.30*	2.40		
Hg^{+2}	1.34*	2.3		
In^{+3}	1.85	2.60	3.00	
K^+	0.96			
La^{+3}	3.82			
Li^+	0.64			
Mg^{+2}	2.36*			
Mn^{+2}	2.28*			
Na^+	0.72			
Ni^{+2}	2.40*			
Pu^{+3}	1.0	1.62		
Pu^{+4}	3.66			
Th^{+4}	3.32	5.70*		

* Neutral molecules in solution.

Simple Ion	pK_1	pK_{12}	pK_{123}	pK_{1234}	pK_{12345}	pK_{123456}
Tl^+	1.37					
U^{+4}	3.24	5.42*				
UO_2^{+2}	2.96*	3.9				
Y^{+3}	3.47					
Zn^{+2}	2.32*					
Zr^{+4}	3.79	6.64*				

Sulfides: See Table 5–4 and Section 6–3

Sulfites (SO_3^{-2})

	pK_1	pK_{12}	pK_{123}	pK_{1234}		
Ag^+	5.60	8.68	9.00			
Cd^{+2}	?	4.19				
Cu^+	7.85	8.70	9.36			
Hg^{+2}	?	24.07	24.96			
Tl^{+3}	?	?	?	≈34.		

Thiocyanates (NCS^-)

	pK_1	pK_{12}	pK_{123}	pK_{1234}	pK_{12345}	pK_{123456}
Ag^+	4.75*	8.23	9.45	9.67		
Au^+	?	25.				
Au^{+3}	?	?	?	42.	42.	42.
Bi^{+3}	1.15	2.26	?	3.41	?	4.23
Cd^{+2}	1.74	2.33*	≈2.	≈3.0		
Co^{+2}	3.0	3.0*	2.3	2.0		
Cr^{+3}	3.08	4.8	5.8*	6.1	5.4	3.8
Cu^+	?	12.11	9.90	10.09	9.59	9.27
Cu^{+2}	?	?	5.19	6.52		
Fe^{+2}	0.95	0.07*				
Fe^{+3}	3.00	4.75	<4.0*	>5.8	≈5.1	≈4.
Hg^{+2}	?	17.47*	19.15	19.77		
In^{+3}	2.58	3.60	4.63*			
Ni^{+2}	1.18	1.64*	1.81			
Pb^{+2}	1.09	2.52*	1.52	2.37		
Th^{+4}	1.08	?	1.78			
$TiOH^{+3}$	1.7					
Tl^+	0.80*	0.65	0.2	0.		
UO_2^{+2}	0.93	0.91*	1.35			
V^{+3}	2.0					
VO^{+2}	0.92					
Zn^{+2}	1.7	2.1*	2.2	3.7		
$ZnOH^+$	2.01*	?	2.66			

Thiosulfates ($S_2O_3^{-2}$)

	pK_1	pK_{12}	pK_{123}	pK_{1234}		
Ag^+	?	13.38	13.93			
Ba^{+2}	2.33*					
Ca^{+2}	1.91*					
Cd^{+2}	3.94*	6.48				
Co^{+2}	2.05*					
Cu^+	?	11.69	13.5			
Cu^{+2}	?	12.29				
Fe^{+2}	2.17*	?	?	<2		
Fe^{+3}	3.25					

* Neutral molecules in solution.

Simple Ion	pK_1	pK_{12}	pK_{123}	pK_{1234}	pK_{12345}	pK_{123456}
Hg^{+2}	?	29.86	32.26	33.61		
K^+	1.00					
La^{+3}	0.8					
Mg^{+2}	1.79*					
Mn^{+2}	1.95*					
Na^+	0.58					
Ni^{+2}	2.06*					
Pb^{+2}	?	5.13	6.35	7.2		
Tl^+	2.00	3.1				
Tl^{+3}	?	?	?	41.		
Zn^{+2}	2.29*	4.59	?	<0.6		
$ZnOH^+$	?	2.13				

* Neutral molecules in solution.

Appendix 7

Solubility Product Constants

Acetates*

Salt	Constant	pK_{sp}	Salt	Constant	pK_{sp}
$AgC_2H_3O_2$	4×10^{-3}	2.4	$Pb(C_2H_3O_2)_2$	1.8×10^{-3}	2.75
$Hg_2(C_2H_3O_2)_2$	3.5×10^{-10}	9.45	$[UO_2](C_2H_3O_2)_2$	5×10^{-6}	5.3

Arsenates*

Salt	Constant	pK_{sp}	Salt	Constant	pK_{sp}
Ag_3AsO_4	1.13×10^{-20}	19.95	$Mn_3(AsO_4)_2$	1.9×10^{-29}	28.72
$AlAsO_4$	1.6×10^{-16}	15.80	$Ni_3(AsO_4)_2$	3.1×10^{-26}	25.51
$Ba_3(AsO_4)_2$	1.1×10^{-13}	12.96	$Pb_3(AsO_4)_2$	4.1×10^{-36}	35.39
$BiAsO_4$	2.8×10^{-10} (?)	9.36(?)	$Sr_3(AsO_4)_2$	1.29×10^{-18}	17.79
$Ca_3(AsO_4)_2$	6.8×10^{-19}	18.17	$Sr[HAsO_4]$	1×10^{-3}	3.
$Ca[HAsO_4]\cdot H_2O$	2.2×10^{-4}	3.7	$[UO_2][HAsO_4]$	3.2×10^{-11}	10.50
$Cd_3(AsO_4)_2$	2.2×10^{-33}	32.66	$[K][UO_2][AsO_4]$	2.5×10^{-23}	22.60
$Co_3(AsO_4)_2$	7.6×10^{-29}	28.12	$[Li][UO_2][AsO_4]$	1.5×10^{-19}	18.82
$CrAsO_4$	7.8×10^{-21}	20.11	$[NH_4][UO_2][AsO_4]$	1.7×10^{-24}	23.77
$Cu_3(AsO_4)_2$	7.6×10^{-36}	35.12	$[Na][UO_2][AsO_4]$	1.3×10^{-22}	21.87
$FeAsO_4$	5.8×10^{-21}	20.24	$Zn_3(AsO_4)_2$	1.07×10^{-27}	26.97
$Mg_3(AsO_4)_2$	2.1×10^{-20}	19.68			

Azides

Salt	Constant	pK_{sp}	Salt	Constant	pK_{sp}
AgN_3	2.9×10^{-9}	8.54	$Pb(N_3)_2$	2.5×10^{-11}	10.6
CuN_3	5.0×10^{-9}	8.3	TlN_3	2.19×10^{-4}	3.66
$Hg_2(N_3)_2$	5.0×10^{-19}	18.3			

Benzoates

Salt	Constant	pK_{sp}	Salt	Constant	pK_{sp}
$Ca(C_7H_5O_2)_2\cdot 3\ H_2O$	4×10^{-3}	2.4	$Mg(C_7H_5O_2)_2\cdot 3\ H_2O$	5×10^{-3}	2.3
$Cd(C_7H_5O_2)_2\cdot 2\ H_2O$	2×10^{-3}	2.7	$Mn(C_7H_5O_2)_2\cdot 3\ H_2O$	5×10^{-3}	2.3

Bromates

Compound			Compound		
AgBrO$_3$	4.28	5.25×10^{-5}	La(BrO$_3$)$_3$·9 H$_2$O	2.5	3×10^{-3}
Ba(BrO$_3$)$_2$	5.26	5.5×10^{-6}	Ni(BrO$_3$)$_2$·6 H$_2$O	0.10	8×10^{-1}
CsBrO$_3$	1.7	2×10^{-2}	Pb(BrO$_3$)$_2$·H$_2$O	3.5	3.2×10^{-4}
Hg(BrO$_3$)$_2$·2 H$_2$O	4.	1×10^{-4}	RbBrO$_3$	1.7	2×10^{-2}
KBrO$_3$	1.5	6×10^{-2}	TlBrO$_3$	3.41	3.89×10^{-4}

Bromides

Compound			Compound		
AgBr	12.27	4.27×10^{-13}	HgBr$_2$	18.95	1.12×10^{-19}
AuBr	16.3	5.0×10^{-17}	PbBr$_2$	5.3	4.6×10^{-6}
AuBr$_3$	35.4	4.0×10^{-36}	PtBr$_4$	40.5	3×10^{-41}
CuBr	8.28	5.25×10^{-9}	TlBr	5.41	3.89×10^{-6}
Hg$_2$Br$_2$	21.9	1.26×10^{-22}			

Carbonates*

Compound			Compound		
Ag$_2$CO$_3$	11.09	8.13×10^{-12}	Li[HCO$_3$]	0.3	5×10^{-1}
BaCO$_3$	8.29	5.13×10^{-9}	Na[HCO$_3$]	0.205	6.24×10^{-1}
BeCO$_3$·4 H$_2$O	3.	1×10^{-3}	MgCO$_3$	4.4	4.0×10^{-5}
CaCO$_3$	8.32	4.79×10^{-9}	MnCO$_3$	10.74	1.82×10^{-11}
CaMg(CO$_3$)$_2$	11.	1×10^{-11}	NH$_4$[HCO$_3$]	1.	1×10^{-1}
CdCO$_3$	11.3	5.2×10^{-12}	NiCO$_3$	8.18	6.61×10^{-9}
CoCO$_3$	12.1	8×10^{-13}	PbCO$_3$	13.0	1.0×10^{-13}
CuCO$_3$	9.6	2.5×10^{-10}	SrCO$_3$	9.03	9.4×10^{-10}
FeCO$_3$	10.46	3.47×10^{-11}	Sr(HCO$_3$)$_2$	5.74	1.83×10^{-6}
Gd(HCO$_3$)$_3$	2.8	1.5×10^{-3}	Tl$_2$CO$_3$	2.4	4×10^{-3}
Hg$_2$CO$_3$	16.05	8.91×10^{-17}	ZnCO$_3$	10.84	1.45×10^{-11}
Li$_2$CO$_3$	2.40	3.98×10^{-3}			

Chlorites, Chlorates, and Perchlorates

Compound			Compound		
AgClO$_2$	3.7	2×10^{-4}	Ni(ClO$_3$)$_2$·6 H$_2$O	4.	1×10^{-4}
Pb(ClO$_2$)$_2$	8.4	4×10^{-9}	RbClO$_3$	0.1	8×10^{-1}
AgClO$_3$	1.3	5.0×10^{-2}	TlClO$_3$	2.4	4.0×10^{-3}
Ba(ClO$_3$)$_2$·H$_2$O	0.	1	CsClO$_4$	2.4	4.0×10^{-3}
CsClO$_3$	1.4	4×10^{-2}	KClO$_4$	1.95	1.12×10^{-2}
Hg(ClO$_3$)$_2$	0.	1	RbClO$_4$	2.3	5.0×10^{-3}
KClO$_3$	0.5	0.32	TlClO$_4$	2.4	4×10^{-2}

457

* Groups inclosed in square brackets, [ ], act as a unit.

Salt	Constant	pK_{sp}	Salt	Constant	pK_{sp}
			Chlorides*		
AgCl	1.78×10^{-10}	9.75	Hg_2Cl_2	2.3×10^{-18}	17.88
AuCl	2.0×10^{-13}	12.7	$HgCl_2$	6.1×10^{-15}	14.60
$AuCl_3$	3.2×10^{-25}	24.5	$PbCl_2$	2.6×10^{-5}	4.79
$BaCl_2 \cdot 2 H_2O$	1.6	−0.2	$PtCl_4$	8.0×10^{-29}	28.1
$[BiO]Cl$	7×10^{-9}	8.85	$RaCl_2 \cdot 2 H_2O$	4×10^{-1}	0.4
CuCl	1.2×10^{-6}	5.92	TlCl	1.81×10^{-4}	3.726
			Chloroplatinates, etc.*		
$Cs[AuCl_4]$	1×10^{-3}	3.	$K_2[PtCl_4]$	8×10^{-3}	2.1
$K[AuCl_4]$	1.65	−0.22	$Cs_2[PtCl_6]$	3×10^{-8}	7.5
$Cs[HgCl_3]$	2×10^{-3}	2.7	$K_2[PtCl_6]$	1.4×10^{-6}	5.85
$K_2[IrCl_6]$	6.8×10^{-5}	4.17	$(NH_4)_2[PtCl_6]$	9×10^{-6}	5.05
$(NH_4)_2[IrCl_6]$	3×10^{-5}	4.5	$Rb_2[PtCl_6]$	6×10^{-8}	7.2
K_3IrCl_6	1.26×10^{-1}	0.9	$Tl_2[PtCl_6]$	4×10^{-12}	11.4
$K_2[PdCl_4]$	1.6×10^{-5}	4.9	$Cs_2[SnCl_6]$	3.6×10^{-8}	7.44
$K_2[PdCl_6]$	6.0×10^{-6}	5.2			
			Chromates		
Ag_2CrO_4	1.3×10^{-12}	11.89	Hg_2CrO_4	5.0×10^{-9}	8.70
$Ag_2Cr_2O_7$	1×10^{-10}	10.0	$K_2Cr_2O_7$	2×10^{-2}	1.7
$BaCrO_4$	1.17×10^{-10}	9.93	$PbCrO_4$	1.78×10^{-14}	13.75
$CaCrO_4$	7.1×10^{-4}	3.15	$Rb_2Cr_2O_7$	1×10^{-2}	2.
$CuCrO_4$	3.6×10^{-6}	5.44	$SrCrO_4$	3.75×10^{-5}	4.44
$Dy_2(CrO_4)_3 \cdot 10 H_2O$	1×10^{-8}	8.	Tl_2CrO_4	9.8×10^{-13}	12.01

Cyanamides ($CN_2{}^{2-}$), Cyanates (NCO^-), Dicyanamides [$N(CN)_2{}^-$], Tricyanomethyls [$C(CN)_3{}^-$], and Fulminates (ONC^-)*

Salt	Constant	pK_{sp}	Salt	Constant	pK_{sp}
$Ag_2[CN_2]$	7.2×10^{-11}	10.14	$Ag[C(CN)_3]$	2.2×10^{-9}	8.34
$Ag[NCO]$	2.3×10^{-7}	6.64	$Ag[ONC]$	3×10^{-6}	5.5
$Ag[N(CN)_2]$	1.4×10^{-9}	8.85	$Hg[ONC]_2$	2.5×10^{-27}	26.6

Cyanides

Compound	K_{sp}	pK
AgCN	1.2×10^{-16}	15.92
Cd(CN)$_2$	1.0×10^{-8}	8.0
CuCN	3.2×10^{-20}	19.49
Hg$_2$(CN)$_2$	$5 \times 10^{-40}(?)$	39.3(?)
Hg(CN)$_2$	3×10^{-33}	32.5
Ni(CN)$_2$	3×10^{-23}	22.5
Zn(CN)$_2$	8×10^{-12}	11.1

Cyanoferrates, etc.*

Compound	K_{sp}	pK
Ag$_4$[Fe(CN)$_6$]	1.55×10^{-41}	40.81
Ba$_2$[Fe(CN)$_6$]·6 H$_2$O	3×10^{-8}	7.5
Ca(NH$_4$)$_2$[Fe(CN)$_6$]	4×10^{-8}	7.4
Cd$_2$[Fe(CN)$_6$]	3.2×10^{-17}	16.49
Co$_2$[Fe(CN)$_6$]	1.8×10^{-15}	14.74
Cu$_2$[Fe(CN)$_6$]	1.3×10^{-16}	15.89
Fe$_4$[Fe(CN)$_6$]$_3$	3.0×10^{-41}	40.52
Ga$_4$[Fe(CN)$_6$]$_3$	1.5×10^{-34}	33.82
In$_4$[Fe(CN)$_6$]$_3$	1.9×10^{-44}	43.72
K$_4$[Fe(CN)$_6$]	11.3	-1.05
Mg$_2$[Fe(CN)$_6$]·12 H$_2$O	8×10^{-1}	0.10
MgK$_2$[Fe(CN)$_6$]	5×10^{-9}	8.3
Mg(NH$_4$)$_2$[Fe(CN)$_6$]	4×10^{-8}	7.4
Mn$_2$[Fe(CN)$_6$]	8.0×10^{-13}	12.10
Ni$_2$[Fe(CN)$_6$]	1.3×10^{-15}	14.89
Pb$_2$[Fe(CN)$_6$]	3.5×10^{-15}	14.46
[UO$_2$]$_2$[Fe(CN)$_6$]	7.0×10^{-14}	13.15
Tl$_4$[Fe(CN)$_6$]·2H$_2$O	5×10^{-10}	9.3
Zn$_2$[Fe(CN)$_6$]	4.1×10^{-16}	15.39
Ag$_3$[Fe(CN)$_6$]	1×10^{-22}	22.
K$_3$[Fe(CN)$_6$]	89.	-1.95
K$_5$[Mn(CN)$_6$]	2.4×10^{-11}	10.62
Ba[Pt(CN)$_4$]·4 H$_2$O	4×10^{-3}	2.4
Tl$_2$[Zn(CN)$_4$]	1.7×10^{-2}	1.8

Fluorides

Compound	K_{sp}	pK
BaF$_2$	9.5×10^{-6}	5.98
CaF$_2$	4.0×10^{-11}	10.40
LiF	3.8×10^{-3}	2.42
MgF$_2$	6.5×10^{-9}	8.19
NaF	4×10^{-1}	0.4
PbF$_2$	2.7×10^{-8}	7.57
SrF$_2$	2.4×10^{-9}	8.61
Na$_4$FPO$_4$·12 H$_2$O	6.2×10^{-2}	1.20

Fluoroborates*

Compound	K_{sp}	pK
Cd(NH$_3$)$_6$][BF$_4$]$_2$	2×10^{-6}	5.7
[Co(NH$_3$)$_6$][BF$_4$]$_2$	4×10^{-6}	5.4
[Cr(NH$_3$)$_6$][BF$_4$]$_3$	6.2×10^{-5}	4.21
Cs[BF$_4$]	2×10^{-5}	4.7
K[BF$_4$]	2×10^{-3}	2.7
[Ni(NH$_3$)$_6$][BF$_4$]$_2$	1×10^{-6}	6.0
Rb[BF$_4$]	1×10^{-3}	3.0

* Groups inclosed in square brackets, [], act as a unit.

Salt	Constant	pK_{sp}	Salt	Constant	pK_{sp}
			*Fluorophosphates**		
$Cs[PF_6]$	9.0×10^{-4}	3.05	$Ba[PO_3F]$	4×10^{-7}	6.4
$K[PF_6]$	2.45×10^{-1}	0.61	$Ca[PO_3F] \cdot 2\ H_2O$	4×10^{-3}	2.4
$[Ni(NH_3)_6][PF_6]_2$	2.3×10^{-8}	7.64	$Hg_2[PO_3F]$	3×10^{-7}	6.5
$Rb[PF_6]$	5.8×10^{-3}	2.24	$Pb[PO_3F]$	1×10^{-7}	7.0
$Ag_2[PO_3F]$	9×10^{-4}	3.05	$Sr[PO_3F] \cdot H_2O$	3×10^{-3}	2.5
			*Fluoroplatinates**		
$Cs_2[PtF_6]$	2.39×10^{-6}	5.62	$Na_2[PtF_6]$	2.0	−0.3
$K_2[PtF_6]$	2.9×10^{-5}	4.54	$Rb_2[PtF_6]$	7.63×10^{-7}	6.12
$(NH_4)_2[PtF_6]$	3.8×10^{-2}	1.42			
			*Fluorosilicates**		
$Ba[SiF_6]$	1×10^{-6}	6.	$(NH_4)_2[SiF_6]$	4.55	−0.658
$Ca[SiF_6]$	8.1×10^{-4}	3.09	$Na_2[SiF_6]$	5×10^{-4}	3.3
$Cs_2[SiF_6]$	1.26×10^{-5}	4.90	$Rb_2[SiF_6]$	5×10^{-7}	6.3
$K_2[SiF_6]$	4×10^{-5}	4.4	$Sr[SiF_6] \cdot 2\ H_2O$	1.5×10^{-2}	1.82
		*Fluoroaluminates, Fluoroberyllates, Fluorosulfonates, etc.**			
$Na_3[AlF_6]$	4.1×10^{-10}	9.39	$K_2[SnF_6]$	6×10^{-3}	2.2
$K_3[AlF_6]$	1.6×10^{-9}	8.80	$[Cr(NH_3)_6][SO_3F]_3$	4.3×10^{-4}	3.37
$(NH_4)_3[AlF_6]$	1.6×10^{-3}	2.80	$Cs[SO_3F]$	1×10^{-2}	2.
$K_2[BeF_4]$	8×10^{-2}	1.1	$K[SO_3F]$	2.5×10^{-1}	0.60
$Na_2[BeF_4]$	7×10^{-3}	2.15	$Li_2[TiF_6]$	11.5	−1.06
$K_2[GeF_6]$	3.0×10^{-5}	4.52	$K_2[TiF_6] \cdot H_2O$	5×10^{-4}	3.3
$K_2[HfF_6]$	2×10^{-3}	2.7	$Rb_2[TiF_6]$	5.5×10^{-5}	4.26
$K_2[NbOF_6]$	6.0×10^{-2}	1.22	$K_2[ZrF_6]$	5×10^{-4}	3.3
			Formates		
$Ca(CHO_2)_2$	2.5×10^{-6}	5.6	$Mn(CHO_2)_2$	56.	−1.75
$Co(CHO_2)_2$	8×10^{-2}	1.1	$Pb(CHO_2)_2$	2×10^{-7}	6.7
$Hg_2(CHO_2)_2$	2×10^{-5}	4.7	$Sr(CHO_2)_2$	5×10^{-2}	1.3
$Mg(CHO_2)_2 \cdot 2\ H_2O$	3×10^{-1}	0.5	$Zn(CHO_2)_2$	5×10^{-4}	3.3

Hydroxides*

Compound	K_{sp}	pK_{sp}	Compound	K_{sp}	pK_{sp}
Ac(OH)₃	10^{-15}	15.	[HfO](OH)₂	4×10^{-26}	25.4
½ Ag₂O	2×10^{-8}	7.7	Hg₂O	1.6×10^{-23}	22.8
Al(OH)₃	2.5×10^{-32}	31.59	HgO	2.5×10^{-26}	25.60
Am(OH)₃	2.7×10^{-20}	19.57	Ho(OH)₃	5×10^{-23}	22.3
Am(OH)₄	10^{-56}	56.	In(OH)₃	5×10^{-34}	33.3
¼ As₂O₃†	9.5×10^{-16}	15.02	½ Ir₂O₃	2×10^{-48}	47.7
Au(OH)₃	10^{-53}	53.	IrO₂	1.6×10^{-72}	71.8
Ba(OH)₂	5.0×10^{-3}	2.3	La(OH)₃	1.0×10^{-19}	19.0
Be(OH)₂	2×10^{-18}	17.7	LiOH	4×10^{-2}	1.4
[BiO]OH	1.0×10^{-12}	12.0	Lu(OH)₃	2.5×10^{-24}	23.6
Bi(OH)₃	3.2×10^{-40}	39.5	Mg(OH)₂	9.0×10^{-12}	11.05
Ca(OH)₂	7.9×10^{-6}	5.1	Mn(OH)₂	4.6×10^{-14}	13.34
Cd(OH)₂	2.0×10^{-14}	13.70	Mn(OH)₃	10^{-36}	36.
Ce(OH)₃	1.5×10^{-20}	19.82	Mo(OH)₄	1×10^{-50}	50.0
CeO₂	8×10^{-37}	36.1	Nd(OH)₃	1.9×10^{-21}	20.32
Cm(OH)₃	1.9×10^{-21}	20.72	Ni(OH)₂	2.8×10^{-16}	15.55
Co(OH)₂	2.5×10^{-16}	15.60	[NpO₂](OH)₂	2.5×10^{-22}	21.6
Co(OH)₃	4×10^{-45}	44.4	Pb(OH)₂	4.0×10^{-15}	14.40
Cr(OH)₂	1.0×10^{-17}	17.00	PbO₂	3×10^{-66}	65.5
Cr(OH)₃	5×10^{-31}	30.3	Pd(OH)₂	1×10^{-31}	31.0
½ Cu₂O	1×10^{-14}	14.0	Pd(OH)₄	6.5×10^{-71}	70.2
Cu(OH)₂	1.6×10^{-19}	18.8	Pm(OH)₃	10^{-21}	21.
Dy(OH)₃	1.4×10^{-22}	21.85	Pr(OH)₃	2.7×10^{-20}	19.57
Er(OH)₃	1.3×10^{-23}	22.88	Pt(OH)₂	10^{-35}	35.
Eu(OH)₃	3.4×10^{-22}	21.47	PtO₂	1.6×10^{-72}	71.8
Fe(OH)₂	7.9×10^{-15}	14.10	Pu(OH)₃	2×10^{-20}	19.7
Fe(OH)₃	6.3×10^{-38}	37.2	Pu(OH)₄	10^{-52}	52.
Ga(OH)₃	5.0×10^{-36}	35.3	[PuO₂]OH	10^{-3}	3.
Gd(OH)₃	2.1×10^{-22}	21.68	[PuO₂](OH)₂	3.2×10^{-21}	20.5
GeO₂	1×10^{-57}	57.0	½ Rh₂O₃	2×10^{-48}	47.7

* Groups inclosed in square brackets, [], act as a unit.

† ¼ As₂O₃ (s) + ¼ H₂O ⇌ AsO⁺ + OH⁻.

Salt	Constant	pK_{sp}	Salt	Constant	pK_{sp}
			Hydroxides—continued		
$\frac{1}{2}Ru_2O_3$	1×10^{-45}	45.0	$Tu(OH)_3$	3.3×10^{-24}	23.48
$\frac{1}{2}Sb_2O_3$	4×10^{-42}	41.4	$U(OH)_3$	1×10^{-19}	19.0
$Sc(OH)_3$	10^{-27}	27.	$U(OH)_4$	1×10^{-45}	45.0
$Sm(OH)_3$	6.8×10^{-22}	21.17	$[UO_2](OH)_2$	1×10^{-22}	22.0
$Sn(OH)_2$	2.0×10^{-26}	25.70	$[VO](OH)_2$	7.4×10^{-23}	22.13
$Sn(OH)_4$	1×10^{-57}	57.0	$\frac{1}{2}V_2O_5\ddagger$	1.6×10^{-15}	14.8
$Sr(OH)_2$	3.2×10^{-4}	3.50	$W(OH)_4$	1×10^{-50}	50.0
$Tb(OH)_3$	2.0×10^{-22}	21.70	$Y(OH)_3$	8×10^{-23}	22.1
$Te(OH)_4$	3.0×10^{-54}	53.52	$Yb(OH)_3$	2.9×10^{-24}	23.54
$Th(OH)_4$	3.2×10^{-45}	44.5	$Zn(OH)_2$	1.9×10^{-17}	16.32
$[TiO](OH)_2$	10^{-29}	29.	$[ZrO](OH)_2$	2.5×10^{-29}	28.6
$TlOH$	6.3×10^{-1}	0.2	$Zr(OH)_4$	1.6×10^{-56}	55.8
$Tl(OH)_3$	1.6×10^{-44}	43.8			
			*Iodates**		
$AgIO_3$	3.1×10^{-8}	7.51	$Mg(IO_3)_2 \cdot 4 H_2O$	3×10^{-3}	2.5
$Ba(IO_3)_2$	1.50×10^{-9}	8.82	NH_4IO_3	2×10^{-2}	1.7
$Ca(IO_3)_2$	7.0×10^{-7}	6.15	$NaIO_3$	2×10^{-1}	0.7
$Ce(IO_3)_3$	3.2×10^{-10}	9.50	$Ni(IO_3)_2$	1.40×10^{-8}	7.85
$Ce(IO_3)_4$	5×10^{-17}	16.3	$Pb(IO_3)_2$	2.6×10^{-13}	12.58
$Co(IO_3)_2$	1.0×10^{-4}	4.0	$Pu(IO_3)_4$	5×10^{-13}	12.3
$CsIO_3$	1.0×10^{-2}	2.0	$Ra(IO_3)_2$	8.8×10^{-10}	9.06
$Cu(IO_3)_2$	7.4×10^{-8}	7.13	$RbIO_3$	1.0×10^{-2}	2.0
$Hg_2(IO_3)_2$	2.45×10^{-14}	13.71	$Sr(IO_3)_2$	3.3×10^{-7}	6.48
$Hg(IO_3)_2$	3×10^{-13}	12.5	$Th(IO_3)_4$	2.5×10^{-15}	14.6
$In(IO_3)_3$	3×10^{-3}	2.5	$TlIO_3$	3.1×10^{-6}	5.51
KIO_3	4×10^{-2}	1.4	$[UO_2](IO_3)_2 H_2O$	3×10^{-8}	7.5
$La(IO_3)_3$	6.2×10^{-12}	11.21	$Zn(IO_3)_2$	2×10^{-8}	7.7

Periodates

Compound	K_{sp}	pK	Compound	K_{sp}	pK
$CsIO_4$	4.4×10^{-3}	2.36	$NaIO_4$	3×10^{-3}	2.5
KIO_4	8.3×10^{-4}	3.08	$RbIO_4$	5.5×10^{-4}	3.26
NH_4IO_4	2×10^{-2}	1.7			

Iodides

Compound	K_{sp}	pK	Compound	K_{sp}	pK
AgI	8.30×10^{-17}	16.081	Hg_2I_2	4.5×10^{-29}	28.35
AuI	1.6×10^{-23}	22.8	HgI_2	4×10^{-29}	28.4
AuI_3	1×10^{-46}	46.	PbI_2	1.05×10^{-9}	8.98
BiI_3	8.1×10^{-19}	18.09	SnI_2	1.0×10^{-4}	4.0
CsI	1.1	−0.04	TlI	6.5×10^{-8}	7.19
CuI	1.1×10^{-12}	11.96			

Manganates and Permanganates*

Compound	K_{sp}	pK	Compound	K_{sp}	pK
$BaMnO_4$	2.45×10^{-10}	9.61	$KMnO_4$	5.6×10^{-2}	1.25
$AgMnO_4$	1.0×10^{-3}	2.79	NH_4MnO_4	3×10^{-1}	0.5
$[Cr(NH_3)_6](MnO_4)_3$	4.0×10^{-8}	7.40	$RbMnO_4$	2.9×10^{-3}	2.54
$CsMnO_4$	9.1×10^{-5}	4.08			

Molybdates

Compound	K_{sp}	pK	Compound	K_{sp}	pK
Ag_2MoO_4	2.8×10^{-12}	11.55	$Na_2Mo_9O_{10} \cdot 7\ H_2O$	1×10^{-6}	6.0
$BaMoO_4$	4×10^{-8}	7.40	$PbMoO_4$	4×10^{-6}	5.4
$BeMoO_4$	3.5×10^{-2}	1.5	$SrMoO_4$	2×10^{-7}	6.7
$La_2(MoO_4)_3$	4×10^{-21}	20.4			

Nitrates

Compound	K_{sp}	pK	Compound	K_{sp}	pK
$Ba(NO_3)_2$	4.5×10^{-3}	2.35	$Ra(NO_3)_2$	6.2×10^{-3}	2.21
$CsNO_3$	1.32×10^{-1}	0.88	$RbNO_3$	2.45	−0.39
KNO_3	9.6	−0.98	$TlNO_3$	7.0×10^{-1}	0.15
$Pb(NO_3)_2$	5.6×10^{-2}	1.25			

* Groups inclosed in square brackets, [], act as a unit.

$\ddagger\ \tfrac{1}{2} V_2O_5 + \tfrac{1}{2} H_2O \rightleftharpoons VO_2^+ + OH^-$.

Salt	Constant	pK_{sp}
Oxalates*		
$Ac_2(C_2O_4)_3$	2×10^{-24}	23.7
$Ag_2C_2O_4$	1×10^{-11}	11.
$Au_2(C_2O_4)_3$	10^{-10}	10.
BaC_2O_4	1.1×10^{-7}	6.96
CaC_2O_4	1.3×10^{-9}	8.8
CdC_2O_4	1.5×10^{-8}	7.8
$Ce_2(C_2O_4)_3 \cdot 10\ H_2O$	2.5×10^{-29}	28.60
CoC_2O_4	4×10^{-8}	7.4
CuC_2O_4	3×10^{-8}	7.5
FeC_2O_4	2×10^{-7}	6.7
$Hg_2C_2O_4$	1×10^{-13}	13.
HgC_2O_4	1×10^{-5}	5.
$K[HC_2O_4] \cdot \frac{1}{2}\ H_2O$	4×10^{-1}	0.4
Hypophosphites, Phosphites, and Hypophosphates		
$Fe(PH_2O_2)_3$	3×10^{-10}	9.5
$Mn(PH_2O_2)_2$	5×10^{-1}	0.3
$BaPHO_3 \cdot \frac{1}{2}\ H_2O$	1×10^{-3}	3.
$MgPHO_3 \cdot 3\ H_2O$	5×10^{-4}	3.3
Phosphates*		
Ag_3PO_4	1.3×10^{-20}	19.89
$AlPO_4$	5.75×10^{-19}	18.24
$Ba_3(PO_4)_2$	6.03×10^{-39}	38.22
$Ba[HPO_4]$	3×10^{-7}	6.5
$Ba_2P_2O_7$	3×10^{-11}	10.5
$BiPO_4$	1.3×10^{-23}	22.89
$Ca_3(PO_4)_2$	2.0×10^{-29}	28.70
$Ca[HPO_4]$	2.7×10^{-7}	6.57
$Ca[H_2PO_4]_2$	1×10^{-3}	3.

Salt	Constant	pK_{sp}
$La_2(C_2O_4)_3 \cdot 9\ H_2O$	4×10^{-26}	25.4
$LiHC_2O_4 \cdot H_2O$	5×10^{-1}	0.3
MgC_2O_4	8.6×10^{-5}	4.1
MnC_2O_4	1×10^{-15}	15.
$(NH_4)_2C_2O_4$	2×10^{-1}	0.7
$Na[HC_2O_4] \cdot H_2O$	3×10^{-2}	1.5
NiC_2O_4	4×10^{-10}	9.4
PbC_2O_4	8.3×10^{-12}	11.1
SrC_2O_4	5.61×10^{-8}	7.2
$Th(C_2O_4)_2$	$2.0 . 10^{-5}$	4.70
$[UO_2]C_2O_4 \cdot 3\ H_2O$	4×10^{-4}	3.4
ZnC_2O_4	1.5×10^{-9}	8.8
$PbPHO_3$	5.6×10^{-7}	6.25
$Na_4P_2O_6 \cdot 10\ H_2O$	2×10^{-8}	7.7
$Na_2H_2P_2O_6 \cdot 6\ H_2O$	1×10^{-3}	3.
$Li_4P_2O_6 \cdot 7\ H_2O$	1×10^{-11}	11.
Na_3PO_4	1.5	-0.17
$Na_4FPO_4 \cdot 12\ H_2O$	6.2×10^{-2}	1.20
$Na_4P_2O_7 \cdot 10\ H_2O$	1×10^{-2}	2.
$NaNH_4[HPO_4] \cdot 4\ H_2O$	5×10^{-4}	3.3
$Pb_3(PO_4)_2$	8.0×10^{-43}	42.10
$Pb[HPO_4]$	1.26×10^{-10}	9.90
$Pb_5(PO_4)_3Cl$	7.5×10^{-80}	79.12
$Sr_3(PO_4)_2$	1×10^{-31}	31.
$Sr[HPO_4]$	2×10^{-4}	3.7

$Ca_5(PO_4)_3OH$	1.6×10^{-58}	57.8	$Th_3(PO_4)_4$	2.57×10^{-79}	78.59
$CrPO_4$ (green)	2.4×10^{-23}	22.62	$Th[HPO_4]_2$	9.1×10^{-22}	21.04
$CrPO_4$ (violet)	1.00×10^{-17}	17.00	Tl_3PO_4	6.7×10^{-8}	7.18
$FePO_4$	1.30×10^{-22}	21.89	$Tl_4P_2O_7$	2.6	−0.42
$Hg_2[HPO_4]$	4.0×10^{-13}	12.40	$[UO_2][HPO_4]$	2.14×10^{-11}	10.67
Li_3PO_4	3.2×10^{-9}	8.5	$K[UO_2]PO_4$	7.8×10^{-24}	23.11
$Mg_3(PO_4)_2 \cdot 4\ H_2O$	1×10^{-13}	13.	$NH_4[UO_2]PO_4$	4.4×10^{-27}	26.36
$Mg[HPO_4]3\ H_2O$	1×10^{-4}	4.	$[VO]_3(PO_4)_2$	8×10^{-25}	24.1
$MgNH_4PO_4$	2.5×10^{-12}	12.6	$Zn_3(PO_4)_2$	9.1×10^{-33}	32.04
$MnNH_4PO_4 \cdot H_2O$	1×10^{-12}	12.	$Zr_3(PO_4)_4$	10^{-132}	132.

*Perrhenates**

$AgReO_4$	7.95×10^{-5}	4.10	$KReO_4$	1.9×10^{-3}	2.72
$Ba(ReO_4)_2$	5.25×10^{-2}	1.28	NH_4ReO_4	5.2×10^{-2}	1.28
$[Co(NH_3)_6](ReO_4)_3$	1.7×10^{-12}	11.77	$[Ni(NH_3)_6](ReO_4)_2$	5.1×10^{-4}	3.29
$[Cr(NH_3)_6](ReO_4)_3$	7.7×10^{-12}	11.11	$RbReO_4$	9.6×10^{-4}	3.02
$CsReO_4$	4.0×10^{-4}	3.40	$TlReO_4$	1.21×10^{-5}	4.92

Selenates

Ag_2SeO_4	5.6×10^{-8}	7.25	$CuSeO_4 \cdot 5\ H_2O$	8×10^{-1}	0.1
$BaSeO_4$	2.8×10^{-11}	10.55	$PbSeO_4$	1.45×10^{-7}	6.84
$CaSeO_4$	5×10^{-1}	0.3	Tl_2SeO_4	5×10^{-4}	3.3

Selenides

Al_2Se_3	4×10^{-25}	24.4	$HgSe$	1×10^{-59}	59.
Bi_2Se_3	1×10^{-146}	146.	$PbSe$	1×10^{-38}	38.
$CuSe$	1×10^{-49}	49.	Tl_2Se	1.0×10^{-35}	35.0
$FeSe$	1×10^{-26}	26.	$ZnSe$	1×10^{-31}	31.

Selenites

Ag_2SeO_3	9.8×10^{-16}	15.01	$HgSeO_3$	1.50×10^{-14}	13.82
$CaSeO_3$	4.7×10^{-6}	5.53	$MgSeO_3$	1.30×10^{-5}	4.89
$CdSeO_3$	1.30×10^{-9}	8.89	$MnSeO_3$	1.26×10^{-7}	6.9
$Ce_2(SeO_3)_3$	3.75×10^{-25}	24.43	$NiSeO_3$	1.0×10^{-5}	5.0
$CoSeO_3$	1.6×10^{-7}	6.8	$PbSeO_3$	3×10^{-12}	11.5
$CuSeO_3$	2.1×10^{-8}	7.68	$SrSeO_3$	8.5×10^{-7}	6.07
$Fe_2(SeO_3)_3$	2×10^{-31}	30.7	$ZnSeO_3$	2.57×10^{-7}	6.59
Hg_2SeO_3	6.3×10^{-15}	14.2			

* Groups inclosed in square brackets, [], act as a unit.

Sulfates*

Salt	Constant	pK_{sp}	Salt	Constant	Kp_{sp}
Ag_2SO_4	1.70×10^{-5}	4.77	$La_2(SO_4)_3$	3×10^{-5}	4.5
$BaSO_4$	8.7×10^{-11}	10.06	Li_2SO_4	7.6	-0.88
$Ba[HSO_4]_2$	2.7	-0.43	Na_2SO_4	1.55	-0.19
$CaSO_4$	2.37×10^{-5}	4.625	$PbSO_4$	1.60×10^{-8}	7.80
$CaK_2(SO_4)_2 \cdot H_2O$	1×10^{-9}	9.	$Pb[HSO_4]_2 \cdot H_2O$	6×10^{-17}	16.2
$Ce_2(SO_4)_3$	2×10^{-2}	1.7	$Po(SO_4)_2$	2.6×10^{-7}	6.58
$CeNH_4(SO_4)_2$	4×10^{-8}	7.4	$RaSO_4$	4.2×10^{-15}	14.38
$CrSO_4$	3×10^{-1}	0.5	Rb_2SO_4	3.6×10^{-1}	0.44
Cs_2SO_4	12.6	-1.10	$SrSO_4$	3.2×10^{-7}	6.49
Hg_2SO_4	6.8×10^{-7}	6.17	$Th(SO_4)_2$	4×10^{-3}	2.4
$HgSO_4$	4.3×10^{-2}	1.43	Tl_2SO_4	4×10^{-3}	2.4
K_2SO_4	2.04×10^{-2}	1.69	$U(SO_4)_2 \cdot 4 H_2O$	1×10^{-1}	1.
$KHSO_4$	2×10^{-1}	0.7	$[UO_2]SO_4 \cdot 3 H_2O$	4×10^{-2}	1.4

Sulfides*

Salt	Constant	pK_{sp}	Salt	Constant	Kp_{sp}
Ag_2S	5.5×10^{-51}	50.26	La_2S_3	3×10^{-14}	13.5
Al_2S_3	2×10^{-7}	6.7	MgS	690	-2.42
Bi_2S_3	1.6×10^{-121}	120.8	MnS (pink)	2.5×10^{-10}	9.6
CaS	5.8×10^{-8}	7.24	MnS (green)	2.5×10^{-13}	12.6
CdS	5×10^{-28}	27.3	NiS (α)	1.0×10^{-22}	22.0
Ce_2S_3	2×10^{-12}	11.7	NiS (β)	3×10^{-28}	27.5
CoS (α)	5×10^{-22}	21.3	NiS (γ)	7.0×10^{-30}	29.15
CoS (β)	6.0×10^{-29}	28.22	$Os[S_2]$	1×10^{-75}	75.
Co_2S_3	1×10^{-124}	124.	PbS	1.3×10^{-28}	27.9
Cu_2S	1.20×10^{-49}	48.92	PoS	5×10^{-29}	28.3
CuS	8.0×10^{-36}	35.10	PtS	8×10^{-73}	72.1
FeS	5×10^{-18}	17.3	$Pt[S_2]$	1.0×10^{-75}	75.0
$Fe[S_2]$	6.3×10^{-31}	30.2	$Ru[S_2]$	3×10^{-66}	65.5
Fe_2S_3	1.0×10^{-88}	88.0	Sb_2S_3	1.6×10^{-93}	92.8
GeS	3×10^{-35}	34.5	SnS	1.3×10^{-27}	26.9

Compound			Compound		
Hg$_2$S	47.0	1.0×10^{-47}	SnS$_2$	10^{-70}	70.
HgS	51.8	1.60×10^{-52}	SrS	500	−2.7
In$_2$S$_3$	88.	1×10^{-88}	Tl$_2$S	6.3×10^{-21}	20.2
Ir[S$_2$]	75.	1×10^{-75}	ZnS (α, sphalerite)	7.0×10^{-26}	25.15
Ir$_2$S$_3$	185.2	6.3×10^{-186}	ZnS (β, wurtzite)	1.60×10^{-23}	22.80

Sulfites

Compound			Compound		
Ag$_2$SO$_3$	13.82	1.50×10^{-14}	Na$_2$SO$_3$·7 H$_2$O	5×10^{-1}	0.3
BaSO$_3$	6.1	8.0×10^{-7}	SrSO$_3$	4×10^{-8}	7.4
CaSO$_3$·2 H$_2$O	7.89	1.3×10^{-8}	Tl$_2$SO$_3$	6.3×10^{-4}	3.2
Hg$_2$SO$_3$	27.0	1.0×10^{-27}	ZnSO$_3$	1×10^{-2}	2.
MgSO$_3$	2.5	3×10^{-3}			

Tellurides

Compound			Compound		
Bi$_2$Te$_3$	164.	1×10^{-164}	PbTe	1×10^{-48}	48.
CdTe	42.	1×10^{-42}	Tl$_2$Te	3×10^{-34}	33.5

Thiocyanates

Compound			Compound		
AgNCS	12.0	1.0×10^{-12}	Hg(NCS)$_2$	3×10^{-21}	20.5
CuNCS	10.8	1.6×10^{-11}	Pb(NCS)$_2$	3×10^{-8}	7.5
Hg$_2$(NCS)$_2$	19.52	3.0×10^{-20}	TlNCS	1.70×10^{-4}	3.77

Thiosulfates

Compound			Compound		
BaS$_2$O$_3$	4.2	6×10^{-5}	SrS$_2$O$_3$·5 H$_2$O	3×10^{-1}	0.5
Hg$_2$S$_2$O$_3$	34.7	2×10^{-35}	Tl$_2$S$_2$O$_3$	2.0×10^{-7}	6.70
PbS$_2$O$_3$	3.2	6×10^{-4}			

Tungstates

Compound			Compound		
Ag$_2$WO$_4$	11.26	5.5×10^{-12}	Hg$_2$WO$_4$	1.10×10^{-17}	16.96
BaWO$_4$	14.6	2.5×10^{-15}	La$_2$(WO$_4$)$_3$·3 H$_2$O	1.25×10^{-4}	3.90
CaWO$_4$	8.06	9.0×10^{-9}	PbWO$_4$	4.5×10^{-7}	6.35
CdWO$_4$	5.7	2×10^{-6}	SrWO$_4$	2.2×10^{-10}	9.77
CuWO$_4$·2 H$_2$O	5.	1×10^{-5}			

* Groups inclosed in square brackets, [], act as a unit.

467

Vanadates*

Salt	Constant	pK_{sp}
$AgVO_3$	5×10^{-7}	6.3
$Ag_2[HVO_4]$	2×10^{-14}	13.7
$Ag_3[HVO_4]OH$	1×10^{-24}	24.
NH_4VO_3	1×10^{-3}	3.
$TlVO_3$	1×10^{-5}	5.
$Tl_4V_2O_7$	1×10^{-11}	11.

Miscellaneous*

Salt	Constant	pK_{sp}
Ag_8AsO_6	1×10^{-17}	17.
$Fe[(CH_3)_2AsO_2]_3$	1×10^{-2}	2.
$K[AuBr_4] \cdot 2 \, H_2O$	1.24×10^{-1}	0.91
$Cs[BH_4]$	2.5×10^{-7}	6.6
$K[BH_4]$	1.3×10^{-3}	2.9
$NaBH_4$	$1.41 \times 10^{+4}$	-4.15
$Rb[BH_4]$	2.5×10^{-4}	3.6
$AgBO_2$	4×10^{-1}	0.4
$K[B(C_6H_5)_4]$	2.25×10^{-8}	7.65
$Na[B(C_6H_5)_4]$	2.14×10^{-2}	1.67
$K_3[Co(NO_2)_6] \cdot \frac{1}{2} \, H_2O$	4.3×10^{-10}	9.37
$K_2Na[Co(NO_2)_6] \cdot H_2O$	2.2×10^{-11}	10.66
$Rb_3[Co(NO_2)_6]$	1.48×10^{-15}	14.83
$Cs_3[Co(NO_2)_6]$	5.8×10^{-16}	15.24
$(NH_4)_3[Co(NO_2)_6]$	7.6×10^{-6}	5.12
$Tl_3[Co(NO_2)_6]$	1.01×10^{-16}	15.996
$[C_2H_5NH_3]_3[Co(NO_2)_6]$	7.5	-0.88
$Co[Hg(NCS)_4]$	1.50×10^{-6}	5.82
$Zn[Hg(NCS)_4]$	2.2×10^{-7}	6.66
$Ag_2[N_2O_2]$	1.6×10^{-30}	29.8
$AgNO_2$	1.6×10^{-4}	3.8
$TlNO_2$	1.6	-0.2
$K_2[PtBr_4]$	4×10^{-3}	2.4
$K_2[PtBr_6]$	6×10^{-5}	4.2
$(NH_4)_2[PtBr_6]$	4×10^{-6}	5.4
$K_2[Pt(NO_2)_4]$	4×10^{-3}	2.4
$Ag[SO_3NH_2]$	1×10^{-1}	1.
$K[Sb(OH)_6]$	4×10^{-3}	2.4
$Na[Sb(OH)_6]$	4×10^{-8}	7.4
$Ag[NCSe]$	4.0×10^{-16}	15.40
$(NH_4)_4[UO_2(CO_3)_3] \cdot 2 \, H_2O$	6×10^{-5}	4.2
$K_4[UO_2(CO_3)_3]$	6×10^{-5}	4.2

* Groups inclosed in square brackets, [], act as a unit.

Electronic Configurations of the Elements

Symbol	Z	1s	2s	2p	3s	3p	3d	4s	4p	4d	4f	5s	5p	5d	5f	6s	6p	6d	7s
H	1	**1***																	
He	2	**2**																	
Li	3	2	**1**																
Be	4	2	**2**																
B	5	2	**2**	**1**															
C	6	2	**2**	**2**															
N	7	2	**2**	**3**															
O	8	2	**2**	**4**															
F	9	2	**2**	**5**															
Ne	10	2	**2**	**6**															
Na	11	2	2	6	**1**														
Mg	12	2	2	6	**2**														
Al	13	2	2	6	**2**	**1**													
Si	14	2	2	6	**2**	**2**													
P	15	2	2	6	**2**	**3**													
S	16	2	2	6	**2**	**4**													
Cl	17	2	2	6	**2**	**5**													
Ar	18	2	2	6	**2**	**6**													
K	19	2	2	6	2	6		**1**											
Ca	20	2	2	6	2	6		**2**											
Sc	21	2	2	6	2	6	**1**	**2**											
Ti	22	2	2	6	2	6	**2**	**2**											
V	23	2	2	6	2	6	**3**	**2**											
Cr	24	2	2	6	2	6	**5**	**1**											
Mn	25	2	2	6	2	6	**5**	**2**											
Fe	26	2	2	6	2	6	**6**	**2**											
Co	27	2	2	6	2	6	**7**	**2**											
Ni	28	2	2	6	2	6	**8**	**2**											
Cu	29	2	2	6	2	6	**10**	**1**											
Zn	30	2	2	6	2	6	10	**2**											
Ga	31	2	2	6	2	6	10	**2**	**1**										
Ge	32	2	2	6	2	6	10	**2**	**2**										

* Electrons in the Valence Levels are Shown in Bold-Faced Type.

Symbol	Z	1s	2s	2p	3s	3p	3d	4s	4p	4d	4f	5s	5p	5d	5f	6s	6p	6d	7s
As	33	2	2	6	2	6	10	2	3										
Se	34	2	2	6	2	6	10	2	4										
Br	35	2	2	6	2	6	10	2	5										
Kr	36	2	2	6	2	6	10	2	6										
Rb	37	2	2	6	2	6	10	2	6										
Sr	38	2	2	6	2	6	10	2	6			2							
Y	39	2	2	6	2	6	10	2	6	1		2							
Zr	40	2	2	6	2	6	10	2	6	2		2							
Nb	41	2	2	6	2	6	10	2	6	4		1							
Mo	42	2	2	6	2	6	10	2	6	5		1							
Tc	43	2	2	6	2	6	10	2	6	6		1							
Ru	44	2	2	6	2	6	10	2	6	7		1							
Rh	45	2	2	6	2	6	10	2	6	8		1							
Pd	46	2	2	6	2	6	10	2	6	10									
Ag	47	2	2	6	2	6	10	2	6	10		1							
Cd	48	2	2	6	2	6	10	2	6	10		2							
In	49	2	2	6	2	6	10	2	6	10		2	1						
Sn	50	2	2	6	2	6	10	2	6	10		2	2						
Sb	51	2	2	6	2	6	10	2	6	10		2	3						
Te	52	2	2	6	2	6	10	2	6	10		2	4						
I	53	2	2	6	2	6	10	2	6	10		2	5						
Xe	54	2	2	6	2	6	10	2	6	10		2	6						
Cs	55	2	2	6	2	6	10	2	6	10		2	6			1			
Ba	56	2	2	6	2	6	10	2	6	10		2	6			2			
La	57	2	2	6	2	6	10	2	6	10		2	6	1		2			
Ce	58	2	2	6	2	6	10	2	6	10	1	2	6	1		2			
Pr	59	2	2	6	2	6	10	2	6	10	3	2	6			2			
Nd	60	2	2	6	2	6	10	2	6	10	4	2	6			2			
Pm	61	2	2	6	2	6	10	2	6	10	5	2	6			2			
Sm	62	2	2	6	2	6	10	2	6	10	6	2	6			2			
Eu	63	2	2	6	2	6	10	2	6	10	7	2	6			2			
Gd	64	2	2	6	2	6	10	2	6	10	7	2	6	1		2			
Tb	65	2	2	6	2	6	10	2	6	10	*	2	6	*		2			
Dy	66	2	2	6	2	6	10	2	6	10	10	2	6			2			
Ho	67	2	2	6	2	6	10	2	6	10	11	2	6			2			
Er	68	2	2	6	2	6	10	2	6	10	12	2	6			2			
Tu	69	2	2	6	2	6	10	2	6	10	13	2	6			2			
Yb	70	2	2	6	2	6	10	2	6	10	14	2	6			2			
Lu	71	2	2	6	2	6	10	2	6	10	14	2	6	1		2			
Hf	72	2	2	6	2	6	10	2	6	10	14	2	6	2		2			
Ta	73	2	2	6	2	6	10	2	6	10	14	2	6	3		2			
W	74	2	2	6	2	6	10	2	6	10	14	2	6	4		2			
Re	75	2	2	6	2	6	10	2	6	10	14	2	6	5		2			
Os	76	2	2	6	2	6	10	2	6	10	14	2	6	6		2			
Ir	77	2	2	6	2	6	10	2	6	10	14	2	6	9					
Pt	78	2	2	6	2	6	10	2	6	10	14	2	6	9		1			
Au	79	2	2	6	2	6	10	2	6	10	14	2	6	10		1			
Hg	80	2	2	6	2	6	10	2	6	10	14	2	6	10		2			
Tl	81	2	2	6	2	6	10	2	6	10	14	2	6	10		2	1		
Pb	82	2	2	6	2	6	10	2	6	10	14	2	6	10		2	2		
Bi	83	2	2	6	2	6	10	2	6	10	14	2	6	10		2	3		

* Terbium has a mixed ground state: $(4f^8 5d^1 + 4f^9 5d^0)$.

Symbol	Z	1s	2s	2p	3s	3p	3d	4s	4p	4d	4f	5s	5p	5d	5f	6s	6p	6d	7s
Po	84	2	2	6	2	6	10	2	6	10	14	2	6	10		2	4		
At	85	2	2	6	2	6	10	2	6	10	14	2	6	10		2	5		
Rn	86	2	2	6	2	6	10	2	6	10	14	2	6	10		2	6		
Fr	87	2	2	6	2	6	10	2	6	10	14	2	6	10		2	6		1
Ra	88	2	2	6	2	6	10	2	6	10	14	2	6	10		2	6		2
Ac	89	2	2	6	2	6	10	2	6	10	14	2	6	10		2	6	1	2
Th	90	2	2	6	2	6	10	2	6	10	14	2	6	10		2	6	2	2
Pa	91	2	2	6	2	6	10	2	6	10	14	2	6	10	2	2	6	1	2
U	92	2	2	6	2	6	10	2	6	10	14	2	6	10	3	2	6	1	2
Np	93	2	2	6	2	6	10	2	6	10	14	2	6	10	4	2	6	1	2
Pu	94	2	2	6	2	6	10	2	6	10	14	2	6	10	6	2	6		2
Am	95	2	2	6	2	6	10	2	6	10	14	2	6	10	7	2	6		2
Cm	96	2	2	6	2	6	10	2	6	10	14	2	6	10	7	2	6	1	2
Bk*	97	2	2	6	2	6	10	2	6	10	14	2	6	10	9	2	6		2
Cf*	98	2	2	6	2	6	10	2	6	10	14	2	6	10	10	2	6		2
Es*	99	2	2	6	2	6	10	2	6	10	14	2	6	10	11	2	6		2
Fm*	100	2	2	6	2	6	10	2	6	10	14	2	6	10	12	2	6		2
Md*	101	2	2	6	2	6	10	2	6	10	14	2	6	10	13	2	6		2
*	102	2	2	6	2	6	10	2	6	10	14	2	6	10	14	2	6		2
	103	2	2	6	2	6	10	2	6	10	14	2	6	10	14	2	6	1	2
	104	2	2	6	2	6	10	2	6	10	14	2	6	10	14	2	6	2	2

* Exact structure of valence level uncertain.

Constants for

Redox Half-Reactions

Half-Reaction*	pK_{ox}
1. $Ba \rightleftharpoons Ba^{+2} + 2\,e^-$	-98.0
2. $Sr \rightleftharpoons Sr^{+2} + 2\,e^-$	-97.6
3. $Ca \rightleftharpoons Ca^{+2} + 2\,e^-$	-97.0
4. $Al \rightleftharpoons Al^{+3} + 3\,e^-$	-84.3
5. $Mg \rightleftharpoons Mg^{+2} + 2\,e^-$	-80.2
6. $Li \rightleftharpoons Li^+ + e^-$	-51.5
7. $Rb \rightleftharpoons Rb^+ + e^-$	-49.4
8. $K \rightleftharpoons K^+ + e^-$	-49.4
9. $Na \rightleftharpoons Na^+ + e^-$	-46.9
10. $Mn \rightleftharpoons Mn^{+2} + 2\,e^-$	-39.8
11. $Te^{-2} \rightleftharpoons Te + 2\,e^-$	-38.0
12. $Cr \rightleftharpoons Cr^{+3} + 3\,e^-$	-37.5
13. $Cr \rightleftharpoons Cr^{+2} + 2\,e^-$	-30.8
14. $Se^{-2} \rightleftharpoons Se + 2\,e^-$	-28.3
15. $Ga \rightleftharpoons Ga^{+3} + 3\,e^-$	-27.0
16. $Zn \rightleftharpoons Zn^{+2} + 2\,e^-$	-25.8
17. $H_2Te\ (aq) \rightleftharpoons Te + 2\,H^+ + 2\,e^-$	-24.4
18. $In \rightleftharpoons In^{+3} + 3\,e^-$	-17.4
19. $S^{-2} \rightleftharpoons S + 2\,e^-$	-15.8
20. $Fe \rightleftharpoons Fe^{+2} + 2\,e^-$	-14.8
21. $Cd \rightleftharpoons Cd^{+2} + 2\,e^-$	-13.6
22. $Co \rightleftharpoons Co^{+2} + 2\,e^-$	-9.4
23. $Ni \rightleftharpoons Ni^{+2} + 2\,e^-$	-8.6
24. $S_2O_6^{-2} + 2\,H_2O \rightleftharpoons 2\,SO_4^{-2} + 4\,H^+ + 2\,e^-$	-7.4
25. $Cr^{+2} \rightleftharpoons Cr^{+3} + e^-$	-6.9
26. $Ti^{+2} \rightleftharpoons Ti^{+3} + e^-$	-6.3
27. $Tl \rightleftharpoons Tl^+ + e^-$	-5.7
28. $CN^- + H_2O \rightleftharpoons NCO^- + 2\,H^+ + 2\,e^-$	-4.8
29. $Sn \rightleftharpoons Sn^{+2} + 2\,e^-$	-4.6

* The powers of α have been omitted.

Half-Reaction	pK_{ox}
30. $Pb \rightleftharpoons Pb^{+2} + 2\,e^-$	-4.2
31. $SO_3^{-2} + H_2O \rightleftharpoons SO_4^{-2} + 2\,H^+ + 2\,e^-$	-3.4
32. $H_2\,(g) \rightleftharpoons 2\,H^+ + 2\,e^-$	0.0
33. $Ti^{+3} + H_2O \rightleftharpoons TiO^{+2} + 2\,H^+ + e^-$	1.7
34. $Cu^+ \rightleftharpoons Cu^{+2} + e^-$	2.6
35. $2\,S_2O_3^{-2} \rightleftharpoons S_4O_6^{-2} + 2\,e^-$	2.8
36. $PHO_3^{-2} + H_2O \rightleftharpoons PO_4^{-3} + 3\,H^+ + 2\,e^-$	3.9
37. $Sb + H_2O \rightleftharpoons SbO^+ + 2\,H^+ + 3\,e^-$	4.7
38. $Sn^{+2} \rightleftharpoons Sn^{+4} + 2\,e^-$	5.0
39. $Fe(CN)_6^{-4} \rightleftharpoons Fe(CN)_6^{-3} + e^-$	6.1
40. $V^{+3} + H_2O \rightleftharpoons VO^{+2} + 2\,H^+ + e^-$	6.1
41. $Bi + H_2O + Cl^- \rightleftharpoons BiOCl\,(s) + 2\,H^+ + 3\,e^-$	8.1
42. $Cu \rightleftharpoons Cu^+ + e^-$	8.8
43. $MnO_4^{-2} \rightleftharpoons MnO_4^- + e^-$	9.5
44. $U^{+4} + 2\,H_2O \rightleftharpoons UO_2^{+2} + 4\,H^+ + 2\,e^-$	11.2
45. $Fe^{+2} \rightleftharpoons Fe^{+3} + e^-$	13.1
46. $Ag \rightleftharpoons Ag^+ + e^-$	13.5
47. $Bi + H_2O \rightleftharpoons BiO^+ + 2\,H^+ + 3\,e^-$	16.2
48. $2\,I^- \rightleftharpoons I_2\,(s) + 2\,e^-$	18.2
49. $2\,SbO^+ + 3\,H_2O \rightleftharpoons Sb_2O_5\,(s) + 6\,H^+ + 4\,e^-$	19.6
50. $NO\,(g) + H_2O \rightleftharpoons NO_2^- + 2\,H^+ + e^-$	20.2
51. $As + 2\,H_2O \rightleftharpoons AsO_2^- + 4\,H^+ + e^-$	21.9
52. $H_2O_2 \rightleftharpoons O_2\,(g) + 2\,H^+ + 2\,e^-$	23.2
53. $Mn^{+2} \rightleftharpoons Mn^{+3} + e^-$	25.6
54. $2\,Hg \rightleftharpoons Hg_2^{+2} + 2\,e^-$	26.6
55. $N_2O_4\,(g) + 2\,H_2O \rightleftharpoons 2\,NO_3^- + 4\,H^+ + 2\,e^-$	27.0
56. $Ce^{+3} \rightleftharpoons Ce^{+4} + e^-$	27.2
57. $NO_2^- + H_2O \rightleftharpoons NO_3^- + 2\,H^+ + 2\,e^-$	28.4
58. $Au \rightleftharpoons Au^+ + e^-$	28.4
59. $SeO_3^{-2} + H_2O \rightleftharpoons SeO_4^{-2} + 2\,H^+ + 2\,e^-$	29.6
60. $Co^{+2} \rightleftharpoons Co^{+3} + e^-$	30.8
61. $Hg_2^{+2} \rightleftharpoons 2\,Hg^{+2} + 2\,e^-$	31.0
62. $AsO_2^- + 2\,H_2O \rightleftharpoons AsO_4^{-3} + 4\,H^+ + 2\,e^-$	33.1
63. $Te + 2\,H_2O \rightleftharpoons TeO_2\,(s) + 4\,H^+ + 4\,e^-$	35.6
64. $2\,Br^- \rightleftharpoons Br_2\,(aq) + 2\,e^-$	35.8
65. $I^- + H_2O \rightleftharpoons IO^- + 2\,H^+ + 2\,e^-$	36.3
66. $S + 3\,H_2O \rightleftharpoons SO_3^{-2} + 6\,H^+ + 4\,e^-$	39.6
67. $ClO_2^- + H_2O \rightleftharpoons ClO_3^- + 2\,H^+ + 2\,e^-$	40.0
68. $Mn^{+2} + 2\,H_2O \rightleftharpoons MnO_2\,(s) + 4\,H^+ + 2\,e^-$	41.6
69. $ClO_3^- + H_2O \rightleftharpoons ClO_4^- + 2\,H^+ + 2\,e^-$	42.0
70. $Tl^+ \rightleftharpoons Tl^{+3} + 2\,e^-$	42.4
71. $S_2O_3^{-2} + 3\,H_2O \rightleftharpoons 2\,SO_3^{-2} + 6\,H^+ + 2\,e^-$	45.6
72. $2\,Cl^- \rightleftharpoons Cl_2\,(aq) + 2\,e^-$	46.0
73. $NO\,(g) + 2\,H_2O \rightleftharpoons NO_3^- + 4\,H^+ + 3\,e^-$	48.6
74. $ClO^- + H_2O \rightleftharpoons ClO_2^- + 2\,H^+ + 2\,e^-$	48.9
75. $Pb^{+2} + 2\,H_2O \rightleftharpoons PbO_2\,(s) + 4\,H^+ + 2\,e^-$	49.2
76. $Se + 3\,H_2O \rightleftharpoons SeO_3^{-2} + 6\,H^+ + 4\,e^-$	50.2
77. $Ni^{+2} + 2\,H_2O \rightleftharpoons NiO_2\,(s) + 4\,H^+ + 2\,e^-$	56.8
78. $I_2\,(aq) + 2\,H_2O \rightleftharpoons 2\,HIO + 2\,H^+ + 2\,e^-$	58.0
79. $2\,H_2O \rightleftharpoons H_2O_2 + 2\,H^+ + 2\,e^-$	59.8
80. $Br_2\,(aq) + 2\,H_2O \rightleftharpoons 2\,BrO^- + 4\,H^+ + 2\,e^-$	62.5
81. $Cl_2\,(aq) + 2\,H_2O \rightleftharpoons 2\,ClO^- + 4\,H^+ + 2\,e^-$	62.5

Half-Reaction	pK_{ox}
82. $2 SO_4^{-2} \rightleftharpoons S_2O_8^{-2} + 2 e^-$	68.0
83. $O_2 (g) + H_2O \rightleftharpoons O_3 (g) + 2 H^+ + 2 e^-$	70.0
84. $Au \rightleftharpoons Au^{+3} + 3 e^-$	76.2
85. $2 H_2O \rightleftharpoons O_2 (g) + 4 H^+ + 4 e^-$	83.2
86. $MnO_2 (s) + 2 H_2O \rightleftharpoons MnO_4^- + 4 H^+ + 3 e^-$	86.1
87. $2 F^- \rightleftharpoons F_2 (g) + 2 e^-$	89.6
88. $N_2O (g) + 3 H_2O \rightleftharpoons 2 NO_2^- + 6 H^+ + 4 e^-$	93.8
89. $Fe^{+3} + 4 H_2O \rightleftharpoons FeO_4^{-2} + 8 H^+ + 3 e^-$	96.3
90. $NH_4^+ + 3 H_2O \rightleftharpoons NO_3^- + 10 H^+ + 8 e^-$	122.4
91. $Mn^{+2} + 4 H_2O \rightleftharpoons MnO_4^- + 8 H^+ + 5 e^-$	128.0
92. $2 Cr^{+3} + 7 H_2O \rightleftharpoons Cr_2O_7^{-2} + 14 H^+ + 6 e^-$	135.0
93. $Br_2 (aq) + 6 H_2O \rightleftharpoons 2 BrO_3^- + 12 H^+ + 10 e^-$	258.0

Standard Oxidation Potentials

Half-Reaction	Oxidation Potential
1. $Li \rightarrow Li^+ + e^-$	3.045
2. $Rb \rightarrow Rb^+ + e^-$	2.925
3. $K \rightarrow K^+ + e^-$	2.925
4. $Cs \rightarrow Cs^+ + e^-$	2.923
5. $Ba \rightarrow Ba^{+2} + 2 e^-$	2.90
6. $Sr \rightarrow Sr^{+2} + 2 e^-$	2.89
7. $Ca \rightarrow Ca^{+2} + 2 e^-$	2.87
8. $Na \rightarrow Na^+ + e^-$	2.714
9. $La \rightarrow La^{+3} + 3 e^-$	2.52
10. $Mg \rightarrow Mg^{+2} + 2 e^-$	2.37
11. $Y \rightarrow Y^{+3} + 3 e^-$	2.37
12. $H^- \rightarrow \frac{1}{2} H_2 + e^-$	2.25
13. $Sc \rightarrow Sc^{+3} + 3 e^-$	2.08
14. $Th \rightarrow Th^{+4} + 4 e^-$	1.90
15. $Be \rightarrow Be^{+2} + 2 e^-$	1.85
16. $U \rightarrow U^{+3} + 3 e^-$	1.80
17. $Al \rightarrow Al^{+3} + 3 e^-$	1.66
18. $Ti \rightarrow Ti^{+2} + 2 e^-$	1.63
19. $Mn \rightarrow Mn^{+2} + 2 e^-$	1.18
20. $V \rightarrow V^{+2} + 2 e^-$	≈ 1.18
21. $B + 3 H_2O \rightarrow H_3BO_3 \text{ (aq)} + 3 H^+ + 3 e^-$	0.87
22. $Si + 2 H_2O \rightarrow SiO_2 \text{ (s)} + 4 H^+ + 4 e^-$	0.86
23. $Zn \rightarrow Zn^{+2} + 2 e^-$	0.763
24. $Cr \rightarrow Cr^{+2} + 2 e^-$	0.74
25. $H_2Te \rightarrow Te + 2 H^+ + 2 e^-$	0.72
26. $U^{+3} \rightarrow U^{+4} + e^-$	0.61
27. $AsH_3 \rightarrow As + 3 H^+ + 3 e^-$	0.60
28. $Ga \rightarrow Ga^{+3} + 3 e^-$	0.53
29. $SbH_3 \rightarrow Sb + 3 H^+ + 3 e^-$	0.51
30. $P + 2 H_2O \rightarrow HPH_2O_2 + H^+ + e^-$	0.51
31. $HPH_2O_2 + H_2O \rightarrow H_2PHO_3 + 2 H^+ + 2 e^-$	0.50
32. $H_2C_2O_4 \text{ (aq)} \rightarrow 2 CO_2 \text{ (g)} + 2 H^+ + 2 e^-$	0.49

Half-Reaction	Oxidation Potential
33. $Fe \rightarrow Fe^{+2} + 2\,e^-$	0.440
34. $H_2 \rightarrow 2\,H^+\,(10^{-7}\,M) + 2\,e^-$	0.414
35. $Cr^{+2} \rightarrow Cr^{+3} + e^-$	0.41
36. $Cd \rightarrow Cd^{+2} + 2\,e^-$	0.403
37. $H_2Se \rightarrow Se + 2\,H^+ + 2\,e^-$	0.40
38. $Ti^{+2} \rightarrow Ti^{+3} + e^-$	≈ 0.37
39. $In \rightarrow In^{+3} + 3\,e^-$	0.342
40. $Tl \rightarrow Tl^+ + e^-$	0.3363
41. $Co \rightarrow Co^{+2} + 2\,e^-$	0.277
42. $H_2PHO_3 + H_2O \rightarrow H_3PO_4 + 2\,H^+ + 2\,e^-$	0.276
43. $V^{+2} \rightarrow V^{+3} + e^-$	0.255
44. $Ni \rightarrow Ni^{+2} + 2\,e^-$	0.250
45. $Sn \rightarrow Sn^{+2} + 2\,e^-$	0.136
46. $Pb \rightarrow Pb^{+2} + 2\,e^-$	0.126
47. $Ge + 2\,H_2O \rightarrow GeO_2\,(s) + 4\,H^+ + 4\,e^-$	0.1
48. $W + 3\,H_2O \rightarrow WO_3 + 6\,H^+ + 6\,e^-$	0.09
49. $H_2 \rightarrow 2\,H^+ + 2\,e^-$	0.00
50. $PH_3 \rightarrow P + 3\,H^+ + 3\,e^-$	-0.06
51. $Ti^{+3} + H_2O \rightarrow TiO^{+2} + 2\,H^+ + e^-$	-0.1
52. $Mo + 3\,H_2O \rightarrow MoO_3\,(s) + 6\,H^+ + 6\,e^-$	-0.1
53. $SiH_4 \rightarrow Si + 4\,H^+ + 4\,e^-$	-0.102
54. $CH_4 \rightarrow C + 4\,H^+ + 4\,e^-$	-0.13
55. $H_2S \rightarrow S + 2\,H^+ + 2\,e^-$	-0.141
56. $Sn^{+2} \rightarrow Sn^{+4} + 2\,e^-$	-0.15
57. $2\,S_2O_3^{-2} \rightarrow S_4O_6^{-2} + 2\,e^-$	-0.15
58. $Cu^+ \rightarrow Cu^{+2} + e^-$	-0.153
59. $H_2SO_3 + H_2O \rightarrow SO_4^{-2} + 4\,H^+ + 2\,e^-$	-0.17
60. $Sb + H_2O \rightarrow SbO^+ + 2\,H^+ + 3\,e^-$	-0.212
61. $As + 2\,H_2O \rightarrow HAsO_2 + 3\,H^+ + 3\,e^-$	-0.247
62. $Bi + H_2O \rightarrow BiO^+ + 2\,H^+ + 3\,e^-$	-0.32
63. $(CN)_2\,(g) + 2\,H_2O \rightarrow 2\,HNCO + 2\,H^+ + 2\,e^-$	-0.33
64. $U^{+4} + 2\,H_2O \rightarrow UO_2^{+2} + 4\,H^+ + 2\,e^-$	-0.334
65. $Fe(CN)_6^{-4} \rightarrow Fe(CN)_6^{-3} + e^-$	-0.36
66. $V^{+3} + H_2O \rightarrow VO^{+2} + 2\,H^+ + e^-$	-0.361
67. $Re + 4\,H_2O \rightarrow ReO_4^- + 8\,H^+ + 7\,e^-$	-0.363
68. $2\,HCN \rightarrow (CN)_2 + 2\,H^+ + 2\,e^-$	-0.37
69. $S + 3\,H_2O \rightarrow H_2SO_3 + 4\,H^+ + 4\,e^-$	-0.45
70. $ReO_2 + 2\,H_2O \rightarrow ReO_4^- + 4\,H^+ + 3\,e^-$	-0.51
71. $Cu \rightarrow Cu^+ + e^-$	-0.521
72. $2\,I^- \rightarrow I_2\,(s) + 2\,e^-$	-0.5355
73. $Te + 2\,H_2O \rightarrow TeO_2H^+ + 3\,H^+ + 4\,e^-$	-0.559
74. $HAsO_2 + 2\,H_2O \rightarrow H_3AsO_4 + 2\,H^+ + 2\,e^-$	-0.559
75. $MnO_4^{-2} \rightarrow MnO_4^- + e^-$	-0.564
76. $2\,SbO^+ + 3\,H_2O \rightarrow Sb_2O_5 + 6\,H^+ + 4\,e^-$	-0.581
77. $H_2O_2 \rightarrow O_2 + 2\,H^+ + 2\,e^-$	-0.682
78. $Pt + 4\,Cl^- \rightarrow PtCl_4^{-2} + 2\,e^-$	-0.73
79. $Mo(CN)_8^{-4} \rightarrow Mo(CN)_8^{-3} + e^-$	-0.73
80. $Se + 3\,H_2O \rightarrow H_2SeO_3 + 4\,H^+ + 4\,e^-$	-0.74
81. $2\,NCS^- \rightarrow (NCS)_2 + 2\,e^-$	-0.77
82. $Fe^{+2} \rightarrow Fe^{+3} + e^-$	-0.771
83. $2\,Hg\,(l) \rightarrow Hg_2^{+2} + 2\,e^-$	-0.789

	Half-Reaction	Oxidation Potential
84.	$Ag \rightarrow Ag^+ + e^-$	-0.7991
85.	$Rh \rightarrow Rh^{+3} + 3\ e^-$	≈ -0.8
86.	$NO_2 + H_2O \rightarrow NO_3^- + 2\ H^+ + e^-$	-0.81
87.	$Os + 4\ H_2O \rightarrow OsO_4 + 8\ H^+ + 8\ e^-$	-0.85
88.	$Hg_2^{+2} \rightarrow 2\ Hg^{+2} + 2\ e^-$	-0.920
89.	$HNO_2 + H_2O \rightarrow NO_3^- + 3\ H^+ + 2\ e^-$	-0.94
90.	$NO + 2\ H_2O \rightarrow NO_3^- + 4\ H^+ + 3\ e^-$	-0.96
91.	$Pu^{+3} \rightarrow Pu^{+4} + e^-$	-0.97
92.	$TeO_2H^+ + 4\ H_2O \rightarrow H_6TeO_6\ (s) + 3\ H^+ + 2\ e^-$	-0.97
93.	$Pt + 2\ H_2O \rightarrow Pt(OH)_2 + 2\ H^+ + 2\ e^-$	-0.98
94.	$Pd \rightarrow Pd^{+2} + 2\ e^-$	-0.987
95.	$Au + 4\ Cl^- \rightarrow AuCl_4^- + 3\ e^-$	-1.00
96.	$VO^{+2} + H_2O \rightarrow VO_2^+ + 2\ H^+ + e^-$	-1.00
97.	$Pu^{+4} + 2\ H_2O \rightarrow PuO_2^{+2} + 4\ H^+ + 2\ e^-$	-1.04
98.	$2\ Br^- \rightarrow Br_2\ (l) + 2\ e^-$	-1.0652
99.	$H_2SeO_3 + H_2O \rightarrow SeO_4^{-2} + 4\ H^+ + 2\ e^-$	-1.15
100.	$ClO_3^- + H_2O \rightarrow ClO_4^- + 2\ H^+ + 2\ e^-$	-1.19
101.	$\frac{1}{2}\ I_2\ (s) + 3\ H_2O \rightarrow IO_3^- + 6\ H^+ + 5\ e^-$	-1.195
102.	$HClO_2 + H_2O \rightarrow ClO_3^- + 3\ H^+ + 2\ e^-$	-1.21
103.	$2\ H_2O \rightarrow O_2 + 4\ H^+ + 4\ e^-$	-1.229
104.	$Mn^{+2} + 2\ H_2O \rightarrow MnO_2 + 4\ H^+ + 2\ e^-$	-1.23
105.	$Tl^+ \rightarrow Tl^{+3} + 2\ e^-$	-1.25
106.	$2\ NH_4^+ \rightarrow N_2H_5^+ + 3\ H^+ + 2\ e^-$	-1.275
107.	$PdCl_4^{-2} + 2\ Cl^- \rightarrow PdCl_6^{-2} + 2\ e^-$	-1.288
108.	$2\ Cr^{+3} + 7\ H_2O \rightarrow Cr_2O_7^{-2} + 14\ H^+ + 6\ e^-$	-1.33
109.	$NH_4^+ + H_2O \rightarrow HONH_3^+ + 2\ H^+ + 2\ e^-$	-1.35
110.	$2\ Cl^- \rightarrow Cl_2\ (aq) + 2\ e^-$	-1.3595
111.	$\frac{1}{2}\ I_2\ (s) + H_2O \rightarrow HIO + H^+ + e^-$	-1.45
112.	$Au + 3\ H_2O \rightarrow Au(OH)_3 + 3\ H^+ + 3\ e^-$	-1.45
113.	$Pb^{+2} + 2\ H_2O \rightarrow PbO_2 + 4\ H^+ + 2\ e^-$	-1.455
114.	$Cl^- + 2\ H_2O \rightarrow ClO_2 + 4\ H^+ + 5\ e^-$	-1.50
115.	$H_2O_2 \rightarrow HO_2 + H^+ + e^-$	-1.5
116.	$Mn^{+2} \rightarrow Mn^{+3} + e^-$	-1.51
117.	$Mn^{+2} + 4\ H_2O \rightarrow MnO_4^- + 8\ H^+ + 5\ e^-$	-1.51
118.	$\frac{1}{2}\ Br_2\ (l) + H_2O \rightarrow HBrO + H^+ + e^-$	-1.59
119.	$2\ BiO^+ + 2\ H_2O \rightarrow Bi_2O_4 + 4\ H^+ + 2\ e^-$	-1.59
120.	$IO_3^- + 3\ H_2O \rightarrow H_5IO_6 + H^+ + 2\ e^-$	-1.6
121.	$\frac{1}{2}\ Cl_2\ (aq) + H_2O \rightarrow HClO + H^+ + e^-$	-1.63
122.	$HClO + H_2O \rightarrow HClO_2 + 2\ H^+ + 2\ e^-$	-1.64
123.	$Au \rightarrow Au^+ + e^-$	≈ -1.68
124.	$Ni^{+2} + 2\ H_2O \rightarrow NiO_2 + 4\ H^+ + 2\ e^-$	-1.68
125.	$MnO_2 + 2\ H_2O \rightarrow MnO_4^- + 4\ H^+ + 3\ e^-$	-1.695
126.	$2\ H_2O \rightarrow H_2O_2 + 2\ H^+ + 2\ e^-$	-1.77
127.	$Co^{+2} \rightarrow Co^{+3} + e^-$	-1.82
128.	$Fe^{+3} + 4\ H_2O \rightarrow FeO_4^{-2} + 8\ H^+ + 3\ e^-$	-1.9
129.	$Ag^+ \rightarrow Ag^{+2} + e^-$	-1.98
130.	$2\ SO_4^{-2} \rightarrow S_2O_8^{-2} + 2\ e^-$	-2.01
131.	$O_2 + H_2O \rightarrow O_3 + 2\ H^+ + 2\ e^-$	-2.07
132.	$2\ F^- \rightarrow F_2 + 2\ e^-$	-2.65
133.	$2\ HF\ (aq) \rightarrow F_2 + 2\ H^+ + 2\ e^-$	-3.06

Solubilities of Salts

TABLE A11–1a. MOLAR SOLUBILITIES OF ALKALI SALTS*

	Lithium	Sodium	Potassium	Rubidium	Cesium	Ammonium
AlF_6^{-3}		0.0020	0.0056			0.039
$AuCl_4^-$	1.75†	1.72†	1.15†	0.27†	0.027	sol.
BF_4^-		9.8†	0.035	0.027	0.047	2.4†
$B(C_6H_5)_4^-$		0.15	0.00014			v. insol.
$B_4O_7^{-2}$	sl. sol.	0.13	0.8†			0.38†
BeF_4^{-2}	0.14	0.12	0.11			2.97†
CO_3^{-2}	0.18	2.1†	8.1†	19.†	8.0†	0.88†
$C_2O_4^{-2}$	0.78†	0.24†	2.0†	1.0†	8.0†	0.30
$HC_4H_4O_6^-$	sol.	0.58†	0.03	0.051	0.34†	0.06
ClO_4^-	5.6†	17.3†	0.12	0.071	0.084	2.14†
$Co(NO_2)_6^{-3}$	v. sol.	v. sol.	0.0019	8.6×10^{-5}	6.8×10^{-5}	0.023
F^-	0.10	1.0†	16.†	12.5†	20.5†	27.† (0°C)
GeO_3^{-2}	0.063	1.5†				
GeF_6^{-2}	2.7†	0.083	0.020	0.017	0.042	
$Hg_2Br_5^-$					0.0086	
$HgCl_3^-$					0.033	
IO_3^-	4.4†	0.44†	0.35†	0.081	0.084	0.13
IO_4^-		0.48†	0.0022	0.023	0.066	0.13
$IrCl_6^{-2}$		1.03†	0.025	0.00097		0.016
MnO_4^-	3.9†	v. sol.	0.40†	0.052	0.009	0.58†
PO_4^{-3}	0.0034	0.70†	9.1†			‡
$P_2O_7^{-4}$		0.24†	sol.			
PF_6^-			0.43	0.076	0.030	4.6†
$H_6PMo_{12}O_{43}^{-3}$		sol.	4×10^{-6}			0.00015
$PtBr_6^{-2}$		v. sol.	0.026			0.0083
$PtCl_4^{-2}$			0.022			sol.
$PtCl_6^{-2}$	sol.	1.2†	0.03	0.0024	0.0020	0.02
PtF_6^{-2}		0.58†	0.079	0.0058	0.0084	0.21†

* Salts more soluble than 0.1 molar are too soluble to be of analytical importance.

† Molal solubility.

‡ Normal salts do not exist.

	Lithium	Sodium	Potassium	Rubidium	Cesium	Ammonium
$Pt(NO_2)_4^{-2}$			0.083			
ReO_4^-	1.30†	3.5†	0.034	0.031	0.020	0.23†
$S_2O_8^{-2}$		sol.	0.20			2.5† (0°C)
$Sb(OH)_6^-$		0.0012	0.11			
SiF_6^{-2}	2.7†	0.035	0.006	0.0050	0.015	1.1†
SnF_6^{-2}			0.11			
TiF_6^{-2}	1.42	0.31†	0.049	0.024	0.059	1.26†
VO_3^-	sol.	1.7†	sol.	0.024		0.044
ZrF_6^{-2}			0.05			

† Molal solubility.

TABLE A11–1b. MOLAR SOLUBILITIES OF SOME DOUBLE ALKALI SALTS

$NaAl(SO_4)_2 \cdot 12\ H_2O$	4.5*
$NH_4Al(SO_4)_2 \cdot 12\ H_2O$	0.33
$KAl(SO_4)_2 \cdot 12\ H_2O$	0.24
$RbAl(SO_4)_2 \cdot 12\ H_2O$	0.050
$CsAl(SO_4)_2 \cdot 12\ H_2O$ (0°C)	0.006
$NaZn(UO_2)_3(C_2H_3O_2)_9 \cdot 6\ H_2O$	0.02
$K_2NaCo(NO_2)_6$	0.0015
$NH_4MgAsO_4 \cdot 6\ H_2O$	0.0013
$NH_4MgPO_4 \cdot 6\ H_2O$	0.00098
$NH_4CaAsO_4 \cdot 6\ H_2O$	0.00065
$NH_4MnPO_4 \cdot 7\ H_2O$	0.00016

* Molal solubility.

TABLE A11–2. MOLAR SOLUBILITIES OF SOME ALKALINE-EARTH SALTS

	Beryllium	Magnesium	Calcium	Strontium	Barium	Radium
AsO_4^{-3}		4.6×10^{-5}	0.00065	8×10^{-11}	0.0008	
CO_3^{-2}	0.025 (0°C)	0.0063	8.3×10^{-5}	2.6×10^{-5}	4×10^{-5}	
$C_2O_4^{-2}$	2.6*	0.0093	3.6×10^{-5}	0.0024	0.00012	
CrO_4^{-2}		8.0*	0.026	0.006	9.2×10^{-6}	
$Fe(CN)_6^{-4}$		0.70*	1.7*	0.76*	0.0029	
F^-	10.7*	0.0027	0.00035	0.00058	0.018	
OH^-	1.4×10^{-7}	0.00013	0.021	0.065	0.28	
IO_3^-		0.22	0.0014	6.0×10^{-5}	3.5×10^{-5}	
PO_4^{-3}		0.00061	3.5×10^{-7}	2.5×10^{-7}	8.9×10^{-9}	
SO_3^{-2}		0.06	0.00012	0.00020	3×10^{-5}	
$S_2O_3^{-2}$		2.5*	4.*	0.86*	0.0080	
SO_4^{-2}	2.4*	1.09*	0.0049	0.00087	3.9×10^{-5}	6×10^{-8}
SeO_4^{-2}	2.5*	2.1*	0.35	0.006	5.3×10^{-6}	
SiF_6^{-2}		2.4*	sl. sol.	0.12	0.0011	

* Molal solubility.

TABLE A11-3. MOLAR SOLUBILITIES OF COMPOUNDS OF THE COINAGE METALS

Copper		Silver		Gold	
(CuF doesn't exist)		AgF	14.*	(AuF doesn't exist)	
CuCl	5.7×10^{-4}	AgCl	1.7×10^{-5}	AuCl	4.5×10^{-7}
CuBr	3.6×10^{-5}	AgBr	7.0×10^{-7}	AuBr	7.0×10^{-9}
CuI	1.0×10^{-6}	AgI	9.2×10^{-9}	AuI	4×10^{-12}
CuCN	1.8×10^{-10}	AgCN	1.3×10^{-7}	AuCN	$\approx 10^{-14}$
		AgNCO	4.7×10^{-4}		
CuNCS	4.0×10^{-6}	AgNCS	1.0×10^{-6}	AuNCS	$\approx 10^{-12}$
		AgNCSe	7.9×10^{-8}		
CuN₃	7.0×10^{-5}	AgN₃	5.4×10^{-5}		
		AgClO₂	1.4×10^{-2}		
		AgClO₃	2.2×10^{-1}		
CuClO₄	dec.	AgClO₄	25.*		
		AgBrO₃	7.0×10^{-3}		
		AgIO₃	1.8×10^{-4}		
		AgNO₂	1.1×10^{-2}		
		AgNO₃	14.*		
		AgMnO₄	2.4×10^{-2}		
		AgReO₄	9×10^{-3}		
CuC₂H₃O₂	dec.	AgC₂H₃O₂	5.3×10^{-2}		
Cu₂O	7.0×10^{-8}	Ag₂O	8.0×10^{-6}	Au₂O	1×10^{-7}
Cu₂S	3.1×10^{-17}	Ag₂S	1.4×10^{-17}	Au₂S	v. insol.
Cu₂CO₃	insol.	Ag₂CO₃	1.3×10^{-4}		
		Ag₂C₂O₄	1.4×10^{-4}		
		Ag₂CrO₄	7.8×10^{-5}		
		Ag₂N₂O₂	7.4×10^{-11}		
Cu₂SO₃·H₂O	insol.	Ag₂SO₃	1.7×10^{-4}		
		Ag₂SO₄	1.8×10^{-2}		
		Ag₂WO₄	1.1×10^{-3}		
		Ag₃AsO₃	2.6×10^{-5}		
		Ag₃AsO₄	1.8×10^{-5}		
		Ag₃Fe(CN)₆	1.2×10^{-6}		
		Ag₃PO₄	1.6×10^{-5}		
Cu₄Fe(CN)₆	insol.	Ag₄Fe(CN)₆	2.3×10^{-9}		
Cu₃(AsO₄)₂	5.9×10^{-8}				
CuF₂	7.4×10^{-3}	AgF₂ (reacts with H₂O)			
Cu(N₃)₂	5.4×10^{-4}				
Cu(IO₃)₂	3.3×10^{-3}				
Cu(OH)₂	3.0×10^{-5}	AgO	2×10^{-11}	AuO	insol.
CuS	2.6×10^{-15}			AuS	7×10^{-40}
CuSeO₃	1×10^{-4}				
CuCO₃	1.6×10^{-5}				
CuC₂O₄	1.7×10^{-4}				
CuWO₄	3×10^{-3}				
				AuF₃ (reacts with H₂O)	
				AuCl₃	2.2†
				AuBr₃	sl. sol.
				AuI₃	$\approx 10^{-12}$
				Au(OH)₃	2.5×10^{-13}
				Au₂S₃	v. insol.
				Au₂(SeO₄)₃	insol.

* Molal.

† Dissolves as $AuCl_3 + 2 H_2O \rightarrow H_3O^+ + AuCl_3OH^-$, not as $Au^{+3} + 3 Cl^-$.

TABLE A11-4. MOLAR SOLUBILITIES OF COMPOUNDS OF MERCURY, THALLIUM, AND LEAD

Mercury(I)	Mercury(II)	Thallium(I)	Thallium(III)	Lead(II)	Lead(IV)
Hg_2F_2 dec.	HgF_2 dec.	TlF 3.5*	TlF_3 dec.	PbF_2 2.6×10^{-3}	PbF_4 dec.
Hg_2Cl_2 6.5×10^{-7}	$HgCl_2$ 0.25	$TlCl$ 1.3×10^{-2}	$TlCl_3$ 2.3*	$PbCl_2$ 3.9×10^{-2}	$PbCl_4$ dec.
Hg_2Br_2 3.2×10^{-8}	$HgBr_2$ 1.4×10^{-2}	$TlBr$ 2.0×10^{-3}	$TlBr_3$ sol.	$PbBr_2$ 1.2×10^{-2}	
Hg_2I_2 2.2×10^{-10}	HgI_2 1.5×10^{-4}	TlI 2.0×10^{-4}		PbI_2 1.5×10^{-3}	
$Hg_2(CN)_2$ 1.8×10^{-16}	$Hg(CN)_2$ 0.34	$TlCN$ 0.73		$Pb(CN)_2$ sl. sol.	
$Hg_2(NCS)_2$ 2.0×10^{-7}	$Hg(NCS)_2$ 2.2×10^{-3}	$TlNCS$ 1.2×10^{-2}		$Pb(NCS)_2$ 1.6×10^{-3}	
$Hg_2(N_3)_2$ 5.0×10^{-7}	$Hg(N_3)_2$	TlN_3 1.5×10^{-2}		$Pb(N_3)_2$ 1.7×10^{-3}	
				$Pb(ClO_2)_2$ 1.0×10^{-3}	
$Hg_2(ClO_3)_2$ 6.55*	$Hg(ClO_3)_2$ 0.68	$TlClO_3$ 6×10^{-2}		$Pb(ClO_3)_2$ 3.8*	
$Hg_2(ClO_4)_2$		$TlClO_4$ 0.64		$Pb(ClO_4)_2$ 0.25	
$Hg_2(BrO_3)_2$	$Hg(BrO_3)_2$ 0.0030	$TlBrO_3$ 2.0×10^{-2}		$Pb(BrO_3)_2$ 2.8×10^{-2}	
$Hg_2(IO_3)_2$ 1.7×10^{-6}	$Hg(IO_3)_2$ 4.2×10^{-5}	$TlIO_3$ 1.8×10^{-3}		$Pb(IO_3)_2$ 2.1×10^{-5}	
$Hg_2(NO_3)_2$ sol.	$Hg(NO_2)_2$ v. sol.	$TlNO_2$ 1.3*		$Pb(NO_2)_2$ sol.	
	$Hg(NO_3)_2$ v. sol.	$TlNO_3$ 0.36		$Pb(NO_3)_2$ 1.1*	
		$TlMnO_4$ sl. sol.			
		$TlReO_4$ 3.4×10^{-3}			
$Hg_2(C_2H_3O_2)_2$ 2.0×10^{-3}	$Hg(C_2H_3O_2)_2$ 0.8	$TlC_2H_3O_2$ v. sol.		$Pb(C_2H_3O_2)_2$ 1.2*	$Pb(C_2H_3O_2)_4$ dec.
Hg_2O 1.7×10^{-5}	HgO 2.4×10^{-4}	$TlOH$ 1.6*	$Tl(OH)_3$ 1.3×10^{-9}	$Pb(OH)_2$ 2.6×10^{-4}	PbO_2 insol.
Hg_2S 3.2×10^{-23}	HgS 1×10^{-25}	Tl_2S 1.2×10^{-7}		PbS 2.0×10^{-13}	
		Tl_2Se 1.4×10^{-12}		$PbTe$ v. insol.	
Hg_2CO_3 9.5×10^{-9}		Tl_2CO_3 8.6×10^{-2}		$PbCO_3$ 4.1×10^{-6}	
$Hg_2C_2O_4$ 3.2×10^{-7}	HgC_2O_4 3.2×10^{-3}	$Tl_2C_2O_4$ 3.8×10^{-2}		PbC_2O_4 5×10^{-6}	
Hg_2CrO_4 4.5×10^{-6}	$HgCrO_4$ insol.	Tl_2CrO_4 6.2×10^{-5}		$PbCrO_4$ 2.2×10^{-7}	
$Hg_2Cr_2O_7$ insol.	$HgCr_2O_7$ insol.	Tl_2PtCl_6 7.8×10^{-5}		$PbPHO_3$ 7.5×10^{-4}	
Hg_2SO_3 3.2×10^{-14}		Tl_2SO_3 6.8×10^{-2}		$PbSO_3$ sl. sol.	
$Hg_2S_2O_3$ 4.5×10^{-18}				PbS_2O_3 9.4×10^{-4}	
				PbS_3O_6 1.8×10^{-8}	

* Molal.

TABLE A11–4—continued

Mercury(I)	Mercury(II)	Thallium(I)	Thallium(III)	Lead(II)	Lead(IV)
Hg_2SO_4 1.2×10^{-3}	$HgSO_4$ 0.21, dec.	Tl_2SO_4 9.6×10^{-2}	$Tl_2(SO_4)_3 \cdot 7\ H_2O$ dec.	$PbSO_4$ 1.4×10^{-4}	
Hg_2SeO_3 8×10^{-8}				$PbSeO_3$ 0.32	
		Tl_2SeO_4 3.9×10^{-2}		$PbSeO_4$ 3.8×10^{-4}	
				$PbMoO_4$ 2×10^{-3}	
	$HgHAsO_4$ insol.			$PbWO_4$ 6.5×10^{-4}	
	$HgHPO_4$ insol.	Tl_3PO_4 7.1×10^{-3}		$Pb_3(AsO_4)_2$ 3.3×10^{-8}	
		$Tl_4Fe(CN)_6$ 3.5×10^{-3}		$Pb_3(PO_4)_2$ 1.7×10^{-7}	
$Hg_2(PO_3)_2$ 6.3×10^{-10}				$Pb_2Fe(CN)_6$ 1×10^{-5}	

* Molal.

TABLE A11–5. MOLAR SOLUBILITIES OF TUNGSTATES AND MOLYBDATES

Tungstate		Molybdate	
Li_2WO_4	v. sol.	$Li_2MoO_4 \cdot \frac{1}{4} H_2O$	2.6*
$Na_2WO_4 \cdot 2 H_2O$	1.4*	$Na_2MoO_4 \cdot 2 H_2O$	1.9*
$Na_{10}W_{12}O_{41} \cdot 28 H_2O$	2.5×10^{-2}	$Na_2Mo_3O_{10} \cdot 7 H_2O$	0.038
$Na_6W_7O_{24} \cdot 16 H_2O$	0.038	$Na_6Mo_7O_{24} \cdot 16 H_2O$	0.74
K_2WO_4	1.4*	K_2MoO_4	7.7*
$(NH_4)_2WO_4$	sol.	$(NH_4)_2MoO_4$	2.0*
Ag_2WO_4	1.1×10^{-3}	Ag_2MoO_4	1.03×10^{-4}
$MgWO_4$	insol.	$MgMoO_4$	0.87*
$CaWO_4$	0.007	$CaMoO_4$	1.25×10^{-7}
$SrWO_4$	4.2×10^{-3}	$SrMoO_4$	4.2×10^{-4}
$BaWO_4$	2.5×10^{-5}	$BaMoO_4$	1.9×10^{-4}
$CuWO_4$	2.9×10^{-3}		
$CdWO_4$	1.4×10^{-3}		
Hg_2WO_4	insol.		
$HgWO_4$	insol.		
$La_2(WO_4)_3$	1.4×10^{-4}	$La_2(MoO_4)_3$	2.4×10^{-5}
$PbWO_4$	6.5×10^{-4}	$PbMoO_4$	2×10^{-3}
$(NH_4)_3[P(W_3O_{10})_4] \cdot 5 H_2O$	sl. sol.	$(NH_4)_3[P(Mo_3O_{10})_4]$	1.2×10^{-5}
$Na_4[Si(W_3O_{10})_4] \cdot 20 H_2O$	v. sol.		
$K_4[Si(W_3O_{10})_4] \cdot 18 H_2O$	0.1		

* Molal.

TABLE A11–6. MOLAR SOLUBILITIES OF SOME CADMIUM AND BISMUTH COMPOUNDS

Cadmium		Bismuth	
$Cd(C_2H_3O_2)_2 \cdot H_2O$	1.7* (0°C)	$Bi(C_2H_3O_2)_3$	dec., sol. in acid
$Cd(BrO_3)_2 \cdot H_2O$	3.3*		
$CdBr_2 \cdot 4 H_2O$	4.2*	$BiBr_3$	dec., sol. in acid
$CdCO_3$	2.3×10^{-6}		
$Cd(ClO_3)_2 \cdot 2 H_2O$	11.*		
$Cd(ClO_4)_2 \cdot 6 H_2O$	1.43*	$Bi(ClO_4)_3 \cdot 5 H_2O$	dec., sol. in acid
$CdCl_2 \cdot 2\frac{1}{2} H_2O$	6.3*	$BiCl_3$	dec., sol. in acid
		$Bi_2(CrO_4)_3$	0.014
$Cd(CN)_2$	0.10		
CdF_2	0.29	BiF_3	insol.
$Cd(OH)_2$	1.8×10^{-5}	$Bi(OH)_3$	5.4×10^{-6}
$Cd(IO_3)_2$	sl. sol.	$Bi(IO_3)_3$	insol.
CdI_2	2.5*	BiI_3	insol., dec. hot H_2O
$Cd(NO_3)_2 \cdot 4 H_2O$	5.5*	$Bi(NO_3)_3 \cdot 5 H_2O$	dec., sol. in acid
$CdC_2O_4 \cdot 3 H_2O$	1.2×10^{-4}	$Bi_2(C_2O_4)_3$	insol.
$Cd_3(PO_4)_2$	insol., sol. in acid	$BiPO_4$	3.5×10^{-12}, sol. in acid
$CdSO_4 \cdot 4 H_2O$	3.7*	$Bi_2(SO_4)_3$	dec., sol. in acid
CdS	9×10^{-6}	Bi_2S_3	0.0035
$CdWO_4$	1.4×10^{-3}		
		$(BiO)Cl$	8×10^{-5}
		$(BiO)OH$	5×10^{-6}

* Molal.

TABLE A11–7. MOLAR SOLUBILITIES OF SOME COMPOUNDS OF ARSENIC, ANTIMONY, AND TIN

Arsenic	Antimony	Tin	
$AsBr_3$ dec.	$SbBr_3$ dec.	$Sn(C_2H_3O_2)_2$ dec.	$Sn(C_2H_3O_2)_4$ dec.
$AsCl_3$ dec.	$SbCl_3$ 40.*, dec.	$SnBr_2$ 3.1* (0°C), dec.	$SnBr_4$ v. sol., dec.
$AsCl_5$ dec.	$SbCl_5$ dec.	$SnCl_2 \cdot 2 H_2O$ 5.2* dec.	$SnCl_4$ v. sol., dec.
			$Sn(CrO_4)_2$ sol.
AsF_3 dec.	SbF_3 27.*	SnF_2 1.9*	SnF_4 v. sol., dec.
AsF_5 sol., dec.	SbF_5 sol.	$SnSiF_6$ v. sol.	
$H_3AsO_4 \cdot \frac{1}{2} H_2O$ 1.1*	$(SbO)OH$ 1×10^{-3}	$Sn(OH)_2$ 2.0×10^{-9}	$Sn(OH)_4$ 1.7×10^{-12}
$(AsO)OH$ 0.19	SbI_3 dec.	SnI_2 3.5×10^{-2}, dec.	SnI_4 dec.
AsI_3 0.13, dec.	Sb_2O_5 insol.	$Sn(NO_3)_2 \cdot 20 H_2O$ dec.	$Sn(NO_3)_4$ dec.
		SnC_2O_4 insol.	
	$SbK_3(C_2O_4)_3 \cdot 3 H_2O$ sol.	$Sn_3(PO_4)_2$ insol.	
As_2S_3 2×10^{-6}	Sb_2S_3 5×10^{-6}	SnS 1×10^{-7}	SnS_2 insol.
As_2S_5 6.5×10^{-6}	$Sb_2(SO_4)_3$ sol., dec.	$SnSO_4$ 0.87, dec.	$Sn(SO_4)_2 \cdot 2 H_2O$ v. sol., dec.
	Sb_2S_5 insol.		

* Molal.

TABLE A11–8. MOLAR SOLUBILITIES OF SOME PHOSPHATES AND ARSENATES

Phosphates		Arsenates	
Ag_3PO_4	4.7×10^{-6}	Ag_3AsO_4	1.4×10^{-6}
$AlPO_4$	7.6×10^{-10}	$AlAsO_4$	1.3×10^{-8}
$Ba_3(PO_4)_2$	insol.	$Ba_3(AsO_4)_2$	3.7×10^{-11}
$BiPO_4$	3.5×10^{-12}	$BiAsO_4$	2.1×10^{-5}†
$Ca_3(PO_4)_2$	8×10^{-7}	$Ca_3(AsO_4)_2$	9.1×10^{-5}
$Cd_3(PO_4)_2$	insol.	$Cd_3(AsO_4)_2$	1.1×10^{-7}
$Co_3(PO_4)_2$	insol.	$Co_3(AsO_4)_2$	9.3×10^{-7}
$CrPO_4$ (green)	4.9×10^{-12}	$CrAsO_4$	8.7×10^{-11}
$CrPO_4$ (violet)	3.2×10^{-9}		
$Cu_3(PO_4)_2 \cdot 3\,H_2O$	insol.	$Cu_3(AsO_4)_2 \cdot 4\,H_2O$	3.7×10^{-8}
$FePO_4$	1.1×10^{-11}	$FeAsO_4$	7.6×10^{-11}
K_3PO_4	0.92*	K_3AsO_4	0.74*
Li_3PO_4	2.3×10^{-3}	Li_3AsO_4	v. sl. sol.
$Mg_3(PO_4)_2 \cdot 8\,H_2O$	6.1×10^{-5}	$Mg_3(AsO_4)_2 \cdot 8\,H_2O$	4.6×10^{-5}
$MgNH_4PO_4$	6.4×10^{-5}	$MgNH_4AsO_4$	1.3×10^{-3}
$Mn_3(PO_4)_2 \cdot 7\,H_2O$	insol.	$Mn_3(AsO_4)_2$	7.1×10^{-7}
$MnNH_4PO_4$	1.7×10^{-4}		
Na_3PO_4	0.75*	Na_3AsO_4	0.63*
$Ni_3(PO_4)_2 \cdot 8\,H_2O$	insol.	$Ni_3(AsO_4)_2$	3.1×10^{-6}
$Pb_3(PO_4)_2$	1.5×10^{-9}	$Pb_3(AsO_4)_2$	3.3×10^{-8}
$Sr_3(PO_4)_2$	insol.	$Sr_3(AsO_4)_2$	1.0×10^{-4}
$Th_3(PO_4)_4$	1.7×10^{-12}		
$(UO_2)_3(PO_4)_2$	6.5×10^{-11}		
		UO_2LiAsO_4	2.1×10^{-7}
$UO_2NH_4PO_4$	1.3×10^{-9}	$UO_2NH_4AsO_4$	1.2×10^{-8}
		UO_2NaAsO_4	5.1×10^{-8}
UO_2KPO_4	2.0×10^{-8}	UO_2KAsO_4	3.0×10^{-8}
$(VO)_3(PO_4)_2$	6.5×10^{-6}		
$Zn_3(PO_4)_2$	1.6×10^{-7}	$Zn_3(AsO_4)_2$	1.1×10^{-6}

* Molal.   † Value questionable.

TABLE A11–9. MOLAR SOLUBILITIES OF SOME SALTS CONTAINING
ANTIMONY, TIN, AND RELATED ELEMENTS IN THE ANION

$NaSb(OH)_6$	0.002	$Na_2Sn(OH)_6$	2.3*
$KSb(OH)_6 \cdot \frac{1}{2} H_2O$	0.11	$K_2Sn(OH)_6$	3.7*
		$Pb_2PbO_4 = (Pb_3O_4)$	$\approx 10^{-17}$
$NaPF_6 \cdot H_2O$	5.5*	Na_2SiF_6	0.035
KPF_6	0.432	K_2SiF_6	0.0054
$RbPF_6$	0.076	$(NH_4)_2SiF_6$	1.04*
$CsPF_6$	0.030	K_2GeF_6	0.024
$NaAsF_6$	v. sol.		
$KAsF_6 \cdot \frac{1}{2} H_2O$	v. sol.	$K_2SnF_6 \cdot H_2O$	0.11
$NaSbF_6$	5.0*	K_2PtF_6	0.019
$KSbF_6$	3.72*	$K_2TiF_6 \cdot H_2O$	0.049
		K_2ZrF_6	0.053
		$(NH_4)_2SnCl_6$	0.90*
		$(NH_4)_2PtCl_6$	0.015

* Molal.

TABLE A11–10. MOLAR SOLUBILITIES OF SALTS OF ALUMINUM, CHROMIUM, IRON, MANGANESE, AND VANADIUM

Aluminum	Vanadium	Chromium	Manganese	Iron
		$CrAc_2$ sl. sol.	$MnAc_2 \cdot 4\,H_2O$ 2.3*	$FeAc_2 \cdot 4\,H_2O$ v. sol., dec.
			$Mn_3(AsO_4)_2$ 7.1×10^{-7}	$Fe_3(AsO_4)_2$ insol.
	VBr_2 sol.	$CrBr_2$ v. sol.	$MnBr_2 \cdot 4\,H_2O$ 2.7*	$FeBr_2 \cdot 6\,H_2O$ 2.5*
		$CrCO_3$ insol.	$MnCO_3$ 9.5×10^{-6}	$FeCO_3$ 5.6×10^{-4}
	VCl_2 sol. dec.	$CrCl_2$ v. sol.	$MnCl_2 \cdot 4\,H_2O$ 3.5*	$FeCl_2 \cdot 4\,H_2O$ 3.3*
			$Mn(ClO_4)_2 \cdot 4\,H_2O$ 5.4*	$Fe(ClO_4)_2 \cdot 6\,H_2O$ 2.7*
			$Mn_2Fe(CN)_6$ 5.9×10^{-5}	$Fe_2Fe(CN)_6$ insol.
	VF_2 dec.	CrF_2 sl. sol.	MnF_2 0.019	FeF_2 sl. sol.
			$MnSiF_6 \cdot 6\,H_2O$ 4.6*	$FeSiF_6 \cdot 6\,H_2O$ 1.68*
		$Cr(OH)_2$ 1.4×10^{-6}	$Mn(OH)_2$ 3.7×10^{-5}	$Fe(OH)_2$ 7.9×10^{-6}
	VI_2 dec.	CrI_2 v. sol.	$MnI_2 \cdot 4\,H_2O$ v. sol.	$FeI_2 \cdot 4\,H_2O$ v. sol.
			$Mn(IO_3)_2 \cdot 4\,H_2O$ 0.22	
			$Mn(NO_3)_2 \cdot 6\,H_2O$ 3.5*	$Fe(NO_3)_2 \cdot 6\,H_2O$ 2.9*
		$CrC_2O_4 \cdot H_2O$ insol.	$MnC_2O_4 \cdot 2\,H_2O$ 1.7×10^{-3}	$FeC_2O_4 \cdot 2\,H_2O$ 4.5×10^{-4}
			$Mn_3(PO_4)_2 \cdot 7\,H_2O$ sl. sol.	$Fe_3(PO_4)_2 \cdot 8\,H_2O$ sl. sol.
			$Mn(PH_2O_2)_2 \cdot H_2O$ 0.62*	$Fe(PH_2O_2)_2 \cdot H_2O$ sol.
			$MnSeO_4 \cdot 5\,H_2O$ 1.9*	$FeSeO_4 \cdot 7\,H_2O$ sol.
			$MnSeO_3 \cdot 2\,H_2O$ 3×10^{-4}	$FeSeO_3$ insol.
	$VSO_4 \cdot 7\,H_2O$ dec.	$CrSO_4 \cdot 7\,H_2O$ 0.45*	$MnSO_4 \cdot 5\,H_2O$ 2.8*	$FeSO_4 \cdot 7\,H_2O$ 0.56*
	VS insol.	CrS insol.	MnS 5.4×10^{-5}	FeS 6.3×10^{-9}
			$Mn(NCS)_2 \cdot 3\,H_2O$ v. sol.	$Fe(NCS)_2 \cdot 3\,H_2O$ v. sol.
			$MnNH_4PO_4 \cdot H_2O$ 2.3×10^{-6}	$FeNH_4PO_4 \cdot H_2O$ insol.
			$Mn(NH_4)_2(SO_4)_2 \cdot 6\,H_2O$ 1.3*	$Fe(NH_4)_2(SO_4)_2 \cdot 6\,H_2O$ 0.68*
$AlAc \cdot H_2O$ dec.	$VAc_3 \cdot H_2O$ sol.	$CrAc_3 \cdot H_2O$ sol.	$MnAc_3 \cdot 2\,H_2O$ dec.	$FeAc_3$ dec.
$AlAsO_4$ 1.25×10^{-8}		$CrAsO_4$ 8.7×10^{-11}	$MnAsO_4$ insol.	$FeAsO_4$ 7.6×10^{-11}
$AlBr_3 \cdot 6\,H_2O$ 6.3*	$VBr_3 \cdot 6\,H_2O$ v. sol.	$CrBr_3 \cdot 6\,H_2O$ 5.0*	$MnBr_3$ does not exist	$FeBr_3 \cdot 6\,H_2O$ v. sol.
$Al(ClO_3)_3 \cdot 9\,H_2O$ v. sol.		$Cr(ClO_3)_3$ sol.		
$Al(ClO_4)_3 \cdot 9\,H_2O$ 4.1*		$Cr(ClO_4)_3 \cdot 9\,H_2O$ 1.6*		$Fe(ClO_4)_3 \cdot 10\,H_2O$ 2.25*
$AlCl_3 \cdot 6\,H_2O$ 1.7*	$VCl_3 \cdot 6\,H_2O$ v. sol.	$CrCl_3 \cdot 6\,H_2O$ 4.4*	$MnCl_3$ v. sol., dec.	$FeCl_3 \cdot 6\,H_2O$ 5.6*

Al	V	Cr	Mn	Fe
$Al_4[Fe(CN)_6]_3$ sl. sol.				$Fe_4[Fe(CN)_6]_3$ 6.4×10^{-6}
$AlF_3 \cdot 3 H_2O$ 0.067	$VF_3 \cdot 3 H_2O$ sl. sol.	$CrF_3 \cdot 3 H_2O$ sl. sol.	$MnF_3 \cdot 2 H_2O$ dec.	FeF_3 0.0081
$Al(OH)_3$ 5×10^{-11}	$V(OH)_3$ insol.	$Cr(OH)_3$ 7×10^{-10}	$Mn(OH)_3$ 1×10^{-15}	$Fe(OH)_3$ 6×10^{-17}
$AlI_3 \cdot 6 H_2O$ v. sol.	$VI_3 \cdot 6 H_2O$ v. sol.	$CrI_3 \cdot 9 H_2O$ sol.	MnI_3 does not exist	FeI_3 does not exist
$Al(NO_3)_3 \cdot 9 H_2O$ 1.7*		$Cr(NO_3)_3 \cdot 9 H_2O$ 1.8*		$Fe(NO_3)_3 \cdot 9 H_2O$ 2.2*
$Al_2(C_2O_4)_3 \cdot 4 H_2O$ insol.		$Cr_2(C_2O_4)_3 \cdot X H_2O$ v. sol.		$Fe_2(C_2O_4)_3 \cdot 5 H_2O$ v. sol.
$AlPO_4$ 7.6×10^{-10}		$CrPO_4 \cdot 3 H_2O$ 7.8×10^{-12}	$MnPO_4 \cdot H_2O$ insol.	$FePO_4$ 1.1×10^{-11}
Al_2S_3 dec.	V_2S_3 insol.	Cr_2S_3 dec.	Mn_2S_3 does not exist	Fe_2S_3 3×10^{-18}
$Al_2(SO_4)_3 \cdot 18 H_2O$ 0.40	$V_2(SO_4)_3 \cdot 3 H_2O$ sol.	$Cr_2(SO_4)_3 \cdot 18 H_2O$ 0.17	$Mn_2(SO_4)_3$ dec.	$Fe_2(SO_4)_3 \cdot 9 H_2O$ 7.9*
$(NH_4)_3AlF_6$ 3.9×10^{-2}	$(NH_4)_3VF_6$ sl. sol.	$(NH_4)_3CrF_6$ sol.	$(NH_4)_2MnF_5$ dec.	$(NH_4)_3FeF_6$ sl. sol.
K_3AlF_6 5.5×10^{-3}	$K_2VF_5 \cdot H_2O$ sl. sol.	K_3CrF_6 sl. sol.	$K_2MnF_5 \cdot H_2O$ dec.	$K_2FeF_5 \cdot H_2O$ 0.018
Na_3AlF_6 1.98×10^{-3}		$Na_2CrF_5 \cdot H_2O$ sl. sol.	Na_2MnF_5 dec.	Na_3FeF_6 sl. sol.
$NH_4Al(SO_4)_2 \cdot 12 H_2O$ 0.33	$NH_4V(SO_4)_2 \cdot 12 H_2O$ 1.04*	$NH_4Cr(SO_4)_2 \cdot 12 H_2O$ 0.44	$NH_4Mn(SO_4)_2 \cdot 12 H_2O$ dec.	$NH_4Fe(SO_4)_2 \cdot 12 H_2O$ 2.6*
$CsAl(SO_4)_2 \cdot 12 H_2O$ 0.006 (0°C)	$CsV(SO_4)_2 \cdot 12 H_2O$ 0.0093		$CsMn(SO_4)_2 \cdot 12 H_2O$ dec.	
$KAl(SO_4)_2 \cdot 12 H_2O$ 0.24	$KV(SO_4)_2 \cdot 12 H_2O$ 4.9*	$KCr(SO_4)_2 \cdot 12 H_2O$ 0.44	$KMn(SO_4)_2 \cdot 12 H_2O$ dec.	$KFe(SO_4)_2 \cdot 12 H_2O$ 0.40
$RbAl(SO_4)_2 \cdot 12 H_2O$ 0.50	$RbV(SO_4)_2 \cdot 12 H_2O$ 0.057	$RbCr(SO_4)_2 \cdot 12 H_2O$ sl. sol.	$RbMn(SO_4)_2 \cdot 12 H_2O$ dec.	
$NaAl(SO_4)_2 \cdot 12 H_2O$ 0.50		$NaCr(SO_4)_2 \cdot 12 H_2O$ sol.	$NaMn(SO_4)_2 \cdot 12 H_2O$ dec.	
$TlAl(SO_4)_2 \cdot 12 H_2O$ 0.2	$TlV(SO_4)_2 \cdot 12 H_2O$ 0.20			
	$VOBr_2$ sol.			
	VCl_2 sol., dec.	$CrCl_4$† dec.	$MnCl_4$‡	
	$VOCl_2$ v. sol., dec.			
	VF_4 sol., dec.	CrF_4 dec.	K_2MnF_6 dec.	
	VOF_2 insol.			
	$VO(OH)_2$ 2.6×10^{-8}	CrO_2 insol.	$MnO(OH)_2$ insol.	
	$(VO)_3(PO_4)_2$ 6.4×10^{-6}			
	$VOSO_4 \cdot 5 H_2O$ v. sol.			
	$Na_2V_4O_9$ v. sol.			
	$K_2V_4O_9$ v. sol.	CrF_5 dec.	$K_2Mn_2O_5$ dec.	
	VF_5 sol., dec.			

* Molal.

† Known only as gas 600–700°C or as solid below −80°C.

‡ Known only in solution.

TABLE A11–10—continued

Aluminum	Vanadium	Chromium	Manganese	Iron
	$Na_3VO_4 \cdot 10\,H_2O$ v. sol.	Na_3CrO_4 sol., dec.	Na_3MnO_4 sol., dec.	Na_3FeO_4 sol., dec.
	Ag_2HVO_4 2×10^{-5}	$Ba_3(CrO_4)_2$ insol.		
	$Pb_3(VO_4)_2$ insol.			
	NH_4VO_3 0.044			
	$K_3V_5O_{14} \cdot 5\,H_2O$ 0.36			
	$NaVO_3$ 1.7*			
		K_2CrO_4 3.2	K_2MnO_4 1.*, dec.	K_2FeO_4 sol., dec.
		$K_2Cr_2O_7$ 0.39	$Na_2MnO_4 \cdot 10\,H_2O$ v. sol., dec.	Na_2FeO_4 sol., dec.
		$Na_2CrO_4 \cdot 10\,H_2O$ 5.4*		
		$Na_2Cr_2O_7 \cdot 2\,H_2O$ 6.8*		
		Tl_2CrO_4 6.5×10^{-5}		Ag_2FeO_4 insol.
		Ag_2CrO_4 6×10^{-5}		
		$Ag_2Cr_2O_7$ 3.7×10^{-3}		
		$BaCrO_4$ 1.1×10^{-5}	$BaMnO_4$ 1.5×10^{-5}	$BaFeO_4 \cdot 2\,H_2O$ insol.
		$CaCrO_4$ 1.34*		$CaFeO_4 \cdot 2\,H_2O$ sl. sol., dec.
				$CoFeO_4$ sol., dec.
		$CuCrO_4$ 1.9×10^{-3}		$CuFeO_4 \cdot 2\,H_2O$ sol., dec.
		$SrCrO_4$ 6×10^{-3}	$PbMnO_4$ insol.	$SrFeO_4 \cdot 2\,H_2O$ insol.
		$PbCrO_4$ 1.3×10^{-7}		$PbFeO_4$ insol.
				$ZnFeO_4$ sol., dec.
			$CsMnO_4$ 9.1×10^{-4}	
			$LiMnO_4 \cdot 3\,H_2O$ 4.*	
			$KMnO_4$ 0.40	
			$NaMnO_4 \cdot 3\,H_2O$ v. sol.	
			$RbMnO_4$ 0.054	
			$AgMnO_4$ 0.041	
			$Ba(MnO_4)_2$ 1.7*	

TABLE A11–11. MOLAR SOLUBILITIES OF SOME SALTS OF COBALT, NICKEL, AND ZINC

Cobalt	Nickel	Zinc
$Co(C_2H_3O_2)_2 \cdot 4\ H_2O$ sol.	$Ni(C_2H_3O_2)_2$ 0.94*	$Zn(C_2H_3O_2)_2 \cdot 2\ H_2O$ 1.6*
$Co_3(AsO_4)_2 \cdot 8\ H_2O$ 9.3×10^{-7}	$Ni_3(AsO_4)_2$ 3.1×10^{-6}	$Zn_3(AsO_4)_2 \cdot 8\ H_2O$ 1.3×10^{-6}
$CoBr_2 \cdot 6\ H_2O$ 3.*	$NiBr_2 \cdot 3\ H_2O$ 6.1*	$ZnBr_2$ 21.*
$Co(BrO_3)_2 \cdot 6\ H_2O$ 1.1*	$Ni(BrO_3)_2 \cdot 6\ H_2O$ 0.66*	$Zn(BrO_3)_2 \cdot 6\ H_2O$ 2.3*
$CoCO_3$ 9×10^{-7}	$NiCO_3$ 3.7×10^{-4}	$ZnCO_3$ 1.4×10^{-5}
$CoCl_2 \cdot 6\ H_2O$ 4.0*	$NiCl_2 \cdot 6\ H_2O$ 5.0*	$ZnCl_2$ 32.*
$Co(ClO_3)_2 \cdot 6\ H_2O$ 16.7*(0°C)	$Ni(ClO_3)_2 \cdot 6\ H_2O$ 5.9*	$Zn(ClO_3)_2 \cdot 4\ H_2O$ 8.6*
$Co(ClO_4)_2 \cdot 6\ H_2O$ 4.2*	$Ni(ClO_4)_2 \cdot 6\ H_2O$ 7.*	$Zn(ClO_4)_2 \cdot 6\ H_2O$ v. sol.
$Co_2Fe(CN)_6 \cdot 7\ H_2O$ 7.8×10^{-6}	$Ni_2Fe(CN)_6 \cdot 11\ H_2O$ 6.9×10^{-6}	$Zn_2Fe(CN)_6$ 4.7×10^{-6}
$CoF_2 \cdot 4\ H_2O$ 0.146	NiF_2 2.1×10^{-3}	$ZnF_2 \cdot 4\ H_2O$ 0.091
$CoSiF_6 \cdot 6\ H_2O$ 3.8*	$NiSiF_6 \cdot 6\ H_2O$ v. sol.	$ZnSiF_6 \cdot 6\ H_2O$ 2.0*
$Co(OH)_2$ 3.4×10^{-5}	$Ni(OH)_2$ 1.4×10^{-4}	$Zn(OH)_2$ 1.0×10^{-5}
$CoI_2 \cdot 6\ H_2O$ 6.8*	NiI_2 4.7*	ZnI_2 2.6*
$Co(IO_3)_2 \cdot 6\ H_2O$ 0.011	$Ni(IO_3)_2 \cdot 4\ H_2O$ 0.030	$Zn(IO_3)_2 \cdot 2\ H_2O$ 0.019
$Co(NO_3)_2 \cdot 6\ H_2O$ 5.5*	$Ni(NO_3)_2 \cdot 6\ H_2O$ 5.3*	$Zn(NO_3)_2 \cdot 6\ H_2O$ 10.9*
CoC_2O_4 2.0×10^{-4}	$NiC_2O_4 \cdot 2\ H_2O$ 2×10^{-5}	$ZnC_2O_4 \cdot 2\ H_2O$ 4.2×10^{-5}
$Co_3(PO_4)_2 \cdot 8\ H_2O$ insol.	$Ni_3(PO_4)_2 \cdot 7\ H_2O$ insol.	$Zn_3(PO_4)_2 \cdot 8\ H_2O$ 1.6×10^{-7}
$CoSO_4 \cdot 7\ H_2O$ 2.3*	$NiSO_4 \cdot 7\ H_2O$ 2.4*	$ZnSO_4 \cdot 7\ H_2O$ 3.8*
CoS 4.2×10^{-5}	NiS 4.0×10^{-5}	ZnS 7.1×10^{-6}
$Co(NCS)_2 \cdot 4\ H_2O$ 2.9*	$Ni(NCS)_2 \cdot 4\ H_2O$ 2.0*	$Zn(NCS)_2$ 0.144 (18°C)
$CoNH_4PO_4 \cdot H_2O$ insol.	$NiNH_4PO_4 \cdot H_2O$ insol.	$ZnNH_4PO_4 \cdot H_2O$ 9×10^{-5}
$Co(NH_4)_2(SO_4)_2 \cdot 6\ H_2O$ 0.52*	$Ni(NH_4)_2(SO_4)_2 \cdot 6\ H_2O$ 0.26	$Zn(NH_4)_2(SO_4)_2 \cdot 6\ H_2O$ 0.56*
$CoK_2(SO_4)_2 \cdot 6\ H_2O$ 0.58* (0°C)	$NiK_2(SO_4)_2 \cdot 6\ H_2O$ 0.16 (0°C)	$ZnK_2(SO_4)_2 \cdot 6\ H_2O$ 0.39
$Co(C_2H_3O_2)_3$ v. sol., dec.		
$CoCl_3$ sol., dec.		
CoF_3 dec.		
K_3CoF_6 dec.		
$Co(OH)_3$ 2.9×10^{-5}	Ni_2O_3 insol.	
$Co_2(SO_4)_3 \cdot 9\ H_2O$ sol., dec.		
$CoK(SO_4)_2 \cdot 12\ H_2O$ sol.		
$[Co(NH_3)_6]Cl_3$ 0.16 (0°C)		
$[Co(NH_3)_6](NO_3)_3$ 0.063		
$[Co(NH_3)_5(H_2O)]Cl_3$ 0.93*		
$[Co(NH_3)_5Cl]Cl_2$ 0.0093 (0°C)		
$[Co(NH_3)_4(H_2O)Cl]Cl_2$ 1.83*		
$K_3Co(CN)_6$ v. sol.		
$K_3[Co(NO_2)_6] \cdot \frac{3}{2} H_2O$ 0.0019		
$K_2Na[Co(NO_2)_6]$ 0.0015		
$K_2Ag[Co(NO_2)_6]$ <0.001		
$(NH_4)_2Na[Co(NO_2)_6]$ 0.001		
CoO_2 insol.	NiO_2 insol.	
K_3CoF_7 dec.	K_2NiF_6 dec.	

* Molal.

Mathematical Review

It is assumed that any student reaching the level of college chemistry will be well-grounded in the principles of high-school algebra and will be capable of carrying out the simple mathematical manipulations required in a course of qualitative analysis. Lest there be some, however, who have slipped by not being properly prepared, the following brief review of simple mathematical manipulations is included.

Exponents. Cumbersome numbers with many digits to the right or left of the decimal point can be eliminated by the use of exponents. Besides taking less space, exponential numbers show their magnitude at a glance. Data concerning equilibrium or rate constants, or indeed most other physical data, very seldom exceed four significant figures in precision and consequently are more properly expressed exponentially.

The magnitude of a number is expressed exponentially by writing the digits multiplied by 10, raised to the appropriate power. For example, the number 1000, which is the product of $10 \times 10 \times 10$, or 10 cubed, may be written 10^3 or 1×10^3. The number 0.001, which is the product of $0.1 \times 0.1 \times 0.1$ is written 10^{-3} or 1×10^{-3}. The number 4000 becomes 4×10^3 or $10^{3.6}$ (see below) and 0.004 becomes 4×10^{-3} or $10^{-2.4}$. The rules for converting ordinary numbers into exponential numbers are:

1. For numbers greater than one, the exponent is the same as the number of zeros in the ordinary number, e.g. $5000 = 5 \times 10^3$, $5300 = 53 \times 10^2$, but note also $5300 = 5.3 \times 10^3$.

2. For numbers less than one, the exponent is negative and is one more than the number of zeros following the decimal point; e.g., $0.005 = 5 \times 10^{-3}$, $0.0053 = 5.3 \times 10^{-3}$, but note also $0.0053 = 53 \times 10^{-4} = 0.53 \times 10^{-2}$.

3. Usual practice is to place one digit to the left of the decimal point in the coefficient; i.e., $0.0053 = 5.3 \times 10^{-3}$ is to be preferred to either 53×10^{-4} or 0.53×10^{-2} although mathematically the latter two are equally correct.

Multiplication of two numbers is accomplished by multiplying the co-

efficients in the ordinary way and adding the exponents algebraically; e.g.,
$540 \times 0.63 = 5.4 \times 10^2 \times 6.3 \times 10^{-1} = 34 \times 10^1 = 340$; or $540 \times 0.63 = 10^{2.73}$
$\times 10^{-0.20} = 10^{2.53} = 340$.

Division is accomplished in like manner, the coefficient of the divisor
being divided into that of the dividend, and the exponent of the divisor being
subtracted from that of the dividend; e.g., $540 \div 0.63 = 5.4 \times 10^2 \div 6.3$
$\times 10^{-1} = 0.85 \times 10^3 = 8.5 \times 10^2$; or $540 \div 0.63 = 10^{2.73} \div 10^{-0.20} = 10^{2.93}$
$= 850$.

Raising a number to a power is accomplished by raising the coefficient to
that power in the usual way and multiplying the exponent by the power

$$(3 \times 10^4)^2 = 9 \times 10^8; \quad \sqrt{4 \times 10^6} = (4 \times 10^6)^{1/2} = 2 \times 10^3;$$

$$\sqrt[3]{2.7 \times 10^{-8}} = (2.7 \times 10^{-8})^{1/3} = (27 \times 10^{-9})^{1/3} = 3 \times 10^{-3};$$

$$(2.7 \times 10^{-8})^{1/3} = (10^{-7.58})^{1/3} = 10^{-2.53} = 3 \times 10^{-3}$$

Logarithms. A logarithm is an exponent which must be applied to a
number taken as a base in order to produce any given number. That is, it is
the exponent or power to which the base number is raised in order to produce
the given number. The base of common logarithms is 10. Thus in the
equation $100 = 10^2$ the exponent 2 is the common logarithm of 100 to the
base 10, or in other words, $\log_{10} 100 = 2$. For $0.01 = 10^{-2}$, $\log_{10} 0.01 = -2$.
Frequently, when it is understood that common logarithms are being used,
the base is not specifically designated, as $\log 0.01 = -2$. The logarithm of
$10 = 10^1$ is 1 and the logarithm of $1 = 10^0$ is zero.

For numbers not exact powers of 10, the logarithms are more complicated. For example, $249 = 10^{2.3962}$ and $\log 249 = 2.3962$, expressing the
logarithm to four decimal places. A logarithm consists of two parts: the
mantissa placed to the right of the decimal point, which is found in the table
of logarithms, and the characteristic, placed at the left of the decimal point.
The mantissa gives the ordinary number of which it is the logarithm, or, in
other words, the antilogarithm. The characteristic shows the location of the
decimal point in the antilogarithm. For example, the logarithm of 249 is
2.3962, where 3962 is the mantissa and 2 is the characteristic.

1. If there are *n* digits before the decimal point, the characteristic is $n-1$.
For example, 249 has three digits and its characteristic is $3-1 = 2$.

2. If there are no numbers to the left of the decimal point, the characteristic is negative and has the value of the first position to the right of the
decimal point in which a digit other than zero occurs. Thus, 0.249 has the
characteristic -1, giving the logarithm $\bar{1}.3962$ and 0.000249 has the characteristic -4, giving the logarithm $\bar{4}.3962$. The same results could have been
obtained by using the first rule, since 0.249 has no digits to the left of the
decimal point and $0-1 = -1$, and 0.000249 has -3 digits to the left of the
decimal point and $-3-1 = -4$. These logarithms can also be expressed as
simple negative numbers, e.g., $\bar{1}.3962 = -1+0.3962 = -0.6038$ and $\bar{4}.3962$

$= -4+0.3962 = -3.6038$. This is convenient when the logarithms are to be used as exponents (as for expressing pH), but must be converted to have a positive mantissa for use with tables of logarithms.

Multiplication and division of numbers using their logarithms is accomplished by adding and subtracting the logarithms. For example, $249 \times 2 = 498$ may be done logarithmically: $2.3962 + 0.3010 = 2.6972$; antilog $2.6972 = 498$. To raise the number to a power, the logarithm is multiplied by the power: $(249)^2 = 62,000$, $2.3962 \times 2 = 4.7924$, antilog $4.7924 = 62,000$; $(0.0249)^2 = 0.00062$, $\bar{2}.3962 \times 2 = \bar{4}.7924$, antilog $\bar{4}.7924 = 6.2 \times 10^{-4} = 0.00062$, or $-1.6038 \times 2 = -3.2076 = \bar{4}.7924$, antilog $\bar{4}.7924 = 0.00062$; $(249)^{1/5} = 3.01$, $2.3962 \div 5 = 0.4792$, antilog $0.4792 = 3.01$; $(0.00249)^{1/5} = 0.301$, $\bar{3}.3962 \div 5 = -2.6038 \div 5 = -0.5208 = \bar{1}.4792$, antilog $\bar{1}.4792 = 3.01 \times 10^{-1} = 0.301$.

pH and pK. Since pH and *pK* are defined as the negative logarithms of $[H^+]$ and K, respectively, it should now be quite apparent that they are handled exactly as are logarithms. Thus, if $[H^+][OH^-] = 10^{-14} = K_w$, then it follows that $(-pH) + (-pOH) = -14 = (-pK_w)$ or $pH + pOH = 14 = pK_w$. Likewise, if $[H^+]$ is raised to a power: $[H^+][H^+] = [H^+]^2$; pH is multiplied by that power: i.e., 2pH. Hydrogen-ion concentrations which are not even powers of 10 give nonintegral pH's. Thus if $[H^+] = 5 \times 10^{-4} M$, $pH = -\log(5 \times 10^{-4}) = -\log 5 - \log 10^{-4} = -0.6990 + 4 = 3.3010$.

The Quadratic Equation. Any quadratic equation may be expressed as

$$ax^2 + bx + c = 0$$

in which a, b, and c may be either positive or negative. A quadratic equation always has two roots, which may be either real or imaginary. If the equation pertains to real physical data, however, the roots must be real, and of the real roots, only the positive ones have physical significance.

The equation given above has the following general solution:

$$x = \frac{-b \pm \sqrt{b^2 - 4ac}}{2a}$$

Simple numerical calculation with the quadratic formula, then, will yield the roots of any quadratic equation.

It should be noted that equations of the sort

$$ax^{2n} + bx^n + c = 0$$

may all be treated as quadratic equations in x^n and may be solved directly for x^n. The result will be $x^n = $ a number. Taking the nth root of the number will then yield the value of x.

For example

$$x^4 + 3x^2 - 10 = 0$$

$$x^2 = \frac{-3 \pm \sqrt{9+40}}{2} = 2, -5$$

$$x = \pm 1.417, \pm 2.236\ i$$

where $i = \sqrt{-1}$. Of these, only $+1.417$ would have physical significance. Again, $2x^5 + 5x^{2.5} - 3 = 0$

$$x^{2.5} = \frac{-5 \pm \sqrt{25+12}}{4} = \frac{-5 \pm 6.1}{4} = 0.275, -2.775$$

Ignoring the negative value

$$x = \sqrt[2.5]{0.275}$$

log $0.275 = \overline{1}.4393 = -0.5607$ and $-0.5607 \div 2.5 = -0.2243 = \overline{1}.7757$. The antilog of $\overline{1}.7757 = 0.597$. Therefore, $x = 0.597$.

List of Reagents

Acids	*Molarity*
Acetic, glacial	17
Acetic, dilute	6
Hydrochloric, concentrated	12
Hydrochloric, dilute	6
Hydrochloric	3
Nitric, concentrated	15
Nitric, dilute	6
Perchloric	0.2
Perchloric	1
Phosphoric	6
Sulfuric, concentrated	18
Sulfuric, dilute	6

Bases	
Ammonium hydroxide, concentrated	15
Ammonium hydroxide, dilute	6
Ammonium hydroxide	3
Potassium hydroxide	6
Sodium hydroxide	6
Sodium hydroxide	0.1

Solutions of Salts and Special Reagents	
Alizarin S (sodium alizarin sulfonate) 2 percent in water	——
Aluminon reagent, 1 g of ammonium aurintricarboxylate in 1 l of water	——
Aluminum nitrate	0.1
Ammonium acetate	3
Ammonium carbonate reagent, 200 g of ammonium carbonate and 500 ml of 3 M NH$_4$OH diluted to 1 l	——
Ammonium chloride	5
Ammonium iodide	1
Ammonium molybdate. Dissolve 40 g of MoO$_3$ in a mixture of 60 ml of 15 M NH$_4$OH and 100 ml of H$_2$O. Add this slowly and with vigorous stirring to a solution of 200 ml of 15 M HNO$_3$ in 450 ml of H$_2$O	——

Solutions of Salts and Special Reagents	*Molarity*
Ammonium nitrate	0.1
Ammonium nitrate	4
Ammonium oxalate	0.2
Ammonium polysulfide	——
Ammonium sulfate	1
Ammonium sulfate	0.2
Ammonium sulfide, light	——
Amyl alcohol	——
Antimony(III) chloride. Dissolve 23 g in 500 ml of 6 M HCl and dilute to 1 l	0.1
Arsenic(III) oxide. Dissolve 20 g in 30 ml of 6 M HCl and dilute to 1 l	0.1
Arsenic(V) oxide. Dissolve 23 g in 1 l of hot water and add a little HCl to obtain a clear solution	0.1
Barium chloride	0.1
Barium hydroxide, saturated	——
Barium nitrate	0.1
Bismuth nitrate. Dissolve 49 g of Bi(NO$_3$)$_3$·5 H$_2$O or 31 g of BiONO$_3$·H$_2$O in 1 l of 1.5 M HNO$_3$	0.1
Bromine, liquid (not on the shelf)	——
Bromine water. Saturate water with a few drops of bromine	——
Cadmium nitrate	0.1
Cadmium sulfate	0.1
Calcium chloride	0.1
Calcium nitrate	0.1
Calcium sulfate, saturated	——
Carbon tetrachloride	——
Cerium(III) nitrate	0.1
Chromium(III) nitrate	0.1
Cobalt nitrate	0.1
Copper(II) nitrate	0.1
Copper(II) sulfate	0.1
Diethylaniline	——
Dimethylglyoxime, 1 percent. Dissolve 10 g in 1 l of alcohol	——
Ethanol	——
Hydrogen peroxide, 3 percent	——
Iron(II) sulfate	0.1
Iron(III) chloride	1
Iron(III) chloride	0.1
Iron(III) nitrate	0.1
Iron(III) sulfate, saturated in 0.1 M H$_2$SO$_4$	——
Lead acetate	0.2
Lead nitrate	0.1
Lithium chloride	1
Magnesia mixture. Dissolve 50 g of MgCl$_2$·6 H$_2$O and 70 g of NH$_4$Cl in 400 ml of H$_2$O, add 100 ml of 15 M NH$_4$OH and dilute to 1 l; filter	——
Magnesium nitrate	0.1
Manganese(II) chloride, saturated in 12 M HCl	——
Manganese(II) nitrate	0.1
Mercury	——
Mercury(II) chloride. Add HCl until clear	0.1
Mercury(II) nitrate. Add HNO$_3$ until clear	0.1
Mercury(I) nitrate. Add HNO$_3$ until clear	0.1
Methanol	——
Methyl orange, 1 g in 1 l	——

Solutions of Salts and Special Reagents	*Molarity*
Miller's reagent. Dissolve 1.7 g $AgNO_3$, 25.3 g KNO_3, and 17.0 ml 15 M NH_4OH in water and dilute with water to 1 l.	——
Nickel nitrate	0.1
Phenolphthalein, 1 percent solution in 50 percent alcohol	——
Potassium antimonate	0.1
Potassium bromide	0.1
Potassium bromate (see also Section 3–11)	0.1
Potassium carbonate, saturated	——
Potassium chlorate	0.1
Potassium chloride	0.1
Potassium chromate	1
Potassium chromate	0.1
Potassium cyanoferrate(III)	0.1
Potassium cyanoferrate(II)	0.1
Potassium fluoride	0.15
Potassium fluoride	5
Potassium iodide	0.1
Potassium nitrate	0.1
Potassium permanganate	0.01
Potassium phosphate	1
Potassium thiocyanate	1
Potassium thiocyanate	0.1
S. and O. reagent. Dissolve 1.2 g of p-nitrobenzeneazoresorcinol in 250 ml of 0.25 M NaOH	——
Selenous acid	0.1
Silver nitrate	0.1
Sodium acetate	2
Sodium arsenate	0.1
Sodium arsenite	0.1
Sodium carbonate	1.5
Sodium carbonate	0.1
Sodium chloride	0.1
Sodium hydrogen sulfate	2
Sodium dihydrogen phosphate	0.5
Sodium monohydrogen phosphate	0.5
Sodium monohydrogen phosphate	0.1
Sodium sulfate	0.1
Sodium sulfate, saturated	——
Sodium sulfide	0.1
Sodium sulfite (Must be made up fresh!)	0.1
Sodium tetraphenylborate. Allow solution to stand overnight and filter	3%
Sodium thiosulfate	0.1
Sodium tungstate	0.1
Sodium vanadate	0.1
Sodium vanadate	0.3
Strontium nitrate	0.1
Thallium(I) nitrate	0.1
Thioacetamide	1
Tin(IV) chloride. Add HCl until clear	0.1
Tin(II) chloride. Dissolve 22 g of $SnCl_2·2 H_2O$ in 75 ml of 12 M HCl. Allow to stand for several hours and then dilute to 1 l. Must be tested frequently	0.1
Titanyl(IV) sulfate	0.1
Zinc nitrate	0.1

Solutions of Salts and Special Reagents *Molarity*

Zinc nitrate 0.5

Zinc sulfate 0.1

Zinc uranyl acetate. Dissolve 20 g of uranyl acetate in 12 g of 30 percent acetic acid, warming if necessary, and dilute to 100 ml. In a separate vessel, mix 60 g of zinc acetate with 6 g of 30 percent acetic acid and dilute to 100 ml. Mix these two solutions, add a pinch of NaCl, allow to stand for 24 hours and then filter ———

Zirconyl(IV) nitrate 0.1

Zirconyl(IV) nitrate 0.003

Solid Reagents

Absorbent cotton

Aluminum, granular, pellets

Ammonium chloride

Ammonium nitrate

Ammonium sulfate

Copper(II) oxide, rods

Copper wire

Iron, fine wire

Iron(II) sulfate

Magnesium, powder

Mercury(II) oxide

Methyl violet paper

Potassium carbonate

Potassium cyanoferrate(III)

Potassium iodomercurate

Potassium nitrate

Potassium nitrite

Potassium permanganate

Sodium bismuthate

Sodium carbonate

Sodium dithionite

Sodium hydrogen carbonate

Sodium nitrate

Sodium nitrite

Sodium nitrocobaltate(III)

Sodium thiosulfate

Sulfur, flowers

Zinc, powdered, granular (arsenic-free)

List of Desk Apparatus

 4 Beakers, Griffin, 2–10 ml, 1–100 ml, 1–250 ml, 1–600 ml
12 Bottles, homeopathic vials, 19 × 65 mm
 8 Bottles, pyrex, tincture, without stopper, 30-ml
 4 Bottles, tincture, g.s., 1 oz
 1 Burner, micro
 1 Casserole, 30-ml
 1 Clamp, micro test tube
 1 Combination lock
 1 Crucible, porcelain (small)
 1 Cylinder, graduated, 10-ml
 8 Dropper adapters, plastic
 8 Dropper pipettes, regular
 1 Flask, Erlenmeyer, 25-ml
 3 Glass tubing 6 mm × 16 in.
 1 Forceps, iron
 1 Pipette, gas absorption, micro
 2 Plates, cobalt glass, 2 in. × 2 in.
 1 Plate, test, porcelain, white
 1 Plate, test, porcelain, black
 1 Platinum wire, 2 in. (on handle)
 1 Policeman (for cleaning centrifuge tubes)
 1 Rubber connection, $\frac{3}{16}$ × $\frac{3}{64}$ × 2 in. long
 1 Rubber stopper, 1 hole, No. 0
 1 Rubber stopper, 1 hole, No. 2
 3 ft Rubber tubing, $\frac{1}{4}$ in. × $1\frac{1}{16}$ in.
 1 Sponge
 1 Spatula, stainless-steel micro
 1 Support, bottle 16 hole
 1 Support, test tube, 42 hole
 2 Stirring rods, glass, 2 mm × 4 in.
12 Test tubes, 3 in.
 6 Test tubes, 6 in.
 2 Triangles, chromel or clay
 8 Tubes, centrifuge, micro, 3-ml
 4 Watch glasses, 2–1$\frac{1}{2}$ in. and 2–90 mm diam.

1 Water bath cover (stainless steel $2\frac{3}{4}$ in. $\times$ $2\frac{3}{4}$ in., corners bent down to fit 100-ml beaker). Hole $1\frac{5}{16}$ in. diam. to take large crucible

1 Wash bottle, polyethylene, 8 oz

1 Wire gauze, 4 in. $\times$ 4 in.

Obtain the following nonreturnable kit at storeroom.

10 Corks, No. 3 (for vials)

2 doz. Labels, No. 2004, ($2\frac{3}{4}$ in. $\times$ 1 in.)

1 Box matches

10 Sheets paper, filter Reeve Angel No. 201, 9-cm (in envelope)

1 Towel

1 File, triangular

8 Bulbs, dropper, plain

1 Vial Accutint Paper, No. 10 12 strips cut in half (24 pcs.)

1 Vial Hydrion B Paper 25 strips cut in half (50 pcs.)

1 Test tube brush

The following items should be issued with the above or made available in the laboratory: soap (liquid or bar), Bunsen burner, fishtail (wingtop).

Index

DD-X 13585

RY OF QUALITATIW 648l 544.C63

MAIN ENTRY CONT

CALL NUMBER

DO NOT REMOVE FROM TH
A FEE WILL BE CHARGED
DAMAGE TO THIS

ACCES. NO.

55388 CL

MAST

HETERICK MEMORIAL
ADA, OHIO
45

OCLC

Heterick Memorial Library
Ohio Northern University
Ada, Ohio 45810

Common Logarithms to the Base 10

N	0	1	2	3	4	5	6	7	8	9	P.P. 1	2	3	4	5
10	0000	0043	0086	0128	0170	0212	0253	0294	0334	0374	4	8	12	17	21
11	0414	0453	0492	0531	0569	0607	0645	0682	0719	0755	4	8	11	15	19
12	0792	0828	0864	0899	0934	0969	1004	1038	1072	1106	3	7	10	14	17
13	1139	1173	1206	1239	1271	1303	1335	1367	1399	1430	3	6	10	13	16
14	1461	1492	1523	1553	1584	1614	1644	1673	1703	1732	3	6	9	12	15
15	1761	1790	1818	1847	1875	1903	1931	1959	1987	2014	3	6	8	11	14
16	2041	2068	2095	2122	2148	2175	2201	2227	2253	2279	3	5	8	11	13
17	2304	2330	2355	2380	2405	2430	2455	2480	2504	2529	2	5	7	10	12
18	2553	2577	2601	2625	2648	2672	2695	2718	2742	2765	2	5	7	9	12
19	2788	2810	2833	2856	2878	2900	2923	2945	2967	2989	2	4	7	9	11
20	3010	3032	3054	3075	3096	3118	3139	3160	3181	3201	2	4	6	8	11
21	3222	3243	3263	3284	3304	3324	3345	3365	3385	3404	2	4	6	8	10
22	3424	3444	3464	3483	3502	3522	3541	3560	3579	3598	2	4	6	8	10
23	3617	3636	3655	3674	3692	3711	3729	3747	3766	3784	2	4	5	7	9
24	3802	3820	3838	3856	3874	3892	3909	3927	3945	3962	2	4	5	7	9
25	3979	3997	4014	4031	4048	4065	4082	4099	4116	4133	2	3	5	7	9
26	4150	4166	4183	4200	4216	4232	4249	4265	4281	4298	2	3	5	7	8
27	4314	4330	4346	4362	4378	4393	4409	4425	4440	4456	2	3	5	6	8
28	4472	4487	4502	4518	4533	4548	4564	4579	4594	4609	2	3	5	6	8
29	4624	4639	4654	4669	4683	4698	4713	4728	4742	4757	1	3	4	6	7
30	4771	4786	4800	4814	4829	4843	4857	4871	4886	4900	1	3	4	6	7
31	4914	4928	4942	4955	4969	4983	4997	5011	5024	5038	1	3	4	6	7
32	5051	5065	5079	5092	5105	5119	5132	5145	5159	5172	1	3	4	5	7
33	5185	5198	5211	5224	5237	5250	5263	5276	5289	5302	1	3	4	5	6
34	5315	5328	5340	5353	5366	5378	5391	5403	5416	5428	1	3	4	5	6
35	5441	5453	5465	5478	5490	5502	5514	5527	5539	5551	1	2	4	5	6
36	5563	5575	5587	5599	5611	5623	5635	5647	5658	5670	1	2	4	5	6
37	5682	5694	5705	5717	5729	5740	5752	5763	5775	5786	1	2	3	5	6
38	5798	5809	5821	5832	5843	5855	5866	5877	5888	5899	1	2	3	5	6
39	5911	5922	5933	5944	5955	5966	5977	5988	5999	6010	1	2	3	4	6
40	6021	6031	6042	6053	6064	6075	6085	6096	6107	6117	1	2	3	4	5
41	6128	6138	6149	6160	6170	6180	6191	6201	6212	6222	1	2	3	4	5
42	6232	6243	6253	6263	6274	6284	6294	6304	6314	6325	1	2	3	4	5
43	6335	6345	6355	6365	6375	6385	6395	6405	6415	6425	1	2	3	4	5
44	6435	6444	6454	6464	6474	6484	6493	6503	6513	6522	1	2	3	4	5
45	6532	6542	6551	6561	6571	6580	6590	6599	6609	6618	1	2	3	4	5
46	6628	6637	6646	6656	6665	6675	6684	6693	6702	6712	1	2	3	4	5
47	6721	6730	6739	6749	6758	6767	6776	6785	6794	6803	1	2	3	4	5
48	6812	6821	6830	6839	6848	6857	6866	6875	6884	6893	1	2	3	4	4
49	6902	6911	6920	6928	6937	6946	6955	6964	6972	6981	1	2	3	4	4
50	6990	6998	7007	7016	7024	7033	7042	7050	7059	7067	1	2	3	3	4
51	7076	7084	7093	7101	7110	7118	7126	7135	7143	7152	1	2	3	3	4
52	7160	7168	7177	7185	7193	7202	7210	7218	7226	7235	1	2	2	3	4
53	7243	7251	7259	7267	7275	7284	7292	7300	7308	7316	1	2	2	3	4
54	7324	7332	7340	7348	7356	7364	7372	7380	7388	7396	1	2	2	3	4

HETERICK MEMORIAL LIBRARY onuu
544 C63
Clifford, Alan F./Inorganic chemistry of
3 5111 00131 4982